An Introduction to Stochastic Processes and Their Applications

An Introduction to Stochastic Processes and Their Applications

CHIN LONG CHIANG

Professor of Biostatistics
University of California, Berkeley

ROBERT E. KRIEGER PUBLISHING COMPANY
HUNTINGTON, NEW YORK

Original Edition 1980, based upon previous title
Introduction to Stochastic Processes in Biostatistics

Printed and Published by
ROBERT E. KRIEGER PUBLISHING CO., INC.
645 NEW YORK AVENUE
HUNTINGTON, NEW YORK 11743

Basic edition

Printed in the United States of America

Library of Congress Cataloging in Publication Data

Chiang, Chin Long
An introduction to stochastic processes and their applications.

Bibliography: p.
1. Applied mathematics
2. Probability
3. Stochastic processes
4. Mathematical statistics
I. Title.
QH323.5.C5 1975 574'.01'82 74-14821
ISBN 0-88275-200-6

To
Fu Chen
and
William, Robert, Harriet and Carol

Preface

This book is intended to be a textbook in stochastic processes or in applied probability. It may be used also as a reference book for courses in mathematical statistics, engineering (reliability theory), biostatistics (survival analysis), and demography (migration processes). The volume consists of an extensive revision of eight chapters of Part I of *Introduction to Stochastic Processes in Biostatistics* (Wiley, 1968) and a collection of nine new chapters on various topics on the subject. The biostatistics component of the 1968 book is eliminated. The 1968 book went out of print within five years of the date of publication; I only just managed to complete the revision, almost six years after the last copy was sold.

The evolution of stochastic processes is envisioned here in a particular sequence. The material is arranged in the order of discrete processes, one-state continuous processes, two-state processes, and multiple-state processes. The preliminaries now include a new chapter (Chapter 3) on exponential type distributions because of their importance and their utility in stochastic processes, in survival analysis, and in reliability theory.

Discrete processes and renewal processes in Chapters 4 through 7 have been added in this volume as they are an essential part of stochastic processes. The algebraic treatment in Chapter 6 is in variation of conventional methods that one may find, for example, in Feller [1968]. The simple and more explicit formulas for the higher order transition probabilities presented in this chapter may help the reader achieve a better understanding of Markov chains and facilitate their application.

Chapters 8 and 10 contain well-known continuous processes describing population growth and queueing processes. The general birth process and the equality in stochastic processes in Chapter 9 provide two additional means for deriving explicit formulas for any increasing process or decreasing process. The epidemic model serves as an example to demonstrate the potential of the equality in resolving difficulties.

The first chapter (Chapter 11) on the simple illness-death process is basically unaltered except for the addition of a section on generating functions and a section on survival and stages of diseases. The material on multiple transition probability and multiple transition time in Chapters 12 and 13 is essentially new. The corresponding formulas in these chapters are now of closed form and thus the process can more easily be subject to practical application. When there are no absorbing states, the two-state model generates an alternating renewal process. Parts of the general renewal theory have been extended to this case.

Explicit solution for the Kolmogorov differential equations for the case where the intensity function matrix (infinitesimal generator) **V** has distinct eigenvalues has been presented in the previous edition and reproduced in Chapter 14. The solution has been extended in Chapter 15 for the general case where matrix **V** has multiple and complex eigenvalues. Chapters 16 and 17 are reproductions of the corresponding chapters in the old book but with some minor changes.

I place the significance of stochastic processes on their potential as an analytic tool for scientific research rather than on the theoretical development of the subject. I believe that this volume as well as the 1968 book reflect this point of view.

I have used the material in this volume in courses that I have taught at the University of California, Berkeley and at Harvard University. I have once again benefitted from comments and encouragement from several friends who have read selected chapters. They include B. J. van den Berg, J. Deming, J. Emerson, J. P. Hsu, E. Peritz, P. Rust, S. Selvin, R. Wong and G. L. Yang. Solutions to the problems at the end of each chapter are in preparation but will not be published together with the text in order to meet the publication date of the book. Finally, my deep appreciation is due to Ms. Bonnie Hutchings who provided secretarial assistance during the course of the revision and expert typing from my handwritten pages to the final version with peerless skill and patience.

CHIN LONG CHIANG

University of California, Berkeley
September, 1979

Preface to The 1968 Book

Time, life, and risks are three basic elements of stochastic processes in biostatistics. Risks of death, risks of illness, risks of birth, and other risks act continuously on man with varying degrees of intensity. Long before the development of modern probability and statistics, men were concerned with the chance of dying and the length of life, and they constructed tables to measure longevity. But it was not until the advances in the theory of stochastic process made in recent years that empirical processes in the human population have been systematically studied from a probabilistic point of view.

The purpose of this book is to present stochastic models describing these processes. Emphasis is placed on specific results and explicit solutions rather than on the general theory of stochastic processes. Those readers who have a greater curiosity about the theoretical arguments are advised to consult the rich literature on the subject.

A basic knowledge in probability and statistics is required for a profitable reading of the test. Calculus is the only mathematics presupposed, although some familiarity with differential equations and matrix algebra is needed for a thorough understanding of the material.

The text is divided into two parts. Part I begins with one chapter on random variables and one on probability generating functions for use in succeeding chapters. Chapter 3 is devoted to basic models of population growth, ranging from the Poisson process to the time-dependent birth-death process. Some other models of practical interest that are not included elsewhere are given in the problems at the end of the chapter.

Birth and death are undoubtedly the most important events in the human population, but what is statistically more complex is the illness process. Illnesses are potentially concurrent, repetitive, and reversible and consequently analysis is more challenging. In this book illnesses are treated as discrete entities, and a population is visualized as consisting of discrete states of illnesses. An individual is said to be in a particular state of illness if he is affected with the corresponding diseases. Since he may leave one illness state for another or enter a death state, consideration of illness opens up a new domain of interest in multiple transition probability and multiple transition time. A basic and important case is that in which there are two illness states. Two chapters (Chapters 4 and 5) are devoted to this simple illness-death process.

In dealing with a general illness-death process that considers any finite number of illness states, I found myself confronted with a finite Markov process. To avoid repetition and to maintain a reasonable graduation of mathematical involvement, I have interrupted the development of illness processes to discuss the Kolmogorov differential equations for a general situation in Chapter 6. This chapter is concerned almost entirely with the derivation of explicit solutions of these equations. For easy reference a section (Section 3) on matrix algebra is included.

Once the Kolmogorov differential equations are solved in Chapter 6, the discussion on the general illness-death process in Chapter 7 becomes straightforward; however, the model contains sufficient points of interest to require a separate chapter. The general illness-death process has been extended in Chapter 8 to account for the population increase through immigration and birth. These two possibilities lead to the emigration-immigration process and the birth-illness-death process, respectively. But my effort failed to provide an explicit solution for the probability distribution function in the latter case.

Part II is devoted to special problems in survival and mortality. The life table and competing risks are classical and central topics in biostatistics, while the follow-up study dealing with truncated information is of considerable practical importance. I have endeavored to integrate these topics as thoroughly as possible with probabilistic and statistical principles. I hope that I have done justice to these topics and to modern probability and statistics.

It should be emphasized that although the concept of illness processes has arisen from studies in biostatistics, it has a wide application to other fields. Intensity of risk of death (force of mortality) is synonymous with "failure rate" in reliability theory; illness states may be alternatively interpreted as geographic locations (in demography), compartments (in compartment analysis), occupations, or other defined conditions. Instead of the illness of a person, we may consider whether a person is unemployed, or whether a gene is a mutant gene, a telephone line is busy, an elevator is in use, a mechanical object is out of order, etc.

The book was written originally for students in biostatistics, but it may be used for courses in other fields as well. The following are some suggestions for teaching plans:

1. As a year course in biostatistics: Chapters 1 and 2 followed by Chapters 10 through 12, and then by Chapters 3 through 8. In this arrangement, a formal introduction of the pure death process is necessary at the beginning of Chapter 10.
2. For a year course in demography: Plan 1 above may be followed, except that the term "illness process" might be more appropriately interpreted as "internal migration process."
3. As a supplementary text for courses in biostatistics or demography: Chapters 9 through 12.
4. For a one-semester course in stochastic processes: Chapters 2 through 8.

As a general reference book, Chapter 9 may be omitted.

The book is an outgrowth partly of my own research, some of which appears here for the first time (e.g., Chapter 5 and parts of Chapter 6), and partly of lecture notes for courses in stochastic processes for which I am grateful to the many contributors to the subject. I have used the material in my teaching at the Universities of California (Berkeley), Michigan, Minnesota, North Carolina; Yale and Emory Universities, and at the London School of Hygiene, University of London.

The work could not have been completed without incurring indebtedness to a number of friends. It is my pleasure to acknowledge the generous assistance of Mrs. Myra Jordan Samuels and Miss Helen E. Supplee, who have read early versions and made numerous constructive criticisms and valuable suggestions. Their help has tremendously improved the quality of the book. I am indebted to the School of Public Health, University of California, Berkeley, and the National Institutes of Health, Public Health Service, for financial aid under Grant No. 5-S01-FR-0544-06 to facilitate the work. An invitation from Peter Armitage to lecture in a seminar course at the London School of Hygiene gave me an opportunity to work almost exclusively on research projects associated with this book. I also wish to express my appreciation to Richard J. Brand and Geoffrey S. Watson who read some of the chapters and provided useful suggestions. My thanks are also due to Mrs. Shirley A. Hinegardner for her expert typing of the difficult material, to Mrs. Dorothy Wyckoff for her patience with the numerical computations, and to Mrs. Cynthia P. Debus for secretarial assistance.

C.L.C.

University of California, Berkeley
Spring, 1968

Table of Contents

CHAPTER 1

Random Variables

1. INTRODUCTION

A large body of probability and statistical theory has been developed to facilitate the study of phenomena arising from random experiments. Some studies take the form of mathematical modeling of observable events, while others are for making statistical inference regarding random experiments. A familiar random experiment is the tossing of dice. When a die is tossed, there are six possible outcomes; it is not certain which one will occur. Similarly, in a laboratory determination of antibody titer, the results vary from one trial to another even if the same blood specimen is used and the laboratory conditions remain constant. Examples of random experiments can be found almost everywhere. In fact, one may extend the concept of random experiments so that any phenomenon may be thought of as the result of some random experiment, be it real or hypothetical.

As a framework for discussing random phenomena, it is convenient to represent each conceivable outcome of a random experiment by a point, called a *sample point*, denoted by s. The totality of all sample points for a particular experiment is called the *sample space,* S. Subsets of S represent certain events such that an event A consists of a certain collection of possible outcomes s. If two subsets contain no points s in common, they are said to be disjoint, and the corresponding events are said to be *mutually exclusive.* Mutually exclusive events cannot occur as a result of a single experiment.

The probability of occurrence of the various events in S is the starting point for analysis of the experiment represented by S. Using $\Pr(A)$ to denote the probability of an event A, we may state the three fundamental assumptions.

(i) The probabilities of events are non-negative:

$$\Pr\{A\} \geq 0 \qquad \text{for any event } A. \tag{1.1}$$

(ii) The probability of the whole sample space is unity:

$$\Pr\{S\} = 1. \tag{1.2}$$

(iii) The probability that one of a sequence of mutually exclusive events $\{A_i\}$ will occur is given by

$$\Pr\{A_1 \text{ or } A_2 \text{ or } \dots\} = \sum_{i=1}^{\infty} \Pr(A_i). \tag{1.3}$$

The last assumption is called the assumption of countable additivity.

2. RANDOM VARIABLES

Any single-valued numerical function $X(s)$ defined on a sample space S is called a *random variable*. We associate a unique real number with each point s in the sample space. We call the number the value at s. We interpret the probability of an event in S as the probability that the value of the random variable $X(s)$ will lie within a certain interval or in a set of real numbers. The most common types of random variables are discrete random variables and continuous random variables. A *discrete random variable* $X(s)$ assumes a finite or denumerable number of values. For each possible value x_i there is a unique probability that the random variable assumes the value x_i:

$$\Pr\{X(s) = x_i\} = p_i, \quad i = 0,1, \dots \tag{2.1}$$

The sequence $\{p_i\}$ is called the *probability distribution* of $X(s)$, and the cumulative probability

$$\Pr\{X(s) \leq x\} = \sum_{x_i \leq x} p_i = F(x), \qquad -\infty < x < \infty \tag{2.2}$$

is called the *distribution function* of $X(s)$.

If $X(s)$ assumes only one value, say x_k, with $p_k = 1$, then we call $X(s)$ a degenerate random variable. In this case $X(s)$ is, in effect, a constant. We say that $X(s)$ is a *proper random variable* if its distribution $\{p_i\}$ satisfies the condition

$$\sum_i p_i = 1. \tag{2.3}$$

Finally, if there is a subset of S on which $X(s)$ is infinite or undefined so that

$$\sum_i p_i < 1, \tag{2.4}$$

then $X(s)$ is an *improper random variable.* The difference $1 - \sum_i p_i$ is the probability that $X(s)$ assumes no (finite) value at all. We shall encounter some improper random variables in later chapters.

Most statistical theory can be developed in terms of random variables without explicit reference to a sample space. Therefore, from now on, we will indicate a random variable simply by X instead of $X(s)$. Three examples of discrete random variables follow.

Example 1. In throwing a fair die, the sample space S consists of six points, one for each face of the die. Let a random variable X be the number of dots on the face shown; then X takes on the values 1, 2, 3, 4, 5, 6, with the corresponding probabilities $p_i = 1/6$, $i = 1, \ldots, 6$. Next, we define a random variable Y such that $Y = 0$ when the number of dots showing is even and $Y = 1$ when the number of dots showing is odd. The corresponding probabilities are $\Pr\{Y = 0\} = 1/2$ and $\Pr\{Y = 1\} = 1/2$. Finally, we let another random variable Z take the value 0 or 1 according to whether the number of dots showing is ≤ 3 or > 3, then $\Pr\{Z = 0\} = 1/2$ and $\Pr\{Z = 1\} = 1/2$. Thus X, Y and Z are different random variables defined on the same sample space. Furthermore, although they are different random variables, Y and Z have the same probability distribution.

Example 2. In tossing a fair coin twice, the sample space S consists of four points: (H,H), (H,T), (T,H), (T,T). Given this sample space we define the random variable X as the number of heads obtained in two tosses. Then X takes on values 0, 1, 2, and the corresponding probabilities are $p_0 = 1/4$, $p_1 = 1/2$, $p_2 = 1/4$.

Tossing a coin is a simple example of *Bernoulli trials.* Bernoulli trials are repeated independent trials, each trial has two possible outcomes, and the corresponding probabilities remain the same for all trials. A more general case is given in Example 3.

Example 3. Consider a sequence of n independent trials. Each trial results in either "success" with probability p or "failure" with probability $1 - p$. If X is the number of successes in the n trials, then X has a *binomial distribution,* and

$$\Pr\{X = k\} = \binom{n}{k} p^k (1-p)^{n-k}, \qquad k = 0, 1, \cdots, n. \tag{2.5}$$

In (2.5) the quantity $p^k(1 - p)^{n-k}$ represents the probability that k specified trials will result in success and the remaining $n - k$ trials in failure; for example, the first k trials may be successes and the last $n - k$ trials will be failures, as represented by the sequence (SS $\cdots$ SFF $\cdots$ F). The combinatorial factor, or *binomial coefficient*

$$\binom{n}{k} = \frac{n!}{k!(n-k)!}, \tag{2.6}$$

is the number of possible ways in which k successes can occur in n trials.

A random variable X is called a *continuous random variable* if there exists a non-negative function f such that, for any $a \le b$,

$$\Pr\{a < X \le b\} = \int_a^b f(x)\,dx. \tag{2.7}$$

The function $f(x)$ is called the *probability density function* (or simply *density function*) of X. The distribution function of X is

$$F(x) = \Pr\{X \le x\} = \int_{-\infty}^{x} f(t)\,dt. \tag{2.8}$$

and

$$\Pr\{a < X \le b\} = F(b) - F(a). \tag{2.9}$$

Note that for a continuous random variable X, $\Pr\{X = x\} = 0$ for any x, and that the values of the density function $f(x)$ are not probabilities; while they are non-negative, they need not be less than unity. The density function is merely a tool which used in conjunction with (2.7) will yield the probability that X lies in any interval.

As in the discrete case, a continuous random variable is proper if its density function satisfies the equation

$$\int_{-\infty}^{\infty} f(x)\,dx = 1,$$

and is improper if the integral is less than one.

Example 4. The *exponential distribution* has the density function

$$f(x) = \begin{cases} \mu e^{-\mu x} & x \geq 0 \\ 0 & x < 0 \end{cases} \tag{2.10}$$

and the distribution function

$$F(x) = \begin{cases} 1-e^{-\mu x} & x \geq 0 \\ 0 & x < 0 \end{cases} \tag{2.11}$$

where the parameter μ is a fixed positive number. The exponential distribution occurs in life table studies, where μ is interpreted as the force of mortality, and in reliability theory, where μ is the failure rate.

Example 5. The standard *normal distribution* has the density function

$$f(x) = \frac{1}{\sqrt{2\pi}} e^{-x^2/2}, \qquad -\infty < x < \infty. \tag{2.12}$$

Its distribution function is

$$F(x) = \int_{-\infty}^{x} \frac{1}{\sqrt{2\pi}} e^{-y^2/2} dy. \tag{2.13}$$

The density function $f(x)$ has the maximum of $(2\pi)^{-1/2}$ at $x = 0$. It is symmetrical with respect to the origin, having two points of inflection at $x = \pm 1$, and approaches zero as $x \to \pm\infty$.

3. MULTIVARIATE PROBABILITY DISTRIBUTIONS

Let X and Y be two discrete proper random variables defined on the same sample space. Their *joint* (or *bivariate*) *probability distribution* $\{p_{ij}\}$ is defined by

$$p_{ij} = \Pr\{X = x_i \quad \text{and} \quad Y = y_j\}, \qquad i,j = 0,1, \ldots, \tag{3.1}$$

with

$$\sum_i \sum_j p_{ij} = 1. \tag{3.2}$$

Let

$$p_i = \sum_j p_{ij} \tag{3.3}$$

and

$$q_j = \sum_i p_{ij}. \tag{3.4}$$

It follows from (3.1) that

$$p_i = \sum_j p_{ij} = \sum_j \Pr\{X = x_i \text{ and } Y = y_j\} = \Pr\{X = x_i\} \tag{3.5}$$

and

$$q_j = \sum_i p_{ij} = \Pr\{Y = y_j\}. \tag{3.6}$$

The sequences $\{p_i\}$ and $\{q_j\}$ are called the *marginal distributions* of X and Y, respectively. They are, of course, simply probability distributions of X and Y; the adjective "marginal" has meaning only in relation to the joint probability distribution $\{p_{ij}\}$. It is clear that the joint distribution $\{p_{ij}\}$ determines distributions $\{p_i\}$ and $\{q_j\}$; however, the reverse is not true in general. We define a joint distribution of improper random variables exactly as in (3.1), but the equations (3.2), (3.5) and (3.6) are no longer valid. Since the concepts to be introduced throughout the remainder of this chapter do not apply to improper random variables, we shall consider only proper random variables.

The *conditional probability distribution* of Y given $X = x_i$ is defined by

$$\Pr\{Y = y_j | X = x_i\} = \frac{\Pr\{X = x_i \text{ and } Y = y_j\}}{\Pr\{X = x_i\}} = \frac{p_{ij}}{p_i}, \text{ for } p_i > 0. \tag{3.7}$$

The conditional distribution of X given $Y = y_j$ is defined analogously. It follows from (3.6) and (3.7) that

$$\Pr\{Y = y_j\} = q_j = \sum_{i=0}^{\infty} \Pr\{Y = y_j | X = x_i\} \Pr\{X = x_i\}.$$

Two random variables X and Y are said to be independently distributed, or *stochastically independent*, if

$$p_{ij} = p_i q_j \tag{3.8}$$

for all i and j. Formula (3.8) is equivalent to the more intuitive condition that

$$\Pr\{Y = y_j | X = x_i\} = \Pr\{Y = y_j\}. \tag{3.9}$$

Similar definitions and relations hold when X and Y are continuous proper random variables. A *joint density function* $h(x,y)$ is defined by the property that

$$\Pr\{a < X \leq b,\, c < Y \leq d\} = \int_c^d \int_a^b h(x,y)\,dx\,dy, \tag{3.10}$$

with $h(x,y)$ satisfying the equation

$$\int_{-\infty}^{\infty} \int_{-\infty}^{\infty} h(x,y)\,dx\,dy = 1. \tag{3.11}$$

Thus, as in the discrete case, *marginal density functions* defined by

$$f(x) = \int_{-\infty}^{\infty} h(x,y)\,dy \quad \text{and} \quad g(y) = \int_{-\infty}^{\infty} h(x,y)\,dx \tag{3.12}$$

satisfy

$$\Pr\{a < X \leq b\} = \int_a^b f(x)\,dx \quad \text{and} \quad \Pr\{c < Y \leq d\} = \int_c^d g(y)\,dy. \tag{3.13}$$

The *conditional density functions are defined by*

$$f(x|y) = \frac{h(x,y)}{g(y)} \quad \text{and} \quad g(y|x) = \frac{h(x,y)}{f(x)} \tag{3.14}$$

for $g(y) > 0, f(x) > 0$; they satisfy the conditions that

$$f(x) = \int_{-\infty}^{\infty} f(x|y)g(y)\,dy \quad \text{and} \quad g(y) = \int_{-\infty}^{\infty} g(y\,|\,x)f(x)\,dx. \tag{3.15}$$

The random variables X and Y are *stochastically independent* if

$$h(x,y) = f(x)\,g(y) \tag{3.16}$$

for all x and y. If X and Y are independent random variables, then the functions $\phi(X)$ and $\psi(Y)$ are also independent random variables.

The above definitions and relations for the bivariate case extend readily to the multivariate case involving several random variables. For example, for three discrete random variables X, Y, and Z with the joint probability distribution

$$p_{ijk} = \Pr\{X = x_i,\ Y = y_j,\ Z = z_k\}, \tag{3.17}$$

there are two "levels" of marginal distributions, one typified by

$$p_{ij} = \Pr\{X = x_i,\ Y = y_j\} = \sum_k p_{ijk} \tag{3.18}$$

and the other by

$$p_i = P\{X = x_i\} = \sum_j \sum_k p_{ijk} = \sum_j p_{ij}. \tag{3.19}$$

We may define two levels of conditional probability in the same way. The relation

$$p_{ijk} = P\{X = x_i\}\ P\{Y = y_j\}\ P\{Z = z_k\} \tag{3.20}$$

defines the stochastic independence of X, Y, and Z. Extension to continuous random variables and to more than three random variables is exactly analogous.

Note that we may regard a set of random variables $(X_1, \ldots, X_n)$ defined on a sample space as a *random vector*

$$\mathbf{X} = \begin{pmatrix} X_1 \\ \vdots \\ X_n \end{pmatrix}$$

defined on that sample space. In later chapters we will find the vector notation convenient.

4. MATHEMATICAL EXPECTATION

We define the *mathematical expectation* of a discrete (proper) random variable X as

$$E(X) = \sum_i x_i p_i, \tag{4.1}$$

and of a continuous random variable as

$$E(X) = \int_{-\infty}^{\infty} x f(x)\, dx. \tag{4.2}$$

Thus, the mathematical expectation of a random variable is the weighted mean of the values that the random variable assumes with the corresponding probabilities used as weights. The mathematical expectation $E(X)$ exists and is finite if the sum in (4.1) or the integral in (4.2) converges absolutely. The terms *mean value, expected value* and *expectation* have the same meaning as mathematical expectation.

Example 6: Let X have the *Poisson* distribution

$$\Pr\{X = k\} = \frac{e^{-\lambda}\lambda^k}{k!} \qquad k = 0, 1, \ldots. \tag{4.3}$$

The expectation of X is

$$E(X) = \sum_{k=0}^{\infty} k \frac{e^{-\lambda}\lambda^k}{k!} = \lambda. \tag{4.4}$$

It is apparent that since the parameter λ is not necessarily an integer, the expectation of a discrete random variable need not coincide with any possible value of the random variable.

Example 7. Let X have the exponential distribution

$$f(x) = \mu e^{-\mu x}. \tag{4.5}$$

The expectation of X is

$$E(X) = \int_0^{\infty} x \mu e^{-\mu x} dx = \frac{1}{\mu}. \tag{4.6}$$

Any function $\phi(X)$ of a random variable X is also a random variable.

Theorem 1. *The expectation of the function $\phi(X)$, if it exists, is given by*

$$E[\phi(X)] = \sum_i \phi(x_i) p_i \tag{4.7}$$

in the discrete case, and by

$$E\,[\phi(X)] = \int_{-\infty}^{\infty} \phi(x) f(x)\, dx \tag{4.8}$$

in the continuous case.

We leave the proof of the theorem to the reader. We will sometimes write expressions of the type $E\,[\phi(X)]$ simply as $E\phi(X)$ when there is no ambiguity.

Theorem 1 extends immediately to multivariate distributions. For example, if X and Y are discrete random variables with joint distribution $\{p_{ij}\}$ and if $\Psi(X,Y)$ is any function of X and Y, then the mathematical expectation of Ψ is

$$E\,[\Psi(X,Y)] = \sum_i \sum_j \Psi(x_i, y_j) p_{ij}. \tag{4.9}$$

The most important property of mathematical expectation is that it is a *linear* operator. Let X and Y be discrete random variables with joint distribution $\{p_{ij}\}$ and respective marginal distributions $\{p_i\}$ and $\{q_j\}$. For any constants a, b, and c, we may use the definition of expectation to write

$$\begin{aligned} E(a + bX + cY) &= \sum_i \sum_j (a + bx_i + cy_j) p_{ij} \\ &= a \sum_i \sum_j p_{ij} + b \sum_i x_i \sum_j p_{ij} + c \sum_j y_j \sum_i p_{ij} \\ &= a + b \sum_i x_i p_i + c \sum_j y_j q_j \\ &= a + bE(X) + cE(Y). \end{aligned}$$

In general we have the following theorem:

Theorem 2. *The expectation of a linear function of random variables is equal to the same linear function of the expectations. If X_1, ..., X_n are random variables and c_0, c_1, ... ,c_n are constants, then*

$$E(c_0 + c_1 X_1 + \ldots + c_n X_n) = c_0 + c_1 E(X_1) + \ldots + c_n E(X_n). \tag{4.10}$$

We leave proofs for continuous random variables to the reader. Note that we do not assume the independence of $X_1, \ldots, X_n$ in (4.10).

Theorem 2 makes it clear that the expectation of a constant is equal to the constant itself.

4.1. A Useful Inequality.

According to Theorem 1, the equality

$$E\phi(X_1, \ldots, X_n) = \phi\,[E(X_1), \ldots, E(X_n)]$$

holds when ϕ is a linear function. This equality does not hold for arbitrary functions ϕ. A case in point is a useful inequality (Jensen's inequality) for the function $\phi(X) = 1/X$.

Theorem 3. *If a non-degenerate random variable X assumes only positive values, then the expectation of the reciprocal of X is greater than the reciprocal of the expectation; that is,*

$$E\left[\frac{1}{X}\right] > \frac{1}{E(X)}. \tag{4.11}$$

The reverse inequality holds if X assumes only negative values.

Proof. Let

$$X = E(X)\left[1 + \frac{X - E(X)}{E(X)}\right] = E(X)(1 + \Delta) \tag{4.12}$$

so that

$$E(\Delta) = E\left[\frac{X - E(X)}{E(X)}\right] = 0. \tag{4.13}$$

From (4.12) we know that

$$E\left[\frac{1}{X}\right] = E\left[\frac{1}{E(X)(1 + \Delta)}\right] = \frac{1}{E(X)}\,E\left[\frac{1}{1 + \Delta}\right]. \tag{4.14}$$

Since

$$\frac{1}{1 + \Delta} = 1 - \Delta + \frac{\Delta^2}{1 + \Delta} \tag{4.15}$$

and since Δ^2 and $1 + \Delta$ are positive random variables, therefore the expectation

$$E\left[\frac{1}{X}\right] = \frac{1}{E(X)} E\left[1 - \Delta + \frac{\Delta^2}{1+\Delta}\right]$$

$$= \frac{1}{E(X)}\left[1 + E\left(\frac{\Delta^2}{1+\Delta}\right)\right] > \frac{1}{E(X)}, \tag{4.16}$$

and we recover (4.11).

4.2. Conditional Expectation.

The conditional expectation of Y given x is the expectation of Y with respect to the conditional distribution of Y given x. For the discrete case

$$E(Y|x_i) = \sum_j y_j \frac{p_{ij}}{p_i}, \qquad p_i > 0. \tag{4.17}$$

For the continuous case

$$E(Y|x) = \int_{-\infty}^{+\infty} y \frac{h(x,y)}{f(x)}\, dy, \qquad f(x) > 0. \tag{4.18}$$

For these conditional expectations to be meaningful, it is necessary that $p_i > 0$ in (4.17) and $f(x) > 0$ in (4.18). The conditional expectations in (4.17) and (4.18) are constant for a given value x (or x_i). If we regard x (or x_i) as a random variable X, then we write these expectations as $E(Y|X)$, and they themselves are random variables. When X assumes the value x_i, $E(Y|X)$ takes on the value $E(Y|x_i)$.

We define conditional expectations of functions, such as $E[\phi(X,Y)|X]$, analogously. When calculating the expectation, we treat the random variable on which the expectation is conditioned as a constant. Thus, for example,

$$E[(X+Y)|X] = X + E(Y|X) \tag{4.19}$$

and

$$E[XY|X] = XE[Y|X]. \tag{4.20}$$

Since expressions like $E(Y|X)$ are random variables, they themselves have expectations.

Theorem 4.[1] *For any two random variables X and Y,*

[1] To aid in interpreting repeated expectations, remember that $E(Y|X)$ is a function of X, therefore the outer expectation refers to the distribution of X.

$$E[E(Y|X)] = E(Y), \tag{4.21}$$

and

$$E(XY) = E[XE(Y|X)]. \tag{4.22}$$

Proof. For the discrete case

$$E[E(Y|X)] = \sum_i p_i \left[\sum_j y_j \frac{p_{ij}}{p_i} \right]$$

$$= \sum_i \sum_j y_j p_{ij} = \sum_j y_j \sum_i p_{ij} = \sum_j y_j q_j = E(Y). \tag{4.23}$$

The proof of the continuous case is similar. Formula (4.22) follows from (4.20) and (4.21).

An important consequence of the independence of random variables is that their expectations are multiplicative.

Theorem 5. *If* $X_1, \ldots, X_n$ *are independent random variables, then*

$$E(X_1 \ldots X_n) = E(X_1) \ldots E(X_n). \tag{4.24}$$

Proof. When X_1 and X_2 are independent, $E(X_2|X_1) = E(X_2)$. Thus, for the case of two random variables, (4.22) implies that $E(X_1 X_2) = E(X_1)E(X_2)$. We may extend the proof to the general case by induction.

5. MOMENTS, VARIANCES, AND COVARIANCES

Expectations of a random variable X that are of particular interest are

(i) the moments

$$E[X^r] \qquad r = 1,2, \ldots; \tag{5.1}$$

(ii) the factorial moments

$$E[X(X-1)\ldots(X-r+1)] \qquad r = 1,2, \ldots; \tag{5.2}$$

and

(iii) the central moments

$$E[X - E(X)]^r \qquad r = 1,2, \ldots. \tag{5.3}$$

The first moment, which is the expectation $E(X)$, is called the *mean* of the distribution. It is a commonly used index of its location. The second central moment

$$\sigma_X^2 = E[X - E(X)]^2 \tag{5.4}$$

$$= E(X^2) - [E(X)]^2, \tag{5.4a}$$

is the *variance* of the distribution and its square root σ_X is the *standard deviation*. We will also use the notation $\text{Var}(X)$ to indicate the variance. The variance and standard deviation are often used to measure the spread, or dispersion, of the distribution. It is therefore reasonable that the variance of a degenerate random variable or a constant is equal to zero:

$$\sigma_c^2 = 0. \tag{5.5}$$

The variance of a random variable depends on the scale of measurement but not on the origin of measurement. Thus

$$\sigma_{a+bX}^2 = b^2 \sigma_X^2. \tag{5.6}$$

Proof of these properties is left to the reader.

Example 8. Let X be a Poisson random variable with the distribution given by (4.3). Then we have

$$E(X^2) = \sum_{k=0}^{\infty} k^2 \frac{e^{-\lambda}\lambda^k}{k!} = \lambda(\lambda + 1) \tag{5.7}$$

and in view of (4.4) and (5.4a),

$$\sigma_X^2 = \lambda. \tag{5.8}$$

Example 9. Let X have the exponential distribution given in (2.10). Then the variance of X is

$$\sigma_X^2 = \int_0^{\infty} \left(x - \frac{1}{\mu}\right)^2 \mu e^{-\mu x}\,dx = \frac{1}{\mu^2}. \tag{5.9}$$

Now, consider two random variables X and Y having a joint distribution. The moments of the marginal distributions describe the properties of X and Y separately. In order to relate X and Y, we introduce the *product-moment* or *covariance of* X and Y:

$$\sigma_{X,Y} = E[X - E(X)][Y - E(Y)] \tag{5.10}$$

$$= E(XY) - E(X)E(Y). \tag{5.10a}$$

Note that $\sigma_{X,X} = \sigma_X^2$. We will also use the notation Cov(X, Y) for the covariance. If X and Y are stochastically independent, then $\sigma_{X,Y}$ vanishes because of Theorem 5; but a zero covariance between random variables does not imply that they are independently distributed. An example to the contrary follows.

Example 10. Suppose that we have two urns. The ith urn contains a proportion p_i of white balls and a proportion q_i of black balls with $p_i + q_i = 1$, $i = 1,2$. From the i-th urn we draw with replacement n_i balls, of which X_i are white. The number n_1 is fixed in advance, but the number n_2 is a random variable set equal to the number of white balls drawn from the first urn; in other words, $n_2 = X_1$. For $n_1 > 0$ and $X_1 > 0$, the proportions of white balls drawn,

$$\hat{p}_1 = \frac{X_1}{n_1} \quad \text{and} \quad \hat{p}_2 = \frac{X_2}{X_1} \tag{5.11}$$

are estimators of the corresponding proportions of white balls in the urns. *It can be shown that* $\hat{p}_1$ and $\hat{p}_2$ *have zero covariance and that they are not independently distributed.* See Problem 16 for proof.

This urn scheme is quite useful for illustrative purposes in life table analysis, where n_1 is taken as the number of individuals starting the first time interval, and X_1 and X_2 represent the survivors of the first and the second time intervals. A more general model has been given in Chiang ([1968], p. 223).

5.1. Variance of a Linear Function of Random Variables.

Using the properties of expectation we can find the variance of a linear function of random variables:

$$\begin{aligned}
\operatorname{Var}(a + bX + cY) &= E\{a + bX + cY - E(a + bX + cY)\}^2 \\
&= E\{b[X - E(X)] + c[Y - E(Y)]\}^2 \\
&= b^2 E[X - E(X)]^2 + c^2 E[Y - E(Y)]^2 \\
&\quad + 2bc\, E[X - E(X)][Y - E(Y)] \\
&= b^2\sigma_X^2 + c^2\sigma_Y^2 + 2bc\sigma_{X,Y}.
\end{aligned}$$

We generalize the above result in the following theorem.

Theorem 6. *The variance of the linear function* $c_0 + c_1 X_1 + \dots + c_n X_n$ *is*

$$\operatorname{Var}(c_0 + c_1 X_1 + \ldots + c_n X_n) = \sum_{i=1}^{n} c_i^2 \sigma_{X_i}^2 + \sum_{\substack{i=1 \\ i \neq j}}^{n} \sum_{j=1}^{n} c_i c_j \sigma_{X_i, X_j}. \tag{5.12}$$

In particular, if $X_1, \ldots, X_n$ are independent random variables, then

$$\operatorname{Var}(c_1 X_1 + \ldots + c_n X_n) = c_1^2 \sigma_{X_1}^2 + \ldots + c_n^2 \sigma_{X_n}^2, \tag{5.13}$$

and if $X_1, \ldots, X_n$ are independent and have the same variance σ_X^2, then the variance of the sample mean $\bar{X} = \frac{1}{n}(X_1 + \ldots + X_n)$ is

$$\operatorname{Var}(\bar{X}) = \frac{1}{n} \sigma_X^2. \tag{5.14}$$

Example 11. Consider a sequence of n independent trials, each with probability p of success and probability $1 - p$ of failure. The number of successes in the i-th trial, X_i, has the *Bernoulli distribution*

$$P\{X_i = 0\} = 1 - p, \qquad P\{X_i = 1\} = p$$

so that

$$E(X_i) = p, \tag{5.15}$$

and

$$\sigma_{X_i}^2 = p(1 - p). \tag{5.16}$$

Let

$$Z = X_1 + \ldots + X_n$$

represent the number of successes in n trials and, hence, have the binomial distribution (2.5). Theorem 2 and (5.15) imply that

$$E(Z) = np, \tag{5.17}$$

and, since $X_1, \ldots, X_n$ are independent, Theorem 6 and (5.16) imply that

$$\sigma_Z^2 = np(1 - p). \tag{5.18}$$

These computations of $E(Z)$ and σ_Z^2 are much simpler than direct computations from binomial distribution (2.5).

Example 12. The *multinomial distribution* is a direct generalization of the binomial distribution. Consider an experiment that results in the mutually exclusive outcomes $E_0, E_1, \ldots, E_m$ with probabilities $p_0, p_1, \ldots, p_m$, respectively, where $\sum_{i=0}^{m} p_i = 1$. The numbers $X_1, \ldots, X_m$ of occurrences of $E_1, \ldots E_m$ in n independent repetitions of the experiment have the joint multinomial distribution[2]

$$\Pr\{X_1 = k_1, \ldots, X_m = k_m\} = \frac{n!}{k_1! \ldots k_m!\,(n-k)!} p_1^{k_1} \ldots p_m^{k_m} p_0^{(n-k)},$$

$$k_i = 0,1, \ldots, n;\ i = 1, \ldots, m, \qquad (5.19)$$

where $k = k_1 + \ldots + k_m$. We are interested in the covariance between X_i and X_j. It is clear that each X_i has a binomial distribution with the variance

$$\sigma_{X_i}^2 = np_i(1 - p_i) \qquad (5.20)$$

and that the sum $X_i + X_j$ also has a binomial distribution with the variance

$$\sigma_{X_i+X_j}^2 = n(p_i + p_j)[1 - (p_i + p_j)]. \qquad (5.21)$$

But from Theorem 6 we can write

$$\sigma_{X_i+X_j}^2 = \sigma_{X_i}^2 + \sigma_{X_j}^2 + 2\sigma_{X_i,X_j}. \qquad (5.22)$$

Substituting (5.20) and (5.21) in (5.22) yields

$$\sigma_{X_i,X_j} = -np_ip_j. \qquad (5.23)$$

5.2. Covariance Between Two Linear Functions of Random Variables.
Let $U = a_1X_1 + \ldots + a_mX_m$ and $V = b_1Y_1 + \ldots + b_nY_n$ be two linear functions of the random variables X_i and Y_j where a_i and b_j are constants, $i = 1, \ldots, m$ and $j = 1, \ldots, n$. The covariance between U and V is given by

$$\sigma_{U,V} = \sum_{i=1}^{m}\sum_{j=1}^{n} a_ib_j\sigma_{X_i,Y_j}. \qquad (5.24)$$

The proof of (5.24) is left to the reader.

---

[2] A random variable X_0 corresponding to the occurrences of E_0 is not explicitly included in (5.19) because the value of X_0 is completely determined by the relation $X_0 = n - X_1 - \ldots - X_m$.

5.3. Variance of a Product of Random Variables.

We have an exact formula for the variance of the product of random variables that are independently distributed. For two random variables, we can prove the formula

$$\operatorname{Var}(XY) = \sigma_X^2\sigma_Y^2 + [E(Y)]^2\sigma_X^2 + [E(X)]^2\sigma_Y^2 \tag{5.25}$$

by direct computation. Using (5.4a) we get

$$\begin{aligned}\operatorname{Var}(XY) &= E[(XY)^2] - [E(XY)]^2 \\ &= E(X^2)E(Y^2) - [E(X)]^2[E(Y)]^2. \end{aligned} \tag{5.26}$$

Again, substituting (5.4a) for $E(X^2)$ and $E(Y^2)$ in (5.26), we obtain (5.25). In general, the variance of the product of n independent random variables is

$$\operatorname{Var}(X_1 \ldots X_n) = \prod_{i=1}^{n}\{\sigma_{X_i}^2 + [E(X_i)]^2\} - \prod_{i=1}^{n}[E(X_i)]^2. \tag{5.27}$$

5.4. Approximate Variance of a Function of Random Variables.

When random variables are not independently distributed, there is no exact formula expressing the variance of their product in terms of the individual variances and covariances. However, we can use Taylor's formula to obtain an approximate formula for the variance of the product, or any function, of random variables. Let $\phi(X)$ be a function of random variables $X = (X_1, \ldots, X_n)$. Taylor's expansion of $\phi(X)$ about the expected value $\mu = (\mu_1, \ldots, \mu_n)$ gives the first two terms

$$\phi(X) \doteq \phi(\mu) + \sum_{i=1}^{n}(X_i - \mu_i)\phi_i(\mu) \tag{5.28}$$

where

$$\phi_i(\mu) = \frac{\partial}{\partial X_i}\phi(X)_{|X=\mu}. \tag{5.29}$$

Applying Theorem 6 to (5.28), we have the approximate variance of $\phi(X)$

$$\operatorname{Var}(\phi(X)) = \sum_{i=1}^{n}[\phi_i(\mu)]^2\sigma_{X_i}^2 + \sum_{\substack{i=1 \\ i\neq j}}^{n}\sum_{j=1}^{n}[\phi_i(\mu)][\phi_j(\mu)]\sigma_{X_i,X_j}. \tag{5.30}$$

It is necessary to apply caution in using this approximation, however, as illustrated by the following example.

Example 13. Consider the product $\phi = XY$ of two independent random variables X and Y so that the covariance $\sigma_{X,Y} = 0$. Formula (5.30) gives the approximation

$$\text{Var}(XY) = [E(Y)]^2\sigma_X^2 + [E(X)]^2\sigma_Y^2. \tag{5.31}$$

Now compare (5.31) with the exact formula in (5.25) and note the error in the missing term $\sigma_X^2\sigma_Y^2$.

5.5. Conditional Variance and Covariance.

Variances and covariances can be conditioned on other random variables just as were expectations (Section 4.2). We define the conditional variance of X given Z as

$$\sigma_{X|Z}^2 = E\{[X - E(X|Z)]^2|Z\}, \tag{5.32}$$

and the conditional covariance of X and Y given Z as

$$\sigma^2_{X,Y|Z} = E\{[X - E(X|Z)][Y - E(Y|Z)]|Z\}. \tag{5.33}$$

The conditional variance and covariance are, of course, random variables. Their moments satisfy the following relationships.

Theorem 7. *For any random variables X, Y, and Z,*

$$\sigma_X^2 = E[\sigma_{X|Z}^2] + \sigma^2_{E(X|Z)} \tag{5.34}$$

and

$$\sigma_{X,Y} = E[\sigma_{X,Y|Z}] + \sigma_{E(X|Z),E(Y|Z)}. \tag{5.35}$$

Proof. To prove (5.34) we use the definition of variance to write

$$\begin{aligned}\sigma_X^2 &= E[X - E(X)]^2 = E[X - E(X|Z) + E(X|Z) - E(X)]^2\\ &= E[X - E(X|Z)]^2 + E[E(X|Z) - E(X)]^2\\ &\quad + 2E\{[X - E(X|Z)][E(X|Z) - E(X)]\}.\end{aligned} \tag{5.36}$$

Applying Theorem 4, the first term after the last equality becomes

$$E[E\{[X - E(X|Z)]^2|Z\}] = E[\sigma_{X|Z}^2],$$

the second term becomes

$$E\{E(X|Z) - E[E(X|Z)]\}^2 = \sigma^2_{E(X|Z)},$$

and, since $E\{[X - E(X|Z)]|Z\} = 0$, the third term is

$$
\begin{aligned}
2E\,[E\{[X - E(X|Z)]\,[E(X|Z) - E(X)]\,|\,Z\}] \\
= 2E\,[[E(X|Z) - E(X)]\,E\{[X - E(X|Z)]\,|\,Z\}] \\
= 0,
\end{aligned}
$$

and (5.34) is proved. The proof of (5.35) is similar.

5.6. Correlation Coefficient.

Consider two random variables X and Y with standard deviations σ_X and σ_Y. Let

$$U = \frac{X - E(X)}{\sigma_X} \quad \text{and} \quad V = \frac{Y - E(Y)}{\sigma_Y}. \tag{5.37}$$

It is easy to see that

$$E(U) = 0 \quad \text{and} \quad E(V) = 0, \tag{5.38}$$

and that

$$\sigma_U^2 = E(U^2) = 1 \quad \text{and} \quad \sigma_V^2 = E(V^2) = 1. \tag{5.39}$$

For these reasons U and V are called *standardized random variables.* We define the correlation coefficient between X and Y, denoted by ρ_{XY}, as the covariance between U and V:

$$\rho_{XY} = \sigma_{U,V} = E(UV) = E\left[\frac{X - E(X)}{\sigma_X}\right]\left[\frac{Y - E(Y)}{\sigma_Y}\right], \tag{5.40}$$

or,

$$\rho_{XY} = \frac{\sigma_{X,Y}}{\sigma_X \sigma_Y}. \tag{5.41}$$

Since the correlation coefficient is calculated from standardized random variables, its value is not affected by changes of scale or origin, i.e.,

$$\rho_{a+bX,c+dY} = \rho_{XY}. \tag{5.42}$$

The correlation coefficient is often used to measure the extent to which X and Y obey a linear relation. If the linear relation $Y = a + bX$ holds exactly, then we say Y and X are *perfectly* correlated. In this case the correlation coefficient between X and Y is either -1 or $+1$. However, X and Y may have a perfect nonlinear relation and nevertheless have a small correlation coefficient. In any case, the inequalities

$$-1 \leq \rho_{XY} \leq 1 \tag{5.43}$$

always hold true, since

$$E(U \pm V)^2 \geq 0 \tag{5.44}$$

so that

$$E(U^2) \pm 2E(UV) + E(V^2) = 1 \pm 2\rho_{XY} + 1 \geq 0. \tag{5.45}$$

We can rearrange the last inequality to yield (5.43).

6. CHEBYSHEV'S INEQUALITY AND LAWS OF LARGE NUMBERS

The general limit theorems in probability theory are fundamental to understanding the connection between probability and statistics. We introduce the most basic theorems in this section, some without proofs.

Give the conservative estimate that a random variable is within k standard deviation from its mean is at least $1 - \frac{1}{k^2}$

6.1. Chebyshev's Inequality.

Theorem 8. *Let X be a random variable with expectation μ and variance σ^2. For any positive number t,*

$$\Pr\{|X - \mu| \geq t\} \leq \frac{\sigma^2}{t^2}. \tag{6.1}$$

Several proofs of (6.1) are available. We prove it with the following lemma.

Lemma 1. *Let Y be a non-negative random variable and c be any positive constant. Then*

$$\Pr\{Y \geq c\} \leq \frac{E(Y)}{c}. \tag{6.2}$$

The lemma is obviously true, because

$$E(Y) \geq \int_{y \geq c} yf(y)\,dy \geq c \int_{y \geq c} f(y)\,dy.$$

Now letting $Y = (X - \mu)^2$ and $c = t^2$ we obtain inequality (6.1) from (6.2).

6.2. Bernoulli's Theorem.

Consider a sequence of Bernoulli trials with a constant probability of success p. Let X_i be the number of successes in the i-th trial for $i = 1,2, \dots,$ so that, if the i-th trial results in success, $X_i = 1$, and, if the i-th trial results in failure, $X_i = 0$. Let

$$S_n = X_1 + \dots + X_n \tag{6.3}$$

be the number of successes in n trials. For sufficiently large n, the relative frequency S_n/n becomes and remains close to p with a probability of one. Formally we have the following theorem.

Theorem 9. *For every* $\varepsilon > 0$, $\delta > 0$ *there exists a number* N *such that, for* $n = N + 1, N + 2, \dots,$

$$\Pr\left\{\left|\frac{S_n}{n} - p\right| < \varepsilon\right\} > 1 - \delta. \tag{6.4}$$

This important theorem was discovered by Jacob Bernoulli and published in his posthumous book *Ars Conjectandi* [1713]. The original proof of the theorem, which may be found in Uspensky [1937], is rigorous and lengthy. We shall here use Chebyshev's inequality to prove the theorem.

Proof. Since the expectation and variance of the relative frequency S_n/n are $E(S_n/n) = p$ and $\mathrm{Var}(S_n/n) = p(1-p)/n$, respectively, Chebyshev's inequality implies that

$$\Pr\left\{\left|\frac{S_n}{n} - p\right| \geq \varepsilon\right\} \leq \frac{p(1-p)}{n\varepsilon^2}. \tag{6.5}$$

For any value of p, $0 \leq p \leq 1$, $p(1-p) \leq \frac{1}{4}$; therefore, (6.5) implies

$$\Pr\left\{\left|\frac{S_n}{n} - p\right| \geq \varepsilon\right\} \leq \frac{1}{4n\varepsilon^2}, \tag{6.6}$$

or

$$\Pr\left\{\left|\frac{S_n}{n} - p\right| < \varepsilon\right\} \geq 1 - \frac{1}{4n\varepsilon^2}. \tag{6.7}$$

To determine N, we let

$$1 - \frac{1}{4n\varepsilon^2} > 1 - \delta$$

so that N may be taken as the smallest integer greater than $1/(4\delta\varepsilon^2)$. Therefore (6.4) holds for all $n > N \geq 1/(4\delta\varepsilon^2)$.

The Bernoulli theorem presented here is a special case of the law of large numbers, to which we now turn.

6.3. Laws of Large Numbers.

We have the strong law of large numbers (SLLN) and the weak law of large numbers (WLLN), depending on the type of convergence to which they refer. Their distinction is made clear in the following definitions. Let $\{X_n\}$ be an infinite sequence of random variables with the common expectation $E(X_i) = \mu$, and let

$$S_n = X_1 + \ldots + X_n. \tag{6.8}$$

Definition. *An infinite sequence of random variables $\{X_n\}$ is said to obey the weak law of large numbers if, for every $\varepsilon > 0$,*

$$\lim_{n\to\infty} \Pr\left\{\left|\frac{S_n}{n} - \mu\right| < \varepsilon\right\} = 1. \tag{6.9}$$

Thus, the ratio S_n/n converges to μ in probability. The difference $|(S_n/n) - \mu|$ may still be large, although large differences occur at infrequent occasions.

Definition. *An infinite sequence of random variables $\{X_n\}$ is said to obey the strong law of large numbers, if, for any $\varepsilon > 0$,*

$$\Pr\left\{\lim_{n\to\infty}\left|\frac{S_n}{n} - \mu\right| < \varepsilon\right\} = 1. \tag{6.10}$$

Thus the ratio S_n/n converges to μ *almost everywhere.* As n becomes large, the ratio S_n/n becomes close to μ and remains close to μ.

There are certain conditions for the laws of large numbers to hold; some are given in the following theorems.

Theorem 10. *Let $\{X_i\}$ be a sequence of mutually independent and identically distributed random variables with expectation $E(X_i) = \mu$ and finite variance* $\text{Var}(X_i) = \sigma^2$, *and let*

$$S_n = X_1 + \ldots + X_n. \tag{6.11}$$

Then, for every $\varepsilon > 0$,

$$\lim_{n\to\infty} \Pr\left\{\left|\frac{S_n}{n} - \mu\right| < \varepsilon\right\} = 1. \tag{6.12}$$

Thus, the WLLN holds.

Proof. Formula (6.12) is a direct consequence of Chebyshev's inequality (6.1). Since $\operatorname{Var}(S_n/n) = \sigma^2/n$, (6.1) implies that for every $\varepsilon > 0$,

$$\Pr\left\{\left|\frac{S_n}{n} - \mu\right| \geq \varepsilon\right\} \leq \frac{\sigma^2}{n\varepsilon^2}. \tag{6.13}$$

The right-hand side of (6.13) tends to zero as n increases indefinitely; (6.12) follows.

Remark 1. The assumption stated in Theorem 10 is more stringent than necessary. The law of large numbers still holds even if the random variables X_i are not identically distributed. To be specific, let us consider the mutually independent random variables, $X_1, X_2, \ldots,$ with finite means $E(X_i) = \mu_i$ and finite variances σ_i^2. For each n, the sum $S_n = X_1 + \ldots + X_n$ also has finite mean and finite variance:

$$E(S_n) = \mu_1 + \ldots + \mu_n \tag{6.14}$$

and

$$\operatorname{Var}(S_n) = \sigma_1^2 + \ldots + \sigma_n^2. \tag{6.15}$$

If $\sqrt{\operatorname{Var}(S_n)}/n \to 0$, then

$$\lim_{n\to\infty} \Pr\left\{\left|\frac{S_n - E(S_n)}{n}\right| < \varepsilon\right\} = 1. \tag{6.16}$$

Proof of (6.16) follows from Chebyshev's inequality.

In the preceding modification, we assume the existence of variances for each X_i. Khintchine has shown that this restriction is unnecessary when the random variables are identically distributed.

Theorem 11. *Let* $\{X_i\}$ *be a sequence of independent and identically distributed random variables with a finite common expectation* $E(X_i) = \mu$. *Then*

$$\lim_{n\to\infty} P\left\{\left|\frac{S_n}{n} - \mu\right| < \varepsilon\right\} = 1. \qquad \text{(WLLN)} \tag{6.9}$$

While the convergence in (6.10) is stronger than that in (6.9), the conditions for the SLLN are surprisingly modest. The following result is due to Kolmogorov.

Theorem 12. *Let $\{X_i\}$ be a sequence of independent and identically distributed random variables with the common expectation $E(X_i) = \mu$. Then*

$$P\left\{\lim_{n\to\infty}\left|\frac{S_n}{n}-\mu\right|<\varepsilon\right\}=1. \qquad \text{(SLLN)} \qquad (6.10)$$

Kolmogorov has shown also that the SLLN applies to a sequence of independent random variables $\{X_i\}$ with different density functions, provided that the expectations $E(X_i) = \mu_i$ exist and the variances $\text{Var}(X_i) = \sigma_i^2$ are such that the series $\Sigma\sigma_i^2/i^2$ converges.

6.4. The Central Limit Theorem.

While the laws of large numbers show the convergence of the sample mean S_n/n to the population mean μ, the central limit theorem provides the probability distribution of the standardized sample mean.

Theorem 13 (Lindeberg). *Let $\{X_i\}$ be an infinite sequence of independent and identically distributed random variables with expectation $E(X_i) = \mu$ and variance $\text{Var}(X_i) = \sigma^2$. Let*

$$\bar{X}=\frac{X_1+\ldots+X_n}{n} \qquad (6.17)$$

be the sample mean. Then for large n the standardized random variable

$$Z_n=\frac{\sqrt{n}\,(\bar{X}-\mu)}{\sigma} \qquad (6.18)$$

is approximately normally distributed with mean zero and variance one. That is, for every real number t,

$$\Pr\{Z_n\le t\}\to\int_{-\infty}^{t}\frac{1}{\sqrt{2\pi}}e^{-x^2/2}\,dx. \qquad (6.19)$$

For proof of (6.19), see Section 4.1 in Chapter 3.

Remark. The necessity of the existence of the mean μ (or μ_i) in the laws of large numbers and in the central limit theorem is intuitively clear since it is to the mean μ that $\bar{X}$ converges. Conversely, if the mean of a distribution does not exist, then the laws of large numbers and the central limit theorem do not apply to that sequence $\{X_i\}$. A classical example is the Cauchy distribution, which has the probability density function

$$f(x) = \frac{\theta}{\pi\,[\theta^2 + (x-\mu)^2]}, \quad \text{for } -\infty < x < +\infty, \tag{6.20}$$

where μ and θ are real numbers with $\theta > 0$. The distribution is symmetrical with respect to μ, but μ is not the mean of the distribution. The mean does not exist, nor does any higher moment. Furthermore, the sample mean $\bar{X}$ has exactly the same distribution as X. Thus the limiting distribution of $\bar{X}$ is independent of sample size n, and the sequence $\{X_i\}$ obeys neither the laws of large numbers nor the central limit theorem.

7. PROBLEMS FOR SOLUTION

1. Let X be a binomial random variable with the probability distribution given in (2.5) and let $Y = n - X$. Find the covariance $\sigma_{X,Y}$.

2. Show that a Poisson distribution with the parameter λ has both an expectation and variance equal to λ.

3. Prove the equation

$$E(c_0 + c_1 X_1 + \dots + c_n X_n) = c_0 + c_1 E(X_1) + \dots + c_n E(X_n) \tag{4.10}$$

for the continuous case.

4. If a, b, and c are constant and the random variable X has finite variance, show that

$$\sigma_c^2 = 0 \tag{5.5}$$

and

$$\sigma_{a+bX}^2 = b^2 \sigma_X^2. \tag{5.6}$$

5. Let X have an exponential distribution with the probability density function

$$f(x) = \mu e^{-\mu x}. \tag{2.10}$$

Show that $F_X(\infty) = 1$ and compute the expectation and variance of X.

6. A lot contains m defective units and $N - m$ acceptable units. The units are tested one at a time without replacement. Let X be the number of defectives found before the first acceptable one. Derive the probability distribution and the expectation of X.

7. *Hypergeometric distribution.* Assume a lot contains m defective units and $N - m$ acceptable units as in Problem 6. A sample of n units is taken without replacement from the lot; let Y be the number of defectives in the sample.

(a) Find the probability distribution of Y.

(b) Show that the sum of the probabilities in (a) for all possible values of Y is unity.

(c) Find the expectation and the variance of Y and compare them with those in a binomial distribution.

8. *Normal distribution.* For the standard normal distribution

$$f(x) = \frac{1}{\sqrt{2\pi}} e^{-x^2/2}$$

(a) Determine the points of inflection.

(b) Show that the integral

$$\int_{-\infty}^{+\infty} f(x)\, dx = 1,$$

so that X is a proper random variable.

9. *Continuation.* Suppose that X has a normal distribution with the expectation μ, variance σ^2, and the probability density function

$$f(x) = \frac{1}{\sqrt{2\pi}\,\sigma} e^{-(x-\mu)^2/2\sigma^2}.$$

Show that the standardized form

$$Z = \frac{X - \mu}{\sigma}$$

has the standard normal distribution in problem 8. Thus, a linear function of a normal random variable is a normal random variable.

10. *Continuation.* Suppose X and Y have the bivariate normal distribution with the joint probability density function given by

$$f(x,y) = \frac{1}{2\pi\sigma_X\sigma_Y\sqrt{1-\rho^2}}$$

$$\times \exp\left\{-\frac{1}{2(1-\rho^2)}\left[\left(\frac{x-\mu}{\sigma_X}\right)^2 - 2\rho\left(\frac{x-\mu}{\sigma_X}\right)\left(\frac{y-\nu}{\sigma_Y}\right) + \left(\frac{y-\nu}{\sigma_Y}\right)^2\right]\right\}.$$

(a) By completing the square in the exponent, show that the density function can be rewritten as

$$f(x,y) = \frac{1}{\sqrt{2\pi}\,\sigma_X} \exp\left\{-\frac{1}{2}\left(\frac{x-\mu}{\sigma_X}\right)^2\right\} \times \frac{1}{\sqrt{2\pi}\,\sigma_Y\sqrt{1-\rho^2}}$$

$$\exp\left\{\frac{-1}{2(1-\rho^2)\sigma_Y^2}\left[(y-\nu)-\rho\frac{\sigma_Y}{\sigma_X}(x-\mu)\right]^2\right\}.$$

(b) Using (a) verify that the marginal density functions of X and Y are normal with means μ and ν and variances σ_X^2 and σ_Y^2, respectively, and that the covariance between X and Y is $\rho\sigma_X\sigma_Y$, so that ρ is the correlation coefficient.

(c) Using (a) show that the conditional density function $g(y \mid x)$ is a normal distribution with the expectation

$$E(Y \mid x) = \nu + \rho\frac{\sigma_Y}{\sigma_X}(x-\mu)$$

and the variance $(1-\rho^2)\sigma_Y^2$. The line represented by this equation is called the regression line of Y on X. How does the value of ρ affect the closeness of the points of the random variables (X, Y) to this line? Discuss the meaning of correlation coefficients in this light.

(d) Show that if two normal random variables X and Y have a zero correlation, then they are independently distributed.

(e) Verify for the bivariate normal case that $E[E(Y \mid X)] = E(Y)$ and $E(XY) = E[XE(Y \mid X)]$.

(f) Use (b) and (c) to verify

$$\sigma_Y^2 = E[\sigma_{Y \mid x}^2] + \sigma_{E(Y \mid X)}^2.$$

11. Prove the following inequality for a nondegenerate positive random variable X

$$E\left(\frac{1}{X}\right) > \frac{1}{E(X)}$$

(a) using the Schwarz inequality, and

(b) using the concept of convexity.

12. Let $X_1, \ldots, X_n$ be a sample of independent random variables having the common expectation $E(X_i) = \mu$ and the common variance $\mathrm{Var}(X_i) = \sigma^2$.

Let

$$\bar{X} = \frac{X_1 + \ldots + X_n}{n} \quad \text{and} \quad S_X^2 = \frac{\sum_{i=1}^{n} (X_i - \bar{X})^2}{n-1}$$

be the sample mean and sample variance.

(a) Show that

$$E(\bar{X}) = \mu \quad \text{and} \quad E(S_X^2) = \sigma^2.$$

In this sense $\bar{X}$ and S_X^2 as defined above are unbiased estimators of μ and σ^2, respectively.

(b) Show that

$$\sum_i (X_i - \bar{X})^2 = \frac{1}{n^2}(n-1) \sum_{i=1}^{n} \sum_{j=1}^{n} (X_i - X_j)^2$$

so that the sample variance may be rewritten as

$$S_x^2 = \frac{1}{n^2} \sum_{i=1}^{n} \sum_{j=1}^{n} (X_i - X_j)^2$$

and is the mean of the squares of the differences $X_i - X_j$.

13. Prove the following identities for the continuous case

$$\sigma_X^2 = E\,[\sigma_{X|Z}^2] + \sigma_{E(X|Z)}^2 \tag{5.34}$$

and

$$\sigma_{X,Y} = E\,[\sigma_{X,Y|Z}] + \sigma_{E(X|Z),\,E(Y|Z)} \tag{5.35}$$

14. Let $U = a_1 X_1 + \ldots + a_m X_m$ and $V = b_1 Y_1 + \ldots + b_n Y_n$ as given in section 5.2. Show that the covariance between U and V is given by

$$\sigma_{U,V} = \sum_{i=1}^{m} \sum_{j=1}^{n} a_i b_j \sigma_{X_i, Y_j} \tag{5.24}$$

15. Show that, if $X_1, \ldots, X_n$ are independent random variables, then the variance of the product $X_1, \ldots, X_n$ is given by

$$\operatorname{Var}(X_1 \ldots X_n) = \prod_{i=1}^{n} \{\sigma_{X_i}^2 + [E(X_i)]^2\} - \prod_{i=1}^{n} [E(X_i)]^2 \tag{5.27}$$

16. Referring to (5.11), show that the two proportions $\hat{p}_1$ and $\hat{p}_2$ of white balls drawn have zero covariance but that they are not independently distributed.

17. Show that if $Y = a + bX$, then $\rho_{X,Y} = \pm 1$.

18. *Multinomial distribution.* Compute the expectation $E(X_i X_j)$ for the multinomial distribution (5.19) and use the result to show that $\sigma_{X_i, X_j} = -np_ip_j$.

19. *Continuation.* Find the conditional distribution of X_j given X_i from (5.19) and the expectation $E(X_j | X_i)$ and the variance $\sigma^2_{X_j | X_i}$.

20. *Continuation.* Verify for the multinomial distribution the identities

$$\sigma^2_{X_j} = E\,[\sigma^2_{X_j | X_i}] + \sigma^2_{E(X_j | X_i)}$$

and

$$\sigma_{X_j, X_k} = E\,[\sigma_{X_j, X_k | X_i}] + \sigma_{E(X_j | X_i), E(X_k | X_i)}.$$

21. Let X_1 and X_2 be two i.i.d. random variables both having the Cauchy distribution:

$$f(x) = \frac{\theta}{\pi\,[\theta^2 + (x - \mu)^2]}, \qquad -\infty < x < \infty. \tag{6.20}$$

Find the density function of the mean

$$\bar{X} = \frac{X_1 + X_2}{2}.$$

22. *Multiple Poisson distribution.* Let a random vector $(X_1, \ldots, X_m)$ have the multiple Poisson distribution with the probability distribution

$$\Pr\{X_1 = k_1, \ldots, X_m = k_m\} = \frac{\lambda_1^{k_1} \ldots \lambda_m^{k_m}}{k_1! \ldots k_m!} e^{-(\lambda_1 + \ldots + \lambda_m)}.$$

Show that the sum of the probabilities for $k_i = 0, 1, \ldots, i = 1, \ldots, m$, is equal to unity.

23. *Continuation.* Compute the expectation $E\,[X_i]$, the variance $V\,[X_i]$, and the covariance $\text{Cov}\,[X_i, X_j]$.

24. *Continuation.* For $m = 3$ in problem 22, find

(a) The marginal distribution of X_1 and the marginal distribution of X_1 and X_2.

(b) The conditional distribution of X_1 given X_2, and the conditional distribution of X_1, X_2 given X_3.

(c) The distribution of the sum $X_1 + X_2 + X_3$.

25. Show that as $n \to \infty$ and $np_i \to \lambda_i$, then the multinomial distribution in equation (5.19) tends to the multiple Poisson distribution in problem 22.

CHAPTER 2

Probability Generating Functions

1. INTRODUCTION

The method of *generating functions* is one of the most important analytic tools in the study of stochastic processes with discrete sample spaces. It has been used in differential and integral calculus and in combinatorial analysis. The generating function of an integer-valued random variable completely determines its probability distribution and provides convenient ways to obtain the moments of the distribution. Furthermore, certain important relations among random variables may be simply expressed in terms of generating functions. Detailed treatments of the subject are given in Feller [1968] and Riordan [1958].

2. GENERAL PROPERTIES

Definition. Let $a_0, a_1, \ldots$ be a sequence of real numbers. If the power series

$$A(s) = a_0 + a_1 s + a_2 s^2 + \ldots \tag{2.1}$$

converges in some interval $-s_0 < s < s_0$, then the function $A(s)$ is called the *generating function* of the sequence $\{a_k\}$. Formula (2.1) in fact defines a transformation which carries the sequence $\{a_k\}$ into the function $A(s)$.

If X is an integer-valued random variable with the probability distribution

$$\Pr\{X = k\} = p_k, \quad k = 0, 1, \ldots, \tag{2.2}$$

then the power series

$$g_X(s) = p_0 + p_1 s + p_2 s^2 + \dots \tag{2.3}$$

is the *probability generating function* (p.g.f.) of X (or of the sequence $\{p_k\}$). Since every p_k is less than unity, the geometric series in (2.3) converges at least for $|s| < 1$. Furthermore, since (2.3) also converges for $|s| = 1$, it converges uniformly for $|s| \leq 1$, and hence the sum is continuous in that interval. Therefore, for every probability distribution $\{p_k\}$, there exists a unique continuous function $g_X(s)$ defined on $[0,1]$. The usefulness of (2.3) lies in the converse fact that every p.g.f. $g_X(s)$ determines a unique probability distribution $\{p_k\}$. In fact, one can obtain the individual probabilities p_k from the function $g_X(s)$ by the relation[1]

$$p_k = \frac{1}{k!} \frac{d^k}{ds^k} g_X(s) \bigg|_{s=0}, \qquad k = 0, 1, \dots. \tag{2.4}$$

When X is a proper random variable so that

$$g_X(1) = \sum_{k=0}^{\infty} p_k = 1, \tag{2.5}$$

the power series in (2.3) defines an expectation

$$g_X(s) = E(s^X). \tag{2.6}$$

In this case, we may use the p.g.f. to obtain the expectation and higher-order factorial moments of X by taking appropriate derivatives as follows:[2]

$$\begin{aligned} E(X) &= p_1 + 2p_2 + 3p_3 + \dots \\ &= \frac{d}{ds} g_X(s) \bigg|_{s=1} \end{aligned} \tag{2.7}$$

---

[1] If a power series $\sum_k^{\infty} c_k s^k$ converges to a function $f(s)$ for $|s| < s_0$, then the differentiated series $\sum_k^{\infty} k\, c_k s^{k-1}$ converges at least for $|s| < s_0$, and is equal to $f'(s)$ in that interval. Repeated application of this argument justifies (2.4). Furthermore, if $\sum_k^{\infty} k c_k s_0^{k-1}$ converges, then it is equal to $f'(s_0)$. See Buck [1965] or Rudin [1953].

[2] If one of the derivatives in (2.7) to (2.9) is infinite, then the corresponding series diverges and the moment is said to be infinite.

$$E[X(X-1)] = \frac{d^2}{ds^2} g_X(s) \Big|_{s=1} \tag{2.8}$$

$$E[X(X-1)\dots(X-r+1)] = \frac{d^r}{ds^r} g_X(s) \Big|_{s=1} \tag{2.9}$$

We obtain the variance of X from

$$\sigma_X^2 = E[X(X-1)] + E(X) - [E(X)]^2. \tag{2.10}$$

3. CONVOLUTIONS

Suppose two independent random variables X and Y have probability distributions

$$\Pr\{X=i\} = p_i \quad \text{and} \quad Pr\{Y=j\} = q_j, \tag{3.1}$$

so that their joint distribution is

$$\Pr\{X=i \text{ and } Y=j\} = p_i q_j. \tag{3.2}$$

Then the sum $Z = X + Y$ has the probability distribution

$$\Pr\{Z=k\} = r_k = p_0 q_k + p_1 q_{k-1} + \dots + p_k q_0. \tag{3.3}$$

The sequence $\{r_k\}$ is called the *convolution* of $\{p_k\}$ and $\{q_k\}$. We denote the convolutional relation by

$$\{r_k\} = \{p_k\} * \{q_k\}. \tag{3.4}$$

Let

$$g_X(s) = \sum_{k=0}^{\infty} p_k s^k$$

and

$$g_Y(s) = \sum_{k=0}^{\infty} q_k s^k$$

be the p.g.f.'s of X and Y respectively. Multiplying the infinite sums for $g_X(s)$ and $g_Y(s)$ and collecting terms according to the powers of s, we find

$$g_X(s) g_Y(s) = \sum_{k=0}^{\infty} r_k s^k$$

$$= g_Z(s), \tag{3.5}$$

where r_k is given in (3.3). Thus, the p.g.f. of the sum of two independently distributed random variables is the product of the two p.g.f.'s. Generalizing to an arbitrary number of random variables by induction, we have the following theorem.

Theorem 1. *Let $X_1, \ldots, X_n$ be independent integer-valued random variables with probability distributions $\{p_{k,1}\}, \ldots, \{p_{k,n}\}$ and* p.g.f.'s *$g_1(s), \ldots, g_n(s)$ respectively. The probability distribution of the sum*

$$Z_n = X_1 + \ldots + X_n, \tag{3.6}$$

which we denote by $\{r_k\}$, *is the convolution of $\{p_{k,1}\}, \ldots,$ and $\{p_{k,n}\}$*

$$\{r_k\} = \{p_{k,1}\} * \ldots * \{p_{k,n}\}. \tag{3.7}$$

The p.g.f. of Z_n is the product of $g_1(s), \ldots, g_n(s)$

$$G_{Z_n}(s) = g_1(s) \ldots g_n(s). \tag{3.8}$$

A more direct proof of (3.8) is available when $X_1, \ldots, X_n$ are proper random variables. In this case

$$\begin{aligned} G_{Z_n}(s) &= E(s^{Z_n}) = E\,[s^{X_1+X_2+\ldots X_n}] \\ &= E\,[s^{X_1} s^{X_2} \ldots s^{X_n}] \\ &= E(s^{X_1})\,E(s^{X_2}) \ldots E(s^{X_n}) \\ &= g_1(s)\,g_2(s) \ldots g_n(s). \end{aligned}$$

Corollary. *If $X_1, \ldots, X_n$ are independent and identically distributed (i.i.d.) random variables with a common probability distribution $\{p_k\}$ and the same p.g.f. $g(s)$, then the probability distribution of the sum $Z_n = X_1 + \ldots + X_n$, $\{r_k\}$, is the n-fold convolution of $\{p_k\}$ with itself,*

$$\{r_k\} = \{p_k\}^{n*}, \tag{3.9}$$

and the p.g.f. of Z_n is $g(s)$ raised to the n-th power,

$$G_{Z_n}(s) = [g(s)]^n. \tag{3.10}$$

4. EXAMPLES

4.1. Binomial Distribution.

A Bernoulli random variable X has the probability distribution (see example 3, section 2, Chapter 1)

$$\Pr\{X = 1\} = p, \qquad \Pr\{X = 0\} = 1 - p, \tag{4.1}$$

and the p.g.f.

$$g_X(s) = (1-p) + ps. \tag{4.2}$$

The number of successes (occurrences of $X = 1$) in n Bernoulli trials, Z_n, is the sum of n independent Bernoulli random variables. According to (3.10), the p.g.f. of Z_n is

$$G_{Z_n}(s) = [(1-p) + ps]^n. \tag{4.3}$$

We can also obtain (4.3) directly from (2.3) with $\{p_k\}$ being the binomial distribution

$$\Pr\{Z_n = k\} = \binom{n}{k} p^k (1-p)^{n-k}, \qquad k = 0, 1, \ldots, n. \tag{4.4}$$

Consider now a more general sequence of independent random variables $X_1, \ldots, X_n$ having distributions

$$\Pr\{X_i = k\} = \binom{m_i}{k} p^k (1-p)^{m_i - k},$$

$$i = 1, \ldots, n; \quad k = 0, 1, \ldots, m_i, \tag{4.5}$$

and p.g.f.'s

$$g_i(s) = [(1-p) + ps]^{m_i}, \qquad i = 1, \ldots, n. \tag{4.6}$$

The p.g.f. of the sum $Z_n = X_1 + \ldots + X_n$ is

$$G_{Z_n}(s) = [(1-p) + ps]^{m_1 + \ldots + m_n} = [(1-p) + ps]^N, \tag{4.7}$$

which is the p.g.f. of the binomial distribution with $N = m_1 + \ldots + m_n$ trials. Hence, the sum of independent binomial random variables with the same parameter p is also a binomial random variable.

4.2. Poisson Distribution.

The p.g.f. of the Poisson distribution

$$\Pr\{X = k\} = \frac{e^{-\lambda}\lambda^k}{k!}, \qquad k = 0, 1, \ldots, \tag{4.8}$$

is

$$g_X(s) = \sum_{k=0}^{\infty} s^k \frac{e^{-\lambda}\lambda^k}{k!} = e^{-\lambda(1-s)}. \tag{4.9}$$

Consider now another Poisson random variable Y, independent of X, having the probability distribution

$$\Pr\{Y = k\} = \frac{e^{-\mu}\mu^k}{k!}, \qquad k = 0, 1, \ldots, \tag{4.10}$$

and the p.g.f.

$$g_Y(s) = \sum_{k=0}^{\infty} s^k \frac{e^{-\mu}\mu^k}{k!} = e^{-\mu(1-s)}. \tag{4.11}$$

The p.g.f. of the sum $Z = X + Y$ is

$$g_Z(s) = g_X(s) g_Y(s) = e^{-(\lambda+\mu)(1-s)}. \tag{4.12}$$

Thus Z also has a Poisson distribution whose parameter is $\lambda + \mu$. Note that X and Y need not have the same parameter value.

4.3. Geometric and Negative Binomial Distributions.

Let X be the number of failures preceding the first success in an infinite sequence of Bernoulli trials. Obviously X has the *geometric distribution*

$$\Pr\{X = k\} = q^k p, \qquad k = 0, 1, \ldots, \tag{4.13}$$

and the p.g.f.

$$g(s) = \sum_{k=0}^{\infty} s^k q^k p = \frac{p}{1 - qs}, \tag{4.14}$$

with expectation

$$E(X) = \frac{d}{ds} g(s) \bigg|_{s=1} = \frac{q}{p}, \tag{4.15}$$

and variance

$$\sigma_X^2 = \frac{q}{p^2}. \tag{4.16}$$

Newton's binomial formula. We now find it useful to recall that, for any real number x,

$$(1 + t)^x = \sum_{k=0}^{\infty} \binom{x}{k} t^k, \qquad |t| < 1 \tag{4.17}$$

where the binomial coefficient is defined by

$$\binom{x}{k} = \frac{x(x-1)\dots(x-k+1)}{k!}. \tag{4.18}$$

If $x = n$ is a positive integer, then (4.18) becomes the ordinary binomial coefficient and is defined only for $n \geq k$, and the summation in (4.17) is taken over $k = 0$ to $k = n$. If $x = -r$ is a negative quantity, then

$$\binom{-r}{k} = (-1)^k \binom{r+k-1}{k}, \tag{4.19}$$

and the summation in (4.17) is extended to $k = \infty$.

Let Y_r be the number of failures preceding the r-th success in an infinite sequence of Bernoulli trials. We seek the probability distribution of Y_r. When $Y_r = k$, there are altogether $k + r$ trials, with the last trial resulting in success (the r-th success). Since there are $\binom{k+r-1}{k}$ possible combinations of k failures and $r - 1$ successes in the first $(k + r - 1)$ trials, the distribution of Y_r is

$$\Pr\{Y_r = k\} = \binom{k+r-1}{k} q^k p^r, \qquad k = 0, 1, \dots, \tag{4.20}$$

which is known as the *negative binomial distribution.* For the p.g.f. of Y_r, we write

$$G_{Y_r}(s) = \sum_{k=0}^{\infty} s^k \binom{k+r-1}{k} q^k p^r. \tag{4.21}$$

Introducing (4.19) in (4.21) and applying (4.17), we find

$$G_{Y_r}(s) = \sum_{k=0}^{\infty} \binom{-r}{k} (-qs)^{-k} p^r$$

$$= \left(\frac{p}{1-qs}\right)^r. \tag{4.22}$$

In deriving (4.20), we assumed that the parameter r is a positive integer. One can easily verify that, with the extended definition of the binomial coefficient in (4.18), (4.20) is a proper probability distribution with p.g.f. (4.22) for any positive number r.

We can now demonstrate a relationship between the geometric distribution (4.13) and the negative binomial distribution (4.20). Consider again an infinite sequence of Bernoulli trials and let X_i be the number of failures between the $(i-1)$-th success and the i-th success, for $i = 1, 2, \dots, r$. Insofar as the trials are independent, every sequence of trails following a success is a replica of any other sequence. Therefore, $X_1, \dots, X_r$ are i.i.d. random variables, each having the geometric distribution

$$\Pr\{X_i = k\} = q^k p, \qquad k = 0, 1, \dots, \quad i = 1, \dots, r, \tag{4.23}$$

and the p.g.f.

$$g(s) = \frac{p}{1 - qs}. \tag{4.24}$$

The sum

$$Y_r = X_1 + \dots + X_r$$

is the number of failures preceding the r-th success, and has a negative binomial distribution (4.20). According to Theorem 1, the negative binomial distribution in (4.20) is the r-fold convolution of the geometric distribution (4.23), and the p.g.f. of Y_r is the p.g.f. (4.24) raised to the r-th power, which is the same as (4.22).

Let $Y_1, \dots, Y_r$ be independent random variables, each having a negative binomial distribution with

$$\Pr\{Y_j = k\} = \binom{k + r_j - 1}{k} q^k p^{r_j}, \qquad j = 1, \dots, n, \quad k = 0, \dots, \tag{4.25}$$

and the p.g.f.

$$G_{Y_j}(s) = \left(\frac{p}{1 - qs}\right)^{r_j}, \qquad j - 1, \dots, n. \tag{4.26}$$

The sum

$$Z_n = Y_1 + \dots + Y_n$$

has a negative binomial distribution with

$$\Pr\{Z_n = k\} = \binom{k + r - 1}{k} q^k p^r, \qquad k = 0, 1, \dots \tag{4.27}$$

and the p.g.f.

$$G_{Z_n}(s) = \left(\frac{p}{1 - qs}\right)^r, \tag{4.28}$$

where $r = r_1 + \ldots + r_n$. While it is tedious to derive probability distribution (4.27) from (4.25) by means of convolution, the relationship between the p.g.f.'s (4.26) and (4.28) is quite clear. Therefore, the sum of independent negative binomial random variables with the same parameter p is a negative binomial random variable.

5. THE CONTINUITY THEOREM

It is well known in a binomial distribution with probability p that, if $n \to \infty$ in such a way that $np \to \lambda$, then the probability function tends to a Poisson probability function and the p.g.f. tends to the p.g.f. of a Poisson distribution. This phenomenon prevails in general. A sequence of probability distributions converges to a limiting distribution if and only if the corresponding probability generating functions converge. Formally, we present the theorem.

Theorem 2. *For every fixed n, let $\{p_{k,n}\}$ be a probability distribution so that*

$$p_{k,n} \geq 0 \quad \text{and} \quad \sum_{k=0}^{\infty} p_{k,n} = 1, \tag{5.1}$$

and let

$$g_n(s) = \sum_{k=0}^{\infty} p_{k,n} s^k \tag{5.2}$$

be the corresponding p.g.f. Suppose that there exists a probability distribution $\{p_k\}$ with the p.g.f.

$$G(s) = \sum_{k=0}^{\infty} p_k s^k. \tag{5.3}$$

Then in order that for each k

$$\lim_{n\to\infty} p_{k,n} = p_k, \tag{5.4}$$

it is necessary and sufficient that

$$\lim_{n\to\infty} g_n(s) = G(s), \quad \text{for all } s,\ |s| < 1. \tag{5.5}$$

Proof. First assume that (5.4) holds for $k = 0, 1, \ldots$. For a fixed s, $|s| < 1$,

$$|g_n(s) - G(s)| \le \sum_{k=0}^{r} |p_{k,n} - p_k| |s|^k + \left| \sum_{k=r+1}^{\infty} (p_{k,n} - p_k) |s|^k \right|$$
$$\le \sum_{k=0}^{r} |p_{k,n} - p_k| |s|^k + \frac{|s|^{r+1}}{1 - |s|}. \tag{5.6}$$

Given $\varepsilon > 0$, choose a sufficiently large integer r so that $|s|^{r+1}/(1 - |s|) < \varepsilon/2$. Also find n_0 such that $|p_{k,n} - p_k| < \varepsilon/2(r + 1)$, for $k = 0, 1, \ldots, r$, and for $n > n_0$. Then $|g_n(s) - G(s)| < \varepsilon$ for all $n \ge n_0$.

Conversely, suppose (5.5) is true. We prove (5.4) by induction. For $k = 0$, $g_n(0) = p_{0,n}$ and $G(0) = p_0$. According to (5.5), $\lim_{n\to\infty} g_n(0) = G(0)$, therefore

$$\lim_{n\to\infty} p_{0,n} = p_0. \tag{5.7}$$

Now assuming $\lim_{n\to\infty} p_{i,n} = p_i$ is true for $i = 0, 1, \ldots, k - 1$, we need to prove $\lim_{n\to\infty} p_{k,n} = p_k$. Clearly,

$$|p_{k,n} - p_k| \le |g_n(s) - G(s)| |s|^{-k} + \sum_{i=1}^{k-1} |p_{i,n} - p_i| |s|^{i-k}$$
$$+ \sum_{i=k+1}^{\infty} |p_{i,n} - p_i| |s|^{i-k} \tag{5.8}$$

where

$$\sum_{i=k+1}^{\infty} |p_{i,n} - p_i| |s|^{i-k} \le \frac{|s|}{1 - |s|}. \tag{5.9}$$

Letting $n \to \infty$ and taking the limit of both sides of (5.8) yields

$$\lim_{n\to\infty} |p_{k,n} - p_k| \le \lim_{n\to\infty} |g_n(s) - G(s)| |s|^{-k}$$
$$+ \sum_{i=0}^{k-1} \lim_{n\to\infty} |p_{i,n} - p_i| |s|^{i-k} + \frac{|s|}{1 - |s|}$$
$$= \frac{|s|}{1 - |s|}. \tag{5.10}$$

Given $\varepsilon > 0$, we choose $0 < s < \varepsilon/(1+\varepsilon)$, so that $\lim_{n\to\infty} |p_{k,n} - p_k| < \varepsilon$. This proves $\lim_{n\to\infty} p_{k,n} = p_k$, for $k = 0, 1, \ldots$.

Example 1. *Binomial Distribution.* In a binomial distribution with probability p, if $n \to \infty$ in such a way that $np \to \lambda$, then

$$\lim_{n\to\infty} \binom{n}{k} p^k (1-p)^{n-k} = \frac{e^{-\lambda}\lambda^k}{k!} \tag{5.11}$$

and

$$\lim_{n\to\infty} [1 - p + ps]^n = e^{-(1-s)\lambda}. \tag{5.12}$$

Example 2. *Negative binomial distribution.* In the probability function (4.20), if $r \to \infty$ in such a way that $rq \to \lambda$, then

$$\lim_{r\to\infty} \binom{k+r-1}{k} q^k p^r = \frac{e^{-\lambda}\lambda^k}{k!} \tag{5.13}$$

and

$$\lim_{r\to\infty} \left(\frac{p}{1-qs}\right)^r = e^{-(1-s)\lambda}. \tag{5.14}$$

6. PARTIAL FRACTION EXPANSIONS

We may obtain individual probabilities of a random variable from the corresponding p.g.f. by taking repeated derivatives as in formula (2.4). In many cases, the necessary calculations involved are so overwhelming that they render this approach undesirable, and one has to resort to some other means to expand the p.g.f. in a power series. The most useful method is that of partial fraction expansion, which we present for the case where a p.g.f. is a rational function.

Suppose that the p.g.f. of a random variable can be expressed as a ratio

$$G(s) = \frac{U(s)}{V(s)} \tag{6.1}$$

where $U(s)$ and $V(s)$ are polynomials with no common roots. If $U(s)$ and $V(s)$ have a common factor, it should be cancelled before the method is applied. By division, if necessary, we can assume that the degree of $V(s)$ is m and the degree of $U(s)$ is less than m.

Suppose that the equation $V(s) = 0$ has m distinct real roots, $s_1, \ldots, s_m$, so that

$$V(s) = (s - s_1)(s - s_2) \ldots (s - s_m). \tag{6.2}$$

Then the ratio in (6.1) can be decomposed into partial fractions

$$G(s) = \frac{a_1}{s_1 - s} + \frac{a_2}{s_2 - s} + \ldots + \frac{a_m}{s_m - s}, \tag{6.3}$$

where the constants $a_1, \ldots, a_m$ are determined from

$$a_r = \frac{-U(s_r)}{V'(s_r)}, \qquad r = 1, \ldots, m. \tag{6.4}$$

Equation (6.3) is well known in algebra. To prove (6.4) for $r = 1$ we substitute (6.2) into (6.1) and multiply by $(s_1 - s)$ to obtain

$$(s_1 - s)\, G(s) = \frac{-U(s)}{(s - s_2)(s - s_3) \ldots (s - s_m)}. \tag{6.5}$$

It is evident from (6.3) that as $s \to s_1$, the left-hand side of (6.5) tends to a_1, the numerator on the right-hand side tends to $-U(s_1)$ and the denominator to $(s_1 - s_2)(s_1 - s_3) \ldots (s_1 - s_m)$, which is the same as $V'(s_1)$. Hence (6.4) is proven for $r = 1$. Since the same argument applies to all roots, (6.4) is true for all r.

Now we use formula (6.3) to derive the coefficient of s^k in $G(s)$. We first write

$$\frac{1}{s_r - s} = \frac{1}{s_r}\left[\frac{1}{1 - s/s_r}\right] = \frac{1}{s_r}\left[1 + \frac{s}{s_r} + \left(\frac{s}{s_r}\right)^2 + \ldots\right]. \tag{6.6}$$

Substituting (6.6) for $r = 1, \ldots, m$ in (6.3) and selecting s such that $|s/s_r| < 1$, we find an exact expression for the coefficient of s^k:

$$p_k = \frac{a_1}{s_1^{k+1}} + \frac{a_2}{s_2^{k+1}} + \ldots + \frac{a_m}{s_m^{k+1}}, \qquad k = 0, 1, \cdots. \tag{6.7}$$

Strict application of this method requires calculation of all m roots, which is usually prohibitive. However, we see from (6.7) that the value of p_k is dominated by the term corresponding to the smallest root in absolute value. Suppose s_1 is smaller in absolute value than any other root. Then

$$p_k \doteq \frac{a_1}{s_1^{k+1}} \tag{6.8}$$

represents an approximation to p_k and the approximation becomes better as k increases. Furthermore, even if the roots $\{s_r\}$ are not all distinct, (6.8) remains valid as long as s_1 is itself a simple root.

7. MULTIVARIATE PROBABILITY GENERATING FUNCTIONS

Let us consider a vector of m integer valued random variables

$$\mathbf{X} = \begin{pmatrix} X_1 \\ \vdots \\ X_m \end{pmatrix} \tag{7.1}$$

with a joint probability distribution

$$\Pr\{X_1 = k_1, \ldots, X_m = k_m\} = p_{k_1 \ldots k_m}, \qquad k_i = 0, 1, \ldots; \quad i = 1, \ldots, m. \tag{7.2}$$

$\mathbf{X}$ is called a *proper random vector* if

$$\sum_{k_1} \cdots \sum_{k_m} p_{k_1 \ldots k_m} = 1 \tag{7.3}$$

and an *improper random vector* if the sum is less than one. The p.g.f. of $\mathbf{X}$ is defined by

$$G_{\mathbf{X}}(\mathbf{s}) = G_{\mathbf{X}}(s_1, \ldots, s_m) = \sum_{k_1} \cdots \sum_{k_m} s_1^{k_1} \cdots s_m^{k_m} p_{k_1 \ldots k_m}, \tag{7.4}$$

for $|s_1| < 1, \ldots, |s_m| < 1$. When $\mathbf{X}$ is a proper random vector,

$$G_{\mathbf{X}}(\mathbf{s}) = E(s_1^{X_1} \cdots s_m^{X_m}) \tag{7.5}$$

and we can expand the p.g.f. $G_{\mathbf{X}}(s_1, \ldots, s_m)$ in a power series in $s_1, \ldots, s_m$ to obtain joint probabilities (7.2).

We see from (7.5) that the p.g.f. of the sum $Z_m = X_1 + \ldots + X_m$ is

$$E(s^{Z_m}) = E(s^{X_1} \ldots s^{X_m}) = G_X(s, \ldots, s). \tag{7.6}$$

Furthermore, if $X_1, \ldots, X_m$ are mutually independent random variables, then

$$E(s_1^{X_1} \dots s_m^{X_m}) = E(s_1^{X_1}) \dots E(s_m^{X_m}). \tag{7.7}$$

The p.g.f. of the sum of independent random vectors is the product of the p.g.f.'s. Explicitly, we state the theorem.

Theorem 5. *If n vectors*

$$\mathbf{Y}_j = \begin{pmatrix} Y_{1j} \\ \vdots \\ Y_{mj} \end{pmatrix}, \qquad j = 1, \dots, n,$$

are independently distributed and have p.g.f.'s $g_j(s_1, \dots, s_m)$, *then the p.g.f. of the vector sum*

$$X = \sum_{j=1}^{n} Y_j = \begin{pmatrix} \sum_{j=1}^{n} Y_{1j} \\ \vdots \\ \sum_{j=1}^{n} Y_{mj} \end{pmatrix}$$

is

$$G_X(s_1, \dots, s_m) = \prod_{j=1}^{n} g_j(s_1, \dots, s_m). \tag{7.8}$$

If $\mathbf{Y}_j$ *are identically distributed with a common p.g.f.* $g(s_1, \dots, s_m)$, *then*

$$G_{\mathbf{X}}(s_1, \dots, s_m) = [g(s_1, \dots, s_m)]^n. \tag{7.9}$$

The proof used for Theorem 1 extends immediately to this case. We leave the details to the reader.

7.1 Probability Generating Functions of Marginal Distributions.

For a random vector of m components

$$\mathbf{X} = \begin{pmatrix} X_1 \\ \vdots \\ X_m \end{pmatrix} \tag{7.1}$$

there are $m - 1$ "levels" of marginal distributions. The k-th "level" marginal distribution is a joint distribution of k components of $\mathbf{X}$. We can find the corresponding p.g.f. from the p.g.f. of $\mathbf{X}$ by substituting unity for appropriate $m - k$ components of the vector $(s_1, \ldots, s_m)'$ into (7.5). For the first two "levels" of marginal distributions, we have

$$G_{X_i}(s_i) = E\,[s_i^{X_i}] = G_{\mathbf{X}}(1, \ldots, s_i, \ldots, 1) \tag{7.10}$$

and

$$G_{X_iX_j}(s_i, s_j) = E\,[S_i^{X_i} s_j^{X_j}] = G_{\mathbf{X}}(1, \ldots, s_i, \ldots, s_j, \ldots, 1). \tag{7.11}$$

It follows that the first two moments are given by

$$E(X_i) = \left.\frac{\partial G_{\mathbf{X}}(s_1, \ldots, s_m)}{\partial s_i}\right|_{\mathbf{s}=\begin{pmatrix}1\\ \vdots\\ 1\end{pmatrix}}, \tag{7.12}$$

$$E\,[X_i(X_i - 1)] = \left.\frac{\partial^2 G_{\mathbf{X}}(s_1, \ldots, s_m)}{\partial s_i^2}\right|_{\mathbf{s}=\begin{pmatrix}1\\ \vdots\\ 1\end{pmatrix}}, \tag{7.13}$$

and

$$E(X_iX_j) = \left.\frac{\partial^2}{\partial s_i \partial s_j} G_{\mathbf{X}}(s_1, \ldots, s_m)\right|_{\mathbf{s}=\begin{pmatrix}1\\ \vdots\\ 1\end{pmatrix}} \tag{7.14}$$

We compute the variances and covariances from

$$\sigma_{X_i}^2 = E\,[X_i(X_i - 1)] + E(X_i) - [E(X_i)]^2, \tag{7.15}$$

and

$$\sigma_{X_i,X_j} = E(X_iX_j) - E(X_i)\,E(X_j). \tag{7.16}$$

7.2. Probability Generating Functions of Conditional Distributions.

Consider the random vector $\mathbf{X} = (X_1, \ldots, X_m)'$ and the p.g.f. $G_{\mathbf{X}}(\mathbf{s})$ in (7.5). The p.g.f. of the conditional distribution of X_2 given $X_1 = k_1$ is defined by

$$G_{X_2|k_1}(s_2) = \sum_{k_2} s_2^{k_2} \frac{\Pr\{X_1 = k_1, X_2 = k_2\}}{\Pr\{X_1 = k_1\}}, \tag{7.17}$$

where $\Pr\{X_1 = k_1\} > 0$. We compute the numerator from

$$\sum_{k_2} s_2^{k_2} \Pr\{X_1 = k_1, X_2 = k_2\} = \frac{1}{k_1!} \frac{\partial^{k_1}}{\partial s_1^{k_1}} G_{\mathbf{X}}(\mathbf{s}) \Bigg|_{\substack{s_1=0 \\ s_3=\ldots=s_m=1}} \tag{7.18}$$

and the denominator from

$$\Pr\{X_1 = k_1\} = \frac{1}{k_1!} \frac{\partial^{k_1}}{\partial s_1^{k_1}} G_{\mathbf{X}}(\mathbf{s}) \Bigg|_{\substack{s_1=0 \\ s_2=s_3=\ldots=s_m=1}} \tag{7.19}$$

As a consequence,

$$G_{X_2|k_1}(s_2) = \frac{D\, G_{\mathbf{X}}(\mathbf{s}) \Big|_{\substack{s_1=0 \\ s_3=\ldots=s_m=1}}}{D\, G_{\mathbf{X}}(\mathbf{s}) \Big|_{\substack{s_1=0 \\ s_2=s_3=\ldots=s_m=1}}} \tag{7.20}$$

where D stands for the differentiation

$$D = \frac{\partial^{k_1}}{\partial s_1^{k_1}}.$$

The p.g.f. of $X_{j+1}, \ldots, X_m$ given $X_1 = k_1, \ldots, X_j = k_j$ is similarly derived from

$$G_{X_{j+1}, \ldots, X_m | k_1, \ldots, k_j}(s_{j+1}^{X_{j+1}} \ldots s_m^{X_m})$$

$$= \frac{D\, G_{\mathbf{X}}(\mathbf{s}) \Big|_{s_1=\ldots=s_j=0}}{D\, G_{\mathbf{X}}(\mathbf{s}) \Big|_{\substack{s_1=\ldots=s_j=0 \\ s_{j+1}=\ldots=s_m=1}}} \tag{7.21}$$

where

$$D = \left(\frac{\partial^{k_1}}{\partial s_1^{k_1}}\right) \cdots \left(\frac{\partial^{k_j}}{\partial s_j^{k_j}}\right).$$

Example 1. *Multinomial Distribution.* The multinomial distribution given by Equation (5.19) in Chapter 1 has the p.g.f.

$$G_{\mathbf{X}}(s_1, \ldots, s_m) = (p_0 + p_1 s_1 + \ldots + p_m s_m)^n. \tag{7.22}$$

This is most easily seen by writing the multinomial random vector as the sum of n independent and identically distributed random vectors and applying (7.9). Using (7.6) and (7.10), we have the p.g.f. of the sum $Z_m = X_1 + \ldots + X_m$,

$$\begin{aligned} G_{\mathbf{X}}(s, \ldots, s) &= [p_0 + p_1 s + \ldots + p_m s]^n \\ &= [p_0 + (1 - p_0)s]^n, \end{aligned} \tag{7.23}$$

and the p.g.f. of the marginal distribution of X_i,

$$G_{\mathbf{X}}(1, \ldots, s_i, \ldots, 1) = [1 - p_i + p_i s_i]^n. \tag{7.24}$$

Thus, both Z_m and X_i are binomial random variables. The marginal distribution of X_i and X_j is trinomial with the p.g.f.

$$G_{\mathbf{X}}(1, \ldots, s_i, \ldots, s_j, \ldots, 1) = [(1 - p_i - p_j) + p_i s_i + p_j s_j]^n. \tag{7.25}$$

It is easily shown that

$$E(X_i) = np_i, \qquad E(X_i X_j) = n(n-1)p_i p_j$$

and

$$\operatorname{Cov}(X_i, X_j) = -np_i p_j \tag{7.26}$$

which agrees with Equation (5.23) in Chapter 1.

For the conditional distribution of X_2 given $X_1 = k_1$, we apply (7.20) to (7.22) to obtain

$$G_{X_2|k_1}(s_2) = \left[1 - \frac{p_2}{1 - p_1} + \frac{p_2}{1 - p_1} s_2\right]^{n - k_1} \tag{7.27}$$

with the expectation

$$E[X_2|k_1] = (n - k_1)\frac{p_2}{1 - p_1}. \tag{7.28}$$

Example 2. *Negative Multinomial Distribution (Multivariate Pascal Distribution).* Consider a sequence of independent trials, each of which results in a success, S, or in one of the failures, $F_1, F_2, \ldots$, or F_m, with corresponding probabilities $p, q_1, q_2, \ldots, q_m$, so that

$$p + q_1 + q_2 + \ldots + q_m = 1. \tag{7.29}$$

Let X_i be the number of failures of type F_i, for $i = 1, \ldots, m$, preceding the rth success in an infinite sequence of trials. The joint probability distribution of $X_1, \ldots, X_m$ is

$$\Pr\{X_1 = k_1, \ldots, X_m = k_m\} = \frac{(k+r-1)!}{k_1! \ldots k_m!(r-1)!} q_1^{k_1} \ldots q_m^{k_m} p^r \tag{7.30}$$

where $k = k_1 + \ldots + k_m$, and the corresponding p.g.f. is

$$G_{\mathbf{X}}(s_1, \ldots, s_m)$$
$$= \sum_{k_1=0}^{\infty} \ldots \sum_{k_m=0}^{\infty} s_1^{k_1} \ldots s_m^{k_m} \frac{(k+r-1)!}{k_1! \ldots k_m!(r-1)!} q_1^{k_1} \ldots q_m^{k_m} p^r$$
$$= \left[\frac{p}{1 - q_1 s_1 - \ldots - q_m s_m}\right]^r. \tag{7.31}$$

Formula (7.31) shows that $(X_1, \ldots, X_m)$ is the sum of r i.i.d. random vectors, which have the same p.g.f.

$$\frac{p}{1 - q_1 s_1 - \ldots - q_m s_m}.$$

We use (7.12), (7.13) and (7.14) to compute from (7.31) expectations

$$E(X_i) = r\frac{q_i}{p}, \qquad i = 1, \ldots, m, \tag{7.32}$$

variances

$$\sigma_{X_i}^2 = r\frac{q_i}{p}\left(1 + \frac{q_i}{p}\right), \qquad i = 1, \ldots, m, \tag{7.33}$$

and covariances

$$\sigma_{X_i, X_j} = r\frac{q_i q_j}{p^2}. \qquad i \neq j; \quad i, j = 1, \ldots, m. \tag{7.34}$$

The distribution of the sum $Z_m = X_1 + \ldots + X_m$ and the marginal distributions of any of the random variables X_i are negative binomial distributions. This is evident from the definitions of these random variables; we may see it explicitly by writing the p.g.f. of the sum as

$$E(s^{Z_m}) = G_X(s, \ldots, s) = \left[\frac{p}{1 - p_1 s - \ldots - q_m s}\right]^r = \left[\frac{p}{1 - qs}\right]^r \tag{7.35}$$

where $q = q_1 + \ldots + q_m$, and the p.g.f. of X_i as

$$E(s_i^{X_i}) = G_{\mathbf{X}}(1, \ldots, s_i, \ldots, 1)$$
$$= \left[\frac{p}{1 - q_1 - \ldots - q_i s_i - \ldots - q_m}\right]^r$$
$$= \left[\frac{p}{p + q_i - q_i s_i}\right]^r = \left[\frac{P_i}{1 - Q_i s_i}\right]^r, \tag{7.36}$$

where

$$P_i = \frac{p}{p + q_i}, \qquad Q_i = \frac{q_i}{p + q_i}, \qquad P_i + Q_i = 1.$$

It may be noted that since

$$\sigma_{Z_m}^2 = \sum_{i=1}^{m} \sigma_{X_i}^2 + \sum_{\substack{i=1 \\ i \neq j}}^{m} \sum_{j=1}^{m} \sigma_{X_i, X_j} \tag{7.37}$$

we have

$$r\frac{q}{p^2} = \sum_{i=1}^{m} r\frac{q_i}{p}\left(1 + \frac{q_i}{p}\right) + \sum_{\substack{i=1 \\ i \neq j}}^{m} \sum_{j=1}^{m} r\frac{q_i q_j}{p^2}, \tag{7.38}$$

which may be verified by direct computation.

To derive the p.g.f. of a conditional distribution for the negative multinomial distribution, we may invoke (7.20) or (7.21). For the conditional distribution of X_2 given $X_1 = k_1$, we apply (7.20) to (7.31) to get the p.g.f.:

$$G_{X_2|k_1}(s_2) = \left[\frac{(p + q_1)/(p + q_1 + q_2)}{1 - \left(\dfrac{q_2}{p + q_1 + q_2}\right) s_2}\right]^{r + k_1} \tag{7.39}$$

The multinomial distribution and the negative multinomial distribution provide an interesting contrast. Table 1 shows the corresponding probability generating functions for $m = 3$. We note that, for the multinomial distribution, the marginal distributions resemble the original joint distribution, whereas for the negative multinomial distribution, the conditional distributions resemble the original joint distribution. For derivation of the p.g.f.'s and comparison of the probability functions, see problems 9 to 13 of this chapter.

Table 1. Probability generating functions: Multinomial distribution vs. negative multinomial distribution

		Multinomial Distribution	Negative Multinomial Distribution
Joint Distribution of X_1, X_2, X_3	$E[s_1^{X_1} s_2^{X_2} s_3^{X_3}]$	$[p_0 + p_1 s_1 + p_2 s_2 + p_3 s_3]^n$	$\left[\dfrac{p}{1 - q_1 s_1 - q_2 s_2 - q_3 s_3}\right]^r$
Marginal Distributions	$E[s_1^{X_1} s_2^{X_2}]$	$[(1 - p_1 - p_2) + p_1 s_1 + p_2 s_2]^n$	$\left[\dfrac{p/(p + q_1 + q_2)}{1 - \dfrac{q_1}{p + q_1 + q_2} s_1 - \dfrac{q_2}{p + q_1 + q_2} s_2}\right]$
	$E[s_1^{X_1}]$	$[(1 - p_1) + p_1 s_1]^n$	$\left[\dfrac{p/(p + q_1)}{1 - \dfrac{q_1}{p + q_1} s_1}\right]^r$
Conditional Distributions	$E[s_1^{X_1} s_2^{X_2} \mid X_3 = k_3]$	$\left[\dfrac{p_0}{p_0 + p_1 + p_2} + \dfrac{p_1}{p_0 + p_1 + p_2} s_1 + \dfrac{p_2}{p_0 + p_1 + p_2} s_2\right]^{n-k_3}$	$\left[\dfrac{1 - q_1 - q_2}{1 - q_1 s_1 - q_2 s_2}\right]^{r+k_3}$
	$E[s_1^{X_1} \mid X_2 = k_2, X_3 = k_3]$	$\left[\dfrac{p_0}{p_0 + p_1} + \dfrac{p_1}{p_0 + p_1} s_1\right]^{n-k_2-k_3}$	$\left[\dfrac{1 - q_1}{1 - q_1 s_1}\right]^{r+k_2+k_3}$

8. SUM OF A RANDOM NUMBER OF RANDOM VARIABLES

If a probability distribution is altered by allowing one of its parameters to behave as a random variable, the resulting distribution is said to be *compound.* An important compound distribution is that of the sum of a random number of random variables.

Theorem 3. *Let* $\{X_k\}$ *be a sequence of independent and identically distributed proper random variables with the common p.g.f.*

$$g(s) = E(s^{X_i}), \qquad i = 1, 2, \dots, \tag{8.1}$$

and let

$$Z_N = X_1 + \dots + X_N \tag{8.2}$$

where N is also a random variable with the p.g.f.

$$h(s) = E(s^N). \tag{8.3}$$

Denote the p.g.f. of the compound distribution of Z_N *by*

$$G(s) = E(s^{Z_N}). \tag{8.4}$$

Then

$$G(s) = h[g(s)]. \tag{8.5}$$

Proof. Since

$$E(s^{Z_N}) = E[E(s^{Z_N} \mid N)] \tag{8.6}$$

and

$$E(s^{Z_N} \mid N) = E(s^{X_1 + \dots + X_N} \mid N) = \{g(s)\}^N, \tag{8.7}$$

we have

$$G(s) = E[\{g(s)\}^N] = h[g(s)]. \tag{8.5}$$

This simple functional relation between the p.g.f. $G(s)$ of the compound distribution of Z_N and the p.g.f's $h(s)$ and $g(s)$ is quite useful, as we will illustrate in an example of branching processes in Chapter 4.

Example: Let X_i have the logarithmic distribution with

$$\Pr\{X_i = k\} = -\frac{p^k}{k \log(1-p)}, \qquad k = 1, 2, \dots, \tag{8.8}$$

where $0 < p < 1$, and the p.g.f.

$$g(s) = \frac{\log(1 - ps)}{\log(1 - p)}. \tag{8.9}$$

Let N have the Poisson distribution with the p.g.f.

$$h(s) = e^{-(1-s)\lambda}. \tag{8.10}$$

According to the theorem, the p.g.f. of $Z_N = X_1 + \ldots + X_N$ is

$$\begin{aligned} G(s) &= e^{-[1-\log(1-ps)/\log(1-p)]\lambda} \\ &= e^{-\lambda}(1 - ps)^{\lambda/\log(1-p)}. \end{aligned} \tag{8.11}$$

Now let

$$r = -\frac{\lambda}{\log(1 - p)} \tag{8.12}$$

so that

$$-\lambda = r\log(1 - p) \quad \text{and} \quad e^{-\lambda} = (1 - p)^r. \tag{8.13}$$

Substituting (8.12) and (8.13) into (8.11) gives

$$G(s) = \left[\frac{1 - p}{1 - ps}\right]^r, \tag{8.14}$$

which is the p.g.f. of the negative binomial distribution in (4.22) with p replaced by $(1 - p)$.

9. PROBLEMS FOR SOLUTION

1. *Binomial distribution.* Derive the p.g.f.

$$G_{Z_n}(s) = [(1 - p) + ps]^n \tag{4.3}$$

for the distribution given in equation (4.4).

2. *Continuation.* Let X_1 and X_2 be two independent binomial random variables with the probability distributions given in equation (4.5). Derive the probability distribution of the sum $Z_2 = X_1 + X_2$. From this distribution find the expectation $E[Z_2]$, the variance $\text{Var}[Z_2]$, and the p.g.f. of Z_2.

3. *Newton's binomial expansion.* Verify the equation

$$(1 + t)^x = \sum_{k=0}^{\infty} \binom{x}{k} t^k, \quad |t| < 1$$

for any real number x by the method of undetermined coefficients.

4. *Continuation.* Newton's binomial formula in Problem 3 can be written as

$$(a_0 + a_1)^x = \sum_{k_1=0}^{\infty} \binom{x}{k_1} a_1^{k_1} a_0^{x-k_1}, \quad |a_1| < |a_0|.$$

Generalize this formula by induction to the multinomial expansion:

$$(a_0 + a_1 + \dots + a_m)^x = \sum_{k_1=0}^{\infty} \cdots \sum_{k_m=0}^{\infty} \binom{x}{k_1, \dots, k_m} a_1^{k_1} \dots a_m^{k_m} a_0^{n-k},$$

where $\left|\sum_{i=1}^{m} a_i\right| < |a_0|$, $k = k_1 + \dots + k_m$, and the multinomial coefficient is defined by

$$\binom{x}{k_1, \dots, k_m} = \frac{x(x-1)\dots(x-k+1)}{k_1! \dots k_m!}$$

for all real x. Use this multinomial expansion to verify the p.g.f. in (7.22).

5. Prove the identify

$$\binom{-r}{k} = (-1)^k \binom{r+k-1}{k} \tag{4.22}$$

and use it to verify the identify

$$\sum_{k=0}^{\infty} \binom{r+k-1}{k} (qs)^k = (1-qs)^{-r}.$$

6. *Negative binomial distribution.* Let Z_r have the negative binomial distribution in (4.27). Show that Z_r is a proper random variable, or

$$\sum_{k=0}^{\infty} \binom{k+r-1}{k} q^k p^r = 1,$$

and find the expectation $E(Z_r)$ from

$$E(Z_r) = \sum_{k=0}^{\infty} k \binom{k+r-1}{k} q^k p^r.$$

7. *Continuation.* Let $Y_1, \dots, Y_n$ be independently distributed negative binomial random variables; each has the probability distribution in (4.25). Derive by induction the probability distribution of the sum $Z_n = Y_1 + \dots + Y_n$.

8. Prove Theorem 5.

9. Use Theorem 5 to derive the p.g.f. of the multinomial distribution in (7.22).

10. *Negative multinomial distribution.* In formula (7.30) let $m = 3$ so that $p + q_1 + q_2 + q_3 = 1$. Find the marginal probability distributions: $\Pr\{X_1 = k_1\}$ and $\Pr\{X_1 = k_1, X_2 = k_2\}$.

11. *Continuation.* Find the conditional probability distributions: $\Pr\{X_1 = k_1 | k_2, k_3\}$, $\Pr\{X_1 = k_1, X_2 = k_2 | k_3\}$, and $\Pr\{X_2 = k_2 | k_1\}$.

12. *Continuation.* Derive the p.g.f. for each of the probability distributions in Problems 10 and 11.

13. *Continuation.* Use the results in Problem 12 and equation (4.22) in Chapter 1 to derive the p.g.f. for the joint probability distribution of X_1, X_2 and X_3.

14. *Multinomial distribution.* Solve Problems 10 through 13 for a multinomial distribution with $p_0 + p_1 + p_2 + p_3 = 1$.

15. Let a random variable X have the p.g.f. $G_X(s)$ and let a and b be constants. Find the p.g.f. for the linear function $a + bX$.

16. Find the p.g.f.'s for the following probabilities in terms of $G_X(s)$:
(a) $\Pr\{X \le n\}$,
(b) $\Pr\{X \ge n\}$.

17. *The continuity theorem.* In a binomial distribution with probability p, if $n \to \infty$ in such a way that $np \to \lambda$, then the probability function

$$\lim_{n\to\infty} \binom{n}{k} p^k (1-p)^{n-k} = \frac{e^{-\lambda}\lambda^k}{k!}$$

and the p.g.f.

$$\lim_{n\to\infty} [1 - p + ps]^n = e^{-\lambda(1-s)}.$$

Prove the equalities.

18. *Continuation.* In the negative binomial distribution (4.20), if $r \to \infty$ in such a way that $rq \to \lambda$, then the probability function

$$\lim_{r\to\infty} \binom{k+r-1}{k} q^k p^r = \frac{e^{-\lambda}\lambda^k}{k!}$$

and the p.g.f.

$$\lim_{r\to\infty} \left(\frac{p}{1-qs}\right)^r = e^{-\lambda(1-s)}.$$

Prove the equalities.

19. In a series of independent trials with a constant probability of success p, if the "success" occurs at least r times in succession, we say that there is a run of r successes. What is the probability of having a run of r successes in n trials, where naturally $n > r$? [Uspensky].

20. Let X be the number of successes in n independent trials with a constant probability of success p. Denote the probability of $X = k$ by $p_{k,n}$, $k = 0,1, \ldots, n$.

(a) Verify the difference equation

$$p_{k,n} = p p_{k-1,n-1} + q p_{k,n-1}.$$

(b) Let $g_X(s)$ be the p.g.f. of X. Derive the formula for $g_X(s)$ from the difference equation in (a) [Uspensky].

21. Let X be the number of failures preceding the r-th success in an infinite series of independent trials with a constant probability of success p. Denote the probability of $X = k$ by $p_{k,r}$, $k = 0,1, \ldots$

(a) Formulate a difference equation for $p_{k,r}$.

(b) Use the difference equation in (a) to derive the p.g.f. of X.

CHAPTER 3

Exponential-Type Distributions and Maximum Likelihood Estimation

1. INTRODUCTION

Exponential-type distributions appear in stochastic processes almost as frequently as the normal distribution does in conventional statistics. They appear in Poisson processes, birth processes, renewal processes, survival analysis, and others. The reason for this is that most stochastic processes result in first order differential equations whose solutions are exponential functions of time. When the time involved in a stochastic process is treated as a random variable, the corresponding distribution is exponential. The purpose of this chapter is to give a brief review of some of the exponential-type distributions appearing in this book. However, to maintain a reasonable graduation of mathematical involvement, we will not discuss more complex functions until later chapters when they appear in conjunction with the corresponding stochastic processes.

In applying stochastic processes to practical problems, we need to estimate the parameters involved. For easy reference, we devote a section of this chapter to a discussion of the maximum-likelihood method of estimation and optimum properties of an estimator.

2. GAMMA FUNCTIONS

The integral

$$\Gamma(\alpha) = \int_0^\infty y^{\alpha-1} e^{-y}\, dy, \qquad \alpha > 0, \tag{2.1}$$

is known as the complete gamma function. Integration by parts gives a recursive relation

$$\Gamma(\alpha + 1) = \alpha \Gamma(\alpha). \tag{2.2}$$

Since obviously $\Gamma(1) = 1$, formula (2.2) implies that, when $\alpha = n$ is a positive integer, $\Gamma(n + 1) = n!$, or

$$\int_0^\infty y^n e^{-y}\, dy = n!. \tag{2.1a}$$

An interesting case is when $\alpha = \frac{1}{2}$. One can show, by using polar coordinates, that

$$\Gamma\left(\frac{1}{2}\right) = \sqrt{\pi}. \tag{2.3}$$

Letting $y = z^2/2$ and $\alpha = \frac{1}{2}$ in (2.1) gives

$$\Gamma\left(\frac{1}{2}\right) = \sqrt{2} \int_0^\infty e^{-z^2/2}\, dz. \tag{2.4}$$

Since the integrand in (2.4) is an even function of z and is symmetrical with respect to the origin, formulas (2.3) and (2.4) imply that the integral

$$\int_{-\infty}^{+\infty} \frac{1}{\sqrt{2\pi}} e^{-z^2/2}\, dz = 1. \tag{2.5}$$

Thus the standard normal distribution is a proper distribution. The essential part of the normal distribution is the function

$$f(z) = e^{-z^2/2}.$$

The factor $1/\sqrt{2\pi}$ is necessary merely to make the distribution proper.

The incomplete gamma function is defined by

$$\int_0^\lambda y^{\alpha-1} e^{-y}\, dy, \qquad \alpha > 0, \lambda > 0, \tag{2.6}$$

or

$$\int_0^\lambda y^n e^{-y}\, dy, \qquad n = 0, 1, \ldots; \lambda > 0. \tag{2.6a}$$

We evaluate the integral in (2.6a):

$$\int_0^\lambda y^n e^{-y}\, dy = \int_0^\infty y^n e^{-y}\, dy - \int_\lambda^\infty y^n e^{-y}\, dy$$

$$= n! - \int_\lambda^\infty y^n e^{-y}\, dy. \tag{2.7}$$

Upon the substitution of $y = x + \lambda$, the last integral becomes

$$\int_\lambda^\infty y^n e^{-y}\, dy = \int_0^\infty (x+\lambda)^n e^{-(x+\lambda)}\, dx$$

$$= e^{-\lambda} \sum_{k=0}^{n} \binom{n}{k} \lambda^k \int_0^\infty x^{n-k} e^{-x}\, dx$$

$$= e^{-\lambda} \sum_{k=0}^{n} \frac{n!}{k!} \lambda^k. \tag{2.8}$$

Therefore, the incomplete gamma function has a simple expression:

$$\int_0^\lambda y^n e^{-y}\, dy = n! \left[1 - \sum_{k=0}^{n} \frac{e^{-\lambda}\lambda^k}{k!} \right]. \tag{2.9}$$

The quantity inside the brackets in (2.9) is the probability that a Poisson random variable (with parameter λ) will take on a value greater than n.

3. CONVOLUTIONS

Let X_1 and X_2 be two independently distributed continuous random variables with the density functions $h_1(x)$ and $h_2(x)$ and the distribution functions $H_1(x)$ and $H_2(x)$, respectively. The density function and the distribution function of the sum

$$Z_2 = X_1 + X_2 \tag{3.1}$$

are

$$f(x) = \int_{-\infty}^{+\infty} h_1(x-\tau) h_2(\tau)\, d\tau \tag{3.2}$$

and

$$F(x) = \int_{-\infty}^{+\infty} H_1(x-\tau)\, dH_2(\tau). \tag{3.3}$$

The density function $\{f(x)\}$ thus is the convolution of the density functions $\{h_1(x)\}$ and $\{h_2(x)\}$, and may be expressed as

$$\{f(x)\} = \{h_1(x)\}*\{h_2(x)\}. \tag{3.4}$$

If X_1 and X_2 have the identical distribution $h(x)$ and $H(x)$, then (3.2), (3.3), and (3.4) reduce to

$$f(x) = \int_{-\infty}^{+\infty} h(x-\tau)h(\tau)\,d\tau, \tag{3.2a}$$

$$F(x) = \int_{-\infty}^{+\infty} H(x-\tau)\,dH(\tau), \tag{3.3a}$$

and

$$\{f(x)\} = \{h(x)\}^{2*}. \tag{3.4a}$$

One can easily generalize the above result to the sum of any finite number of independent continuous random variables. For example, the density function of the sum of n i.i.d. random variables X_i is the n-fold convolution of the density function of X_i. Symbolically,

$$\{f(x)\} = \{h(x)\}^{n*}.$$

If there is some value x for which

$$\Pr\{X_1 = x\} > 0 \qquad \text{or} \qquad \Pr\{X_2 = x\} > 0, \tag{3.5}$$

then the convolutional relation (3.2) for the density function no longer holds true, but relation (3.3) for the distribution function does. In such cases, we use (3.3) to find the distribution function $F(t)$, and then use the relation

$$f(t) = dF(t)$$

to find the density function. An example may be found in the queueing process {cf. Chapter 10, equation (4.38)}.

Example 1. Let $X_1, X_2, \ldots, X_r$ be independent and identically distributed random variables, having the same exponential distribution with parameter μ and density function

$$h(x) = \mu e^{-\mu x}. \tag{3.6}$$

The sum

$$Z_r = X_1 + \ldots + X_r$$

has a gamma distribution with density function

$$f(x) = \frac{\mu^r x^{r-1}}{(r-1)!} e^{-\mu x}. \tag{3.7}$$

This may be shown by induction.

4. MOMENT GENERATING FUNCTIONS

The moment generating function (m.g.f.) is defined for both discrete distributions and continuous distributions. The m.g.f. of a distribution, if it exists, is defined by

$$M_x(s) = E\,[e^{Xs}], \tag{4.1}$$

where the expectation is

$$E\,[e^{Xs}] = \int_{-\infty}^{+\infty} e^{xs} f(x)\,dx \tag{4.2}$$

for a continuous distribution, and is

$$E\,[e^{Xs}] = \sum_{x=0}^{\infty} e^{xs} p_x$$

for a discrete distribution. In any event, for the existence of the moment generating function, it is necessary that there be a positive real number s_0 such that the expectation (4.1) is finite for all s for $|s| \leq s_0$. To derive moments from $M_x(s)$, we expand e^{Xs} in an infinite series,

$$e^{Xs} = 1 + Xs + X^2 \frac{s^2}{2!} + \ldots$$

and take the expectations

$$M_X(s) = 1 + E(X)\,s + E(X^2)\frac{s^2}{2!} + \ldots. \tag{4.3}$$

We obtain moments of the distribution by taking derivatives of $M_X(s)$:

$$E(X^r) = \frac{d^r}{ds^r} M_X(s)\bigg|_{s=0}. \tag{4.4}$$

Example 2. *Exponential distribution* with parameter μ:

$$f(x) = \mu e^{-\mu x}, \qquad x > 0. \tag{4.5}$$

The m.g.f. is

$$M_X(s) = \int_0^\infty e^{xs}\, \mu e^{-\mu x}\, dx$$

$$= \frac{\mu}{\mu - s}. \tag{4.6}$$

The first two moments are

$$E(X) = \frac{d}{ds}\left(\frac{\mu}{\mu - s}\right)\bigg|_{s=0} = \frac{1}{\mu}$$

and

$$E(X^2) = \frac{d^2}{ds^2}\left(\frac{\mu}{\mu - s}\right)\bigg|_{s=0} = \frac{2}{\mu^2}.$$

Example 3. *Normal distribution with* $E(X) = 0$ and $\mathrm{Var}(X) = 1$:

$$f(x) = \frac{1}{\sqrt{2\pi}}\, e^{-x^2/2}. \tag{4.7}$$

The m.g.f. is

$$M_X(s) = \int_{-\infty}^{+\infty} e^{sx} \frac{1}{\sqrt{2\pi}}\, e^{-x^2/2}\, dx$$

$$= \left[\frac{1}{\sqrt{2\pi}} \int_{-\infty}^{+\infty} e^{-(x-s)^2/2}\, dx\right] e^{s^2/2}$$

$$= e^{s^2/2}. \tag{4.8}$$

The first two moments are

$$E(X) = \frac{d}{ds}(e^{s^2/2})\bigg|_{s=0} = 0$$

and

$$E(X^2) = \frac{d^2}{ds^2}(e^{s^2/2})\bigg|_{s=0} = 1.$$

The moment generating function $M_X(s)$ of a discrete random variable has a simple relationship with the probability generating function $G_X(s)$:

$$M_X(s) = E[e^{Xs}] = G_X(e^s).$$

A probability distribution uniquely determines its moment generating function, if it exists. Under some mild restrictions, a moment generating function also uniquely determines the distribution function.

Corresponding to the p.g.f. for discrete distributions, the following theorem concerns the m.g.f. of the sum of independent and identically distributed random variables.

Theorem 1. *Let $X_1, \ldots, X_n$ be independent and identically distributed random variables with a common density function $f(x)$ and the same m.g.f. $m_X(s)$. Then the m.g.f. $M_Z(s)$ of the sum*

$$Z = X_1 + \ldots + X_n,$$

is the n-th power of the m.g.f. $m_X(s)$, or

$$M_Z(s) = [m_X(s)]^n. \tag{4.9}$$

Proof. By definition,

$$\begin{aligned} M_Z(s) &= E[e^{Zs}] = E[e^{(X_1+\ldots+X_n)s}] \\ &= E[e^{X_1 s}] \ldots E[e^{X_n s}] = [m_X(s)]^n, \end{aligned}$$

as required.

Example 4. Gamma distribution with parameters μ and r:

$$f(x) = \frac{\mu^r x^{r-1}}{\Gamma(r)} e^{-\mu x}; \qquad x > 0. \tag{4.10}$$

Example 1 shows that (4.10) is the density function of the sum of r i.i.d. variables, each having an exponential density function (4.5). Using the m.g.f. (4.6) and applying Theorem 1 yield the m.g.f.

$$M_X(s) = \left(\frac{\mu}{\mu - s}\right)^r. \tag{4.11}$$

We can obtain formula (4.11) directly from (4.2) with the density function (4.10).

4.1. The Central Limit Theorem.

Theorem 2. *If $X_1, \ldots, X_n$ are a sample of n independent and identically distributed random variables with $E(X_i) = \mu$ and $\mathrm{Var}(X_i) = \sigma^2$, then as $n \to \infty$, the standardized sample mean has the normal distribution with a mean zero and variance one.*

This theorem has been given in Section 6 of Chapter 1. We now prove it by using the moment generating function.

Proof. Let $m(s)$ be the moment generating function of $(X_i - \mu)/\sigma$,

$$m(s) = E\left[e^{s(X_i-\mu)/\sigma}\right], \qquad \text{for } i = 1, \ldots \tag{4.12}$$

and let $M_{Z_n}(s)$ be the moment generating function of the standardized sample mean

$$Z_n = \frac{\sqrt{n}\,(\bar{X} - \mu)}{\sigma}. \tag{4.13}$$

We need to show that, as $n \to \infty$,

$$M_{Z_n}(s) = e^{s^2/2}. \tag{4.14}$$

We rewrite Z_n as

$$Z_n = \sum_{i=1}^{n} \frac{X_i - \mu}{\sqrt{n}\,\sigma} \tag{4.13a}$$

to establish a relationship between the m.g.f. of Z_n and $m(s)$ in (4.12). Using (4.13a), we write the m.g.f. of Z_n

$$\begin{aligned} M_{Z_n}(s) &= E\left[e^{s\Sigma_{i=1}^{n}(X_i-\mu)/\sqrt{n}\sigma}\right] = \left\{E\left[e^{s(X_i-\mu)/\sqrt{n}\sigma}\right]\right\}^n \\ &= \left\{m\left(\frac{s}{\sqrt{n}}\right)\right\}^n. \end{aligned} \tag{4.15}$$

We expand the function $m(s/\sqrt{n})$ as in equation (4.3) to obtain

$$\begin{aligned} m\left[\frac{s}{\sqrt{n}}\right] &= 1 + E\left(\frac{X_i-\mu}{\sigma}\right)\frac{s}{\sqrt{n}} + E\left(\frac{X_i-\mu}{\sigma}\right)^2\frac{s^2}{2n} + 0\left(\frac{s^2}{n}\right) \\ &= 1 + \frac{s^2}{2n} + 0\left(\frac{s^2}{n}\right). \end{aligned} \tag{4.16}$$

Substituting (4.16) into (4.15) yields

$$M_{Z_n}(s) = \left[1 + \frac{s^2}{2n} + 0\left(\frac{s^2}{n}\right)\right]^n, \tag{4.17}$$

where $0\left(\dfrac{s^2}{n}\right)$ has the same order of magnitude as $\dfrac{s^2}{n}$. Using the definition $\lim_{n\to\infty}\left(1 + \dfrac{a}{n}\right)^n = e^a$ we obtain

$$\lim_{n\to\infty} M_{Z_n}(s) = e^{s^2/2}. \tag{4.18}$$

Thus, the limiting distribution of Z_n is normal with parameters zero and one, proving the central limit theorem.

5. SUM OF NON-IDENTICALLY DISTRIBUTED RANDOM VARIABLES

Let $X_1, \ldots, X_n$ be a sample of n independently distributed random variables, and let the density function of X_i be

$$h_i(x) = \lambda_i e^{-\lambda_i x}, \qquad i = 1, \ldots, n, \qquad x > 0, \tag{5.1}$$

so that the distribution function of X_i is

$$H_i(x) = 1 - e^{-\lambda_i x}, \qquad i = 1, \ldots, n, \qquad x > 0, \tag{5.2}$$

where $\lambda_i \neq \lambda_j$ for $i \neq j$. The ratio

$$\frac{h_i(x)}{1 - H_i(s)} = \lambda_i, \qquad i = 1, \ldots, n \qquad x > 0, \tag{5.3}$$

is known as the intensity function, force of mortality, or failure rate. We see from (5.2) that, as $t \to \infty$,

$$H_i(\infty) = 1, \qquad i = 1, \ldots, n,$$

and every one of the variables $X_1, \ldots, X_n$ is proper.

Before deriving the distribution of the sum of $X_1, \ldots, X_n$, let us introduce a useful lemma.

Lemma 1. *For distinct numbers $\lambda_1, \ldots, \lambda_n$, we have*

$$\sum_{i=1}^{n} \frac{1}{\prod_{\substack{j=1\\j\neq i}}^{n} (\lambda_i - \lambda_j)} = 0. \tag{5.4}$$

The lemma is a special case of lemma 2 in Chapter 6, Section 2.1, where a proof is given.

Theorem 3. *Let $X_1, \ldots, X_n$ be independently distributed random variables, and let the density function of X_i be given in* (5.1). *The density function of the sum*

$$Z_n = X_1 + \ldots + X_n \tag{5.5}$$

is

$$f_n(x) = (-1)^{n-1} \lambda_1 \ldots \lambda_n \sum_{i=1}^{n} \frac{e^{-\lambda_i x}}{\prod_{\substack{j=1\\j\neq i}}^{n} (\lambda_i - \lambda_j)}. \tag{5.6}$$

Proof. When $n = 1$, the right-hand side of (5.6) becomes

$$f_1(x) = \lambda_1 e^{-\lambda_1 x},$$

which is the same as (5.1) for $i = 1$. Suppose (5.6) holds true for n; we need to show that the density function for the sum

$$Z_{n+1} = X_1 + \ldots + X_{n+1}$$

is

$$f_{n+1}(x) = (-1)^{n} \lambda_1 \ldots \lambda_{n+1} \sum_{i=1}^{n+1} \frac{e^{-\lambda_i x}}{\prod_{\substack{j=1\\j\neq i}}^{n+1} (\lambda_i - \lambda_j)}. \tag{5.7}$$

Since $Z_{n+1} = Z_n + X_{n+1}$, we use the convolutional formula (3.2) to write

$$f_{n+1}(x) = \int_0^x f_n(\tau)\, h_{n+1}(x - \tau)\, d\tau. \tag{5.8}$$

Introducing (5.6) and (5.1) in (5.8) gives

$$f_{n+1}(x) = \int_0^x (-1)^{n-1} \lambda_1 \dots \lambda_n \sum_{i=1}^{n} \frac{e^{-\lambda_i \tau}}{\prod_{\substack{j=1 \\ j\neq i}}^{n} (\lambda_i - \lambda_j)} [\lambda_{n+1} e^{-\lambda_{n+1}(x-\tau)}] \, d\tau$$

$$= (-1)^{n-1} \lambda_1 \dots \lambda_{n+1} \sum_{i=1}^{n} \frac{1}{\prod_{\substack{j=1 \\ j\neq i}}^{n} (\lambda_i - \lambda_j)} \int_0^x e^{-\lambda_i \tau - \lambda_{n+1}(x-\tau)}] \, d\tau$$

where

$$\int_0^x e^{-\lambda_i \tau - \lambda_{n+1}(x-\tau)} \, d\tau = \frac{-1}{\lambda_i - \lambda_{n+1}} [e^{-\lambda_i x} - e^{-\lambda_{n+1} x}] .$$

Therefore, the density function becomes

$$f_{n+1}(x) = (-1)^n \lambda_1 \dots \lambda_{n+1} \left[\sum_{i=1}^{n} \frac{e^{-\lambda_i x}}{\prod_{\substack{j=1 \\ j\neq i}}^{n+1} (\lambda_i - \lambda_j)} - \sum_{i=1}^{n} \frac{e^{-\lambda_{n+1} x}}{\prod_{\substack{j=1 \\ j\neq i}}^{n+1} (\lambda_i - \lambda_j)} \right]. \tag{5.9}$$

According to lemma 1,

$$\sum_{i=1}^{n} \frac{1}{\prod_{\substack{j=1 \\ j\neq i}}^{n+1} (\lambda_i - \lambda_j)} = - \frac{1}{\prod_{j=1}^{n} (\lambda_{n+1} - \lambda_j)} . \tag{5.10}$$

Substituting (5.10) in the second summation of (5.9), we recover (5.7), proving the theorem.

The distribution function of Z_n is

$$F_n(x) = \int_0^x f_n(\tau) \, d\tau$$

$$= (-1)^{n-1} \lambda_1 \dots \lambda_n \sum_{i=1}^{n} \frac{1}{\prod_{\substack{j=1 \\ j\neq i}}^{n} (\lambda_i - \lambda_j) \lambda_i} [1 - e^{-\lambda_i x}] . \tag{5.11}$$

As $x \to \infty$,the exponential vanishes, and

$$F_n(\infty) = (-1)^{n-1} \lambda_1 \ldots \lambda_n \sum_{i=1}^{n} \frac{1}{\prod_{\substack{j=1 \\ j \neq i}}^{n} (\lambda_i - \lambda_j) \lambda_i}. \tag{5.12}$$

Since every one of the distributions in (5.1) is proper, we expect $F_n(\infty) = 1$. To evaluate the right-hand side of (5.12) directly, we introduce a number λ_{n+1} distinct from $\lambda_1, \ldots, \lambda_n$ and use lemma 1 to find the equation

$$\sum_{i=1}^{n} \frac{1}{\prod_{\substack{j=1 \\ j \neq i}}^{n} (\lambda_i - \lambda_j)(\lambda_i - \lambda_{n+1})} = \frac{-1}{\prod_{j=1}^{n} (\lambda_{n+1} - \lambda_j)}. \tag{5.13}$$

For $\lambda_{n+1} = 0$, (5.13) becomes

$$\sum_{i=1}^{n} \frac{1}{\prod_{\substack{j=1 \\ j \neq i}}^{n} (\lambda_i - \lambda_j) \lambda_i} = (-1)^{n+1} \frac{1}{\prod_{j=1}^{n} \lambda_j}. \tag{5.14}$$

Substituting (5.14) into (5.12) gives

$$F_n(\infty) = 1. \tag{5.15}$$

We can derive the expectation and the variance of Z_n from the definition of Z_n in (5.5). We then get

$$E[Z_n] = \sum_{i=1}^{n} \frac{1}{\lambda_i} \tag{5.16}$$

and

$$V[Z_n] = \sum_{i=1}^{n} \frac{1}{\lambda_i^2}. \tag{5.17}$$

6. SUM OF CONSECUTIVE RANDOM VARIABLES

Events occur in sequences in stochastic processes. Births in a family take place in order of parity; replacement of items in a renewal system is done in succession; service to customers in a queueing process is provided by order of arrival. Let a random variable t_i be the length of time between the occurrence of the $(i-1)$-th event and the occurrence of the i-th event, and let the sum

$$T_n = t_1 + t_2 + \dots + t_n \tag{6.1}$$

be the total length of time up to the occurrence of the n-th event. There is a significant difference between equations (6.1) and (5.5). In equation (5.5), Z_n is an ordinary algebraic sum of $X_1, \dots, X_n$, while in equation (6.1) the t's are observed in succession. The difference is pronounced when the distributions of t's are time dependent.

Consider a time interval (τ, t) for a random variable t_i, for $0 \leq \tau < t < \infty$, such that τ is the beginning of observation of t_i. Let the density function of t_i be

$$h_i(\tau, t) = \lambda_i \mu(t)\, e^{-\lambda_i \int_\tau^t \mu(\xi)\, d\xi}, \qquad i = 1, \dots, n, \tag{6.2}$$

and the distribution function

$$H_i(\tau, t) = \int_\tau^t h_i(\tau, x)\, dx$$

$$= 1 - e^{-\lambda_i \int_\tau^t \mu(\xi)\, d\xi}, \tag{6.3}$$

where $\mu(\xi)$ is a positive continuous function of ξ such that as $t \to \infty$,

$$\int_\tau^t \mu(\xi)\, d\xi \to \infty. \tag{6.4}$$

Formula (6.3) shows that $H_i(\tau, \infty) = 1$.

For clarity, let $n = 2$ and derive the density function $f_2(0, t)$ of the sum $T_2 = t_1 + t_2$. According to the structure of the problem,

$$f_2(0,t) = \int_0^t h_1(0,\tau)\, h_2(\tau,t)\, d\tau, \tag{6.5}$$

which is different from the convolutional formula in (3.2). For the density function in (6.2),

$$f_2(0,t) = \int_0^t [\lambda_1 \mu(\tau)\, e^{-\lambda_1 \int_0^\tau \mu(\xi)\, d\xi}]\, [\lambda_2 \mu(t)\, e^{-\lambda_2 \int_\tau^t \mu(\xi)\, d\xi}]\, d\tau$$

$$= \lambda_1 \lambda_2 \mu(t)\, e^{-\lambda_2 \int_0^t \mu(\xi)\,d\xi} \int_0^t \mu(\tau)\, e^{-(\lambda_1-\lambda_2)\int_0^\tau \mu(\xi)\,d\xi}\, d\tau, \tag{6.6}$$

where the integral

$$\int_0^t \mu(\tau)\, e^{-(\lambda_1-\lambda_2)\int_0^\tau \mu(\xi)\,d\xi}\, d\tau = \frac{-1}{\lambda_1 - \lambda_2}\left[e^{-(\lambda_1-\lambda_2)\int_0^t \mu(\xi)\,d\xi} - 1\right]. \tag{6.7}$$

Substituting (6.7) into (6.6) and simplifying yields the formula

$$f_2(0,t) = (-1)\,\lambda_1 \lambda_2 \mu(t) \sum_{i=1}^{2} \frac{e^{-\lambda_i \int_0^t \mu(\xi)\,d\xi}}{\lambda_i - \lambda_j}, \quad j \neq i;\, j = 1, 2. \tag{6.8}$$

The distribution function of T_2 is easily computed from (6.8):

$$\begin{aligned} F_2(0,t) &= \int_0^t f_2(0,x)\,dx \\ &= (-1)\lambda_1\lambda_2 \sum_{\substack{i=1 \\ j\neq i}}^{2} \frac{1}{(\lambda_i - \lambda_j)\lambda_i}\left[1 - e^{-\lambda_i \int_0^t \mu(\xi)\,d\xi}\right]. \end{aligned} \tag{6.9}$$

As $t \to \infty$,

$$\begin{aligned} F_2(0,\infty) &= (-1)\,\lambda_1 \lambda_2 \sum_{\substack{i=1 \\ j\neq i}}^{2} \frac{1}{(\lambda_i - \lambda_j)\lambda_i} \\ &= 1. \end{aligned} \tag{6.10}$$

Formulas (6.8) and (6.9) can be generalized to an arbitrary number of variables.

Theorem 4. *Let* $t_1, \ldots, t_n$ *be independently distributed random variables and let the density function of* t_i *be given in* (6.2). *Then the density function and the distribution function of the sum* T_n *in* (6.1) *are*

$$f_n(0,t) = (-1)^{n-1}\,\lambda_1 \ldots \lambda_n\, \mu(t) \sum_{i=1}^{n} \frac{e^{-\lambda_i \int_0^t \mu(\xi)\,d\xi}}{\prod_{\substack{j=1 \\ j\neq i}}^{n} (\lambda_i - \lambda_j)} \tag{6.11}$$

and

$$F_n(0,t) = (-1)^{n-1} \lambda_1 \dots \lambda_n \sum_{i=1}^{n} \frac{1}{\prod_{\substack{j=1 \\ j \neq i}}^{n} (\lambda_i - \lambda_j) \lambda_i} \left[1 - e^{-\lambda_i \int_0^t \mu(\xi) d\xi}\right] \tag{6.12}$$

respectively. As $t \to \infty$,

$$F_n(0,\infty) = 1. \tag{6.13}$$

Proof of Theorem 4 is almost identical to the proof of the formulas for the sum Z_n in section 5, and is left to the reader.

Formulas (6.11) and (6.12) are symmetrical with respect to $\lambda_1, \dots, \lambda_n$. This means that, while it is based on consecutive observations of $t_1, \dots, t_n$, the distribution of the sum T_n is independent of the order in which the random variables are observed. In practical problems, however, events involved often follow natural sequences; disturbance of the order in a sequence would render the problem meaningless. For example, in hunting for food, a wild animal needs to go through five phases in the process: search, recognition, pursuit, attack, and kill and devour. The time an animal spends in these phases, t_1, t_2, t_3, t_4, and t_5, forms a logical order. Other examples are cascade phenomena in nuclear physics, stages in developing diseases, engagement-marriage-divorce in demography, and others.

7. MAXIMUM-LIKELIHOOD ESTIMATION

Applications of stochastic processes to practical problems require estimation of the parameters involved. Methods of estimation based on various criteria have been derived in statistical theory. We will briefly review the method of maximum-likelihood estimation for future reference. For simplicity, our discussion will be confined to independent and identically distributed random variables, but the argument holds equally well when the random variables are dependent.

Let $X_1, \dots, X_n$ be a sample of random variables from the same distribution having the density function $f(x;\theta)$, where θ is the parameter to be estimated. The joint density function of $X_1, \dots, X_n$ is called the *likelihood function,* or

$$L(\theta; \mathbf{x}) = f(x_1; \theta) \dots f(x_n; \theta), \tag{7.1}$$

where L is a function of θ. For discrete distributions, the density function $f(x;\theta)$ is replaced by the probability function $p_k(\theta)$ and the following discussion applies.

A statistic $\hat{\theta}(x_1, \ldots, x_n)$ is called a maximum-likelihood (m.l.) estimator of θ if the function $L(\hat{\theta};\mathbf{x})$ is a maximum. Thus, the principle of maximum-likelihood is to find a function $\hat{\theta}$ of $(x_1, \ldots, x_n)$ for which the likelihood function L attains a maximum. Since a maximizing value of L also maximizes the logarithm of L, for convenience, we usually determine an m.l. estimator from the equation

$$\frac{d}{d\theta} \ln L(\theta;\mathbf{x}) = 0, \tag{7.2}$$

which is known as the *maximum-likelihood equation*. If a distribution involves two parameters, $f(x;\ \theta_1,\ \theta_2)$, then the likelihood function (7.1) will contain two parameters, and there will be two simultaneous equations in (7.2).

A maximum-likelihood estimator, however, does not always exist and equation (7.2) may have more than one solution. But, a unique m.l. estimator does exist in enough well-known distributions to render this method of estimation practical. A few examples will help to illustrate the procedure of finding estimators.

Example 5. Let $X_1, \ldots, X_n$ be a sample of n i.i.d. random variables from a normal distribution with the density function

$$f(x;\theta) = \frac{1}{\sqrt{2\pi}}\, e^{-(x-\theta)^2/2}. \tag{7.3}$$

The likelihood function is

$$L(\theta;\mathbf{x}) = \left(\frac{1}{\sqrt{2\pi}}\right)^n e^{-\sum_{i=1}^n (x_i-\theta)^2/2} \tag{7.4}$$

and its logarithm is

$$\ln L(\theta;\mathbf{x}) = -n \ln \sqrt{2\pi} - \frac{1}{2}\sum_{i=1}^{n} (x_i - \theta)^2. \tag{7.5}$$

The maximum-likelihood equation

$$\frac{d}{d\theta} \ln L(\theta;\mathbf{x}) = 0$$

has the unique solution

$$\hat{\theta} = \frac{1}{n} \sum_{i=1}^{n} x_i = \bar{X}. \tag{7.6}$$

Thus the sample mean is the m.l. estimator of the population mean for the normal distribution.

Example 6. If the density function in Example 5 is replaced by

$$f(x; \theta_1, \theta_2) = \frac{1}{\sqrt{2\pi\theta_2}} e^{-(x-\theta_1)^2/2\theta_2}, \tag{7.7}$$

then the logarithm of the likelihood function contains two parameters, the mean θ_1 and the variance θ_2:

$$\ln L(\theta_1, \theta_2; \mathbf{x}) = -n \ln \sqrt{2\pi} - \frac{n}{2} \ln \theta_2 - \sum_{i=1}^{n} (x_i - \theta_1)^2/2\theta_2. \tag{7.8}$$

Differentiating (7.8) with respect to θ_1 and θ_2, respectively, yields two simultaneous equations:

$$\left.\begin{aligned} \frac{\partial}{\partial\theta_1} \ln L = 0: \quad & \sum_{i=1}^{n} (x_i - \hat{\theta}_1) = 0 \\ \frac{\partial}{\partial\theta_2} \ln L = 0: \quad & n\hat{\theta}_2 - \sum_{i=1}^{n} (x_i - \hat{\theta}_1)^2 = 0 \end{aligned}\right\} \tag{7.9}$$

The solutions are

$$\hat{\theta}_1 = \bar{X}, \tag{7.10}$$

and

$$\hat{\theta}_2 = \frac{1}{n} \sum_{i=1}^{n} (x_i - \bar{X})^2. \tag{7.11}$$

Example 7. Let $X_1, \ldots, X_n$ be a sample from the exponential distribution

$$f(x;\theta) = \theta e^{-\theta x}. \tag{7.12}$$

The log likelihood function is

$$\ln L(\theta;\mathbf{x}) = n \ln \theta - \theta \sum_{i=1}^{n} x_i, \tag{7.13}$$

and the derivative is

$$\frac{d}{d\theta} \ln L(\theta;\mathbf{x}) = \frac{n}{\theta} - \sum_{i=1}^{n} x_i .$$

Setting the derivative equal to zero yields the m.l. estimator

$$\hat{\theta} = \frac{1}{\bar{X}}. \tag{7.14}$$

Remark. When the exponential function is used in survival analysis, each of the random variables $X_1, \ldots, X_n$ is a failure time, or the length of lifetime before a failure occurs. The estimator

$$\hat{\theta} = \frac{n}{\sum_{i=1}^{n} x_i} \tag{7.14a}$$

is the ratio of the number of failures to the total length of lifetime. This interpretation applies also to other estimators in exponential-type distributions and will appear again in later chapters.

7.1. Optimum Properties of the M-L Estimator.

Unbiasedness. An estimator $\hat{\theta}(X_1, \ldots, X_n)$ is said to be unbiased if the expectation $E[\hat{\theta}(X_1, \ldots, X_n)] = \theta$. In Example 6, the sample mean is an unbiased estimator of the population mean, but the estimator of the variance in (7.11) is a biased estimator, since

$$E\left[\frac{1}{n}\sum_{i=1}^{n}(X_i - \bar{X})^2\right] = \frac{n-1}{n}\theta_2 .$$

An unbiased estimator of the variance is

$$S^2 = \frac{1}{n-1}\sum_{i=1}^{n}(X_i - \bar{X})^2 .$$

Since the factor $(n - 1)/n \to 1$, as $n \to \infty$, the bias of (7.11) is negligible for large n. Generally, an m.l. estimator is unbiased, at least asymptotically.

Consistency. An estimator $\hat{\theta}_n$ is said to be consistent if it converges in probability to the true value θ_0 of the parameter; symbolically, if, for every $\varepsilon > 0$,

$$\lim_{n\to\infty} \Pr\{|\hat{\theta}_n - \theta_0| > \varepsilon\} = 0.$$

The maximum-likelihood estimator is consistent.

Efficiency **(minimum-variance).** An m.l. estimator is efficient in the sense that it has a variance as small or smaller than the variance of any other estimator. If $\hat{\theta}$ is an m.l. (unbiased) estimator and $\tilde{\theta}$ is any other (unbiased) estimator, then

$$V(\hat{\theta}) \le V(\tilde{\theta}).$$

Asymptotic normality. When the sample size n is sufficiently large, the distribution of the m.l. estimator $\hat{\theta}_n$ is approximately normal with mean θ and variance

$$V(\hat{\theta}_n) = \frac{1}{-E\left[\dfrac{d^2}{d\theta^2}\ln L(\theta;\mathbf{X})\right]}. \tag{7.15}$$

Example 8. In Example 7 of the exponential distribution, we take the second derivative of the log likelihood function in (7.13) to find

$$E\left[\frac{d^2}{d\theta^2}\ln L(\theta;\mathbf{X})\right] = -\frac{n}{\theta^2}.$$

Therefore, when the sample size n is large, the estimator $\hat{\theta}$ in (7.14) has an approximately normal distribution with mean θ and variance

$$V(\hat{\theta}_n) = \frac{\theta^2}{n}. \tag{7.16}$$

8. PROBLEMS FOR SOLUTION

1. *The Gamma Function.* Derive the following recursive relation for the complete gamma function,

$$\Gamma(\alpha + 1) = \alpha\Gamma(\alpha). \tag{2.2}$$

2. *Continuation.* Evaluate the gamma function $\Gamma(\frac{1}{2})$.

3. *Continuation.* Evaluate $[(2n + 1)/2]!$ for a positive integer n.

4. *The Gamma Distribution.* Replacing y with βx in the gamma function $\Gamma(\alpha)$ yields the equation

$$\int_0^\infty \frac{\beta^\alpha x^{\alpha-1}}{\Gamma(\alpha)} e^{-\beta x}\,dx = 1.$$

The integrand

$$f(x) = \frac{\beta^\alpha x^{\alpha-1}}{\Gamma(\alpha)} e^{-\beta x}, \quad x > 0$$

is the density function of a *gamma distribution.* Find the mean and the variance of the distribution.

5. *Continuation.* Derive the distribution function

$$F(x) = \int_0^x \frac{\beta^\alpha t^{\alpha-1}}{\Gamma(\alpha)} e^{-\beta t}\,dt, \quad x > 0$$

for a positive integer α.

6. *Continuation.* Let $X_1, \ldots, X_n$ be independent random variables having the density functions

$$f_i(x) = \frac{\beta^{\alpha_i} x^{\alpha_i - 1}}{\Gamma(\alpha_i)} e^{-\beta x}, \quad i = 1, \ldots, n.$$

Find the density function of the sum $Z_n = X_1 + \ldots + X_n$. [HINT: Use induction and the identity in problem 8.]

7. *The Chi-square Distribution.* When $\beta = \frac{1}{2}$ and $\alpha = n/2$, the gamma density function in problem 4 becomes

$$f(x) = \frac{x^{(n-2)/2}}{2^{n/2}\left(\dfrac{n-2}{2}\right)!} e^{-x/2}, \quad x > 0$$

which is known as the chi-square distribution with n degrees of freedom.

(a) Show that, if Z is a standard normal random variable with a mean zero and a variance unity, then Z^2 has a chi-square distribution with one degree of freedom.

(b) Let $Z_1, \ldots, Z_n$ be n i.i.d. standard normal random variables; then the sum of squares

$$Z_1^2 + \ldots + Z_n^2$$

has a chi-square distribution with n degrees of freedom.

8. *The Beta Functions.* Show that

$$\int_0^1 t^m (1-t)^n\,dt = \frac{m!\,n!}{(m+n+1)!}.$$

The left-hand side quantity in the above equation is called the (complete) *beta function*. When the upper limit of the integral is less than one, we have the *incomplete beta function*.

$$\int_0^x t^m (1-t)^n \, dt, \quad 0 < x < 1.$$

9. *The Beta Distribution.* The function

$$f(x) = \frac{(m+n+1)!}{m!\,n!} x^m (1-x)^n, \quad 0 < x < 1,$$

is the density function of a beta distribution. Find the mean and the variance of the distribution.

10. *The Moment Generating Function.* Find the m.g.f. of the gamma distribution for each X_i in problem 6. And then find the m.g.f. for the sum $Z_n = X_1 + \ldots + X_n$.

11. Find the m.g.f. for each of the following distributions:
(a) The binomial distribution
(b) The Poisson distribution
(c) The negative binomial distribution

12. *Multinomial distribution.* The moment generating function for a multivariate distribution with m components $(X_1, \ldots, X_m)$ is defined by

$$G_X(s_1, \ldots, s_m) = E\,[e^{X_1 s_1 + \ldots + X_m s_m}]$$

when the expectation exists for $e^{s_i} < s_0$, $i = 1, \ldots, m$, for some $s_0 > 1$. Find the m.g.f. for the multinomial distribution in equation (5.19), Chapter 1,

$$\Pr\{X_1 = k_1, \ldots, X_m = k_m\} = \frac{n!}{k_1! \ldots k_m!\,(n-k)!} p_1^{k_1} \ldots p_m^{k_m} p_0^{n-k}$$

for $k_i = 0, 1, \ldots, n$; $i = 1, \ldots, m$ where $k = k_1 + \ldots + k_m$.

From the m.g.f. derive the expectation $E(X_i)$, the variance $V(X_i)$, the covariance $\mathrm{Cov}(X_i, X_j)$, and the correlation coefficient ρ_{X_i, X_j}.

13. *Continuation.* Derive the m.g.f.'s for the marginal distribution of X_1 and X_2, and for the conditional distribution of X_1 and X_2 given X_3 in problem 12.

14. *Negative multinomial distribution.* Derive the m.g.f. for the negative multinomial distribution in equation (7.30), Chapter 2:

$$\Pr\{X_1 = k_1, \ldots, X_m = k_m\} = \frac{(k+r-1)!}{k_1! \ldots k_m!\,(r-1)!} q_1^{k_1} \ldots q_m^{k_m} p^r$$

for $k_i = 0, 1, \ldots$, where $k = k_1 + \ldots + k_m$.

15. *Bivariate normal distribution.* The density function of a bivariate normal distribution is given by

$$f(x,y) = \frac{1}{2\pi\sigma_x\sigma_y\sqrt{1-\rho^2}}$$

$$\exp\left\{\frac{-1}{2(1-\rho^2)}\left[\left(\frac{x-\mu}{\sigma_x}\right)^2 - 2\rho\left(\frac{x-\mu}{\sigma_x}\right)\left(\frac{y-\nu}{\sigma_y}\right) + \left(\frac{y-\nu}{\sigma_y}\right)^2\right]\right\}$$

for $-\infty < x < +\infty$, $-\infty < y < +\infty$. Find the m.g.f.'s for

(a) the joint distribution X and Y,

(b) the marginal distribution of X, and

(c) the conditional distribution of Y given X and the variance of the distribution.

16. *Continuation.* A random sample of size n, $[(X_1, Y_1), \ldots, (X_n, Y_n)]$, is taken from a bivariate normal distribution as given in problem 15.

(a) Find the maximum-likelihood estimators of the parameters μ, ν, σ_x, σ_y, and ρ.

(b) Find the maximum-likelihood estimator of the variance of the conditional distribution of Y given X in problem 15, part (c).

(c) Determine if these estimators are unbiased.

17. *Exponential type distribution.* The random variable Z_n in equation (5.5) has the density functions

$$f_n(x) = (-1)^{n-1}\lambda_1, \ldots, \lambda_n \sum_{i=1}^{n} \frac{e^{-\lambda_i x}}{\prod\limits_{\substack{j=1 \\ j\neq i}}^{n} (\lambda_i - \lambda_j)} \tag{5.6}$$

for $0 \leq x < \infty$.

(a) Derive the m.g.f. of Z_n.

(b) Find the mean and the variance of Z_n.

(c) Verify from the m.g.f. that Z_n is a sum of n independently distributed random variables each having an exponential distribution.

18. *Continuation.* Show that if $\lambda_i = i\lambda$, then the density function in problem 17 becomes

$$f_n(x) = n\lambda\,[1 - e^{-\lambda x}]^{n-1} e^{-\lambda x},$$

which is the density function of the maximum life time in a sample of n i.i.d. random variables each having an exponential distribution with parameter λ [cf. equation (3.38), Chapter 7].

19. *Continuation.* The random variable T_n defined in equation (6.1) has the density function

$$f_n(0,t) = (-1)^{n-1}\lambda_1 \dots \lambda_n \mu(t) \sum_{i=1}^{n} \frac{\exp\left\{-\lambda_i \int_0^t \mu(\xi)\, d\xi\right\}}{\prod_{\substack{j=1 \\ j \neq i}}^{n} (\lambda_i - \lambda_j)}. \tag{6.11}$$

The function $\mu(t)$ signifies the intensity of the transition at time t. Derive the density and the distribution function of T_n when $\mu(t) = Bc^t$.

20. *Continuation.* Derive the density function and the distribution function of T_n in problem 19 when $\mu(t) = A + Bc^t$.

21. *Continuation.* Derive the density function and the distribution function of T_n in problem 19 when $\mu(t) = \mu a t^{a-1}$.

22. *Continuation.* Derive the density function and the distribution function of T_n in problem 19 when $\mu(t) = \beta e^{-\alpha t}$, for $\alpha > 0$, $\beta > 0$.

23. *Multinomial distribution.* A trial can result in $m + 1$ mutually exclusive outcomes $E_0, E_1, \dots, E_m$ with probabilities $p_0, p_1, \dots, p_m$, respectively, so that $p_0 + \dots + p_m = 1$ as in example 12, Chapter 1. A number n independent trials are performed. For each trial we introduce a vector of indicators $(\varepsilon_{0i}, \varepsilon_{1i}, \dots, \varepsilon_{mi})$ such that $\varepsilon_{li} = 1$ if E_l occurs in the i-th trial for $i = 1, \dots, n$. Derive a likelihood function for the n vectors and from which find the maximum-likelihood estimators of the probabilities $p_0, \dots, p_m$.

24. *Negative multinomial distribution.* Derive from the density function of a negative multinomial distribution in equation (7.30), Chapter 2,

$$\Pr\{X_1 = k_1 \dots X_m = k_m\} = \frac{(k + r - 1)!}{k_1 \dots k_m!(r-1)!} q_1^{k_1} \dots q_m^{k_m} p^r$$

where $k = k_1 + \dots + k_m$, the maximum-likelihood estimators of the probabilities $q_1, \dots, q_m$, and p.

25. *Life table urns.* In example 10, Chapter 1, we considered drawing balls consecutively from two urns. Each urn contains a proportion p_i of white balls and a proportion q_i of black balls, $i = 1,2$. From the first urn we draw with replacement n_1 balls, of which X_1 are white, and from the second urn we draw with replacement X_1 balls, of which X_2 are white.

(a) Find the joint probability function of X_1 and X_2 for $X_1 \neq 0$.

(b) Derive from the joint probability the maximum-likelihood estimator of p_1 and p_2 when $n_1 = 3$.

(c) Show that, for any $X_1 > 0$, the estimators $\hat{p}_1$ and $\hat{p}_2$ have a zero correlation but that they are not independently distributed.

CHAPTER 4

Branching Process, Random Walk and Ruin Problem

1. A SIMPLE BRANCHING PROCESS

The idea of branching processes seems to have been first suggested by Francis Galton and the Reverend H. W. Watson in 1874, when they published their solution to the problem of the extinction of family names. Their mathematical model and its generalizations have been used to study frequencies of mutant genes (Fisher [1922] and [1930]), other problems in genetics (Haldane [1927]), epidemics (Neyman and Scott [1964]), nuclear chain reactions, and similar problems. For an extensive theoretical treatment of the subject see Harris [1963].

The basic mechanism of a branching process is as follows: An individual (the 0th generation) is capable of producing 0, 1, 2, ... offspring to form the first generation; each of these offspring in turn produces offspring, which together constitute the second generation; and so on. Let the number of individuals in the nth generation be Z_n. If we now impose a probability structure on the process of reproduction, then $Z_1, Z_2, \ldots$ are random variables whose probability distributions can be calculated.

We shall assume the simplest reproductive structure, that is, (i) that the number X of offspring produced by an individual has the probability distribution

$$P\{X = k\} = p_k, \qquad k = 0, 1, \ldots \tag{1.1}$$

which is the same for each individual in a given generation; (ii) that this probability distribution remains fixed from generation to generation; and (iii) that individuals produce offspring independently of each other. Thus we are dealing with independent and identically distributed random variables.

Let $g_n(s)$ be the p.g.f. of Z_n, $n = 1, 2, \ldots$, and let

$$g(s) = \sum_{k=0}^{\infty} p_k s^k \tag{1.2}$$

be the p.g.f. of X. Since $Z_0 = 1$, the size of the first generation Z_1 has the same probability distribution as X,

$$\Pr\{Z_1 = k\} = p_k, \tag{1.3}$$

and the same p.g.f. $g(s)$. The second generation consists of the direct descendants of the Z_1 members of the first generation, so that Z_2 is the sum of the Z_1 independent random variables, each of which has the probability distribution (1.1) and the p.g.f. $g(s)$. Therefore Z_2 has a compound distribution with the p.g.f. obtained from formula (8.5), Chapter 2,

$$g_2(s) = g\,[g(s)]\,. \tag{1.4}$$

Similarly, the $(n + 1)$th generation consists of the direct descendants of the Z_n members of the nth generation, so that Z_{n+1} is the sum of the Z_n independent random variables and each has p.g.f. $g(s)$. Hence by (8.5), Chapter 2, the p.g.f. of Z_{n+1} is

$$g_{n+1}(s) = g_n\,[g(s)]\,. \tag{1.5}$$

The $(n + 1)$th generation consists of the nth generation descendants of the Z_1 members of the first generation. Therefore the p.g.f. of Z_{n+1} can also be written as

$$g_{n+1}(s) = g\,[g_n(s)]\,, \tag{1.6}$$

an alternative form of (1.5).

The explicit form for the p.g.f. of Z_n depends upon the probability distribution $\{p_k\}$. Consider, for example, organisms which can either die or split into two so that

$$p_0 = (1 - p),$$

$$p_2 = p,$$

$$p_k = 0, \quad \text{for } k = 1, 3, 4, \ldots.$$

The p.g.f's of the $\{Z_n\}$ are

$$g_1(s) = (1-p) + ps^2,$$
$$g_2(s) = (1-p) + p[(1-p) + ps^2]^2,$$
$$g_3(s) = (1-p) + p\{(1-p) + p[(1-p) + ps^2]^2\}^2, \text{ etc.}$$

This simple example demonstrates that although the probability $\Pr\{Z_n = k\}$ can be obtained from $g_n(s)$, actual computations are quite involved when n is large.

1.1. Probability of Extinction.

An interesting problem with a particularly pleasing solution is the question of the ultimate extinction of a population. The probability that a population starting with a single ancestor will become extinct at or before the nth generation is

$$q_n = \Pr\{Z_n = 0\} = g_n(0). \tag{1.7}$$

We wish to investigate the limit of q_n as n tends to infinity. If $p_0 = 1$ the population will never start and if $p_0 = 0$ it will never become extinct; therefore we shall assume that $0 < p_0 < 1$. Then the generating function $g(s)$ in (1.2) is a strictly monotone increasing function of s in $(0,1)$ with

$$0 < g(0) = p_0 < 1. \tag{1.8}$$

Using (1.5) and (1.8) and the monotonicity property of $g(s)$ we have

$$q_{n+1} = g_{n+1}(0) = g_n[g(0)] > g_n(0) = q_n. \tag{1.9}$$

The sequence $\{q_n\}$ is bounded above by unity, and the inequality (1.9) shows that it is monotonically increasing; therefore the sequence will tend to a limit ζ as n tends to infinity. On the other hand, (1.6) implies the relation

$$q_{n+1} = g(q_n). \tag{1.10}$$

Taking limits of both sides of (1.10) we see that ζ satisfies the equation

$$\zeta = g(\zeta). \tag{1.11}$$

In fact, the limit ζ is the smallest root of the equation. To prove this we let x be an arbitrary positive root of the equation $x = g(x)$; then

$$q_1 = g(0) < g(x) = x \tag{1.12}$$

and hence

$$q_2 = g(q_1) < g(x) = x. \tag{1.13}$$

By induction

$$q_{n+1} = g(q_n) < g(x) = x, \tag{1.14}$$

demonstrating that $\zeta \leq x$.

We may now study the behavior of the function $y = g(s)$ for $0 \leq s \leq 1$. If $p_0 + p_1 = 1$, then $g(s)$ is linear and, since $p_0 > 0$, the line $y = g(s)$ intersects the line $y = s$ only at the point (1,1). Hence $\zeta = 1$ and ultimate extinction is certain. We now consider the case $p_0 + p_1 < 1$; it is apparent from (1.2) that in this case the derivative $g'(s)$ is a strictly increasing function of s. Thus the curve $y = g(s)$ is convex and can intercept the line $y = s$ in at most two points. One of these points is (1,1) and therefore the equation (1.11) has at most one root between 0 and 1. Whether such a root exists depends entirely upon the derivative $g'(1)$. If $g'(1) > 1$, the root $\zeta < 1$ exists; for tracing the curve $y = g(s)$ backward from the point (1,1), we find that it must fall below the line $y = s$ and eventually cross the line to reach the point $(0, p_0)$. If on the other hand $g'(1) \leq 1$, then the curve must be entirely above the line and there is no root less than unity, so that ζ must be unity.

Now the derivative $g'(1)$ is the expected number of offspring of any individual in the population. According to the preceding argument, if this expected number is greater than one, the probability of extinction

Figure 1

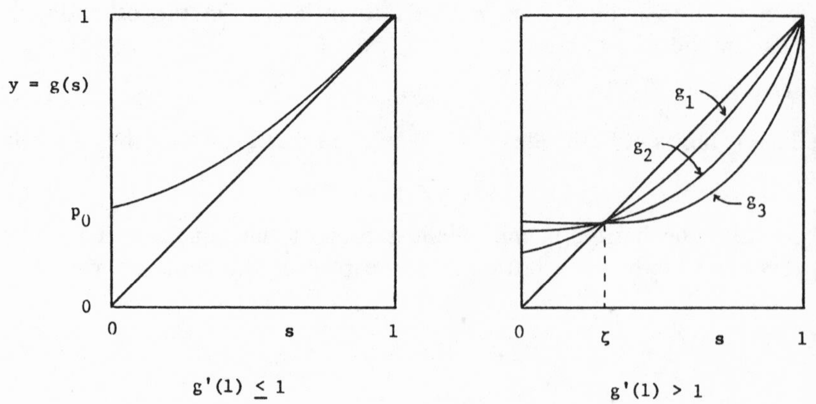

tends to a quantity ζ that is less than one; if the expected number of offspring is less than or equal to one, the probability that the population will eventually become extinct tends to unity.

Further investigation of the case $g'(1) > 1$ yields even more dramatic results. It is easily seen from Figure 1 that

$$\begin{aligned} g(s) &\geq s \quad \text{for} \quad 0 \leq s \leq \zeta \\ g(s) &\leq s \quad \text{for} \quad \zeta \leq s < 1. \end{aligned} \tag{1.15}$$

Hence by arguments similar to those used above to show the convergence of q_n, we have

$$\begin{aligned} s \leq g_1(s) \leq g_2(s) \leq \ldots \leq \zeta, &\quad 0 \leq s \leq \zeta \\ 1 > g_1(s) \geq g_2(s) \geq \ldots \geq \zeta, &\quad \zeta \leq s < 1. \end{aligned} \tag{1.16}$$

Equations (1.16) show that the limit

$$\lim_{n \to \infty} g_n(s) = G(s) \tag{1.17}$$

must exist for all s, and that $G(s) = 1$ only for $s = 1$. Passing to the limit in (1.6), we get

$$G(s) = \begin{cases} \zeta & 0 \leq s < 1 \\ 1 & s = 1. \end{cases} \tag{1.18}$$

This limiting function $G(s)$ is clearly not a p.g.f., since it is discontinuous at $s = 1$. However, if we redefine $G(1)$ to be equal to ζ, then we may interpret $G(s)$ as the p.g.f. of an improper random variable Z, the "ultimate size" of the population, which has the probability distribution

$$\begin{aligned} &\Pr\{Z = 0\} = \zeta, \\ &\Pr\{Z = k\} = 0, \quad k = 1, 2, \ldots. \\ &\Pr\{Z = \infty\} = 1 - \zeta. \end{aligned} \tag{1.19}$$

Thus the population either becomes extinct with a probability ζ, or grows without limit with a probability $1 - \zeta$; no intermediate course is possible. Of course, in practical applications to the growth of real populations, the assumptions of the branching process model are violated long before an infinite population is approached; on the other hand, the investigation of extinction phenomena through the use of branching processes is more useful, since extinction often occurs early in the process.

2. RANDOM WALK AND DIFFUSION PROCESS

The random walk, an extension of the Bernoulli trials, is of considerable interest in the study of the diffusion process in physics and sequential analysis in statistics (see Wald [1947]). It bears a close relationship to the branching process presented in Section 1. The concept of random walk is also akin to the gambler's ruin problem. An excellent discussion of the ruin problem may be found in Uspensky [1937] and Feller [1968]. We shall treat the random walk as a preliminary to the discrete time Markov chain discussed in Chapter 5.

The random walk is typically described by the motion of a particle on a real line. The particle is subject to collisions from the left or from the right, and will move one step to the right with probability p or one step to the left with probability q, $p + q = 1$. Movement takes place at times $t = 1, 2, \ldots$. The problem is to determine the position of a particle after a number of moves. Suppose a particle is initially located at $x = 0$: What is the probability of it being at $x = c$ after n moves? If there is an absorbing barrier at $x = -a$, $a > 0$, what is the probability that it will be absorbed at $t \to \infty$? If there is also an absorbing barrier at $x = +b$, $b > 0$, what is the probability that it will be absorbed at $x = -a$?; at $x = b$?

Gambler's Ruin. Two players, A and B, play a series of independent games at the stake of one dollar per game. Player A will win a game with probability p and lose a game (B wins) with probability $q = 1 - p$. Suppose the initial capital of player A is a and that of player B is b. What are their respective capitals after n games? What is the probability of A's ruin (his capital is reduced to zero) in n games?; if player B is a very rich man ($b = \infty$)? The parallelism between the random walk and the ruin problem is thus apparent.

2.1. Random Walk.

Let us consider a one dimensional random walk by a particle initially located at the origin. The particle will subsequently move to positions on the real line designated by $\pm 1, \pm 2, \ldots$. Let X_i be the outcome of the i-th move, with values $+1$ and -1 and probabilities p and q $(=1 - p)$ respectively. Let $\{X_i\}$ be the corresponding sequence of independent and identically distributed (i.i.d.) random variables. We want to know the probability distribution of the sum

$$Z_n = X_1 + \ldots + X_n, \tag{2.1}$$

or the position of the particle after n moves.

Each X_i is a Bernoulli random variable with the expectation

$$E(X_i) = p - q, \tag{2.2}$$

and the variance

$$\operatorname{Var}(X_i) = 4pq. \tag{2.3}$$

The probability generating function (p.g.f.)[1] is

$$g_i(s) = ps + qs^{-1}. \tag{2.4}$$

Since X_i's are i.i.d., the probability distribution of Z_n is the n-fold convolution of the probability distribution of X_i, and the p.g.f. of Z_n is the n-th power of the p.g.f. in (2.4), or

$$G_{Z_n}(s) = [ps + qs^{-1}]^n = s^{-n}[ps^2 + q]^n. \tag{2.5}$$

Expanding the binomial function in (2.5) gives

$$G_{Z_n}(s) = \sum_{i=0}^{n} \binom{n}{i} p^i q^{n-i} s^{2i-n}. \tag{2.6}$$

Substituting $k = 2i - n$ so that $i = (n + k)/2$, we find

$$\Pr\{Z_n = k\} = \binom{n}{\frac{n+k}{2}} p^{(n+k)/2} q^{(n-k)/2}, \tag{2.7}$$

with

$$E(Z_n) = n(p - q) \tag{2.8}$$

and

$$\operatorname{Var}(Z_n) = 4npq. \tag{2.9}$$

The value that Z_n assumes may be odd or even according to whether n is odd or even. If n is odd, the probability that Z_n will be an even number is zero. Also, for Z_n to assume a value of k, the particle must take $(n + k)/2$ steps to the right and $(n - k)/2$ steps to the

[1] We introduce the probability generating function here merely for the convenience of deriving the probability distribution of Z_n. Since each X_i may take on negative values, some of the general properties of a probability generating function discussed in Chapter 2 do not hold true here. For example, the probability distribution of X_i or of Z_n cannot be obtained by differentiation.

left, so that the difference

$$\left(\frac{n+k}{2}\right) - \left(\frac{n-k}{2}\right) = k \tag{2.10}$$

is the net displacement: k steps to the right. Of course, k can be either positive or negative. When $Z_n = 0$, the particle returns to the original position. When n is odd, the probability of return to the origin is

$$\Pr\{Z_n = 0\} = 0;$$

when n is even

$$\Pr\{Z_n = 0\} = \binom{n}{\frac{n}{2}} p^{n/2} q^{n/2}. \tag{2.11}$$

2.2 Diffusion Process.

The random walk described above can be extended almost immediately to the (one dimensional) diffusion process when both the size of step and time required for each move are infinitesimal. Consider a random walk taking place on the real line during a time interval $(0,t)$; a move of length Δx occurs with every time element Δt. Let δ be the corresponding random variable, with $\Pr\{\delta = +\Delta x\} = p$ and $\Pr\{\delta = -\Delta x\} = 1 - p(= q)$, so that the expectation is

$$E(\delta) = (p - q)\Delta x \tag{2.12}$$

and the variance

$$V(\delta) = 4pq(\Delta x)^2. \tag{2.13}$$

During the interval $(0,t)$, $t/\Delta t$ moves take place, and there are $t/\Delta t$ independent and identically distributed random variables δ_i. According to the central limit theorem, when $t/\Delta t$ becomes infinitely large the total net displacement during $(0,t)$, or the position of the particle at time t,

$$Z_t = \sum_{i=1}^{t/\Delta t} \delta_i, \tag{2.14}$$

has a normal distribution, with

$$E[Z_t] = (p-q)t\frac{\Delta x}{\Delta t} \tag{2.15}$$

and

$$V[Z_t] = 4pqt\frac{(\Delta x)^2}{\Delta t}. \tag{2.16}$$

In a diffusion process $\Delta x \to 0$ and $\Delta t \to 0$, and both p and q are close to $1/2$. For Z_t to have a finite expectation and a bounded variance, we let $\Delta x \to 0$, $\Delta t \to 0$ and $p \to 1/2$ in such a way that

$$(p-q)\frac{\Delta x}{\Delta t} = c \tag{2.17}$$

and

$$\frac{(\Delta x)^2}{\Delta t} = D, \tag{2.18}$$

where both c and D are positive constants. Therefore

$$\frac{(p-q)}{\Delta x} = \frac{c}{D}, \tag{2.19}$$

$$p = 1/2 + \frac{c}{2D}\Delta x, \qquad q = 1/2 - \frac{c}{2D}\Delta x, \tag{2.20}$$

and

$$V(Z_t) = Dt + o(\Delta x). \tag{2.21}$$

Consequently, the density function of the limiting distribution of Z_t is given by

$$f_{Z_t}(x) = \frac{1}{\sqrt{2\pi Dt}}e^{-(x-ct)^2/2Dt}. \tag{2.22}$$

We can also arrive at (2.22) by means of differential equations. Let

$$\Pr\{Z_t = x\} = v(x,t), \tag{2.23}$$

and consider a particle being at x at time $t + \Delta t$. For this to occur, the particle must be located either at $x - \Delta x$ at time t followed by a shift of Δx to the right in $(t, t + \Delta t)$, or at $x + \Delta x$ at t followed by a shift of Δx to the left in $(t, t+\Delta t)$. Therefore the corresponding probabilities satisfy the equation

$$\nu(x, t+\Delta t) = p\,\nu(x-\Delta x, t) + q\,\nu(x+\Delta x, t). \tag{2.24}$$

Using Taylor's expansion at the point (x, t), we can write

$$\left.\begin{aligned} \nu(x, t+\Delta t) &= \nu(x, t) + \Delta t \frac{\partial}{\partial t}\nu(x, t) + o(\Delta t), \\ &\text{and} \\ \nu(x \pm \Delta x, t) &= \nu(x, t) \pm \Delta x \frac{\partial}{\partial x}\nu(x, t) \\ &\quad + \frac{(\Delta x)^2}{2}\frac{\partial^2}{\partial x^2}\nu(x, t) + o\,[(\Delta x)^2]. \end{aligned}\right\} \tag{2.25}$$

Substituting (2.25) into (2.24) gives

$$\frac{\partial}{\partial t}\nu(x, t) = (q-p)\frac{\Delta x}{\Delta t}\frac{\partial}{\partial x}\nu(x, t) + (1/2)\frac{(\Delta x)^2}{\Delta t}\frac{\partial^2}{\partial x^2}\nu(x, t) + o(\Delta t) + o\,[(\Delta x)^2]. \tag{2.26}$$

Using (2.17) and (2.18) and letting $\Delta t \to 0$, $\Delta x \to 0$, we obtain

$$\frac{\partial}{\partial t}\nu(x, t) = -c\frac{\partial}{\partial x}\nu(x, t) + (1/2)\,D\frac{\partial^2}{\partial x^2}\nu(x, t), \tag{2.27}$$

which is the Fokker-Planck diffusion equation. The constant c is the drift coefficient and D, the diffusion coefficient. Equation (2.27) is essentially the same as the differential equation for the conduction of heat. Although direct integration of the equation is beyond the scope of this book, it is relatively easy to verify that the normal density function

$$\nu(x, t) = \frac{1}{\sqrt{2\pi Dt}}\,e^{-(x-ct)^2/2Dt} \tag{2.22a}$$

satisfies the differential equation (2.27).

3. GAMBLER'S RUIN

Consider again players A and B with their initial fortunes a and b and their respective probabilities of winning p and q. In the classical ruin problem, one seeks to determine the probability R_a that the ruin of A will eventually occur if the game is to be played until one of the players goes broke. Before attempting to provide the solution, we shall first give a formal definition of R_a. Let $r_{a1}, r_{a2}, \dots, r_{an}$ be the probabilities that player A is to be ruined at the first, second, . . ., the n-th games, respectively. The probability of ruin within n games is

$$R_{an} = r_{a1} + \cdots + r_{an}.$$

Since they are probabilities, $r_{ai} \geq 0$ and $R_{an} < 1$. Thus, for each given a, the infinite sequence $\{R_{an}\}$ increases monotonically, bounded above by unity and hence converges to a limit as $n \to \infty$. This limit, denoted by R_a, is the probability of player A's eventual ruin. The probability of player B's eventual ruin (A's eventual win) is defined similarly. In the language of random walk, these are the probabilities that a particle will be absorbed at the barriers $x = 0$ and $x = a + b$, respectively.

To determine R_a essentially requires that we establish a system of difference equations and find the solution of that system. Consider more generally R_x, the ruin probability if A's initial capital is x, and the outcome of the first subsequent game. Using the definition of p and q, we arrive at the difference equations:

$$R_x = pR_{x+1} + qR_{x-1}, \qquad \text{for } x = 1, \dots, a + b - 1. \tag{3.1}$$

If $x = 0$, A's ruin is certain. If $x = a + b$, A's ruin is impossible. Therefore, the boundary conditions are

$$R_0 = 1 \qquad \text{and} \qquad R_{a+b} = 0. \tag{3.2}$$

With our understanding of (3.2), we allow (3.1) to hold for $x = 1$ and $x = a + b - 1$. For the solution of equation (3.1), we let

$$R_x = \lambda^x, \tag{3.3}$$

where λ is an unknown constant. Substituting (3.3) in (3.1) yields the quadratic equation

$$\lambda = p\lambda^2 + q \tag{3.4}$$

with roots

$$\lambda_1 = 1 \qquad \text{and} \qquad \lambda_2 = \frac{q}{p}. \tag{3.5}$$

If $p \neq q$, the two roots in (3.5) are distinct and lead to two distinct solutions:

$$R_x = 1 \quad \text{and} \quad R_x = \left(\frac{q}{p}\right)^x. \tag{3.6}$$

It follows that the general solution of (3.1) is a linear function of unity and $(q/p)^x$:

$$R_x = c + d\left(\frac{q}{p}\right)^x. \tag{3.7}$$

To determine the constants c and d, we use the boundary conditions in (3.2):

$$c + d = 1$$

and

$$c + d\left(\frac{q}{p}\right)^{a+b} = 0. \tag{3.8}$$

Solving (3.8) gives us

$$c = \frac{-(q/p)^{a+b}}{1-(q/p)^{a+b}} \quad \text{and} \quad d = \frac{1}{1-(q/p)^{a+b}}, \tag{3.9}$$

and hence the desired solution

$$R_x = \frac{(q/p)^x - (q/p)^{a+b}}{1-(q/p)^{a+b}}. \tag{3.10}$$

For $x = a$, we have the probability of player A's ruin

$$R_a = \frac{(q/p)^a - (q/p)^{a+b}}{1-(q/p)^{a+b}}. \tag{3.11}$$

We can obtain the probability of player B's eventual ruin (A's win) in exactly the same manner. The formula is

$$W_a = \frac{1-(q/p)^a}{1-(q/p)^{a+b}}. \tag{3.12}$$

Since the sum $R_a + W_a = 1$, it is certain that either A or B will eventually lose all his initial capital, and an infinite series of games should not be expected.

When $p = q = 1/2$, we use L'Hopital's rule to obtain the probabilities of

$$R_a = \frac{b}{a+b} \tag{3.11a}$$

and

$$W_a = \frac{a}{a+b}. \tag{3.12a}$$

Equations (3.11) and (3.12) represent the respective probabilities of A's eventual gains of $-a$ and $+b$. The expected gain is thus

$$E[G] = -aR_a + bW_a. \tag{3.13}$$

When $a = b$,

$$E[G] = a\frac{1-(q/p)^a}{1+(q/p)^a}. \tag{3.14}$$

In this case $E[G] > 0$ if $q < p$, and $E[G] < 0$ if $p < q$. When $p = q = 1/2$, $E[G] = 0$.

The probabilities R_a and R_b depend not only on the probability of losing (or winning) a single game, but also on the amount of a player's initial capital. Suppose player B is so enormously rich that $b = \infty$ as compared to a. Taking the limit on both sides of (3.11) and (3.11a) as $b \to \infty$, we get the probability of A's eventual ruin

$$\begin{aligned} R_a &= 1 && \text{if } p < q \\ &= 1 && \text{if } p = q \\ &= (q/p)^a && \text{if } p > q. \end{aligned} \tag{3.15}$$

The habitual visitor to Monte Carlo or Las Vegas casinos might draw a warning from the second case stated in (3.15). Since the house capital is usually much greater than the customers', even if the game is fair, an impulsive gambler is certain to lose all his vacation money if he does not know when to stop.

3.1. Expected Number of Games.

We can derive a formula for the expectation without using the probability distribution for the number of games. Suppose player A has an initial capital x; the series ends as soon as A loses all his capital or its value becomes $a + b$. Let D_x be the expected number of games to be played. It is easy to show that D_x satisfies the difference equation

$$D_x = pD_{x+1} + qD_{x-1} + 1, \qquad 0 < x < a + b. \tag{3.16}$$

The series terminates when $x = 0$ or $x = a + b$. Therefore the boundary conditions are

$$D_0 = 0 \qquad \text{and} \qquad D_{a+b} = 0. \tag{3.17}$$

The difference equation in (3.16) is almost the same as for the ruin probability R_x in (3.1), except for the addition of unity, which makes (3.16) a non-homogeneous equation. We already know that the homogeneous equation (3.1) has a formal solution

$$c + d\left(\frac{q}{p}\right)^x. \tag{3.18}$$

Now, in order to obtain a general solution of equation (3.16), we need a solution that satisfies the non-homogeneous equation (3.16). In searching for such a solution, we let $D_x = \alpha x$ in (3.16) and find $\alpha = (q - p)^{-1}$. Hence,

$$D_x = \frac{x}{q - p}. \tag{3.19}$$

The general solution of (3.16) is the sum of (3.19) and the solution for the homogeneous equation (3.18), that is,

$$D_x = \frac{x}{q - p} + c + d\left(\frac{q}{p}\right)^x. \tag{3.20}$$

Using the boundary conditions (3.17), we find the desired solution

$$D_x = \frac{x}{q - p} - \frac{a + b}{q - p}\left[\frac{1 - (q/p)^x}{1 - (q/p)^{a+b}}\right]. \tag{3.21}$$

The expected number of games depends on the value of p and q. For any given $a + b$ and x, D_x increases as p (and q) approaches 1/2. When $p = q = 1/2$, we replace (3.19) with $D_x = -x^2$ and (3.20) with

$$D_x = -x^2 + c + dx \tag{3.22}$$

and obtain the expectation

$$D_x = x(a + b - x). \tag{3.23}$$

D_x assumes a maximum value of

$$D_x = \left(\frac{a+b}{2}\right)^2 \tag{3.24}$$

when $x = (a + b)/2$. For example, if two players, each with an initial amount of \$100, are to play a series of fair games at a stake of one dollar per game, on the average they will play 10,000 games before either one of them loses his entire capital.

3.2. Ruin Probability in a Finite Number of Games.

The ruin probability in a given number of games is not as easy to determine as when the number of games is unlimited; the final formula is also more complicated. But this very problem stimulated the interest of many early mathematicians who devised various solutions. The method described below requires only a minimum amount of mathematics and is quite instructive (cf., Feller [1968]). For convenience we shall use the terminology of the random walk to develop the ruin probability.

Given two absorbing barriers at $x = 0$ and $x = a + b$, we let

$$\pi_{x,n} = \Pr\{\text{a particle in position } x \text{ will be absorbed at } x = 0 \text{ in } n \text{ moves}\},$$

$$0 < x < a + b$$

$$n = 1, 2, \ldots. \tag{3.25}$$

The probability $\pi_{x,n}$ is analogous to the ruin probability R_a formulated in (3.1) and satisfies the difference equation

$$\pi_{x,n+1} = p\pi_{x+1,n} + q\pi_{x-1,n}, \qquad \text{for } n = 1, 2, \ldots,; 1 \le x < a + b, \tag{3.26}$$

with the boundary conditions

$$\pi_{0,n} = 0, \qquad \pi_{a+b,n} = 0, \qquad \text{for } n \ge 1,$$

and

$$\pi_{0,0} = 1, \qquad \pi_{x,0} = 0, \qquad \text{for } 1 \le x \le a + b.$$

The probability $\pi_{x,n}$ has two indices, x and n; it is difficult to solve (3.26) directly. We resort to the method of the probability generating function. For each x, we let

$$g(x;s)=\sum_{n=0}^{\infty}\pi_{x,n}s^n \tag{3.27}$$

be the p.g.f. of $\pi_{x,n}$, with the boundary conditions

$$g(0,s)=1 \qquad \text{and} \qquad g(a+b,\,s)=0. \tag{3.28}$$

Multiplying both sides of (3.26) by s^{n+1}, and summing over n from 0 to infinity, we arrive at a difference equation for the probability generating function:

$$g(x;s)=psg(x+1;s)+qsg(x-1;s), \qquad \text{for } 1\le x<a+b. \tag{3.29}$$

To find a solution for (3.29), we let

$$g(x;s)=[\lambda(s)]^x. \tag{3.30}$$

Substituting (3.30) in (3.29), we get the equation

$$ps\lambda^2(s)-\lambda(s)+qs=0. \tag{3.31}$$

Thus the roots of (3.31)

$$\lambda_1(s)=\frac{1+\sqrt{1-4pqs^2}}{2ps} \qquad \text{and} \qquad \lambda_2(s)=\frac{1-\sqrt{1-4pqs^2}}{2ps}, \tag{3.32}$$

are the only values of $\lambda(s)$ for which (3.30) is a valid solution of equation (3.29). The two roots $\lambda_1(s)$ and $\lambda_2(s)$ are distinct and since s is between -1 and 1, the discriminant is positive and the two roots are real. Therefore we may form a general solution of (3.29):

$$g(x;s)=c(s)\lambda_1^x(s)+d(s)\lambda_2^x(s). \tag{3.33}$$

To determine the values of $c(s)$ and $d(s)$, we use the boundary conditions in (3.28). As a result, we have

$$c(s)+d(s)=1$$

and (3.34)

$$c(s)\lambda_1^{a+b}(s)+d(s)\lambda_2^{a+b}(s)=0;$$

hence

$$c(s) = \frac{\lambda_2^{a+b}(s)}{\lambda_2^{a+b}(s) - \lambda_1^{a+b}(s)} \quad \text{and} \quad d(s) = \frac{\lambda_1^{a+b}(s)}{\lambda_1^{a+b}(s) - \lambda_2^{a+b}(s)}. \tag{3.35}$$

Consequently, the p.g.f. is

$$g(x;s) = \frac{\lambda_1^{a+b}(s)\lambda_2^x(s) - \lambda_1^x(s)\lambda_2^{a+b}(s)}{\lambda_1^{a+b}(s) - \lambda_2^{a+b}(s)}, \tag{3.36}$$

or, since $\lambda_1(s)\cdot\lambda_2(s) = q/p$,

$$g(x;s) = \left(\frac{q}{p}\right)^x \frac{\lambda_1^{a+b-x}(s) - \lambda_2^{a+b-x}(s)}{\lambda_1^{a+b}(s) - \lambda_2^{a+b}(s)}. \tag{3.37}$$

Both the numerator and the denominator in (3.37) are polynomials in s, so one may use the partial fraction expansion discussed in Chapter 2 to derive the probability $\pi_{x,n}$. However, the roots $\lambda_1(s)$ and $\lambda_2(s)$ contain s under the square root sign; we must remove the square root sign before we proceed further. To do this, we let[2]

$$1 - 4pqs^2 = -\frac{\sin^2\theta}{\cos^2\theta} \tag{3.38}$$

so that

$$\lambda_1(s) = (\sqrt{q/p})[\cos\theta + i\sin\theta]. \tag{3.39}$$

We then use Euler's formula to write

$$\lambda_1(s) = (\sqrt{q/p})e^{i\theta} \quad \text{and} \quad \lambda_2 = (\sqrt{q/p})e^{-i\theta}. \tag{3.40}$$

Introducing (3.40) in (3.37) and applying Euler's formula once again, we have

$$g(x;s) = (\sqrt{q/p})^x \frac{\sin(a+b-x)\theta}{\sin(a+b)\theta}. \tag{3.41}$$

Now we use the partial fraction expansion to write

$$(\sqrt{q/p})^{-x} g(x;s) = \frac{\alpha_1}{s_1 - s} + \cdots + \frac{\alpha_{a+b-1}}{s_{a+b-1} - s}, \tag{3.42}$$

[2] We introduce formula (3.38) solely for obtaining explicit solutions for the problem; complex values of θ corresponding to $-1 < s < 1$ have no effect on the final solution.

where s_r are the roots of the denominator (but not roots of the numerator) of (4.17). Since for $(a+b)\theta = r\pi$, $r = 1, \dots, (a+b-1)$, the denominator of (3.41) vanishes and, by the definition of θ provided in (3.38)

$$s = \frac{1}{2\sqrt{pq}\cos\theta}, \tag{3.43}$$

the roots are

$$s_r = \frac{1}{2\sqrt{pq}\cos\,[r\pi/(a+b)]}, \qquad r = 1, \dots, (a+b-1). \tag{3.44}$$

According to Chapter 2, equation (6.4), the formula used to compute the coefficient α_r in (3.42), is

$$\alpha_r = \frac{-\sin\,[(a+b-x)\theta_r]}{\left.\dfrac{d}{ds}\sin\,[(a+b)\theta]\right|_{\theta=\theta_r}}. \tag{3.45}$$

Here θ_r and s_r are related by equation (3.43); their differentials have the relationship

$$\frac{d\theta}{ds} = 2\sqrt{pq}\,\cos^2\theta\cdot\sin^{-1}\theta. \tag{3.46}$$

To find the denominator of (3.45), we use the rule for differentiating an implicit function to write

$$\frac{d}{ds}\sin\,[(a+b)\theta] = \frac{d}{d\theta}\sin\,[(a+b)\theta]\cdot\frac{d\theta}{ds}. \tag{3.47}$$

Substituting (3.46) in (3.47) yields the derivative evaluated at $\theta_r = r\pi/(a+b)$:

$$\left.\frac{d}{ds}\sin\,[(a+b)\theta]\right|_{\theta=\theta_r} = (-1)^r 2\sqrt{pq}\,(a+b) \{\cos^2\,[r\pi/(a+b)]\}\sin^{-1}\,[r\pi/(a+b)] \tag{3.48}$$

where $(-1)^r$ has been written for $\cos(r\pi)$. The numerator of (3.45) is simply

$$\sin[(a+b-x)\theta_r] = \sin\left[r\pi - \frac{xr\pi}{a+b}\right] = (-1)^{r+1}\sin\left(\frac{xr\pi}{a+b}\right). \tag{3.49}$$

As a result,

$$\alpha_r = \frac{\sin[r\pi/(a+b)]\sin[xr\pi/(a+b)]}{2\sqrt{pq}\,(a+b)\cos^2[r\pi/(a+b)]}, \quad r = 1, \ldots, (a+b-1). \tag{3.50}$$

One can expand each ratio on the right hand side of (3.42) in a geometric series:

$$\frac{\alpha_r}{s_r - s} = \frac{\alpha_r}{s_r}\left[1 + \frac{s}{s_r} + \left(\frac{s}{s_r}\right)^2 + \ldots\right], \tag{3.51}$$

with s_r being given in (3.44). Finally, introducing (3.50) and (3.51) in (3.45) and collecting terms of the power of s, we obtain the desired formula for the probability $\pi_{x,n}$:

$$\pi_{x,n} = \frac{2^n}{a+b}p^{(x-n)/2}q^{(x+n)/2}\sum_{r=1}^{a+b-1}\sin\frac{r\pi}{a+b}\sin\frac{xr\pi}{a+b}\cos^{n-1}\frac{r\pi}{a+b} \tag{3.52}$$

for $0 < x < a+b$, $n = 1, 2, \ldots$.

4. PROBLEMS FOR SOLUTION

1. *Branching process.* In the simple branching process, let the expectation and the variance of X be μ and σ^2, respectively. Use the identities

$$E(Z_{n+1}) = E[E(Z_{n+1} \mid Z_n)]$$

and

$$\text{Var}(Z_{n+1}) = E[\text{Var}(Z_{n+1} \mid Z_n)] + \text{Var}[E(Z_{n+1} \mid Z_n)]$$

to derive the formulas for the expectation $E(Z_n)$ and the variance $\text{Var}(Z_n)$.

2. *Continuation.* Use the relationship $g_{n+1}(s) = g_n[g(s)]$ to derive the formulas for $E(Z_n)$ and $\text{Var}(Z_n)$ in problem 1.

3. *Fokker-Planck diffusion equation.* Show that the normal density function

$$v(x,t) = \frac{1}{\sqrt{2\pi Dt}} e^{-(x-ct)^2/2Dt} \tag{2.22a}$$

satisfies the Fokker-Planck diffusion equation

$$\frac{\partial}{\partial t} v(x,t) = -c\frac{\partial}{\partial x} v(x,t) + (1/2)D\frac{\partial^2}{\partial x^2} v(x,t). \tag{2.27}$$

4. *Gambler's ruin.* Derive the formula

$$W_a = \frac{1-(q/p)^a}{1-(q/p)^{a+b}} \tag{3.12}$$

of the probability of A's eventual win (B's ruin) in an infinite series of games.

5. *Continuation.* Formulas (3.11) and (3.12) for the probability of A's ruin and of B's ruin were derived for the case where $p \neq q$. Derive formulas for R_a and W_a when $p = q = 1/2$ without resorting to L'Hopital's rule.

6. Two players take turns drawing one ball at a time out of an urn containing m white balls and n black balls. The player who extracts the first white ball wins the game. Let A be the player who draws the first ball and P his probability of winning the game. Let B be the other player and Q his probability of winning. Derive the formulas for the probabilities P and Q and show that $P + Q = 1$.

7. Three players, A, B and C, agree to play a series of games according to the following rules: Two players participate in each game while the third is idle. The winner of a game plays the one who is idle. The player who succeeds in winning successively over both opponents wins the series. Supposing that the probability for each player to win a single game is 1/2 and that the first game is played by A and B, find the probabilities for A, B, and C, respectively, to win the series, if

(a) the number of games to be played may not exceed a given number n;

(b) the number of games is unlimited.

8. Three players, A, B, and C, in turn draw balls from an urn with 10 white balls and 10 black balls, taking one ball at a time. He who extracts the first white ball wins the game. Supposing that they draw in order (A, B, C) find the probabilities for each of them to win the game.

9. Two players, A and B, toss two dice. A starts the game. The game is won by A if he casts 6 points before B casts 7 points and it is won by B if he casts 7 points before A casts 6 points. What are the probabilities for A and B to win the game if they agree to cast dice not more than n times? What is the probability of a tie?

10. The game known as "craps" is played with two dice. The caster wins unconditionally if he produces 7 or 11 points (which are called "naturals"); he loses the game in case of 2, 3 or 12 points (called "craps"). But if he produces 4, 5, 6, 8, 9 or 10 points, he is entitled to cast the dice steadily until he throws the same number of points he had before or until he throws a 7. If he rolls 7 before obtaining his point, he loses the game; otherwise, he wins. What is the probability of his winning?

11. If a person playing a certain game can win \$1 with the probability of $1/3$, and lose 25¢ with the probability $2/3$, what is the probability of winning at least \$3 in 20 games?

12. In a series of $2s$ trials with the probability $p = 1/2$, find the most probable number of successes (i.e., the number which occurs with the largest probability) and the corresponding probability. Show also that this probability is less than $1/\sqrt{2s + 1}$.

13. Show that the probability T_n corresponding to the most probable number of successes in n trials with probability T_n tends to $(2\pi npq)^{-1/2}$ as $n \to \infty$.

14. Two players, A and B, agree to play until one of them wins a certain number of games. The probabilities for A and B to win a single game are p and $q = 1 - p$. However, the players are forced to quit when A has a games still to win and B has b games to win. How should they divide their total stake to be fair?

This problem is known as "problème de parties," one of the first problems on probability discussed and solved by Fermat and Pascal in their correspondence. The problem was reproduced by J. V. Uspensky in his remarkable book *Introduction to Mathematical Probability* (1937). Professor Uspensky's book, which is no longer readily available, contains many interesting problems, some of which are classical gems. Several problems in this section are taken from his book.

15. A and B have, respectively, $n + 1$ and n coins. If they toss their coins simultaneously, what is the probability that

(a) A will have more heads than B?

(b) A and B will have an equal number of heads?

(c) B will have more heads than A?

16. Two players, A and B, agree to play a series of games on the condition that A wins the series if he succeeds in winning a games before B wins b games. The probability of winning a single game is p for A and $q = 1 - p$ for B. What is the probability that A will win the series?

17. A and B, each possessing \$2, agree to play a series of games. The probability of winning a single game is p for A and $q = 1 - p$ for B, and the loser pays \$1 to his adversary after each game. Find the probability that each one of them will be ruined at or before the n-th game. What is the probability if $p = 1/2$?

18. Find the probabilities in problem 17 if each players enters the game with \$3.

19. Three players, A, B, and C, play a series of games, each game being won by one of them. If the probabilities for A, B, and C to win a single game are p, q, r, with $p + q + r = 1$, find the probability of A winning a games before B and C win b and c games, respectively.

20. Players A and B with \$50 and \$100, respectively, agree to play until one of them is ruined. The probability of winning a single game is $2/3$ for A and $1/3$ for B, and they stake \$1 at each game. What is the probability of ruin for player A?

21. Player A whose fortune is \$10 agrees to play not more than 20 games against an infinitely rich adversary; both stake \$1 with an equal probability of winning a single game. What is the probability that A will not be ruined in the course of 20 games?

22. Players A and B with \$1 and \$2, respectively, agree to play not more than n equitable games, staking \$1 at each game. What are the probabilities of their ruin? What are the probabilities when $n = 20$?

23. Find the probabilities in problem 22, when A and B have \$2 and \$3 initially.

CHAPTER 5

Markov Chains

1. INTRODUCTION

Most probability and statistical theory has been developed for cases where the random variables involved are independent. The classical central limit theorem and the laws of large numbers are prominent examples. In many practical situations, however, the random variables involved are neither independent nor identically distributed. Such phenomena are especially prevalent when the observations are made in sequence.

For example, in sampling without replacement from a dichotomous population consisting of "successes" and "failures," the probability of choosing a "success" is a function of the previous elements sampled. In the random walk discussed in the previous chapter, the location of a particle after a given move depends on the previous moves. In the Markov chain, we study dependence of a particular kind. When random variables are observed in sequence, the distribution of a random variable is dependent only on the immediately preceding observed random variable and not on those that come before it.

The theory of Markov chains, which is a special case of Markov processes, is named after A. A. Markov, who in 1906 introduced the concept of chains with a discrete parameter and finite number of states. Kolmogorov in 1937 extended the theory for the denumerable case, J. Doob in 1945 and Paul Levy in 1951 introduced continuous parameter chains. While many others have contributed to the advancement of Markov theory, Feller and K. L. Chung are among those who are responsible for the present status in probability theory that the Markov chain enjoys. Chung in [1960] gave a comprehensive theoretical treatment of the subject and Feller in [1968] made a most lucid account of Markov chains for both theoretical interest and practical applications.

The purpose of this chapter is to introduce the Markov chain purely for practical consumption. Included are the essentials necessary for the understanding and appreciation of the topic. For ease of application, an algebraic treatment of finite chains is given in Chapter 6. Let us first consider a practical example as an entree to the main body of discussion.

Life table urns. Balls are drawn with replacement from an infinite sequence of urns numbered 0, 1, ... In the αth urn, there is a proportion p_α of white balls and a proportion q_α of black balls with $0 < p_\alpha < 1$ and $p_\alpha + q_\alpha = 1$. Beginning with the 0th urn a number $X_0 = i_0$ balls is drawn of which $X_1 = i_1$ are white; a total of i_1 balls is drawn from the first urn of which $X_2 = i_2$ are white; i_2 balls are then drawn from the second urn of which $X_3 = i_3$ are white, and so on. In general, the number $X_{\alpha+1} = i_{\alpha+1}$ of white balls drawn from the αth urn is the number of balls to be drawn from the next or the $(\alpha + 1)^{\text{th}}$ urn. The experiment terminates as soon as the number of white balls drawn from an urn is zero. Clearly, X_1, the number of white balls drawn from the 0th urn, has a binomial distribution:

$$\Pr\{X_1 = i_1 \mid i_0\} = \binom{i_0}{i_1} p_0^{i_1} q_0^{i_0 - i_1}, \qquad i_1 = 0, \ldots, i_0. \tag{1.1}$$

The number of white balls drawn (X_2) from the first urn depends only on the number of drawings (X_1) from that urn but not on i_0. Therefore, given $X_0 = i_0$, $X_1 = i_1$, the probability of X_2 is given by

$$\begin{aligned} \Pr\{X_2 = i_2 \mid i_0, i_1\} &= \Pr\{X_2 = i_2 \mid i_1\} \\ &= P_{i_1, i_2} \qquad 0 \le i_2 \le i_1 \le i_0. \end{aligned} \tag{1.2}$$

Generally, the conditional probability of X_β given $X_0 = i_0, \ldots, X_\alpha = i_\alpha$, for $\alpha < \beta$, is a function of i_α only:

$$\begin{aligned} \Pr\{X_\beta = i_\beta \mid i_0, \ldots, i_\alpha\} &= \Pr\{X_\beta = i_\beta \mid i_\alpha\} \\ &= P_{i_\alpha, i_\beta}, \qquad i_\alpha > 0; \quad i_\beta = 0, \ldots, i_\alpha. \end{aligned} \tag{1.3}$$

This urn model, which is an example of a (finite) Markov chain, is devised to describe the life table where $X_0 = i_0$ is the original cohort with which a life table starts and X_α is the number of people of exact age α and $X_{\alpha+1}$ is the number surviving to the end of the

α^{th} age interval. For a discussion on various aspects of the model, the reader is referred to Chiang ([1968], Chapter 10). In the following section, a formal definition of Markov chains is presented.

2. DEFINITION OF MARKOV CHAINS AND TRANSITION PROBABILITIES

Definition: A sequence of random variables $\{X_\alpha, \alpha = 0, 1, \ldots\}$ is called a Markov chain if, for every collection of integers, $\alpha_0 < \alpha_1 < \ldots < \alpha_n < \beta$, the conditional distributions of X_β satisfy the relation:

$$\Pr\{X_\beta = i_\beta \mid X_{\alpha_0}, \ldots, X_{\alpha_n}\} = \Pr\{X_\beta = i_\beta \mid X_{\alpha_n}\}, \qquad \text{for all } i_\beta. \tag{2.1}$$

Thus, given the knowledge of a present state (X_{α_n}), the outcome in the future $(X_\beta = i_\beta)$ is no longer dependent upon the past $(X_{\alpha_0}, \ldots, X_{\alpha_{n-1}})$, a useful motto for those who dwell upon the past in conducting their daily lives.

For each X_α we denote the absolute probability by

$$\Pr\{X_\alpha = i_\alpha\} = a_{i_\alpha} \tag{2.2}$$

and for every pair of random variables, X_α and X_β, $\alpha < \beta$, the conditional probability by

$$\Pr\{X_\beta = i_\beta \mid X_\alpha = i_\alpha\} = P_{i_\alpha, i_\beta}, \tag{2.3}$$

with the conditions that

$$\sum_{i_\alpha} \Pr\{X_\alpha = i_\alpha\} = \sum_{i_\alpha} a_{i_\alpha} = 1 \tag{2.4}$$

and

$$\sum_{i_\beta} P_{i_\alpha, i_\beta} = 1. \tag{2.5}$$

Therefore, the joint probabilities of $X_\alpha, X_\beta, X_\gamma$, for $\alpha < \beta < \gamma$ are given by

$$\Pr\{X_\alpha = i_\alpha, X_\beta = i_\beta, X_\gamma = i_\gamma\} = a_{i_\alpha} P_{i_\alpha, i_\beta} P_{i_\beta, i_\gamma}, \tag{2.6}$$

and

$$\Pr\{X_\alpha = i_\alpha, X_\beta = i_\beta\} = a_{i_\alpha} P_{i_\alpha, i_\beta}. \tag{2.7}$$

Generally, for any collection of integers

$$\alpha < \beta < \cdots < \delta < \varepsilon \tag{2.8}$$

the joint probabilities are

$$\Pr\{X_\alpha = i_\alpha,\ X_\beta = i_\beta,\ \ldots,\ X_\delta = i_\delta,\ X_\varepsilon = i_\varepsilon\}$$
$$= a_{i_\alpha} P_{i_\alpha, i_\beta} \cdots P_{i_\delta, i_\varepsilon}. \tag{2.9}$$

An important feature of the Markov chain, and indeed of stochastic processes in general, is that the random variables are observed in sequence and the order of the sequence, such as the one in (2.9) should not be disturbed. In using a Markov chain to describe a stochastic system, all the possible values of random variables X_α constitute the space of states of the system. The event associated with the absolute probability in (2.2) is that the system is in state i_α at time α (or the αth step). The conditional probability in (2.3) describes a transition from state i_α at α to state i_β at β. A Markov chain with state space being the set of all the non-negative integers is completely determined by the initial absolute probability distribution

$$\Pr\{X_0 = i_0\} = a_{i_0}, \qquad i_0 = 1, 2, \ldots \tag{2.2a}$$

and the transition probabilities

$$\Pr\{X_{\alpha+1} = i_{\alpha+1} \mid X_\alpha = i_\alpha\} = P_{i_\alpha, i_{\alpha+1}}, \qquad i_\alpha, i_{\alpha+1} = 1, 2, \ldots \tag{2.10}$$

for $\alpha = 0, 1, \ldots$. A Markov chain is said to be non-homogeneous with respect to time if the transition probabilities in (2.10) are functions of α (time), and is homogeneous with respect to time if the transition probabilities

$$\Pr\{X_{\alpha+1} = j \mid X_\alpha = i\} = p_{ij} \tag{2.11}$$

are independent of α. We shall be studying mainly time homogeneous Markov chains in this chapter. A chain is a finite chain if there are a finite number of states, an infinite chain if there are an infinite number of states. In any case, the transition probabilities p_{ij} can be arranged in the form of a matrix

$$\mathbf{P} = \begin{pmatrix} p_{11} & p_{12} & p_{13} & \cdots \\ p_{21} & p_{22} & p_{23} & \cdots \\ \cdot & \cdot & \cdot & \cdots \\ \cdot & \cdot & \cdot & \cdots \end{pmatrix} \tag{2.12}$$

if the state space contains 1, 2, ..., or

$$\mathbf{P} = \begin{pmatrix} p_{00} & p_{01} & p_{02} & \cdots \\ p_{10} & p_{11} & p_{12} & \cdots \\ \cdot & \cdot & \cdot & \cdots \\ \cdot & \cdot & \cdot & \cdots \end{pmatrix} \tag{2.12a}$$

if the state space contains non-negative integers. These matrices are known as *stochastic matrices* with the transition probabilities p_{ij} as their elements. The subscripts of each probability are the states associated with a transition from i to j or the values of two random variables X_α and $X_{\alpha+1}$; the first subscript stands for the value of the first random variable, while the second stands for the value of the second random variable. Given $X_\alpha = i$, we have

$$\sum_j \Pr\{X_{\alpha+1} = j \mid X_\alpha = i\} = \sum_j p_{ij} = 1, \tag{2.13}$$

so that each row sum in a stochastic matrix is unity.

Example 1. In the example of life table urns, the proportion of white balls p_α varies from urn to urn. The transition probability

$$p_{ij} = \binom{i}{j} p_\alpha^j q_\alpha^{i-j}$$

is a function of α, and the chain is non-homogeneous. If $p_\alpha = p$, for $\alpha = 0, 1, \ldots$, the transition probability becomes

$$p_{ij} = \binom{i}{j} p^j q^{i-j},$$

and the chain is time homogeneous. The corresponding stochastic matrix is an $(i_0 + 1) \times (i_0 + 1)$ matrix, where i_0 is the number of drawings from urn 0; the first row (column) is the 0th row (column) and the last row (column) is the i_0-th row (column). The number of drawings (i_α) from a particular urn is equal to i_0 if all balls drawn from preceding urns are white, and $i_\alpha < i_0$, otherwise. This restriction is not necessary in Markov chains in general. The $(i_0 + 1) \times (i_0 + 1)$ matrix of the transition probabilities for the homogeneous case appears as follows:

$$\mathbf{P} = \begin{pmatrix} 1 & 0 & 0 & \cdots & 0 \\ q & p & 0 & \cdots & 0 \\ q^2 & \binom{2}{1} qp & p^2 & \cdots & 0 \\ \cdot & \cdot & \cdot & & \cdot \\ q^{i_0} & \binom{i_0}{1} q^{i_0-1} p & \binom{i_0}{2} q^{i_0-2} p^2 & \cdots & p^{i_0} \end{pmatrix}$$

Example 2. *A simple illness-death model.* In their analysis of survival of patients afflicted with cancer, Fix and Neyman [1951] proposed a model consisting of two health states, S_1 and S_2, and two death states, R_1 and R_2 (or S_3 and S_4). An individual is said to be in state S_1 if he is free from the disease or in S_2 if he is afflicted with the disease. He may, from each of the two states S_1 and S_2, enter the state S_3 or S_4. A stochastic matrix describing the transitions is a 4×4 matrix:

$$\mathbf{P} = \begin{pmatrix} p_{11} & p_{12} & p_{13} & p_{14} \\ p_{21} & p_{22} & p_{23} & p_{24} \\ 0 & 0 & 1 & 0 \\ 0 & 0 & 0 & 1 \end{pmatrix}.$$

Here p_{12} is the probability of relapse, p_{21} is the probability of recovery, and p_{13} and p_{23} are the probabilities of entering the death state S_3 from S_1 and S_2, respectively. The elements in the last two rows are (0,0,1,0) and (0,0,0,1) since once an individual enters a state of death, he will remain there forever. An extensive study of this model is given in Chapters 11, 12 and 13.

Example 3. *Gambler's ruin.* The possible states of the system, which range from 0 to $a + b$, represent the amount of money that player A may possess during the course of the game. For $0 < i < a + b$, $p_{i,i+1} = p$ and $p_{i,i-1} = q$; and the game ends at 0 or $a + b$. The transition probability matrix is $(a + b + 1) \times (a + b + 1)$ [Cf. Section 3, Chapter 4].

$$
\mathbf{P} = \begin{pmatrix}
1 & 0 & 0 & 0 & \dots & 0 & 0 & 0 \\
q & 0 & p & 0 & \dots & 0 & 0 & 0 \\
0 & q & 0 & p & \dots & 0 & 0 & 0 \\
. & . & . & . & \dots & . & . & . \\
. & . & . & . & \dots & . & . & . \\
. & . & . & . & \dots & . & . & . \\
0 & 0 & 0 & 0 & \dots & q & 0 & p \\
0 & 0 & 0 & 0 & \dots & 0 & 0 & 1
\end{pmatrix}.
$$

Example 4. *Random walk with reflecting barriers.* The gambler's ruin problem in Example 3 may be modified by an agreement that the player with only one dollar left is allowed to retain the money if he loses the next game. This modification has the same effect as placing reflecting barriers at $x = .5$ and $x = a + b - .5$ in the random walk problem. Given a particle is at $x = 1$, there is a probability q that it will move to $x = .5$ and back to $x = 1$ instead of moving into the absorbing state 0. Similarly, given $x = a + b - 1$, there is a probability p that a particle will move to $x = a + b - .5$ and back to $a + b - 1$ rather than going into the absorbing state $a + b$. In this modification of the game, the system has $a + b - 1$ states. The transition probabilities are of three types: For $1 < i < a + b - 1$, $p_{i,i+1} = p$ and $p_{i,i-1} = q$; for $i = 1$, $p_{i,i} = q$ and $p_{i,i+1} = p$; and for $i = a + b - 1$, $p_{i,i} = p$ and $p_{i,i-1} = q$. The stochastic matrix now is $(a + b - 1) \times (a + b - 1)$:

$$
\mathbf{P} = \begin{pmatrix}
q & p & 0 & 0 & \dots & 0 & 0 \\
q & 0 & p & 0 & \dots & 0 & 0 \\
0 & q & 0 & p & \dots & 0 & 0 \\
. & . & . & . & \dots & . & . \\
0 & 0 & 0 & 0 & \dots & q & p
\end{pmatrix}.
$$

3. HIGHER ORDER TRANSITION PROBABILITIES, $p_{ij}(n)$

The transition probability p_{ij} defined in (2.11) is associated with a transition taking place in one step, from $X_\alpha = i$ to $X_{\alpha+1} = j$. When a transition from i to j occurs in two steps, we have a two-step transition probability:

$$\Pr\{X_{\alpha+2} = j \mid X_\alpha = i\} = p_{ij}(2) \tag{3.1}$$

where the number (2) indicates the number of steps involved in the transition. In accordance with this designation, the one-step transition probability occasionally will be denoted by $p_{ij}(1)$:

$$\Pr\{X_{\alpha+1} = j \mid X_\alpha = i\} = p_{ij}(1). \tag{3.2}$$

It is easy to show that the transition probabilities in (3.1) and (3.2) satisfy the following equation

$$p_{ik}(2) = \sum_j p_{ij}(1)p_{jk}(1), \qquad i, k = 1, 2, \ldots . \tag{3.3}$$

To prove (3.3), we write

$$\begin{aligned}
\Pr\{X_{\alpha+2} = k \mid X_\alpha = i\} &= \sum_j \Pr\{X_{\alpha+2} = k, X_{\alpha+1} = j \mid X_\alpha = i\} \\
&= \sum_j \Pr\{X_{\alpha+1} = j \mid X_\alpha = i\} \\
&\qquad \times \Pr\{X_{\alpha+2} = k \mid X_{\alpha+1} = j, X_\alpha = i\} \\
&= \sum_j \Pr\{X_{\alpha+1} = j \mid X_\alpha = i\} \\
&\qquad \times \Pr\{X_{\alpha+2} = k \mid X_{\alpha+1} = j\},
\end{aligned} \tag{3.4}$$

and equation (3.3) follows.

For all possible values of i, j, k, equation (3.3) may be written in terms of the transition probability matrices:

$$\mathbf{P}(2) = \mathbf{P}(1) \cdot \mathbf{P}(1), \tag{3.5}$$

where $\mathbf{P}(1) = \mathbf{P}$ is the (one-step) transition probability matrix given in (2.12) and

$$\mathbf{P}(2) = \begin{pmatrix} p_{11}(2) & p_{12}(2) & \cdots \\ p_{21}(2) & p_{22}(2) & \cdots \\ \cdot & \cdot & \cdots \\ \cdot & \cdot & \cdots \end{pmatrix} \tag{3.6}$$

is a two-step transition probability matrix. The matrix multiplication on the right-hand side of (3.5) is performed in the usual manner. The $(i,k)^{\text{th}}$ element of the product is obtained by multiplying each (the jth) element in the ith row of the first matrix by the corresponding (the jth) element in the kth column of the second matrix and adding the products over j. In general, higher order transition probabilities have the relationship

$$p_{ik}(m+n) = \sum_j p_{ij}(m)p_{jk}(n), \qquad i, k = 1, 2, \ldots, \tag{3.7}$$

or, in terms of the transition probability matrices:

$$\mathbf{P}(m+n) = \mathbf{P}(m)\mathbf{P}(n), \tag{3.8}$$

where the matrix $\mathbf{P}(n)$ has $p_{ij}(n)$ as its elements. Equation (3.5) shows that

$$\mathbf{P}(2) = [\mathbf{P}(1)]^2 \tag{3.9}$$

and generally

$$\mathbf{P}(n) = [\mathbf{P}(1)]^n. \tag{3.10}$$

Equation (3.7), known as the Chapman-Kolmogorov equation, is often used to derive basic formulas in a given problem. While the Markov chains discussed here are time homogeneous, Chapman-Kolmogorov equations can be derived for non-homogeneous Markov chains as well. In that case, the multiple transition probabilities in (3.7) are all time dependent.

Example 5. In the life table urn example with $p_\alpha = p$, for $\alpha = 0, 1, \ldots$, the two-step transition probabilities are given by

$$p_{ik}(2) = \binom{i}{k}(p^2)^k(1-p^2)^{i-k} \tag{3.11}$$

and the one-step transition probabilities by

$$p_{ij}(1) = \binom{i}{j}p^j(1-p)^{i-j}. \tag{3.12}$$

Substituting (3.11) and (3.12) in (3.3) yields a relationship between the two binomial probabilities:

$$\binom{i}{k}(p^2)^k(1-p^2)^{i-k} = \sum_{j=k}^{i}\binom{i}{j}p^j(1-p)^{i-j}\binom{j}{k}p^k(1-p)^{j-k}. \tag{3.13}$$

For a non-homogeneous chain, with $p_1 \neq p_2$, relationship (3.13) becomes

$$\binom{i}{k}(p_1p_2)^k(1-p_1p_2)^{i-k}$$
$$= \sum_{j=k}^{i}\binom{i}{j}p_1^j(1-p_1)^{i-j}\binom{j}{k}p_2^k(1-p_2)^{j-k}. \tag{3.14}$$

Corresponding to the general Chapman-Kolmogorov equation in (3.7), we have for the homogeneous case

$$\binom{i}{k}(p^{m+n})^k(1-p^{m+n})^{i-k}$$
$$= \sum_{j=k}^{i}\binom{i}{j}p^{mj}(1-p^m)^{i-j}\binom{j}{k}p^{nk}(1-p^n)^{j-k}, \tag{3.15}$$

and for the non-homogeneous case

$$\binom{i}{k}(\pi_1\pi_2)^k(1-\pi_1\pi_2)^{i-k}$$
$$= \sum_{j=k}^{i}\binom{i}{j}\pi_1^j(1-\pi_1)^{i-j}\binom{j}{k}\pi_2^k(1-\pi_2)^{j-k} \tag{3.16}$$

where $\pi_1 = p_1p_2 \ldots p_m$ and $\pi_2 = p_{m+1} \ldots p_{m+n}$. Equations (3.13) through (3.16) can be shown with straightforward computations.

4. CLASSIFICATION OF STATES

A transition from one state to another is not always possible depending upon the type of states. The state j is said to be reachable from state i if there exists some positive integer n such that the probability $p_{ij}(n) > 0$, and we write $i \to j$. For $n = 0$, we define

$p_{ii}(0) = 1$ and $p_{ij}(0) = 0$ for $j \neq i$. If state j is reachable from state i and state i is reachable from state j, the two states are said to be communicative, and we write $i \leftrightarrow j$. If state k is reachable from state j and state j is reachable from state i, then state k is reachable from state i. This transitive property can be shown as follows: The assumption that $j \to k$ and $i \to j$ implies the existence of two positive integers, say m and n, such that

$$p_{ij}(m) > 0 \qquad \text{and} \qquad p_{jk}(n) > 0.$$

Using the Chapman-Kolmogorov equation in (3.7) we write

$$p_{ik}(m+n) = \sum_{l} p_{il}(m) p_{lk}(n) \geq p_{ij}(m) p_{jk}(n) > 0.$$

Therefore, state k is reachable from state i.

It is clear that the communication relation has the following properties:

(1) Reflexivity: $i \leftrightarrow i$, as $p_{ii}(0) = 1$.
(2) Symmetry: If $i \leftrightarrow j$, then $j \leftrightarrow i$.
(3) Transitivity: If $i \leftrightarrow j$ and $j \leftrightarrow k$, then $i \leftrightarrow k$.

Therefore the communication relation is an equivalence relation.

For every two states i and j, $p_{ij}(n)$ is the probability that, starting from state i, the system will enter state j at the nth step, regardless of the number of entrances into j prior to n. Now we introduce the probability that state j is reached for the first time at the nth step, or the *first passage probability*:

$$f_{ij}(n) = \Pr\{X_n = j \text{ and } X_m \neq j;\ m = 1, \ldots, n-1 \mid X_0 = i\}. \quad (4.1)$$

The two types of probabilities are related as follows:

$$p_{ij}(1) = f_{ij}(1), \qquad p_{ij}(2) = f_{ij}(1)p_{jj}(1) + f_{ij}(2)p_{jj}(0) \quad (4.2)$$

where $p_{jj}(0) = 1$; and in general,

$$p_{ij}(n) = \sum_{l=1}^{n} f_{ij}(l) p_{jj}(n-l). \quad (4.3)$$

and

$$f_{ij}(n) = p_{ij}(n) - \sum_{l=1}^{n-1} f_{ij}(l) p_{jj}(n-l). \quad (4.4)$$

We may compute the probabilities $p_{ij}(n)$ successively from the probabilities $f_{ij}(n)$ using (4.3), or compute $f_{ij}(n)$ from $p_{ij}(n)$ using (4.4).

Formulas (4.3) and (4.4), which are intuitively clear, may be verified by means of induction. Equations (4.2) show that (4.3) is true for $n = 1, 2$. Assuming (4.3) is true for $n - 1$:

$$p_{ij}(n-1) = \sum_{l=1}^{n-1} f_{ij}(l) p_{jj}(n-1-l), \tag{4.3a}$$

we use the Chapman-Kolmogorov equation to write

$$p_{ij}(n) = p_{ij}(1) p_{jj}(n-1) + \sum_{k \neq j} p_{ik}(1) p_{kj}(n-1) \tag{4.5}$$

where $p_{ij}(1) = f_{ij}(1)$. Substituting (4.3a) in (4.5) we have

$$\begin{aligned} p_{ij}(n) &= f_{ij}(1) p_{jj}(n-1) + \sum_{k \neq j} f_{ik}(1) \left[\sum_{l=1}^{n-1} f_{kj}(l) p_{jj}(n-1-l) \right] \\ &= f_{ij}(1) p_{jj}(n-1) + \sum_{l=1}^{n-1} \left[\sum_{k \neq j} f_{ik}(1) f_{kj}(l) \right] p_{jj}(n-1-l) \\ &= f_{ij}(1) p_{jj}(n-1) + \sum_{l=1}^{n-1} f_{ij}(l+1) p_{jj}(n-1-l) \\ &= \sum_{l=1}^{n} f_{ij}(l) p_{jj}(n-l), \end{aligned}$$

proving (4.3). Formula (4.4) may be obtained from formula (4.3).

The sum

$$\sum_{n=1}^{\infty} f_{ij}(n) = f_{ij} \tag{4.6}$$

is the probability that, starting from state i, a system will enter j eventually. If $f_{ij} = 1$, the sequence $\{f_{ij}(n)\}$ is the probability distribution of first passage time to state j. In this case, the expectation

$$\mu_{ij} = \sum_{n=1}^{\infty} n f_{ij}(n) \tag{4.7}$$

is the mean passage time from state i to state j.

When $j = i$, we have the first return (recurrence) probability at the nth step

$$f_{ii}(n) = \Pr\{X_n = i \text{ and } X_m \neq i;\ m = 1, \ldots, n-1 \,|\, X_0 = i\}, \qquad n = 1, 2, \ldots. \tag{4.8}$$

Corresponding to (4.3) and (4.4), the probabilities $p_{ii}(n)$ and $f_{ii}(n)$ are related as follows:

$$p_{ii}(n) = \sum_{l=1}^{n} f_{ii}(l)\, p_{ii}(n-l) \tag{4.9}$$

and

$$f_{ii}(n) = p_{ii}(n) - \sum_{l=1}^{n-1} f_{ii}(l)\, p_{ii}(n-l). \tag{4.10}$$

The sum

$$\sum_{n=1}^{\infty} f_{ii}(n) = f_{ii} \tag{4.11}$$

is the probability of eventual return to the original state i.

Now we introduce various types of states in terms of the first return probabilities and the transition probabilities.

Transient state. A state i is called a transient state if $f_{ii} < 1$. In this case there is a positive probability $1 - f_{ii}$ that starting from state i a system will not return to state i in a finite number of steps.

Recurrent state. A state i is called a recurrent state if $f_{ii} = 1$. In this case, the sequence $\{f_{ii}(n)\}$ represents the probability distribution of the first return (recurrence) time. The expectation

$$\mu_{ii} = \sum_{n=1}^{\infty} n f_{ii}(n) \tag{4.12}$$

is the mean recurrence time for state i.

Recurrent null state and recurrent non-null state. A recurrent state i is called a null state if the expectation $\mu_{ii} = \infty$, a non-null state if $\mu_{ii} < \infty$.

Periodic state and aperiodic state. A state i is periodic with period $t > 1$ if $p_{ii}(n) = 0$ except for $n = t, 2t, \ldots$, where t is the largest integer with this property. A state which is not periodic is an aperiodic state. In the gambler's ruin problem, the event that a player will break even has a period of $t = 2$. His winning being zero at the nth game is possible only for $n = 2, 4, \ldots$. The number of white balls drawn from an urn in the life table example is aperiodic.

Ergodic state. An aperiodic recurrent state with a finite mean recurrence time ($\mu_{ii} < \infty$) is called ergodic.

Absorbing state. A state i is an absorbing state if and only if $f_{ii}(1) = 1$. Clearly, if i is an absorbing state, $f_{ii} = 1$, $\mu_{ii} = 1$.

The above definitions of states, which were introduced with respect to the first return probabilities, may be alternately presented in terms of the transition probabilities. The following theorems in effect express further relations between $f_{ii}(n)$ and $p_{ii}(n)$ by way of these definitions.

Theorem 1. *State j can be reached from state i if and only if $f_{ij} > 0$; states i and j communicate if and only if $f_{ij}f_{ji} > 0$.*

Proof. The theorem follows directly from the inequalities

$$p_{ij}(n) \le f_{ij} \le \sum_{n=1}^{\infty} p_{ij}(n). \tag{4.13}$$

Theorem 2. *State i is transient if and only if*

$$\sum_{n=0}^{\infty} p_{ii}(n) < \infty; \tag{4.14}$$

state i is recurrent, if the infinite sum diverges.

Proof. Using relationship (4.9) we write the series

$$\begin{aligned}\sum_{n=0}^{\infty} p_{ii}(n) &= p_{ii}(0) + \sum_{n=1}^{\infty}\sum_{l=1}^{n} f_{ii}(l)p_{ii}(n-l)\\ &= 1 + \sum_{l=1}^{\infty}\sum_{n=l}^{\infty} f_{ii}(l)p_{ii}(n-l)\\ &= 1 + \left[\sum_{l=1}^{\infty} f_{ii}(l)\right]\left[\sum_{m=0}^{\infty} p_{ii}(m)\right],\end{aligned}$$

so that

$$\sum_{n=0}^{\infty} p_{ii}(n) = \frac{1}{1-f_{ii}}. \tag{4.15}$$

It follows that the series $\sum_{n=0}^{\infty} p_{ii}(n)$ converges or diverges according to $f_{ii} < 1$ (state i is transient) or $f_{ii} = 1$ (state i is recurrent), proving the theorem.

Theorem 3. *For any two states i and j*

$$\frac{\sum_{n=1}^{\infty} p_{ij}(n)}{\sum_{n=0}^{\infty} p_{jj}(n)} = f_{ij}. \tag{4.16}$$

Proof. Using relationship (4.3) we write the series

$$\begin{aligned}\sum_{n=1}^{\infty} p_{ij}(n) &= \sum_{n=1}^{\infty}\sum_{l=1}^{n} f_{ij}(l)p_{jj}(n-l)\\ &= \sum_{l=1}^{\infty}\sum_{n=l}^{\infty} f_{ij}(l)p_{jj}(n-l)\\ &= \left[\sum_{l=1}^{\infty} f_{ij}(l)\right]\left[\sum_{m=0}^{\infty} p_{jj}(m)\right],\end{aligned} \tag{4.17}$$

which completes the proof.

Equations (4.15) and (4.16) may be restated formally in the following corollary.

Corollary. *If state j is transient, then*

$$\sum_{n=0}^{\infty} p_{jj}(n) = (1 - f_{jj})^{-1} \tag{4.15}$$

and

$$\sum_{n=1}^{\infty} p_{ij}(n) = f_{ij}(1 - f_{jj})^{-1}. \tag{4.18}$$

Theorem 4. *If two states i and j communicate and if i is recurrent, then* $f_{ji} = 1$.

Proof. Suppose $f_{ji} < 1$; then there is a probability $(1 - f_{ji}) > 0$ that i will not be reached from j in a finite number of steps. This means there is a positive probability that the system will not return to i in a finite number of steps, which implies $f_{ii} < 1$ and contradicts the assumption that i is a recurrent state.

Theorem 5. *If state j is transient, then*

$$\sum_{n=1}^{\infty} p_{ij}(n) < \infty, \tag{4.19}$$

and in this case

$$\lim_{n\to\infty} p_{ij}(n) = 0.$$

Proof. Since j is transient, according to Theorem 2, the sum

$$\sum_{n=0}^{\infty} p_{jj}(n) < \infty.$$

The inequality in (4.19) follows from (4.17).

5. ASYMPTOTIC BEHAVIOR OF $p_{ij}(n)$

We have seen in the preceding section that the series of the transient probabilities $p_{ij}(n)$ behave differently for different types of states. The following theorem describes the limiting probability of $p_{ij}(n)$ as $n \to \infty$.

Theorem 6. *If state i is either transient or recurrent null, then*

$$\lim_{n\to\infty} p_{ii}(n) = 0. \tag{5.1}$$

If state i is recurrent with period t, then

$$\lim_{n\to\infty} p_{ii}(nt) = \frac{t}{\mu_{ii}} \tag{5.2}$$

where μ_{ii} is the mean recurrent time for state i. If state i is ergodic, then

$$\lim_{n\to\infty} p_{ii}(n) = \frac{1}{\mu_{ii}}. \tag{5.3}$$

The theorem may be proven with different approaches, but they are too complex to be presented at the level of this book. The mathematically oriented reader may consult Feller [1950], Chung [1960], Cox and Miller [1965], Karlin [1966] or Prabhu [1965] for detail. Now we use the result in the theorem to investigate the limiting behavior of $p_{ij}(n)$, for $i \neq j$.

Theorem 7. *If state j is either transient or recurrent null, then for all i*

$$\lim_{n\to\infty} p_{ij}(n) = 0; \tag{5.4}$$

if state j is ergodic, then for all i

$$\lim_{n\to\infty} p_{ij}(n) = \frac{1}{\mu_{jj}}. \tag{5.5}$$

Proof. If j is transient, then the series $\sum_{n=1}^{\infty} p_{ij}(n) < \infty$ [cf. (4.19)], so that $\lim_{n\to\infty} p_{ij}(n) = 0$. If j is recurrent null, we use the relation

$$p_{ij}(n) = \sum_{l=1}^{n} f_{ij}(l)\, p_{jj}(n-l). \tag{4.3}$$

Choose $m < n$ and write

$$\begin{aligned} p_{ij}(n) &= \sum_{l=1}^{m} f_{ij}(l)\, p_{jj}(n-l) + \sum_{l=m+1}^{n} f_{ij}(l)\, p_{jj}(n-l) \\ &\le \sum_{l=1}^{m} f_{ij}(l)\, p_{jj}(n-l) + \sum_{l=m+1}^{\infty} f_{ij}(l). \end{aligned}$$

Now by first letting $n \to \infty$ and then letting $m \to \infty$, if j is recurrent null, we find by (5.1) $p_{jj}(n-l) \to 0$ and, since the series $\sum_{l=1}^{\infty} f_{ij}(l)$ is bounded above by one,

$$\sum_{l=m+1}^{\infty} f_{ij}(l) \to 0. \tag{5.6}$$

Therefore $p_{ij}(n) \to 0$.

If, on the other hand, j is ergodic, then according to (5.3) $p_{jj}(n-l) \to \dfrac{1}{\mu_{jj}}$, and by Theorem 4 $\sum_{l=1}^{n} f_{ij}(l) \to f_{ij} = 1$. Therefore $p_{ij}(n) \to \dfrac{1}{\mu_{jj}}$.

6. CLOSED SETS AND IRREDUCIBLE CHAINS

Closed Set. A set C of states is closed if for every i in C

$$\sum_{j \in C} p_{ij} = 1 \tag{6.1}$$

where the summation is taken over all states j belonging to the set C. Generally, for every $n \geq 1$

$$\sum_{j \in C} p_{ij}(n) = 1, \tag{6.2}$$

since, starting from a state i, the system must be in one of the states in the set at the nth step. Thus, if C is a closed set, any state k outside the set cannot be reached from any state inside the set. If i belongs to the set C and k is outside the set, then $p_{ik} = 0$; and generally $p_{ik}(n) = 0$ for all $n \geq 1$. Therefore, any closed subset of a system can be studied independently of all other states.

The totality of all states that can be reached from a given state i form a closed set. A closed set may contain states which do not communicate. A closed set of communicating states is a *class*. If C is a class, then for every pair i and j in C, there exists a positive integer n for which $p_{ij}(n) > 0$. An absorbing state is considered a class.

Irreducible chain. A Markov chain is called an irreducible chain if there exists no closed subset other than the set of all states.

Theorem 8. *In an irreducible Markov chain every state can be reached from every other state.*

Proof. Let C be a set constituting an irreducible Markov chain; in this case, C contains no proper closed subset. Suppose that there are two states i and j in C such that j cannot be reached from i. Then either i is an absorbing state or else it belongs to a closed subset of which j is not a member, which contradicts the fact that C contains no proper closed subset.

Theorem 9. *The states in a class are of the same type; they are either all transient or all recurrent null or all ergodic.*

Proof. Let i and j be two states belonging to a class C so that $i \leftrightarrow j$. There exist two positive integers l and n such that $p_{ij}(l) > 0$ and $p_{ji}(n) > 0$. Now for every $m > 0$,

$$p_{ii}(l + m + n) \geq p_{ij}(l)p_{jj}(m)p_{ji}(n)$$

and

$$p_{jj}(l + m + n) \geq p_{ji}(n)p_{ii}(m)p_{ij}(l)$$

so that the two series $\sum_{m=0}^{\infty} p_{ii}(m)$ and $\sum_{m=0}^{\infty} p_{jj}(m)$ either both converge or both diverge. Furthermore, as $m \to \infty$, $p_{ii}(m) \to 0$ if and only if $p_{jj}(m) \to 0$. Thus i and j are either both transient or both recurrent null or both ergodic. This shows that all states in a class are of the same type.

Corollary. *The states in an irreducible Markov chain are of the same type.*

The corollary follows directly from Theorems 8 and 9.

Theorem 10. *All states in a class have the same period.*

Proof. Let i and j be two arbitrary states in a class C with periods t_i and t_j, respectively. There exist two numbers $l > 0$ and $n > 0$ such that $p_{ij}(l) > 0$ and $p_{ji}(n) > 0$. For every $m > 0$ for which $p_{jj}(m) > 0$,

$$p_{ii}(l + m + n) \geq p_{ij}(l)p_{jj}(m)p_{ji}(n) > 0, \tag{6.4}$$

since $p_{jj}(m) > 0$ implies $p_{jj}(2m) > 0$ and $p_{ii}(l + 2m + n) > 0$. The period t_i thus divides the difference $(l + 2m + n) - (l + m + n) = m$, this being true for every $m > 0$ for which $p_{jj}(m) > 0$. Therefore t_i divides the period t_j. Since this argument holds when i and j are interchanged, it follows that t_j divides t_i, and thus $t_i = t_j$.

Corollary. *All states in an irreducible Markov chain have the same period.*

The corollary follows directly from Theorems 8 and 10.

Ergodic chain. An irreducible Markov chain with ergodic states is called an ergodic chain.

The above concepts are illustrated by an example.

Example 6.

$$\mathbf{P} = \begin{pmatrix} 1 & 0 & 0 & 0 & 0 & 0 & 0 & 0 & 0 \\ 0 & 0 & 1 & 0 & 0 & 0 & 0 & 0 & 0 \\ 0 & 1 & 0 & 0 & 0 & 0 & 0 & 0 & 0 \\ 0 & 0 & 0 & 1 & 0 & 0 & 0 & 0 & 0 \\ 0 & 0 & 0 & 3/8 & 1/6 & 11/24 & 0 & 0 & 0 \\ 0 & 0 & 0 & 3/8 & 1/2 & 1/8 & 0 & 0 & 0 \\ 0 & 0 & 0 & 0 & 0 & 0 & 0 & 1/3 & 2/3 \\ 0 & 0 & 0 & 0 & 0 & 0 & 2/4 & 1/4 & 1/4 \\ 0 & 0 & 0 & 0 & 0 & 0 & 1/2 & 1/2 & 0 \end{pmatrix} \tag{6.5}$$

The above stochastic matrix describes the transitions in a system of nine states numbered from 1 to 9. We divide these states into four subsets, C_1: {1}; C_2: {2,3}, C_3: {4,5,6}; and C_4: {7,8,9}. The set C_1 consists of a single absorbing state 1; it is a closed set and a class. In set C_2 states 2 and 3 communicate and both have a period $t = 2$; C_2 is closed and is a class. C_3 is also a closed set but not a class since neither state 5 nor state 6 can be reached from state 4. State 4 is a class and is a proper closed subset of C_3; the subset {5,6} is not a class because it is not closed. Finally, the set C_4 is closed and is a class where states 7, 8 and 9 communicate.

It is clear then that a Markov chain corresponding to subset C_2 is an irreducible chain with period $t = 2$, while a chain corresponding to subset C_3 is not an irreducible chain since C_3 contains a proper closed subset; neither is a chain corresponding to the subset {5,6} an irreducible chain since the subset is not closed. A Markov chain corresponding to set C_4 is obviously irreducible.

To summarize, we have considered examples of the following types:

(1) Irreducible periodic chains – C_2.

(2) Chains which are not irreducible, because

  (a) the corresponding state set contains a proper closed subset – C_3;

  (b) the state set is not closed – (5, 6).

(3) Irreducible and aperiodic chains – C_4.

Matrix **P** in (6.5) can be decomposed into four submatrices corresponding to these four subsets:

$$\mathbf{P} = \begin{pmatrix} \mathbf{P}_1 & \mathbf{0} & \mathbf{0} & \mathbf{0} \\ \mathbf{0} & \mathbf{P}_2 & \mathbf{0} & \mathbf{0} \\ \mathbf{0} & \mathbf{0} & \mathbf{P}_3 & \mathbf{0} \\ \mathbf{0} & \mathbf{0} & \mathbf{0} & \mathbf{P}_4 \end{pmatrix} \tag{6.6}$$

where the zeros are matrices of various dimensions. The zeros in the first row, for example, (from left to right) are 1×2, 1×3, and 1×3 matrices (or row vectors), respectively. The non-zero submatrices are:

$$\mathbf{P}_1 = [1], \qquad \mathbf{P}_2 = \begin{pmatrix} 0 & 1 \\ 1 & 0 \end{pmatrix}, \qquad \mathbf{P}_3 = \begin{pmatrix} 1 & 0 & 0 \\ 3/8 & 1/6 & 11/24 \\ 3/8 & 1/2 & 1/8 \end{pmatrix}$$

and

$$\mathbf{P}_4 = \begin{pmatrix} 0 & 1/3 & 2/3 \\ 2/4 & 1/4 & 1/4 \\ 1/2 & 1/2 & 0 \end{pmatrix}$$

each corresponding to a sub-Markov chain.

The matrix on the right hand side of (6.6) having submatrices on the diagonal line and zero elsewhere is known as a quasi-diagonal matrix. Direct computations show that the square of the matrix **P** is also a quasi-diagonal matrix with the squares of the submatrices on the diagonal line:

$$\mathbf{P}^2 = \begin{pmatrix} \mathbf{P}_1^2 & \mathbf{0} & \mathbf{0} & \mathbf{0} \\ \mathbf{0} & \mathbf{P}_2^2 & \mathbf{0} & \mathbf{0} \\ \mathbf{0} & \mathbf{0} & \mathbf{P}_3^2 & \mathbf{0} \\ \mathbf{0} & \mathbf{0} & \mathbf{0} & \mathbf{P}_4^2 \end{pmatrix} \tag{6.7}$$

In general, the nth power of a quasi-diagonal matrix **P** is also a quasi-diagonal matrix with the nth power of the submatrices on the diagonal line. In the present example,

$$\mathbf{P}^n = \begin{pmatrix} \mathbf{P}_1^n & \mathbf{0} & \mathbf{0} & \mathbf{0} \\ \mathbf{0} & \mathbf{P}_2^n & \mathbf{0} & \mathbf{0} \\ \mathbf{0} & \mathbf{0} & \mathbf{P}_3^n & \mathbf{0} \\ \mathbf{0} & \mathbf{0} & \mathbf{0} & \mathbf{P}_4^n \end{pmatrix} \tag{6.8}$$

The relation in (6.8) reveals interesting properties of the transitions in a Markov chain. First, the states in different classes do not communicate: $p_{ik} = 0$ whenever i and k belong to two different classes. Second, for every i and j belonging to the same class C_α, the transition probabilities $p_{ij}(n)$ are computed from the corresponding submatrix only and are independent of the other matrices. This is true even if C_α is not a class (such as C_3) and the corresponding Markov chain is reducible. Therefore, a Markov chain may be studied in terms of individual subchains each corresponding to a closed set of states.

7. STATIONARY DISTRIBUTION

Definition: A probability distribution $\{\pi_i\}$ in a Markov chain is called *stationary* if it satisfies the relation

$$\pi_j = \sum_i \pi_i p_{ij}. \tag{7.1}$$

For a stationary distribution, we have

$$\pi_k = \sum_j \pi_j p_{jk} = \sum_j \left(\sum_i \pi_i p_{ij} \right) p_{jk}$$

$$= \sum_i \pi_i \sum_j p_{ij} p_{jk} = \sum_i \pi_i p_{ik}(2), \tag{7.2}$$

and generally,

$$\pi_j = \sum_i \pi_i p_{ij}(n). \tag{7.3}$$

If the initial distribution $a_i(0)$ is stationary, then according to (7.1), the absolute probability $\Pr\{X_1 = j\} = a_j(1)$ is given by

$$a_j(1) = \sum_i a_i(0) p_{ij}(1) = a_j(0) \tag{7.4}$$

and, in general, the absolute probability

$$\Pr\{X_n = j\} = a_j(n)$$

is given by

$$a_j(n) = \sum_i a_i(0)p_{ij}(n) = a_j(0).$$

Therefore, the distribution of X_n is independent of n (time) and the corresponding process is in a statistical equilibrium.

We have seen from Section 5 that if state j is transient or recurrent null, then for every $i \to j$, the probability $p_{ij}(n)$ tends to zero as $n \to \infty$; if j is ergodic, the limiting probability of $p_{ij}(n)$ exists and is non-zero for all i. The above asymptotic proterties are summarized in the following theorem.

Theorem 11. *If all the states in an irreducible Markov chain are ergodic, then the limits*

$$\lim_{n\to\infty} p_{ij}(n) = \pi_j \tag{7.5}$$

exist and are independent of the initial state i. Furthermore, $\pi_j > 0$,

$$\sum_j \pi_j = 1, \tag{7.6}$$

and the limiting distribution $\{\pi_j\}$ *is stationary so that*

$$\sum_i \pi_i p_{ij} = \pi_j. \tag{7.7}$$

Conversely, if a stationary distribution of an irreducible Markov chain exists and satisfies (7.6) *and* (7.7), *then all the states of the Markov chain are ergodic and the stationary distribution is the limiting distribution of the chain.*

Proof. If all the states of an irreducible Markov chain are transient or recurrent null, then $p_{ij}(n) \to 0$ as $n \to \infty$, and no limiting distribution exists. If all the states are ergodic, then limiting probabilities exist and, according to Theorem 7 in Section 5, are given by

$$\pi_j = \frac{1}{\mu_{jj}}. \tag{7.8}$$

Since $\mu_{jj} < \infty$, $\pi_j > 0$ for every j. To show that the distribution $\{\pi_j\}$ is stationary, we use the Chapman-Kolmogorov equation and write

$$p_{hj}(n+1) = \sum_i p_{hi}(n)p_{ij}. \tag{7.9}$$

Taking the limit on both sides of (7.9), as $n \to \infty$, and applying Fatou's lemma, we find

$$\lim_{n\to\infty} p_{hj}(n+1) = \lim_{n\to\infty} \sum_i p_{hi}(n)p_{ij} \geq \sum_i \left[\lim_{n\to\infty} p_{hi}(n)\right] p_{ij} \tag{7.10}$$

or

$$\pi_j \geq \sum_i \pi_i p_{ij}. \tag{7.11}$$

Suppose the strict inequality sign holds in (7.11); then

$$\sum_j \pi_j > \sum_j \sum_i \pi_i p_{ij} = \sum_i \pi_i \tag{7.12}$$

which is impossible. Therefore,

$$\pi_j = \sum_i \pi_i p_{ij}. \tag{7.7}$$

Now, using (7.7), we write for $n = 1, 2, \ldots,$

$$\pi_j = \sum_i \pi_i p_{ij}(n). \tag{7.13}$$

As $n \to \infty$, (7.13) becomes

$$\pi_j = \sum_i \pi_i \pi_j$$

and we recover

$$\sum_i \pi_i = 1. \tag{7.6}$$

Conversely, suppose a stationary distribution $\{\pi_j\}$ of an irreducible Markov chain exists with $\pi_j > 0$ for every j and satisfies (7.6) and (7.7). By induction

$$\pi_j = \sum_i \pi_i p_{ij}(n)$$

for $n = 1, 2, \ldots$. Since the chain is irreducible, all the states are of the same type. As $n \to \infty$, we have either

$$\lim_{n\to\infty} p_{ij}(n) = \frac{1}{\mu_{jj}} \tag{7.14}$$

if all the states are ergodic, or

$$\lim_{n\to\infty} p_{ij}(n) = 0 \tag{7.15}$$

if all the states are transient or recurrent null. The latter case is impossible since $\Sigma\,\pi_j = 1$. Therefore, the states must be ergodic and

$$\pi_j = \sum_i \pi_i \frac{1}{\mu_{jj}} = \frac{1}{\mu_{jj}}, \tag{7.16}$$

so that the stationary distribution is the same as the limiting distribution of the chain.

8. AN APPLICATION TO GENETICS

Genetics, the science of heredity, has been developed to explain the heredity of living things. The field provides an excellent opportunity for application of probability concepts. Flower color, shape of peas, and many other phenomena first observed by G. J. Mendel more than 100 years ago seem to follow specific probability laws. In the passing of heritable traits from one generation to the next, we see the Markov chains at work in nature. The reader may consult textbooks on the subject (e.g., C. C. Li [1968] and Curt Stern [1960]) to gain knowledge in genetics; the present description is provided for the convenience of application of Markov chains.

An important element of heredity is chromosomes. In the nucleus of human somatic cells, for example, there are 23 pairs of chromosomes. One pair is called the sex chromosomes, designated by X and Y; the rest are autosomes. Each reproductive cell, sperm or egg, has only a set (a genome) of 23 single chromosomes, and is said to be haploid. A progeny which inherits two sets (or 23 pairs) of chromosomes, one set from each parent, is said to be diploid. Carriers of heritable traits are called genes and they are located on the chromosomes. The location of a gene on the chromosome is called a locus. Genes appear in pairs; paired genes occupy the same locus of the paired chromosomes. Generally, each gene of a pair can assume two alternate forms (alleles) A and a. The proportions of genes in a population that are A and a are gene frequencies, denoted by p and q ($p + q = 1$), respectively. The two alleles form three genotypes,

AA, Aa, aa (there is no distinction between Aa and aA) with respect to a particular locus. The genotypes AA and aa are called homozygotes; the genotype Aa, heterozygote. If A is dominant over a so that Aa has the same observable properties as AA, then there are two phenotypes. AA individuals produce only A-gametes, aa individuals produce only a-gametes, and Aa individuals produce A-gametes and a-gametes in equal number.

A diploid progeny receives one gene from the father and one gene from the mother to form a pair. According to Mendelian law, a progeny receives either one of the two genes from a parent with a probability of 1/2. Thus, the mating $Aa \times Aa$ produces genotypes AA, Aa, aa with respective probabilities 1/4, 1/2, 1/4. The mating $AA \times Aa$ produces genotypes AA and Aa with an equal probability of 1/2. Finally, the mating $AA \times AA$ produces only AA genotype.

Choice of mates in the human population generally is made through selection or by preference. To demonstrate the Mendelian theory, we consider an idealized situation of the natural environment where pairings of mates are made at random and are independent of one another. This is called random mating. Under random mating both genes and genotypes of a progeny are selected at random. In the case of two alleles, a pair of genes may be chosen from $(A,a) \times (A,a)$ so that there are 2×2 ways of choosing a pair. But since there are three genotypes, a genotype may be chosen from $(AA, Aa, aa) \times (AA, Aa, aa)$ so that there are 3×3 ways of choosing a genotype. A salient feature of the random mating model is that selection of genes and selection of genotypes when made independently yield the same result. The following example will elucidate the point.

Consider a population in which the males and females have the same genotype frequency distribution: $AA{:}Aa{:}aa = d{:}2h{:}r$ with $d + 2h + r = 1$. The gene frequencies for A and a are

$$p = d + h \quad \text{and} \quad q = h + r. \tag{8.1}$$

Under random mating, a progeny can have one A gene with a probability p and can have two A genes (one from each parent) with a probability p^2. That is, a progeny will carry genotype AA with a probability p^2. Similar computations show that a progeny will carry genotypes AA, Aa, or aa with probabilities p^2, $2qp$, or q^2. These probabilities can be derived also through the selection of genotypes. For this purpose, we formulate the product $(dAA + 2hAa + raa) \times (dAA + 2hAa + raa)$ where one factor represents the father and the other represents the mother and d, $2h$ and r are numerical coefficients of the three genotypes, respectively. Since a genotype AA offspring may come from the mating $AA \times AA$ with a probability 1, from $AA \times Aa$ with a probability 1/2 and from $Aa \times Aa$ with a probability 1/4, a simple multiplication of the two factors shows that the probability of a genotype AA offspring is

$$d^2 + 2\,dh + h^2$$

or

$$(d + h)^2 = p^2. \tag{8.2}$$

From the multiplication we also find the probability of a genotype Aa offspring:

$$2dh + 2dr + 2hr + 2h^2 = 2(d + h)(h + r) = 2pq, \tag{8.3}$$

and the probability of a genotype aa offspring:

$$h^2 + 2hr + r^2 = (h + r)^2 = q^2. \tag{8.4}$$

These are exactly the same probabilities determined from the selection of genes.

Hardy-Weinberg law of equilibrium. A careful inspection of the above results leads to an even more remarkable discovery. In equations (8.1) there are three genotype frequencies $(d,\ 2hr,\ r)$ to determine two gene frequencies (p and q). Therefore, there are infinitely many values of $(d,\ 2h,\ r)$ that satisfy equations (8.1); one of the values is $(d,\ 2h,\ r) = (p^2,\ 2pq,\ q^2)$. However, equations (8.2), (8.3) and (8.4) show that, *whatever the parent genotype frequency compositions* $(d, 2h, r)$ *may be, under random mating assumptions, the first generation progenies will have the genotype composition* $(p^2,\ 2pq,\ q^2)$ *and this composition will remain in equilibrium forever.* This law of equilibrium was established independently by G. H. Hardy and W. Weinberg in 1908. Since then, numerous experimental findings and actual observations on real phenomena have been used to prove the validity of this discovery. The most often cited example in the human population is the MN blood typing, which involves one pair of genes and all three genotypes are distinguishable. In problem 14 we shall demonstrate the Hardy-Weinberg law in this case.

To describe the heredity process in one given locus in terms of Markov chains, we number the three genotypes AA, Aa, and aa by 1, 2, and 3 and denote by p_{ij} the probability that an offspring has genotype j given that a specified parent has genotype i. Using mother-child pair as an example for clarity, we let

$$p_{ij} = \Pr\{\text{a child has genotype } j \mid \text{his mother has genotype } i\}, \qquad i,j = 1,2,3. \tag{8.5}$$

When $i = 2$, $j = 1$, p_{21} is the probability that a genotype Aa mother will produce a genotype AA son. Table 1 shows the entire 3×3 transitions and their probabilities:

Table 1. One-Step Transition Probabilities

Genotype of Mother		Genotype of Son AA 1	Aa 2	aa 3
AA	1	p_{11}	p_{12}	p_{13}
Aa	2	p_{21}	p_{22}	p_{23}
aa	3	p_{31}	p_{32}	p_{33}

The one-step transition probability matrix is:

$$\mathbf{P}(1) = \begin{pmatrix} p_{11} & p_{12} & p_{13} \\ p_{21} & p_{22} & p_{23} \\ p_{31} & p_{32} & p_{33} \end{pmatrix}. \tag{8.6}$$

We can determine the transition probabilities in (8.5) by enumerating all possible genotypes of the father AA, Aa, aa with the corresponding frequencies d, $2h$, r. However, since selection of genes and selection of genotypes lead to the same result, we shall determine the probabilities on the basis of gene selection. Consider the probability

$$p_{21} = \Pr\{\text{a child will have genotype } AA \mid \text{his mother has genotype } Aa\}. \tag{8.7}$$

For the child to have a pair of AA genes, he must inherit one A gene from his mother with a probability $1/2$ and acquire another A gene from the male population (through his father) with a probability p. Therefore, $p_{21} = \frac{1}{2}p$. Similar computations yield the other probabilities:

$$\mathbf{P}(1) = \begin{pmatrix} p & q & 0 \\ \frac{1}{2}p & \frac{1}{2} & \frac{1}{2}q \\ 0 & p & q \end{pmatrix}. \tag{8.8}$$

Each p_{ij} in equation (8.8) is interpreted as the conditional probability of a genotype of an individual given a genotype of a specified member of the preceding generation, but it is also equal to the conditional probability of a genotype of an individual given a genotype of a specified member of the succeeding generation. Let us verify the probability

$$p_{21} = \Pr\{\text{a mother has genotype } AA \mid \text{her child has genotype } Aa\}. \tag{8.9}$$

The child could have inherited either A gene or a gene from his mother with an equal probability of 1/2. If he inherits A gene from the mother, then she *has* an A gene. The probability of her having another A gene is p. If the child inherited a gene from his mother, then the probability of her having AA genotype is zero. Therefore, the required probability is $\frac{1}{2}p + \frac{1}{2}0 = \frac{1}{2}p$, which is equal to p_{21}.

The reader may verify the other probabilities in equation (8.8). This type of conditional probability is quite useful in genetic research when inference is to be made about the genotype of an ancestor on the basis of the information of a present generation.

We have labeled p_{ij} one-step transition probability to be consistent with the term introduced earlier in this chapter. A two-step transition probability, denoted by $p_{ij}(2)$, refers to a transition from a grandparent to a grandchild, or from a grandchild to a grandparent. For example,

$$p_{23}(2) = \Pr\{\text{a man has genotype } aa \mid \text{a specified grandfather has genotype } Aa\} \tag{8.10}$$

or

$$p_{23}(2) = \Pr\{\text{a man has genotype } aa \mid \text{a specified grandchild has genotype } Aa\}. \tag{8.10a}$$

Generally a two-step transition probability can be derived from the equation:

$$p_{ik}(2) = \sum_{j=1}^{3} p_{ij}p_{jk}, \tag{8.11}$$

and the two-step transition probability matrix $\mathbf{P}(2)$ is the square of the one-step transition probability matrix:

$$\mathbf{P}(2) = [\mathbf{P}(1)]^2. \tag{8.12}$$

Substituting (8.8) in (8.12) gives the matrix:

$$\mathbf{P}(2) = \begin{pmatrix} p^2 + \frac{1}{2}pq & pq + \frac{1}{2}q & \frac{1}{2}q^2 \\ \frac{1}{2}p^2 + \frac{1}{4}p & pq + \frac{1}{4} & \frac{1}{4}q + \frac{1}{2}q^2 \\ \frac{1}{2}p^2 & \frac{1}{2}p + pq & \frac{1}{2}pq + q^2 \end{pmatrix} \tag{8.13}$$

On the right-hand side of equation (8.11) there are two groups of transition probabilities, p_{ij} and p_{jk}. If the probabilities p_{ij} are interpreted as in (8.9) and p_{jk} as in (8.7), then $p_{ik}(2)$ is also the probability that a man has genotype k given that a specified half-brother has genotype i.

Formulas (8.11) and (8.12) can be extended to n-step transition probabilities, for $n = 1,2, \ldots$. For a given n,

$$p_{ij}(n) = \Pr\{\text{a man has genotype } j \,|\, \text{a specified } n\text{-th generation ancestor has genotype } i\} \tag{8.14}$$

or

$$p_{ij}(n) = \Pr\{\text{a man has genotype } j \,|\, \text{a specified } n\text{-th generation decendant has genotype } i\}, \quad i, j = 1,2,3. \tag{8.15}$$

These conditional probabilities are the elements of the n-step transition probability matrix $\mathbf{P}(n)$. By induction and using the relationship in equation (8.12), we find

$$\mathbf{P}(n) = [\mathbf{P}(1)]^n. \tag{8.16}$$

Substituting (8.8) in (8.16) yields

$$\mathbf{P}(n) = \begin{pmatrix} p & q & 0 \\ \frac{1}{2}p & \frac{1}{2} & \frac{1}{2}q \\ 0 & p & q \end{pmatrix}^n. \tag{8.17}$$

Direct expansion of the n-th power of a matrix is tedious. But we can use the general formula provided in equation (3.2), Chapter 6, to determine the elements of $\mathbf{P}(n)$. The resulting formulas are:

$$\mathbf{P}(n) = \begin{pmatrix} p^2 + pq/2^{n-1} & 2pq + q(q-p)/2^{n-1} & q^2 - q^2/2^{n-1} \\ p^2 + p(q-p)/2^n & 2pq + (p-q)^2/2^n & q^2 + q(p-q)/2^n \\ p^2 - p^2/2^{n-1} & 2pq + p(p-q)/2^{n-1} & q^2 + pq/2^{n-1} \end{pmatrix}. \tag{8.18}$$

This shows that the influence of the original genotype decreases from generation to generation with a factor of 1/2. As n tends to infinity, the influence disappears completely and the limiting transition probability matrix,

$$\lim_{n\to\infty} \mathbf{P}(n) = \begin{pmatrix} p^2 & 2pq & q^2 \\ p^2 & 2pq & q^2 \\ p^2 & 2pq & q^2 \end{pmatrix}, \tag{8.19}$$

becomes independent of the initial genotype i.

To appreciate the result in (8.19), we let the limiting distribution be denoted by:

$$(\pi_1, \pi_2, \pi_3) = (p^2, 2pq, q^2). \tag{8.20}$$

Then it is easily verified that

$$\pi_j = \pi_1 p_{1j}(n) + \pi_2 p_{2j}(n) + \pi_3 p_{3j}(n), \quad j = 1,2,3, \tag{8.21}$$

whatever may be positive integer n. For example, for $j = 1$, we have the identity

$$p^2 = p^2(p^2 + pq/2^{n-1}) + 2pq(p^2 + p(q-p)/2^n) + q^2(p^2 - p^2/2^{n-1}).$$

Equation (8.21) reaffirms the Hardy-Weinberg law: Random matings take place generation after generation, but the stationary genotype distribution (p^2, $2pq$, q^2) remains forever.

Probability $p_{ij}(n)$ refers to the genotypes of an ancestor and his n-th generation decendent regardless of appearances of genotype j in the intermediate generations. We can determine if genotype j has ever appeared before the n-th generation by introducing the following probability.

$$f_{ij}(n) = \Pr\{\text{a man has genotype } j \text{ for the first time in } n \text{ generations since a specified } n\text{-th generation ancestor has genotype } i\},$$
$$i, j = 1,2,3; \quad n = 1,2,\ldots \tag{8.22}$$

If $j = i$, $f_{ii}(n)$ is the first return (recurrence) probability of genotype i at the n-th generation. If $j \neq i$, $f_{ij}(n)$ is the first passage probability to genotype j at the n-th generation. These probabilities can be derived from probabilities $p_{ij}(n)$ via the following formulas (Cf. equation (4.4), Section 4):

$$f_{ij}(n) = p_{ij}(n) - \sum_{l=1}^{n-1} f_{ij}(l) p_{jj}(n-l), \quad i, j = 1,2,3. \tag{8.23}$$

We shall consider only the return probability $f_{ii}(n)$ and leave the discussion on the passage probability $f_{ij}(n)$ to the reader as an exercise.

For $i = j = 1$, and $n = 1, 2, 3$, we have the first return probability of genotype AA at the first, the second, or the third generation:

$$f_{11}(1) = p_{11}(1) = p,$$

$$f_{11}(2) = p_{11}(2) - f_{11}(1) p_{11}(1) = p^2 + pq/2 - p^2 = pq/2,$$

and

$$f_{11}(3) = P_{11}(3) - f_{11}(1) p_{11}(2) - f_{11}(2) p_{11}(1) = pq/4.$$

A general formula for $f_{ii}(n)$ can be found. For each i, the sum

$$f_{ii}(1) + f_{ii}(2) + \ldots = f_{ii} \tag{8.24}$$

is the probability of eventual return of the original genotype i. We have established in equation (4.15), Section 4, a relationship between f_{ii} and the sum of $p_{ii}(n)$:

$$\sum_{i=0}^{\infty} p_{ii}(n) = (1 - f_{ii})^{-1}. \tag{8.25}$$

In the present case, $p_{ii}(n) > 0$ for each n, the infinite sum on the left hand side of (8.25) diverges, and hence $f_{ii} = 1$. This means that for every i the sequence $\{f_{ii}(n)\}$ forms a proper probability distribution with the mean first return time given by the familiar formula

$$\mu_{ii} = \sum_{i=1}^{\infty} n f_{ii}(n). \tag{8.26}$$

However, we can find the value of μ_{ii} without explicit formulas of the probabilities $f_{ii}(n)$. Equation (5.3) in Theorem 6 shows that the mean return time μ_{ii} and the corresponding limiting probability π_i are reciprocal to one another, and provides the following simple formula for μ_{ii}:

$$\mu_{ii} = \frac{1}{\pi_i}. \tag{8.27}$$

Using the limiting probabilities π_i in (8.20), we obtain immediately the mean first return time for the genotypes AA, Aa, and aa:

$$\mu_{11} = \frac{1}{p^2}, \; \mu_{22} = \frac{1}{2pq}, \quad \text{and} \quad \mu_{33} = \frac{1}{q^2}. \tag{8.28}$$

respectively. Thus the more there are A genes in a population, the smaller will be the expected number of generations needed for the return of genotype AA. However, the shortest expected return time for genotype Aa is $\mu_{22} = 2$ generations, when $p = q = 1/2$.

8.1. Two Loci Each with Two Alleles

Consider now two pairs of genes: Genes (A,a) and genes (B,b) in two different loci on the same pair of chromosomes. The gene frequencies of A and a in the population are denoted by p_A and q_a $(p_A + q_a = 1)$, and genotype frequencies of AA, Aa, aa are denoted by d_a, $2h_a$, r_a with $p_A = d_a + h_a$ and $q_a = h_a + r_a$. For genes (B,b) we use similar notations with the subscript a replaced by b and p_A, q_a, etc. replaced by p_B, q_b, etc. When the four alleles $(A,a;\ B,b)$ are considered jointly, there are nine genotypes in the population.

$$\left.\begin{matrix} AABB, & AABb, & AAbb, \\ AaBB, & AaBb, & Aabb, \\ aaBB, & aaBb, & aabb, \end{matrix}\right\} \tag{8.29}$$

with the corresponding frequencies:

$$\left.\begin{matrix} f_{AABB}, & f_{AABb}, & f_{AAbb}, \\ f_{AaBB}, & f_{AaBb}, & f_{Aabb}, \\ f_{aaBB}, & f_{aaBb}, & f_{aabb}. \end{matrix}\right\}. \tag{8.30}$$

The sum of the frequencies is equal to one. We seek the required condition that would lead to an equilibrium of genotype distribution in one generation.

Suppose that the genotype distributions of (A,a) and of (B,b) in the population are mutually independent so that the conditional genotype distribution of (A,a) is given by

$$(AA:Aa:aa\,|\,(B,b)) = d_a : 2h_a : r_a \tag{8.31}$$

where (B,b) stands for the condition BB, or Bb, or bb, and the conditional genotype distribution of (B,b) is given by

$$(BB:Bb:bb\,|\,(A,a)) = d_b : 2h_b : r_b, \tag{8.32}$$

where (A,a) stands for the condition AA, or Aa, or aa. Then the frequencies of the nine genotypes $AABB, AABb, \ldots, aabb$ for males and for females in the population are

$$\left.\begin{array}{ccc} d_a d_b, & 2d_a h_b, & d_a r_b, \\ 2h_a d_b, & 4h_a h_b, & 2h_a r_b, \\ r_a d_b, & 2r_a h_b, & r_a r_b. \end{array}\right\} \tag{8.33}$$

A random mating that takes place in the population may be represented by the product

$$\begin{aligned} &(d_a d_b AABB + 2d_a h_b AABb + \ldots + r_a r_b aabb) \\ &\times (d_a d_b AABB + 2d_a h_b AABb + \ldots + r_a r_b aabb). \end{aligned} \tag{8.34}$$

The first factor in (8.34) represents the father, the second factor represents the mother, and each factor contains nine terms corresponding to the nine genotypes in (8.29). The constants $d_a d_b$, $2d_a h_b, \ldots, r_a r_b$ are numerical coefficients of the corresponding genotypes. We can derive the probabilities of the nine genotypes of the progeny directly from the multiplication of the two factors in (8.34). Thus we find the probability that the progeny will have genotype $AABb$ is

$$\begin{aligned} P(AABb) &= 2(d_a^2 + 2d_a h_a + h_a^2)(d_b h_b + h_b^2 + d_b r_b + h_b r_b) \\ &= 2(d_a + h_a)^2 (d_b + h_b)(h_b + r_b), \end{aligned}$$

that is,

$$P(AABb) = 2p_A^2 p_B q_b. \tag{8.35}$$

The probabilities for the entire nine genotypes are:

$$\left.\begin{array}{ccc} p_A^2 p_B^2, & 2p_A^2 p_B q_b, & p_A^2 q_b^2, \\ 2p_A q_a p_B^2, & 4p_A q_a p_B q_b, & 2p_A q_a q_b^2, \\ q_a^2 p_B^2, & 2q_a^2 p_B q_b, & q_a^2 q_b^2. \end{array}\right\} \tag{8.36}$$

This means that, *if the independence assumption in* (8.31) *and* (8.32) *holds true, then whatever the parent population genotype composition in* (8.33) *may be, the first generation progenies will have the genotype composition given in* (8.36) *and this composition will remain in equilibrium persistently.*

In this case of two loci with two alleles each, there are four kinds of gametes, AB, Ab, aB, and ab, with the respective frequencies and their sums shown below:

	B	b	Sums
A	f_{AB}	f_{Ab}	p_A
a	f_{aB}	f_{ab}	q_a
Sums	p_B	q_b	1

(8.37)

The assumptions in (8.31) and (8.32) are equivalent to the assumption that each gamete frequency is the product of the corresponding (A,a) and (B,b) gene frequencies, that is,

$$\begin{pmatrix} f_{AB} & f_{Ab} \\ f_{aB} & f_{ab} \end{pmatrix} = \begin{pmatrix} p_A p_B & p_A q_b \\ q_a p_B & q_a q_b \end{pmatrix}. \tag{8.38}$$

Under this assumption, the gamete distribution of the first generation offspring will remain the same as the parent population in (8.38). That is

$$\begin{pmatrix} f_{AB} & f_{Ab} \\ f_{aB} & f_{ab} \end{pmatrix} \times \begin{pmatrix} f_{AB} & f_{Ab} \\ f_{aB} & f_{ab} \end{pmatrix} = \begin{pmatrix} p_A p_B & p_A q_b \\ q_a p_B & q_a q_b \end{pmatrix}. \tag{8.39}$$

a reassurance of the Hardy-Weinberg law.

Consider now an arbitrary population for which equation (8.38) does not hold and the gamete distribution is given by[1]

$$\begin{pmatrix} f_{AB} & f_{Ab} \\ f_{aB} & f_{ab} \end{pmatrix} = \begin{pmatrix} p_A p_B + \Delta & p_A q_b - \Delta \\ q_a p_B - \Delta & q_a q_b + \Delta \end{pmatrix}, \qquad \Delta \neq 0. \tag{8.40}$$

Let us compute the frequency of gamete AB in the first generation offspring:

$$\begin{aligned} f_{AB}(1) = f_{AB}&\left[f_{AB} + \frac{1}{2} f_{Ab} + \frac{1}{2} f_{aB} + \frac{1}{4} f_{ab} \right] \\ &+ f_{Ab}\left[\frac{1}{2} f_{AB} + \frac{1}{4} f_{aB} \right] + f_{aB}\left[\frac{1}{2} f_{AB} + \frac{1}{4} f_{Ab} \right] \\ &+ f_{ab}\left[\frac{1}{4} f_{AB} \right]. \end{aligned} \tag{8.41}$$

[1]The author benefited from a discussion with B. J. van den Berg.

Making the substitutions of

$$f_{Ab} = p_A - f_{AB}, \quad f_{aB} = p_B - f_{AB} \quad \text{and}$$
$$f_{ab} = 1 + f_{AB} - p_A - p_B \tag{8.42}$$

in the right-hand side member of (8.41) and simplifying yield

$$f_{AB}(1) = \frac{1}{2}(f_{AB} + p_A p_B), \quad \text{or} \quad f_{AB}(1) = p_A p_B + \frac{1}{2}\Delta. \tag{8.43}$$

From equations (8.43) and (8.42) we find also the frequencies $f_{Ab}(1)$, $f_{aB}(1)$, and $f_{ab}(1)$, and hence the gamete distribution in the first generation:

$$\begin{pmatrix} f_{AB}(1) & f_{Ab}(1) \\ f_{aB}(1) & f_{ab}(1) \end{pmatrix} = \begin{pmatrix} p_A p_B + \frac{1}{2}\Delta & p_A q_b - \frac{1}{2}\Delta \\ q_a p_B - \frac{1}{2}\Delta & q_a q_b + \frac{1}{2}\Delta \end{pmatrix}. \tag{8.44}$$

This shows that *Hardy-Weinberg's law does not apply to any arbitrary population.*

Proceeding further, we find the frequency of gamete AB in the second generation:

$$f_{AB}(2) = \frac{1}{2}(f_{AB}(1) + p_A p_B) = p_A p_B + \left(\frac{1}{2}\right)^2 \Delta,$$

and generally in the n-th generation:

$$f_{AB}(n) = p_A p_B + \left(\frac{1}{2}\right)^n \Delta. \tag{8.45}$$

The gamete distribution in the n-th generation follows:

$$\begin{pmatrix} f_{AB}(n) & f_{Ab}(n) \\ f_{aB}(n) & f_{ab}(n) \end{pmatrix} = \begin{pmatrix} p_A p_B + \left(\frac{1}{2}\right)^n \Delta & p_A q_b - \left(\frac{1}{2}\right)^n \Delta \\ q_a p_B - \left(\frac{1}{2}\right)^n \Delta & q_a q_b + \left(\frac{1}{2}\right)^n \Delta \end{pmatrix}. \tag{8.46}$$

Thus, while the equilibrium law does not hold in an arbitrary population, the original difference Δ decreases from one generation to the next with a factor of $\frac{1}{2}$, and it vanishes in the limit, as n tends to infinity. The equilibrium state in (8.38) is reached eventually.

9. PROBLEMS FOR SOLUTION

1. Equations (3.13) and (3.14) are examples of the relationship between two-step transition probabilities and one-step transition probabilities in the case of the binomial distribution. Verify these algebraic equations.

2. Verify equations (3.15) and (3.16).

3. The Chapman-Kolmogorov equation in (3.7) may be extended as follows:

$$P_{il}(n_1 + n_2 + n_3) = \sum_j \sum_k p_{ij}(n_1) p_{jk}(n_2) p_{kl}(n_3).$$

Verify this equation.

4. Show that the probability distribution

$$p_{ij}(n) = \binom{i}{j} (p_1 \dots p_n)^j (1 - p_1 \dots p_n)^{i-j}$$

satisfy the equation in problem 3.

5. The transition probability p_{ij} for a Poisson distribution is

$$p_{ij} = \frac{e^{-\lambda} \lambda^{j-i}}{(j-i)!}.$$

Show that the Poisson distribution satisfies the Chapman-Kolmogorov equation in (3.3) and the equation

$$p_{il}(3) = \sum_j \sum_k p_{ij}(1) p_{jk}(1) p_{kl}(1)$$

where $p_{ij}(1) = p_{ij}$. What are the limits of j and k?

6. The transition probability for a non-homogeneous Poisson distribution may be represented by

$$p_{ij}(t_{r-1}, t_r) = \frac{\exp\left\{-\int_{t_{r-1}}^{t_r} \lambda(\tau)\, d\tau\right\} \left[\int_{t_{r-1}}^{t_r} \lambda(\tau)\, d\tau\right]^{j-i}}{(j-i)!}$$

Show that the following equations hold true for the non-homogenous Poisson distribution:

$$p_{ik}(t_0, t_2) = \sum_j p_{ij}(t_0, t_1) p_{jk}(t_1, t_2)$$

and

$$p_{il}(t_0, t_3) = \sum_j \sum_k p_{ij}(t_0, t_1) p_{jk}(t_1, t_2) p_{kl}(t_2, t_3).$$

7. The geometric distribution has the following stochastic matrix

$$\mathbf{P} = \begin{pmatrix} p & qp & q^2p & q^3p & \cdots \\ 0 & p & qp & q^2p & \cdots \\ 0 & 0 & p & qp & \cdots \\ 0 & 0 & 0 & p & \cdots \\ . & . & . & . & \cdots \end{pmatrix}$$

From the equation

$$\mathbf{P}(n) = \mathbf{P}^n$$

find the transition probability $p_{ij}(n)$.

8. Show that the negative binomial distribution with

$$p_{ij}(n) = \binom{j-i+n-1}{j-i} q^{j-i} p^n$$

satisfy the equations

$$p_{ik}(n_1 + n_2) = \sum_j p_{ij}(n_1) p_{jk}(n_2)$$

and

$$p_{il}(n_1 + n_2 + n_3) = \sum_j \sum_k p_{ij}(n_1) p_{jk}(n_2) p_{kl}(n_3).$$

9. Classify the states for each of the chains represented by the stochastic matrices $\mathbf{P}_1$, $\mathbf{P}_2$, $\mathbf{P}_3$, $\mathbf{P}_4$ and $\mathbf{P}_5$, respectively.

$$\mathbf{P}_1 = \begin{pmatrix} \frac{1}{3} & \frac{2}{3} \\ \frac{1}{2} & \frac{1}{2} \end{pmatrix} \qquad \mathbf{P}_2 = \begin{pmatrix} 1 & 0 & 0 \\ \frac{1}{2} & 0 & \frac{1}{2} \\ \frac{1}{2} & \frac{1}{2} & 0 \end{pmatrix}$$

$$\mathbf{P}_3 = \begin{pmatrix} 1 & 0 & 0 \\ \frac{1}{4} & \frac{1}{2} & \frac{1}{4} \\ 0 & 0 & 1 \end{pmatrix}$$

$$\mathbf{P}_4 = \begin{pmatrix} \frac{1}{4} & \frac{1}{2} & \frac{1}{4} & 0 \\ \frac{1}{2} & \frac{1}{2} & 0 & 0 \\ 0 & \frac{1}{2} & 0 & \frac{1}{2} \\ 0 & 0 & 1 & 0 \end{pmatrix} \qquad \mathbf{P}_5 = \begin{pmatrix} \frac{1}{3} & \frac{1}{3} & \frac{1}{3} & 0 \\ 0 & 1 & 0 & 0 \\ \frac{1}{2} & 0 & \frac{1}{2} & 0 \\ 0 & \frac{3}{4} & 0 & \frac{1}{4} \end{pmatrix}$$

10. *Continuation.* Compute two-step transition probabilities for each of the chains in problem 9.

11. *Continuation.* For stochastic matrices $\mathbf{P}_1$ and $\mathbf{P}_2$ in problem 9, compute the n-step transition probabilities $P_{ij}(n)$ and examine the behavior of $p_{ij}(n)$, as $n \to \infty$ in each case. (HINT: Use formula (3.2), Chapter 6.)

12. *The Hardy-Weinberg law.* Derive from the mating

$$(dAA + 2hAa + raa) \times (dAA + 2hAa + raa)$$

the genotype frequencies of AA, Aa, aa in equations (8.2), (8.3), and (8.4).

13. *Continuation.* Find the genotype distribution of the progenies for each of the following genotype frequencies of the parents:

(a) AA:Aa:aa = 50:20:30
(b) AA:Aa:aa = 45:30:25
(c) AA:Aa:aa = 40:40:20
(d) AA:Aa:aa = 36:48:16

14. MN blood typing, discovered by Landsteiner and Levine in 1927, is a prominant example of Mendelian inheritance. The theory postulates two allelic genes, M and N, which are specific in detecting the presence of the corresponding antigens in the red blood cells. Neither one of the two alleles is dominant over the other so that there are three phenotypes, M, MN, N associated with the three genotypes, MM, MN, NN. The following phenotype frequencies for 1279 English people are taken from Race and Sanger [1958]: M:MN:N = 363:634:282. Use this example to test the hypothesis that the M and N blood typing obey the Hardy-Weinberg law.

15. Assuming genotype distribution AA:Aa:aa = d:2h:r for both parent populations, find the probability that two full brothers will have the same genotypes AA, Aa, or aa.

16. *Continuation.* What is the probability that two brothers described in problem 15 will have different genotypes?

17. *Continuation.* Two men who have one parent in common are half-brothers. Find the probability that two half-brothers will have the same genotypes AA, Aa, or aa.

18. *Continuation.* What is the probability that a man will have genotype AA given his half-brother has genotype Aa?

19. *Transition probability matrix.* Number the genotypes AA, Aa, aa by 1, 2, 3, respectively and let p_{ij} be the one-step transition probability defined in (8.5). Show that the one-step transition probability matrix is given by

$$\mathbf{P}(1) = \begin{pmatrix} p & q & 0 \\ \frac{1}{2}p & \frac{1}{2} & \frac{1}{2}q \\ 0 & p & q \end{pmatrix} \tag{8.8}$$

20. *Continuation.* Find the probability that a man will have genotype i given that a specified grandparent has genotype i, for $i = 1, 2, 3$.

21. *Continuation.* The probabilities in problem 20 are two-step transition probabilities and may be obtained from one-step transition probabilities via the relationship

$$p_{ik}(2) = \sum_{j=1}^{3} p_{ij} \cdot p_{jk}$$

so that the two-step transition probability matrix may be obtained from

$$\mathbf{P}(2) = [\mathbf{P}(1)]^2.$$

Find all the nine elements of $\mathbf{P}(2)$ from the above equations.

22. *Continuation.* In equation (3.2), Chapter 6, there is a general formula for the n-th step transition probabilities $p_{ij}(n)$. For now, prove the following n-step transition probability matrix by induction:

$$\mathbf{P}(n) = \begin{pmatrix} p^2 + pq/2^{n-1} & 2pq + q(q-p)/2^{n-1} & q^2 - q^2/2^{n-1} \\ p^2 + p(q-p)/2^n & 2pq + (p-q)^2/2^n & q^2 + q(p-q)/2^n \\ p^2 - p^2/2^{n-1} & 2pq + p(p-q)/2^{n-1} & q^2 + pq/2^{n-1} \end{pmatrix}$$

23. *Continuation.* Find the elements of the transition probability matrix in problem 22 for $n = 1, 2, 3$.

24. Verify equation (8.21) for $j = 1, 2, 3$.

25. Find the first return probabilities $f_{ii}(n)$ for $i = 1, 2, 3$; $n = 1, 2, 3$.

26. Find the first passage probabilities $f_{12}(n)$, $f_{13}(n)$, $f_{23}(n)$ for $n = 1, 2, 3$.

27. *Two pairs of genes.* Derive the probabilities of the nine genotypes in equation (8.36) from the product in (8.34).

CHAPTER 6

Algebraic Treatment of Finite Markov Chains

1. INTRODUCTION

The higher order transition probabilities $p_{ij}(n)$ can be computed from p_{ij} by repeated multiplications and summations as shown in Section 2.1 of the preceding chapter; but the work involved is prohibitive even for a chain with a small number of states and for a moderate number n. It is therefore of fundamental importance to derive explicit formulas for these probabilities. The general formulas also play an important role in the investigation of the type of states and the nature of a Markov chain. The purpose of this chapter is to present explicit formulas for $p_{ij}(n)$ derived from matrix multiplications. Since the set of states constituting a Markov chain can always be decomposed into closed subsets, it is sufficient to consider only a finite Markov chain with the smallest closed set containing a given state. However, the formulas are equally valid even if a chain is not irreducible or the states involved are not all communicating.

A method of determining the elements of the nth power of a matrix is described in some detail in Chapter 14, Section 4. We shall not repeat the theoretical background here; nor shall we explain the terminologies involved, such as characteristic matrix, eigenvalues, eigenvectors, etc. We shall only present essential steps needed in arriving at the formulas without justifying each step in the derivation. Examples will be given in Section 5 to illustrate the computations.

2. EIGENVALUES OF STOCHASTIC MATRIX P AND A USEFUL LEMMA

For a finite Markov chain having states 1, 2, ..., s, and a stochastic matrix

$$\mathbf{P} = \begin{pmatrix} p_{11} & p_{12} & \cdots & p_{1s} \\ p_{21} & p_{22} & \cdots & p_{2s} \\ \cdot & \cdot & \cdots & \cdot \\ p_{s1} & p_{s2} & \cdots & p_{ss} \end{pmatrix} \tag{2.1}$$

with

$$\sum_{j=1}^{s} p_{ij} = 1, \qquad i = 1, \ldots, s, \tag{2.2}$$

we introduce a characteristic matrix

$$\mathbf{A}(\lambda) = (\lambda \mathbf{I} - \mathbf{P}) = \begin{pmatrix} (\lambda - p_{11}) & -p_{12} & \cdots & -p_{1s} \\ -p_{21} & (\lambda - p_{22}) & \cdots & -p_{2s} \\ \cdot & \cdot & \cdots & \cdot \\ -p_{s1} & -p_{s2} & \cdots & (\lambda - p_{ss}) \end{pmatrix} \tag{2.3}$$

where **I** is an $s \times s$ unit matrix. The characteristic equation

$$|\mathbf{A}(\lambda)| = |\lambda \mathbf{I} - \mathbf{P}| = 0 \tag{2.4}$$

is an s degree polynomial in λ. By the fundamental theorem of algebra, equation (2.4) has s roots, denoted by $\lambda_1, \lambda_2, \ldots, \lambda_s$. They are known as eigenvalues of the matrix **P**. These eigenvalues may be real or complex numbers, and some of them may be equal. The magnitude of these eigenvalues is given by the following theorem

Theorem 1. *The eigenvalues of the stochastic matrix* **P** *in* (2.1) *are not greater than unity in absolute value and one of the eigenvalues is* $\lambda = 1$.

Proof. Since every row sum of matrix **P** is equal to one, $\lambda = 1$ is a solution of (2.4).

To prove that $|\lambda| \leq 1$, let λ be a root of the equation (2.4); then there is a non-zero column vector

$$\mathbf{C} = (c_1, \ldots, c_s)' \tag{2.5}$$

such that

$$(\lambda \mathbf{I} - \mathbf{P})\mathbf{C} = \mathbf{0}, \tag{2.6}$$

or, equivalently,

$$\lambda c_i = p_{i1} c_1 + p_{i2} c_2 + \dots + p_{is} c_s, \quad i = 1, \dots, s. \tag{2.7}$$

Since p_{ij} are non-negative, we have the inequality

$$|\lambda c_i| \leq \sum_{j=1}^{s} p_{ij} |c_j|, \quad i = 1, \dots, s. \tag{2.8}$$

Let c_k be the largest component in absolute value of the vector $\mathbf{C}$. Then we have from (2.8)

$$|\lambda c_i| \leq |c_k|, \quad i = 1, \dots, s. \tag{2.9}$$

For $i = k$, (2.9) becomes

$$|\lambda c_k| \leq |c_k|, \tag{2.10}$$

which means that

$$|\lambda| \leq 1, \tag{2.11}$$

proving the theorem.

A cofactor of matrix $\mathbf{A}(\lambda)$ is an $(s-1) \times (s-1)$ determinant obtained from $\mathbf{A}(\lambda)$ by deleting the row and the column corresponding to the element of interest and multiplying by an appropriate sign. Specifically, the cofactor of the (i,j)th element of the matrix $\mathbf{A}(\lambda)$ is an $(s-1) \times (s-1)$ determinant after the i-th row and the j-th column have been deleted from $\mathbf{A}(\lambda)$ and multiplied by $(-1)^{i+j}$, and is denoted by $A_{ij}(\lambda)$. When $\lambda = 1$, the cofactors $A_{ij}(1)$ have some interesting properties.

Lemma 1. *All the elements in each row of matrix* $\mathbf{A}(1)$ *have the same cofactor:*

$$A_{ij}(1) = A_{ii}(1), \qquad i, j = 1, \dots, s. \tag{2.12}$$

Proof. For notational convenience, we prove the lemma for $i = 1$ and $j = 2$. The corresponding cofactors are

$$A_{11}(1) = \begin{vmatrix} 1 - p_{22} & -p_{23} & \cdots & -p_{2s} \\ -p_{32} & 1 - p_{33} & \cdots & -p_{3s} \\ \vdots & \vdots & \vdots\vdots\vdots & \vdots \\ -p_{s2} & -p_{s3} & \cdots & 1 - p_{ss} \end{vmatrix} \tag{2.13}$$

and

$$\mathbf{A}_{12}(1) = (-1) \begin{vmatrix} -p_{21} & -p_{23} & \cdots & -p_{2s} \\ -p_{31} & 1 - p_{33} & \cdots & -p_{3s} \\ \vdots & \vdots & \vdots\vdots\vdots & \vdots \\ -p_{s1} & -p_{s3} & \cdots & 1 - p_{ss} \end{vmatrix} \tag{2.14}$$

with the only difference in the first column. Replacing the first column in (2.13) by the sum of all the columns[1] and making the substitution

$$-p_{i2} - \cdots - p_{i,i-1} + (1 - p_{ii}) - p_{i,i+1} - \cdots - p_{is} = p_{i1},$$
$$i = 2, \ldots, s, \tag{2.15}$$

for each row, we recover (2.14) and hence $A_{11}(1) = A_{12}(1)$.

2.1. A Useful Lemma.

In a further discussion of eigenvalues and at other times in the subsequent chapters, the following lemma is frequently used [Cf. Lemma 1, Chapter 3].

Lemma 2. *For any distinct numbers* $\lambda_1, \lambda_2, \ldots, \lambda_s$, *we have*

$$\sum_{i=1}^{s} \frac{\lambda_i^r}{\prod_{\substack{j=1 \\ j \neq i}}^{s} (\lambda_i - \lambda_j)} = 0 \qquad r = 0, 1, \ldots, (s-2),$$
$$= 1 \qquad r = s - 1. \tag{2.16}$$

The lemma can be proven by using Lagrange's interpolation formula, partial fractions, and other methods. In the following proof, we use the double induction method (see Chiang [1963]). A slightly different form of the lemma may be found in Polya and Szegö [1964].

Before proving the lemma, let us introduce a well-known determinant. A *Vandermonde determinant* of order s is of the form

---

[1] Here we use the well-known result in algebra that replacement of any column (or any row) of a determinant by the sum of all columns (or all rows) does not change the value of the determinant.

$$|\mathbf{W}| = \begin{vmatrix} 1 & 1 & \dots & 1 \\ \lambda_1 & \lambda_2 & \dots & \lambda_s \\ \vdots & \vdots & & \vdots \\ \lambda_1^{s-1} & \lambda_2^{s-1} & & \lambda_s^{s-1} \end{vmatrix}. \tag{2.17}$$

When $\lambda_1, \lambda_2, \dots, \lambda_s$, are distinct non-zero numbers, the determinant is given by

$$|\mathbf{W}| = \prod_{i=1}^{s-1} \prod_{j=i+1}^{s} (\lambda_j - \lambda_i). \tag{2.18}$$

Let W_{ij} be the cofactor of W. Then

$$\sum_{j=1}^{s} W_{ij} = 0, \qquad \text{for } i = 2, \dots, s. \tag{2.19}$$

For example, for $i = s$,

$$\sum_{j=1}^{s} W_{sj} = \begin{vmatrix} 1 & 1 & \dots & 1 \\ \lambda_1 & \lambda_2 & \dots & \lambda_s \\ \vdots & \vdots & & \vdots \\ \lambda_1^{s-2} & \lambda_2^{s-2} & \dots & \lambda_s^{s-2} \\ 1 & 1 & & 1 \end{vmatrix} = 0. \tag{2.19a}$$

Proof of Lemma 2 We shall prove the lemma in two parts.

Part 1. $r = 0$, we need to show that

$$\sum_{i=1}^{s} \frac{1}{\prod\limits_{\substack{j=1 \\ j \neq i}}^{s} (\lambda_i - \lambda_j)} = 0. \tag{2.16a}$$

The left hand side of (2.16a) may be rewritten as

$$\sum_{i=1}^{s} \frac{(-1)^{s-i}}{\prod\limits_{h=1}^{i-1} (\lambda_i - \lambda_h) \prod\limits_{j=i+1}^{s} (\lambda_j - \lambda_i)}. \tag{2.20}$$

Making the same denominator in (2.20), we find the first term

$$\frac{(-1)^{s-1}}{\prod_{i=1}^{s-1}\prod_{j=i+1}^{s}(\lambda_j-\lambda_i)}\prod_{i=2}^{s-1}\prod_{j=i+1}^{s}(\lambda_j-\lambda_i)$$

$$=\frac{(-1)^{s-1}}{\prod_{i=1}^{s-1}\prod_{j=i+1}^{s}(\lambda_j-\lambda_i)}(-1)^{s+1}W_{s1}$$

and, in general, the l-th term

$$\frac{(-1)^{s-l}}{\prod_{i=1}^{s-1}\prod_{j=i+1}^{s}(\lambda_j-\lambda_i)}\prod_{\substack{i=1\\ i\neq l}}^{s-1}\prod_{\substack{j=i+1\\ j\neq l}}^{s}(\lambda_j-\lambda_i)=\frac{(-1)^{s-l}}{\prod_{i=1}^{s-1}\prod_{j=i+1}^{s}(\lambda_j-\lambda_i)}(-1)^{s+l}W_{sl},$$

$$l=1,2,\ldots,s. \quad (2.21)$$

Substituting (2.21) in (2.20) gives

$$\sum_{i=1}^{s}\frac{1}{\prod_{i=1}^{s-1}\prod_{j=i+1}^{s}(\lambda_j-\lambda_i)}[W_{s1}+\ldots+W_{ss}]=0 \quad (2.22)$$

and proves (2.16a).

Part 2. $0<r\leq s-1$. We shall prove (2.16) by double induction on r and s. We let

$$\theta_{s,r}=\sum_{i=1}^{s}\frac{\lambda_i^r}{\prod_{\substack{j=1\\ j\neq i}}^{s}(\lambda_i-\lambda_j)}. \quad (2.23)$$

When $s=2$, it is easy to show that

$$\theta_{2,0}=0 \quad \text{and} \quad \theta_{2,1}=1. \quad (2.24)$$

Assuming the lemma is true for s and r, i.e.,

$$\begin{aligned}\theta_{s,r} &= 1 \qquad \text{for } r = s-1 \\ &= 0 \qquad \text{for } 0 \le r < s-1,\end{aligned} \tag{2.25}$$

we need to show that

$$\begin{aligned}\theta_{s+1,r+1} &= 1 \qquad \text{for } r+1 = s \\ &= 0 \qquad \text{for } 0 \le r+1 < s,\end{aligned} \tag{2.26}$$

where

$$\theta_{s+1,r+1} = \sum_{i=1}^{s} \frac{\lambda_i^{r+1}}{\prod_{\substack{j=1\\ j\neq i}}^{s} (\lambda_i - \lambda_j)(\lambda_i - \lambda_{s+1})} + \frac{\lambda_{s+1}^{r+1}}{\prod_{j=1}^{s} (\lambda_{s+1} - \lambda_j)}. \tag{2.27}$$

Now, for every $i = 1, \ldots, s$,

$$\frac{\lambda_i^{r+1}}{\lambda_i - \lambda_{s+1}} = \lambda_i^r + \lambda_i^{r-1}\lambda_{s+1} + \ldots + \lambda_{s+1}^r + \frac{\lambda_{s+1}^{r+1}}{\lambda_i - \lambda_{s+1}}. \tag{2.28}$$

Substituting (2.28) in (2.27) we find

$$\begin{aligned}\theta_{s+1,r+1} &= \\ &\sum_{i=1}^{s} \frac{1}{\prod_{\substack{j=1\\ j\neq i}}^{s} (\lambda_i - \lambda_j)} \left[\lambda_i^r + \lambda_i^{r-1}\lambda_{s+1} + \ldots + \lambda_{s+1}^r + \frac{\lambda_{s+1}^{r+1}}{\lambda_i - \lambda_{s+1}}\right] \\ &+ \frac{\lambda_{s+1}^{r+1}}{\prod_{i=1}^{s} (\lambda_{s+1} - \lambda_i)} \\ &= \theta_{s,r} + \lambda_{s+1}\theta_{s,r-1} + \ldots + \lambda_{s+1}^r \theta_{s,0} + \lambda_{s+1}^{r+1}\theta_{s+1,0}.\end{aligned} \tag{2.29}$$

By the inductive hypothesis (2.24),

$$\begin{aligned}\theta_{s,r-k} = 0 \qquad &\text{for } k = 1, \ldots, r-1 \\ &r = 1, \ldots, s-1.\end{aligned} \tag{2.30}$$

and by Part 1, $\theta_{s,0} = \theta_{s+1,0} = 0$. Therefore (2.29) becomes

$$\begin{aligned}\theta_{s+1,r+1} = \theta_{s,r} \qquad &\text{for } 0 < r \le s-1 \\ &s = 2, 3, \ldots .\end{aligned} \tag{2.31}$$

This means that (2.25) implies (2.26) and completes the inductive proof.

3. FORMULAS FOR HIGHER ORDER TRANSITION PROBABILITIES

For each eigenvalue λ_l, $l = 1, \ldots, s$, we have the corresponding characteristic matrix

$$\mathbf{A}(\lambda_l) = (\lambda_l \mathbf{I} - \mathbf{P}) = \begin{pmatrix} (\lambda_l - p_{11}) & -p_{12} & \cdots & -p_{1s} \\ -p_{21} & (\lambda_l - p_{22}) & \cdots & -p_{2s} \\ \cdot & \cdot & \cdots & \cdot \\ -p_{s1} & -p_{s2} & \cdots & (\lambda_l - p_{ss}) \end{pmatrix} \tag{3.1}$$

and the cofactors $A_{ij}(\lambda_l)$, $i, j = 1, \ldots, s$.

Theorem 2. *If the stochastic matrix* **P** *in* (2.1) *of a Markov chain has distinct eigenvalues* $\lambda_1, \lambda_2, \ldots, \lambda_s$, *then the n-th order transition probabilities are given by*

$$p_{ij}(n) = \sum_{l=1}^{s} A_{ji}(\lambda_l)\lambda_l^n \frac{1}{\prod\limits_{\substack{m=1 \\ m \neq l}}^{s} (\lambda_l - \lambda_m)}, \quad \begin{matrix} i, j = 1, \ldots, s; \\ n = 1, 2, \ldots \end{matrix} \tag{3.2}$$

Furthermore, the right hand side of formula (3.2) *is a real function of* p_{ij} *even if the equation* (2.4) *has complex roots.*

Formula (3.2) is easy to compute. The cofactor $A_{ji}(\lambda_l)$ is the only quantity in the formula which varies with (i,j); the remaining factors are constant for all the probabilities $p_{ij}(n)$, $i, j = 1, \ldots, s$.

Proof. The last assertion regarding complex roots can be shown as follows.[2] It is well known that the sum, or product, of complex conjugates is real, and that a polynomial of the conjugate of a complex number with real coefficients is the conjugate of the polynomial of the complex number.

---

[2] The author benefitted greatly from a discussion with Joan Skurnick regarding complex roots of the matrix **P**.

Now the complex roots of (2.4), if they exist, appear in complex conjugates. Without loss of generality, let us assume that there is only one pair of complex conjugate roots, denoted by λ_k and $\bar{\lambda}_k$, the remaining $s - 2$ roots being real. For a real root λ_l, the corresponding term in (3.2) may be written

$$A_{ji}(\lambda_l)\lambda_l^n \frac{1}{(\lambda_l - \lambda_k)(\lambda_l - \bar{\lambda}_k)\prod_{m=1}^{s}(\lambda_l - \lambda_m)} \tag{3.3}$$

where $\lambda_m \neq \lambda_l, \neq \lambda_k, \neq \bar{\lambda}_k$. The factors $A_{ji}(\lambda_l)$ and λ_l^n and $(\lambda_l - \lambda_m)$ are real. The product of the two complex conjugates $(\lambda_l - \lambda_k)$ and $(\lambda_l - \bar{\lambda}_k)$ is also real. Therefore, the term in (3.3) is real. The terms corresponding to the complex conjugates λ_k and $\bar{\lambda}_k$ are

$$A_{ji}(\lambda_k)\lambda_k^n \frac{1}{(\lambda_k - \bar{\lambda}_k)\prod_{m=1}^{s}(\lambda_k - \lambda_m)} \tag{3.3a}$$

and

$$A_{ji}(\bar{\lambda}_k)\bar{\lambda}_k^n \frac{1}{(\bar{\lambda}_k - \lambda_k)\prod_{m=1}^{s}(\bar{\lambda}_k - \lambda_m)} \tag{3.3b}$$

where $\lambda_m \neq \lambda_k, \neq \bar{\lambda}_k$. Every factor in (3.3b) is the complex conjugate of the corresponding factor in (3.3a). Therefore, the two terms in (3.3a) and (3.3b) are complex conjugates, and hence their sum is real. It follows that the sum on the right hand side of (3.2) is real, proving the assertion.

To derive formula (3.2), we formulate for each eigenvalue the adjoint matrix

$$\begin{pmatrix} A_{11}(\lambda_l) & A_{21}(\lambda_l) & \dots & A_{s1}(\lambda_l) \\ A_{12}(\lambda_l) & A_{22}(\lambda_l) & \dots & A_{s2}(\lambda_l) \\ \cdot & \cdot & \dots & \cdot \\ A_{1s}(\lambda_l) & A_{2s}(\lambda_l) & \dots & A_{ss}(\lambda_l) \end{pmatrix}, \qquad l = 1, \dots, s. \tag{3.4}$$

Each column in (3.4) is an eigenvector of the matrix $\mathbf{P}$ corresponding to the eigenvalue λ_l and satisfies the equation

$$(\lambda_l \mathbf{I} - \mathbf{P})\begin{pmatrix} A_{k1}(\lambda_l) \\ A_{k2}(\lambda_l) \\ \vdots \\ A_{ks}(\lambda_l) \end{pmatrix} = \begin{pmatrix} 0 \\ 0 \\ \vdots \\ 0 \end{pmatrix}, \qquad l, k = 1, \dots, s. \tag{3.5}$$

Taking a non-zero (say, the k_l-th) column from each of the s matrices in (3.4), for $l = 1, \dots, s$, we have a new matrix

$$\mathbf{T}(\cdot) = \begin{pmatrix} A_{k_1,1}(\lambda_1) & A_{k_2,1}(\lambda_2) & \dots & A_{k_s,1}(\lambda_s) \\ A_{k_1,2}(\lambda_1) & A_{k_2,2}(\lambda_2) & \dots & A_{k_s,2}(\lambda_s) \\ \cdot & \cdot & \dots & \cdot \\ A_{k_1,s}(\lambda_1) & A_{k_2,s}(\lambda_2) & \dots & A_{k_s,s}(\lambda_s) \end{pmatrix} \tag{3.6}$$

where the symbol $(\cdot)$ represents a vector $(k_1, k_2, \dots, k_s)$. There are s^s possible choices of vectors to form $\mathbf{T}(\cdot)$, but the final result is independent of the choice of particular (non-zero) vectors. When $\lambda_1, \lambda_2, \dots, \lambda_s$, are distinct, the columns in (3.6) are linearly independent and hence the inverse $\mathbf{T}^{-1}(\cdot)$ of the matrix $\mathbf{T}(\cdot)$ exists and is given by

$$\mathbf{T}^{-1}(\cdot) = \begin{vmatrix} \dfrac{T_{11}(\cdot)}{|T(\cdot)|} & \dfrac{T_{21}(\cdot)}{|T(\cdot)|} & \dots & \dfrac{T_{s1}(\cdot)}{|T(\cdot)|} \\ \dfrac{T_{12}(\cdot)}{|T(\cdot)|} & \dfrac{T_{22}(\cdot)}{|T(\cdot)|} & \dots & \dfrac{T_{s2}(\cdot)}{|T(\cdot)|} \\ \cdot & \cdot & \dots & \cdot \\ \dfrac{T_{1s}(\cdot)}{|T(\cdot)|} & \dfrac{T_{2s}(\cdot)}{|T(\cdot)|} & \dots & \dfrac{T_{ss}(\cdot)}{|T(\cdot)|} \end{vmatrix} \tag{3.7}$$

where $|\mathbf{T}(\cdot)|$ is the determinant of the matrix $\mathbf{T}(\cdot)$ and $T_{ji}(\cdot)$ is the (j, i)th cofactor of $\mathbf{T}(\cdot)$.

The matrix $\mathbf{T}(\cdot)$ in (3.6) diagonalizes the stochastic matrix P in the sense that

$$\mathbf{T}^{-1}(\cdot)\mathbf{P}\mathbf{T}(\cdot) = \begin{pmatrix} \lambda_1 & 0 & \dots & 0 \\ 0 & \lambda_2 & \dots & 0 \\ \cdot & \cdot & \dots & \cdot \\ 0 & 0 & \dots & \lambda_s \end{pmatrix} \tag{3.8}$$

so that

$$\mathbf{P} = \mathbf{T}(\cdot) \begin{pmatrix} \lambda_1 & 0 & \dots & 0 \\ 0 & \lambda_2 & \dots & 0 \\ \cdot & \cdot & \dots & \cdot \\ 0 & 0 & \dots & \lambda_s \end{pmatrix} \mathbf{T}^{-1}(\cdot). \tag{3.9}$$

Direct computations give the square of the matrix P:

$$\mathbf{P}^2 = \mathbf{T}(\cdot) \begin{pmatrix} \lambda_1^2 & 0 & \dots & 0 \\ 0 & \lambda_2^2 & \dots & 0 \\ \cdot & \cdot & \dots & \cdot \\ 0 & 0 & \dots & \lambda_s^2 \end{pmatrix} \mathbf{T}^{-1}(\cdot), \tag{3.10}$$

and in general the nth power of P:

$$\mathbf{P}^n = \mathbf{T}(\cdot) \begin{pmatrix} \lambda_1^n & 0 & \dots & 0 \\ 0 & \lambda_2^n & \dots & 0 \\ \cdot & \cdot & \dots & \cdot \\ 0 & 0 & \dots & \lambda_s^n \end{pmatrix} \mathbf{T}^{-1}(\cdot). \tag{3.11}$$

Now it is a simple matter of performing the matrix multiplication on the right hand side of (3.11) to obtain the probability

$$p_{ij}(n) = \sum_{l=1}^{s} A_{k_l,i}(\lambda_l)\lambda_l^n \frac{T_{jl}(\cdot)}{|T(\cdot)|}, \qquad \begin{matrix} i, j = 1, \dots, s; \\ n = 1, \dots . \end{matrix} \tag{3.12}$$

In the formulation of the matrix $\mathbf{T}(\cdot)$ in (3.6), the numbers k_l may be different for different columns. However, if $k_l = k$ for $l = 1, \dots, s$, then the diagonalizing matrix in (3.6) may be written as

$$\mathbf{T}(k) = \begin{vmatrix} A_{k1}(\lambda_1) & A_{k1}(\lambda_2) & \dots & A_{k1}(\lambda_s) \\ A_{k2}(\lambda_1) & A_{k2}(\lambda_2) & \dots & A_{k2}(\lambda_s) \\ \cdot & \cdot & \dots & \cdot \\ A_{ks}(\lambda_1) & A_{ks}(\lambda_2) & \dots & A_{ks}(\lambda_s) \end{vmatrix} \tag{3.6a}$$

and formula (3.11) becomes

$$p_{ij}(n) = \sum_{l=1}^{s} A_{ki}(\lambda_l)\lambda_l^n \frac{T_{jl}(k)}{|T(k)|}, \qquad i, j = 1, \dots, s. \tag{3.13}$$

It is shown in Chapter 14, Section 3.4 that when k is the same for all the s columns, then the components of the kth column of the inverse $\mathbf{T}^{-1}(k)$ are independent of k and are given by

$$\frac{T_{kl}(k)}{|\mathbf{T}(k)|} = \frac{1}{\prod_{\substack{m=1\\m\neq l}}^{s}(\lambda_l - \lambda_m)}, \qquad \text{for } l = 1, \ldots, s. \tag{3.14}$$

Letting $k = j$ and substituting (3.14) in (3.13), we recover the formula

$$p_{ij}(n) = \sum_{l=1}^{s} A_{ji}(\lambda_l)\lambda_l^n \frac{1}{\prod_{\substack{m=1\\m\neq l}}^{s}(\lambda_l - \lambda_m)}, \qquad i, j = 1, \ldots, s, \tag{3.2}$$

proving the theorem.

Equation (3.2) for higher order transition probabilities is for the case where a stochastic matrix **P** has single eigenvalues. We can derive formulas for higher order transition probabilities when matrix **P** has multiple eigenvalues. However, to keep from interrupting the present line of presentation, we postpone the solution for the multiple eigenvalues case to the exercises of this chapter. Reference should also be made to Chapter 15 where the case is treated for continuous processes.

4. LIMITING PROBABILITY DISTRIBUTION

We have shown in Section 7, Chapter 5, that the limiting probability distribution $\{\pi_j\}$ of an irreducible ergodic Markov chain exists and is stationary. We now provide explicit formulas for the limiting probabilities.

Theorem 3. *Let* **P** *defined in* (2.1) *be the stochastic matrix of a finite ergodic Markov chain. The limiting probabilities*

$$\lim_{n\to\infty} p_{ij}(n) = \pi_j, \qquad i, j = 1, \ldots, s \tag{4.1}$$

are given by

$$\pi_j = \frac{A_{jj}(1)}{\sum_{k=1}^{s} A_{kk}(1)}, \qquad j = 1, \ldots s \tag{4.2}$$

and the mean recurrent time by

$$\mu_{jj} = \frac{\sum_{k=1}^{s} A_{kk}(1)}{A_{jj}(1)}, \qquad j = 1, \ldots, s, \tag{4.3}$$

where $A_{jj}(1)$ *is the* (j,j)th *cofactor of the matrix* $\mathbf{A}(1) = (\mathbf{I} - \mathbf{P})$.

Proof. Denote the limiting probabilities by a column vector

$$\boldsymbol{\pi} = (\pi_1, \ldots, \pi_s)', \tag{4.4}$$

and write equation (7.7), Chapter 5, in matrix notation as

$$(\mathbf{I} - \mathbf{P}')\boldsymbol{\pi} = \mathbf{0}. \tag{4.5}$$

This means that $\boldsymbol{\pi}$ is an eigenvector of $\mathbf{P}'$ corresponding to eigenvalue $\lambda = 1$. Let

$$\mathbf{A}(1) = (\mathbf{I} - \mathbf{P}) \tag{4.6}$$

be the characteristic matrix corresponding to $\lambda = 1$, and $\mathbf{A}'(1)$ the transpose of $\mathbf{A}(1)$. Then the vector $\boldsymbol{\pi}$ is given by (cf., equation (3.5))

$$(\pi_1, \pi_2, \ldots, \pi_s)' = c\,[A'_{k1}(1), A'_{k2}(1), \ldots, A'_{ks}(1)]' \tag{4.7}$$

where c is a scalar and $A'_{kj}(1)$ is the (k,j)th cofactor of $\mathbf{A}'(1)$. Since $A'_{kj}(1) = A_{jk}(1)$ and, according to lemma 1, $A_{jk}(1) = A_{jj}(1)$, (4.7) becomes

$$(\pi_1, \pi_2, \ldots, \pi_s)' = c\,[A_{11}(1), A_{22}(1), \ldots, A_{ss}(1)]'. \tag{4.8}$$

In order for $\{\pi_j\}$ to be a probability distribution, the sum $\pi_1 + \ldots + \pi_s = 1$, and therefore

$$c = \sum_{k=1}^{s} A_{kk}(1) \tag{4.9}$$

and

$$\pi_j = \frac{A_{jj}(1)}{\sum_{k=1}^{s} A_{kk}(1)}, \tag{4.2}$$

as is required to be shown.

Formula (4.3) for the mean recurrent time follows from Theorem 6, Chapter 5 and equation (4.2) above.

We have derived in section 3, equation (3.2), a formula for the transition probability $p_{ij}(n)$. Obviously, the limiting probabilities π_j can be obtained also from (3.2) by taking the limit as n approaches infinity:

$$\lim_{n\to\infty} p_{ij}(n) = \lim_{n\to\infty} \sum_{l=1}^{s} A_{ji}(\lambda_l)\lambda_l^n \frac{1}{\prod_{\substack{m=1\\m\neq l}}^{s}(\lambda_l - \lambda_m)}. \tag{4.10}$$

Formulas for the limiting probabilities in (4.2) and (4.10) should be the same. The following theorem establishes their identity.

Theorem 4. *The limiting probabilities given in* (4.2) *and* (4.10) *are identical. That is,*

$$\lim_{n\to\infty} \sum_{l} A_{ji}(\lambda_l)\lambda_l^n \frac{1}{\prod_{\substack{m=1\\m\neq l}}^{s}(\lambda_l - \lambda_m)} = \frac{A_{jj}(1)}{\sum_{k=1}^{s} A_{kk}(1)} \tag{4.11}$$

Proof. According to Theorem 1, we let $\lambda_1 = 1$, $|\lambda_l| < 1$, for $l = 2, \ldots, s$. As $n \to \infty$, $\lambda_l^n \to 0$ for $l = 2, \ldots, s$, equation (4.11) is in fact:

$$A_{ji}(1)\frac{1}{\prod_{m=2}^{s}(1 - \lambda_m)} = \frac{A_{jj}(1)}{\sum_{k=1}^{s} A_{kk}(1)}. \tag{4.12}$$

Since $A_{ji}(1) = A_{jj}(1)$, (4.12) is reduced to

$$\frac{1}{\prod_{m=2}^{s}(1 - \lambda_m)} = \frac{1}{\sum_{k=1}^{s} A_{kk}(1)}, \tag{4.13}$$

or

$$\prod_{m=2}^{s}(1 - \lambda_m) = \sum_{k=1}^{s} A_{kk}(1). \tag{4.14}$$

To prove the equality in (4.14), we introduce the equation

$$|\mathbf{A}(1) - \rho\mathbf{I}| = 0 \tag{4.15}$$

and determine the roots $\rho_1, \rho_2, \dots \rho_s$. It is well known (see also Chapter 14, equation (3.17)) that

$$\rho_1\rho_2 \cdots \rho_{s-1} + \rho_1\rho_3 \cdots \rho_s + \dots + \rho_2\rho_3 \cdots \rho_s = \sum_{k=1}^{s} A_{kk}(1). \tag{4.16}$$

Since $\mathbf{A}(1) = (\mathbf{I} - \mathbf{P})$, we can write

$$|\mathbf{A}(1) - \rho\mathbf{I}| = |(1-\rho)\mathbf{I} - \mathbf{P}| = |\lambda\mathbf{I} - \mathbf{P}|, \tag{4.17}$$

where $\rho = 1 - \lambda$, and rewrite equation (4.15) as

$$|\lambda\mathbf{I} - \mathbf{P}| = 0. \tag{4.18}$$

The roots of equations (4.15) and (4.18) have the relationship

$$\rho_l = 1 - \lambda_l, \qquad l = 1, 2, \dots, s. \tag{4.19}$$

Substituting (4.19) in (4.16) and recognizing that $\rho_1 = 1 - \lambda_1 = 0$, we recover the relation

$$(1-\lambda_2)(1-\lambda_3)\dots(1-\lambda_s) = \sum_{k=1}^{s} A_{kk}(1) \tag{4.20}$$

and equation (4.12).

5. EXAMPLES

In this section we use the formulas described in the preceding sections to compute the higher order transition probabilities and limiting probability distributions for Markov chains based on given stochastic matrices. These examples are presented not merely for the review of the algebraic formulas, but also to acquaint the reader with Markov chains through computations of practical examples. In passing, the reader may notice that in each example there is one eigenvalue $\lambda = 1$ and all other eigenvalues are not greater than unity in absolute value. While in some cases the characteristic equation $|\lambda\mathbf{I} - \mathbf{P}| = 0$ admits complex roots, the formulas for the probabilities are real functions nevertheless. The limiting probabilities computed from the matrix $\mathbf{A}(1)$ using formula (4.2) are equal to those obtained by taking the limit of $p_{ij}(n)$ as $n \to \infty$. Some well-known examples are included to show that computations of $p_{ij}(n)$ are simpler and more explicit using formula

(3.2) than using conventional formulas as given, for example, in Chapter XVI in Feller [1968].

Example 1. We use the subsets in the example in Section 6, Chapter 5, to compute the high order transition probabilities. The states in each subset are renumbered from 1 on in this illustration in order to avoid confusion in notation.

(1) Subset C_2: {1,2}

$$\mathbf{P}_2 = \begin{pmatrix} 0 & 1 \\ 1 & 0 \end{pmatrix}.$$

The characteristic matrix is

$$\mathbf{A}(\lambda) = (\lambda \mathbf{I} - \mathbf{P}_2) = \begin{pmatrix} \lambda & -1 \\ -1 & \lambda \end{pmatrix}$$

The characteristic equation $|\mathbf{A}(\lambda)| = 0$ has two roots: $\lambda_1 = 1$ and $\lambda_2 = -1$. Therefore

$$\mathbf{A}(\lambda_1) = \begin{pmatrix} 1 & -1 \\ -1 & 1 \end{pmatrix} \quad \text{and} \quad \mathbf{A}(\lambda_2) = \begin{pmatrix} -1 & -1 \\ -1 & -1 \end{pmatrix}.$$

In this case, the system has $s = 2$ states; formula (3.2) for the transition probabilities becomes

$$p_{ij}(n) = A_{ji}(\lambda_1)\lambda_1^n \frac{1}{\lambda_1 - \lambda_2} + A_{ji}(\lambda_2)\lambda_2^n \frac{1}{\lambda_2 - \lambda_1}$$

and hence the numerical values are

$$p_{11}(n) = 1/2 + 1/2\,(-1)^n \qquad p_{12}(n) = 1/2 - 1/2\,(-1)^n$$
$$p_{21}(n) = 1/2 - 1/2\,(-1)^n \qquad p_{22}(n) = 1/2 + 1/2\,(-1)^n.$$

As n approaches infinity, we find

$$\lim_{n\to\infty} \mathbf{P}_2^{2n} = \begin{pmatrix} 1 & 0 \\ 0 & 1 \end{pmatrix} \quad \text{and} \quad \lim_{n\to\infty} \mathbf{P}_2^{2n+1} = \begin{pmatrix} 0 & 1 \\ 1 & 0 \end{pmatrix}.$$

Consequently, each of the two states in C_2 are periodic with period $t = 2$.

(2) Subset C_3: {1,2,3}

$$\mathbf{P}_3 = \begin{pmatrix} 1 & 0 & 0 \\ 3/8 & 1/6 & 11/24 \\ 3/8 & 1/2 & 1/8 \end{pmatrix}.$$

We find the eigenvalues $\lambda_1 = 1$, $\lambda_2 = 5/8$, and $\lambda_3 = -1/3$. The corresponding characteristic matrices are

$$\mathbf{A}(\lambda_1) = \begin{pmatrix} 0 & 0 & 0 \\ -3/8 & 5/6 & -11/24 \\ -3/8 & -1/2 & 7/8 \end{pmatrix},$$

$$\mathbf{A}(\lambda_2) = \begin{pmatrix} -3/8 & 0 & 0 \\ -3/8 & 11/24 & -11/24 \\ -3/8 & -1/2 & 1/2 \end{pmatrix}$$

and

$$\mathbf{A}(\lambda_3) = \begin{pmatrix} -4/3 & 0 & 0 \\ -3/8 & -1/2 & -11/24 \\ -3/8 & -1/2 & -11/24 \end{pmatrix}.$$

Using the formula

$$p_{ij}(n) = \sum_{l=1}^{3} A_{ji}(\lambda_l)\,\lambda_l^n \frac{1}{\prod\limits_{\substack{m=1\\ m\neq l}}^{3} (\lambda_l - \lambda_m)} \tag{3.2}$$

we find the matrix

$$\mathbf{P}_3^n = \begin{pmatrix} 1 & 0 & 0 \\ 1-\left(\frac{5}{8}\right)^n & \frac{12}{23}\left(\frac{5}{8}\right)^n + \frac{11}{23}\left(\frac{-1}{3}\right)^n & \frac{11}{23}\left(\frac{5}{8}\right)^n - \frac{11}{23}\left(\frac{-1}{3}\right)^n \\ 1-\left(\frac{5}{8}\right)^n & \frac{12}{23}\left(\frac{5}{8}\right)^n - \frac{12}{23}\left(\frac{-1}{3}\right)^n & \frac{11}{23}\left(\frac{5}{8}\right)^n + \frac{12}{23}\left(\frac{-1}{3}\right)^n \end{pmatrix}.$$

The reader may check these values for $n = 1, 2$. As $n \to \infty$,

$$\lim_{n\to\infty} \mathbf{P}_3^n = \begin{pmatrix} 1 & 0 & 0 \\ 1 & 0 & 0 \\ 1 & 0 & 0 \end{pmatrix},$$

which are consistent with the fact that states 2 and 3 are transient states while state 1 is absorbing.

(3) Subset C_4: $\{1,2,3\}$

$$\mathbf{P}_4 = \begin{pmatrix} 0 & 1/3 & 2/3 \\ 1/2 & 1/4 & 1/4 \\ 1/2 & 1/2 & 0 \end{pmatrix}.$$

We solve the characteristic equation

$$|\mathbf{A}(\lambda)| = |\lambda \mathbf{I} - \mathbf{P}_4| = 0$$

to find the eigenvalues $\lambda_1 = 1$, $\lambda_2 = -1/2$ and $\lambda_3 = -1/4$, and the corresponding characteristic matrices:

$$\mathbf{A}(\lambda_1) = \begin{pmatrix} 1 & -1/3 & -2/3 \\ -1/2 & 3/4 & -1/4 \\ -1/2 & -1/2 & 1 \end{pmatrix},$$

$$\mathbf{A}(\lambda_2) = \begin{pmatrix} -1/2 & -1/3 & -2/3 \\ -1/2 & -3/4 & -1/4 \\ -1/2 & -1/2 & -1/2 \end{pmatrix}$$

and

$$\mathbf{A}(\lambda_3) = \begin{pmatrix} -1/4 & -1/3 & -2/3 \\ -1/2 & -1/2 & -1/4 \\ -1/2 & -1/2 & -1/4 \end{pmatrix}.$$

Therefore,

$$
\mathbf{P}_4^n = \begin{pmatrix}
\frac{1}{3}+\frac{2}{3}\left(-\frac{1}{2}\right)^n & \frac{16}{45}+\frac{4}{9}\left(-\frac{1}{2}\right)^n-\frac{4}{5}\left(-\frac{1}{4}\right)^n & \frac{14}{45}-\frac{10}{9}\left(-\frac{1}{2}\right)^n+\frac{4}{5}\left(-\frac{1}{4}\right)^n \\
\frac{1}{3}-\frac{1}{3}\left(-\frac{1}{2}\right)^n & \frac{16}{45}-\frac{2}{9}\left(-\frac{1}{2}\right)^n+\frac{13}{15}\left(-\frac{1}{4}\right)^n & \frac{14}{45}+\frac{5}{9}\left(-\frac{1}{2}\right)^n-\frac{13}{15}\left(-\frac{1}{4}\right)^n \\
\frac{1}{3}-\frac{1}{3}\left(-\frac{1}{2}\right)^n & \frac{16}{45}-\frac{2}{9}\left(-\frac{1}{2}\right)^n-\frac{2}{15}\left(-\frac{1}{4}\right)^n & \frac{14}{45}+\frac{5}{9}\left(-\frac{1}{2}\right)^n+\frac{2}{15}\left(-\frac{1}{4}\right)^n
\end{pmatrix}
$$

It is easy to check that each row sum equals one for every $n = 1, 2, \ldots$. As $n \to \infty$,

$$
\lim_{n\to\infty} \mathbf{P}_4^n = \begin{pmatrix} 15/45 & 16/45 & 14/45 \\ 15/45 & 16/45 & 14/45 \\ 15/45 & 16/45 & 14/45 \end{pmatrix}
$$

with identical rows. Thus all the three states in the set C_4 are ergodic. These limiting probabilities can be computed also from (4.2). Matrix $\mathbf{A}(1)$ is the same as $\mathbf{A}(\lambda_1)$ with the cofactors $A_{11}(1) = 5/8$, $A_{22}(1) = 2/3$, $A_{33}(1) = 7/12$, so that $\Sigma A_{kk}(1) = 45/24$. Therefore the limiting distribution is

$$(\pi_1, \pi_2, \pi_3) = (15/45,\ 16/45,\ 14/45),$$

which is the same as each row in the above matrix. Easy computations show that

$$(\pi_1, \pi_2, \pi_3)\boldsymbol{P}_4 = (\pi_1, \pi_2, \pi_3)$$

and thus the distribution (15/45, 16/45, 14/45) is stationary.

Example 2. A two-state Markov chain with the stochastic matrix:

$$\mathbf{P} = \begin{pmatrix} 1-p_1 & p_1 \\ p_2 & 1-p_2 \end{pmatrix}.$$

where $0 < p_1 < 1$ and $0 < p_2 < 1$. The equation $|\lambda \mathbf{I} - \mathbf{P}| = 0$ admits two roots: $\lambda_1 = 1$ and $\lambda_2 = +(1 - p_1 - p_2)$. We find the differences $(\lambda_1 - \lambda_2) = p_1 + p_2$, and $(\lambda_2 - \lambda_1) = -(p_1 + p_2)$ and the characteristic matrices

$$\mathbf{A}(\lambda_1) = \begin{pmatrix} p_1 & -p_1 \\ -p_2 & p_2 \end{pmatrix}, \qquad \mathbf{A}(\lambda_2) = \begin{pmatrix} -p_2 & -p_1 \\ -p_2 & -p_1 \end{pmatrix}.$$

Substituting these values in formula (3.2) yields

$$\mathbf{P}^n = \frac{1}{p_1 + p_2} \begin{bmatrix} p_2 + p_1(1 - p_1 - p_2)^n & p_1 - p_1(1 - p_1 - p_2)^n \\ p_2 - p_2(1 - p_1 - p_2)^n & p_1 + p_2(1 - p_1 - p_2)^n \end{bmatrix}.$$

Since $\lambda_1 = 1$, we find from $\mathbf{A}(\lambda_1) = \mathbf{A}(1)$ the limiting probabilities

$$\pi_1 = \frac{p_2}{p_1 + p_2}$$

and

$$\pi_2 = \frac{p_1}{p_1 + p_2}$$

which can be obtained also from $\mathbf{P}^n$ by taking the limit as $n \to \infty$. Therefore the mean recurrence times for the two states are

$$\mu_{11} = \frac{p_1 + p_2}{p_2} \quad \text{and} \quad \mu_{22} = \frac{p_1 + p_2}{p_1}$$

Example 3. This example has appeared in Feller [1968] with the stochastic matrix

$$\mathbf{P} = \begin{pmatrix} 0 & 0 & 0 & 1 \\ 0 & 0 & 0 & 1 \\ 1/2 & 1/2 & 0 & 0 \\ 0 & 0 & 1 & 0 \end{pmatrix}.$$

The transitions are $1 \to 4$, $2 \to 4$, $3 \to 1$, $3 \to 2$, and $4 \to 3$. Therefore, all the four states communicate. There are four roots of the equation $|\lambda\mathbf{I} - \mathbf{P}| = 0$; two of the roots are complex conjugates: $\lambda_1 = 0$, $\lambda_2 = 1$, $\lambda_3 = (-1 + i\sqrt{3})/2$, and $\lambda_4 = (-1 - i\sqrt{3})/2$. With these values we find $\lambda_3^2 = \lambda_4$, $\lambda_4^2 = \lambda_3$, $\lambda_3^3 = \lambda_4^3 = 1$,

$$\prod_{m=2}^{4} (\lambda_1 - \lambda_m) = -1, \qquad \prod_{\substack{m=1 \\ m \neq l}}^{4} (\lambda_l - \lambda_m) = 3, \qquad \text{for } l = 2, 3, 4,$$

and

$$\mathbf{A}(\lambda_l) = \begin{pmatrix} \lambda_l & 0 & 0 & -1 \\ 0 & \lambda_l & 0 & -1 \\ -1/2 & -1/2 & \lambda_l & 0 \\ 0 & 0 & -1 & \lambda_l \end{pmatrix}, \qquad l = 1, 2, 3, 4.$$

The Formula for $p_{ij}(n)$ varies with n. For $n = 3k$, $3k + 1$, $3k + 2$ we use (3.2) and compute

$$\mathbf{P}^{3k} = \begin{pmatrix} 1/2 & 1/2 & 0 & 0 \\ 1/2 & 1/2 & 0 & 0 \\ 0 & 0 & 1 & 0 \\ 0 & 0 & 0 & 1 \end{pmatrix},$$

$$\mathbf{P}^{3k+1} = \begin{pmatrix} 0 & 0 & 0 & 1 \\ 0 & 0 & 0 & 1 \\ 1/2 & 1/2 & 0 & 0 \\ 0 & 0 & 1 & 0 \end{pmatrix}.$$

and

$$\mathbf{P}^{3k+2} = \begin{pmatrix} 0 & 0 & 1 & 0 \\ 0 & 0 & 1 & 0 \\ 0 & 0 & 0 & 1 \\ 1/2 & 1/2 & 0 & 0 \end{pmatrix}.$$

Therefore, the corresponding Markov chain is periodic with period $t = 3$; the system starts from scratch after every three steps.

To find the stationary probability distribution, we formulate the matrix

$$\mathbf{A}(1) = \begin{pmatrix} 1 & 0 & 0 & -1 \\ 0 & 1 & 0 & -1 \\ -1/2 & -1/2 & 1 & 0 \\ 0 & 0 & -1 & 1 \end{pmatrix}$$

and compute the cofactors

$$A_{11}(1) = 1/2, \qquad A_{22}(1) = 1/2, \qquad A_{33}(1) = 1, \qquad A_{44}(1) = 1.$$

Therefore, the stationary distribution is

$$(\pi_1, \pi_2, \pi_3, \pi_4) = (1/6, 1/6, 1/3, 1/3).$$

It is easy to check that

$$(1/6, 1/6, 1/3, 1/3) \begin{pmatrix} 0 & 0 & 0 & 1 \\ 0 & 0 & 0 & 1 \\ 1/2 & 1/2 & 0 & 0 \\ 0 & 0 & 1 & 0 \end{pmatrix}$$

$$= (1/6, 1/6, 1/3, 1/3).$$

Example 4. In a 4-state cyclical random walk, the (one step) transition probabilities are $p_{j,j-1} = q$ and $p_{j,j+1} = p$, with $p + q = 1$ for $j = 1,2,3,4$. When $j = 1$, $j - 1 = 4$ and when $j = 4$, $j + 1 = 1$, so that the stochastic matrix assumes the form

$$\mathbf{P} = \begin{pmatrix} 0 & p & 0 & q \\ q & 0 & p & 0 \\ 0 & q & 0 & p \\ p & 0 & q & 0 \end{pmatrix}.$$

The roots of the equation $|\lambda\mathbf{I} - \mathbf{P}| = 0$ are $\lambda_1 = 1$, $\lambda_2 = -1$, $\lambda_3 = \sqrt{-1}\,(q - p)$ and $\lambda_4 = -\sqrt{-1}\,(q - p)$, and hence

$$\prod_{m=2}^{4} (\lambda_1 - \lambda_m) = 4(p^2 + q^2)$$

$$\prod_{\substack{m=1 \\ m\neq 2}}^{4} (\lambda_2 - \lambda_m) = -4(p^2 + q^2)$$

$$\prod_{\substack{m=1 \\ m\neq 3}}^{4} (\lambda_3 - \lambda_m) = 4\sqrt{-1}\,(p^4 - q^4)$$

$$\prod_{m=1}^{3} (\lambda_4 - \lambda_m) = -4\sqrt{-1}\,(p^4 - q^4).$$

From the characteristic matrices

$$\mathbf{A}(\lambda_l) = \begin{pmatrix} \lambda_l & -p & 0 & -q \\ -q & \lambda_l & -p & 0 \\ 0 & -q & \lambda_l & -p \\ -p & 0 & -q & \lambda_l \end{pmatrix}, \qquad l = 1, 2, 3, 4,$$

we compute the cofactors

$$A_{ji}(\lambda_1) = (p^2 + q^2), \qquad i, j = 1, 2, 3, 4,$$
$$A_{ji}(\lambda_2) = (-1)^{i+j+1}(p^2 + q^2), \qquad i, j = 1, 2, 3, 4,$$
$$A_{ji}(\lambda_3) = (\sqrt{-1})^{j-i+1}(p^4 - q^4), \qquad i, j = 1, 2, 3, 4,$$

and

$$A_{ji}(\lambda_4) = (\sqrt{-1})^{i-j-1}(p^4 - q^4), \qquad i, j = 1, 2, 3, 4.$$

Substituting these cofactors in the formula

$$p_{ij}(n) = \sum_{l=1}^{4} \frac{A_{ji}(\lambda_l)}{\prod_{\substack{m=1 \\ m\neq l}}^{4} (\lambda_l - \lambda_m)} \lambda_l^n \qquad (3.2)$$

yields

$$p_{ij}(n) = \tfrac{1}{4}\,[1 + (-1)^{i+j+n} + (\sqrt{-1})^{j-i+n}(q-p)^n + (\sqrt{-1})^{i-j-n}(q-p)^n] \qquad i, j = 1, \dots, 4;\ n = 1, 2, \dots$$

which may be simplified. The final formula of $p_{ij}(n)$ assumes slightly different forms for different values of n. The following are the matrices of $\mathbf{P}^n$ for $n = 4k+1$, $4k+2$, $4k+3$, and $4k+4$, with $\Delta = q - p$:

$$\mathbf{P}^{4k+1} = \tfrac{1}{2}\begin{pmatrix} 0 & 1-\Delta^{4k+1} & 0 & 1+\Delta^{4k+1} \\ 1+\Delta^{4k+1} & 0 & 1-\Delta^{4k+1} & 0 \\ 0 & 1+\Delta^{4k+1} & 0 & 1-\Delta^{4k+1} \\ 1-\Delta^{4k+1} & 0 & 1+\Delta^{4k+1} & 0 \end{pmatrix}$$

$$\mathbf{P}^{4k+2} = \tfrac{1}{2}\begin{pmatrix} 1-\Delta^{4k+2} & 0 & 1+\Delta^{4k+2} & 0 \\ 0 & 1-\Delta^{4k+2} & 0 & 1+\Delta^{4k+2} \\ 1+\Delta^{4k+2} & 0 & 1-\Delta^{4k+2} & 0 \\ 0 & 1+\Delta^{4k+2} & 0 & 1-\Delta^{4k+2} \end{pmatrix}$$

$$\mathbf{P}^{4k+3} = \tfrac{1}{2}\begin{pmatrix} 0 & 1+\Delta^{4k+3} & 0 & 1-\Delta^{4k+3} \\ 1-\Delta^{4k+3} & 0 & 1+\Delta^{4k+3} & 0 \\ 0 & 1-\Delta^{4k+3} & 0 & 1+\Delta^{4k+3} \\ 1+\Delta^{4k+3} & 0 & 1-\Delta^{4k+3} & 0 \end{pmatrix}$$

and

$$\mathbf{P}^{4k+4} = \tfrac{1}{2}\begin{pmatrix} 1+\Delta^{4k+4} & 0 & 1-\Delta^{4k+4} & 0 \\ 0 & 1+\Delta^{4k+4} & 0 & 1-\Delta^{4k+4} \\ 1-\Delta^{4k+4} & 0 & 1+\Delta^{4k+4} & 0 \\ 0 & 1-\Delta^{4k+4} & 0 & 1+\Delta^{4k+4} \end{pmatrix}$$

for $k = 0, 1, \dots$.

Example 5. The Random walk with reflecting barriers discussed in Section 2, Chapter 4, is more interesting than the cyclical random walk in Example 4. We shall consider a 4-state case for illustration. The stochastic matrix is

$$\mathbf{P} = \begin{pmatrix} q & p & 0 & 0 \\ q & 0 & p & 0 \\ 0 & q & 0 & p \\ 0 & 0 & q & p \end{pmatrix}$$

and the eigenvalues are $\lambda_1 = 0, \lambda_2 = 1, \lambda_3 = \sqrt{2pq}, \lambda_4 = -\sqrt{2pq}$. Therefore

$$\prod_{m=2}^{4} (\lambda_1 - \lambda_m) = 2pq; \qquad \prod_{\substack{m=1 \\ m\neq 2}}^{4} (\lambda_2 - \lambda_m) = p^2 + q^2;$$

$$\prod_{\substack{m=1 \\ m\neq 3}}^{4} (\lambda_3 - \lambda_m) = -4pq(1 - \sqrt{2pq});$$

$$\prod_{m=1}^{3} (\lambda_4 - \lambda_m) = -4pq(1 + \sqrt{2pq}).$$

The terms containing $\lambda_1 = 0$ contribute zero to $p_{ij}(n)$. The adjoint matrix of $\mathbf{A}(\lambda_2) = \mathbf{A}(1)$ has the identical row:

$$(q^3, pq^2, p^2, qp^3).$$

This means that

$$(A_{11}(1), A_{22}(1), A_{33}(1), A_{44}(1)) = (q^3, pq^2, p^2, qp^3)$$

and the stationary distribution is

$$(\pi_1, \pi_2, \pi_3, \pi_4) = \left(\frac{q^3}{p^2 + q^2}, \frac{pq^2}{p^2 + q^2}, \frac{p^2 q}{p^2 + q^2}, \frac{p^3}{p^2 + q^2}\right).$$

Therefore the mean recurrence times for the four states are

$$(\mu_{11}, \mu_{22}, \mu_{33}, \mu_{44}) = \left(\frac{p^2+q^2}{q^3}, \frac{p^2+q^2}{pq^2}, \frac{p^2+q^2}{p^2q}, \frac{p^2+q^2}{p^3}\right).$$

When $p = q = 1/2$

$$(\pi_1, \pi_2, \pi_3, \pi_4) = (1/4, 1/4, 1/4, 1/4)$$

and

$$(\mu_{11}, \mu_{22}, \mu_{33}, \mu_{44}) = (4, 4, 4, 4)$$

as expected.

The adjoint matrices of $\mathbf{A}(\lambda_3)$ and $\mathbf{A}(\lambda_4)$ are alike:

$$\begin{pmatrix} -p^2q & -p^2(\lambda-q) & p^2(\lambda-p) & p^3 \\ -pq(\lambda-q) & pq(2\lambda-1-p) & -p(\lambda-3pq) & p^2(\lambda-q) \\ q^2(\lambda-p) & -q(\lambda-3pq) & pq(2\lambda-1-q) & -pq(\lambda-p) \\ q^3 & q^2(\lambda-q) & -q^2(\lambda-p) & -pq^2 \end{pmatrix}$$

where $\lambda = \lambda_3 = \sqrt{2pq}$ or $\lambda = \lambda_4 = -\sqrt{2pq}$. Using the formula

$$p_{ij}(n) = \sum_{l=1}^{4} A_{ji}(\lambda_l)\lambda_l^n \frac{1}{\prod_{m=1}^{4}(\lambda_l - \lambda_m)} \tag{3.2}$$

we obtain the matrices of the transition probabilities $p_{ij}(n)$ for $n = 2k$ and for $n = 2k + 1$:

$$\mathbf{P}^{2k} = \frac{1}{1-2pq}\begin{bmatrix} q^3 + p^2q\theta^{k-1} & pq^2 + p^2q(p-q)\theta^{k-1} & p^2q + p^3(p-q)\theta^{k-1} & p^3(1-\theta^{k-1}) \\ q^3 + pq^2(p-q)\theta^{k-1} & pq^2 + pq[(p-q)^2 + p]\theta^{k-1} & p^2q(1-\theta^{k-1}) & p^3 - p^2q(p-q)\theta^{k-1} \\ q^3 + pq^2(p-q)\theta^{k-1} & pq^2(1-\theta^{k-1}) & p^2q + pq[(p-q)^2 + q]\theta^{k-1} & p^3 - p^2q(p-q)\theta^{k-1} \\ q^3(1-\theta^{k-1}) & pq^2 - q^3(p-q)\theta^{k-1} & p^2q - pq^2(p-q)\theta^{k-1} & p^3 + pq^2\theta^{k-1} \end{bmatrix}$$

for $k = 1, 2, \ldots$, where $\theta = 2pq$, and

$$\mathbf{P}^{2k+1} = \frac{1}{1-2pq}\begin{bmatrix} q^3 + p^2q\theta^k & pq^2 + p^3\theta^k & p^2q(1-\theta^k) & p^3(1-\theta^k) \\ q^3 + p^2q\theta^k & pq^2(1-\theta^k) & p^2q + p(1-3pq)\theta^k & p^3(1-\theta^k) \\ q^3(1-\theta^k) & pq^2 + q(1-3pq)\theta^k & p^2q(1-\theta^k) & p^3 + pq^2\theta^k \\ q^3(1-\theta^k) & pq^2(1-\theta^k) & p^2q + q^3\theta^k & p^3 + pq^2\theta^k \end{bmatrix}$$

for $k = 0, 1 \ldots$.

6. PROBLEMS FOR SOLUTION

1. *Lemma 1 in Section 2*: Let $A_{ij}(1)$ be the (i,j)th cofactor of the matrix $A(1) = (\mathbf{I} - \mathbf{P})$ in (2.3). Show that

$$A_{ij}(1) = A_{ii}(1) \tag{2.12}$$

for a given i, and whatever may be $j = 1, \ldots, s$.

2. Let $|\mathbf{W}|$ be a Vandermonde determinant of order s as given in (2.17). Prove the equality

$$|\mathbf{W}| = \prod_{i=1}^{s-1} \prod_{j=i+1}^{s} (\lambda_j - \lambda_i). \tag{2.18}$$

3. The second equality in (2.19a) is based on the fact that a determinant with two identical rows (or columns) is equal to zero. Prove this assertion.

4. Justify equation (2.21).

5. Verify equation (2.28).

6. *Lemma 2.* For any distinct numbers $\lambda_1, \ldots, \lambda_s$

$$\sum_{i=1}^{s} \frac{\lambda_i^r}{\prod_{\substack{j=1\\ j\neq i}}^{s} (\lambda_i - \lambda_j)} = 0, \qquad r = 0, 1, \ldots, (s-2)$$

$$= 1, \qquad r = s - 1. \tag{2.16}$$

Prove the lemma by using Lagrange's interpolation formula.

7. *Continuation.* Show that if

$$\sum_{i=1}^{s} \frac{\lambda_i^{s-1}}{\prod_{\substack{j=1\\ j\neq i}}^{s} (\lambda_i - \lambda_j)} = 1$$

then

$$\sum_{i=1}^{s} \frac{\lambda_i^r}{\prod_{\substack{j=1\\ j\neq i}}^{s} (\lambda_i - \lambda_j)} = 0, \qquad r = 0, 1, \ldots, s-2.$$

8. *Continuation.* Prove the lemma in problem 7 by the method of partial fraction (M. Hills) with

$$G(\lambda) = \frac{\lambda^r}{(\lambda - \lambda_1) \ldots (\lambda - \lambda_s)}.$$

9. Prove the equality

$$\frac{T_{kl}(k)}{|\mathbf{T}(k)|} = \frac{1}{\prod_{\substack{m=1 \\ m \neq l}}^{s} (\lambda_l - \lambda_m)}, \qquad l = 1, \dots, s \tag{3.14}$$

10. Let $\rho_1, \dots, \rho_s$ be distinct roots of the equation

$$|\mathbf{A}(1) - \rho \mathbf{I}| = 0. \tag{4.15}$$

Show that

$$\rho_1 \rho_2 \dots \rho_{s-1} + \rho_1 \rho_3 \dots \rho_s + \dots + \rho_2 \dots \rho_s = \sum_{k=1}^{s} A_{kk}(1). \tag{4.16}$$

The following problems are for further application of Markov chains to genetics. Reference should be made to Section 8, Chapter 5, for background information.

11. *Application to genetics.* At the equilibrium state, the transition probability matrix is given by

$$\mathbf{P} = \begin{pmatrix} p & q & 0 \\ \frac{1}{2}p & \frac{1}{2} & \frac{1}{2}q \\ 0 & p & q \end{pmatrix}$$

where the gene frequencies $p > 0$, $q > 0$ and $p + q = 1$.

(a) Find the eigenvalues $\lambda_1, \lambda_2, \lambda_3$ of matrix P.

(b) Determine the characteristic matrices $A(\lambda_l)$, $l = 1, 2, 3$.

(c) Show that $A_{ij}(1) = A_{ii}(1)$, for $i, j = 1, 2, 3$.

(d) Show that for a particular k the non-zero vector,

$$\mathbf{T}_l(k) = \begin{pmatrix} A_{k1}(\lambda_l) \\ A_{k2}(\lambda_l) \\ A_{k3}(\lambda_l) \end{pmatrix},$$

satisfies the equation

$$(\lambda_l \mathbf{I} - \mathbf{P}) \begin{pmatrix} A_{k1}(\lambda_l) \\ A_{k2}(\lambda_l) \\ A_{k3}(\lambda_l) \end{pmatrix} = \begin{pmatrix} 0 \\ 0 \\ \vdots \\ 0 \end{pmatrix}, \qquad l = 1, 2, 3. \tag{3.5}$$

(e) For a particular k of your choice, formulate a matrix

$$\mathbf{T}(k) = [\mathbf{T}_1(k), \mathbf{T}_2(k), \mathbf{T}_3(k)].$$

Verify that

$$\mathbf{T}^{-1}(k)\mathbf{P}\mathbf{T}(k) = \begin{pmatrix} \lambda_1 & 0 & 0 \\ 0 & \lambda_2 & 0 \\ 0 & 0 & \lambda_3 \end{pmatrix} \tag{3.8}$$

and

$$\mathbf{T}(k)\begin{pmatrix} \lambda_1 & 0 & 0 \\ 0 & \lambda_2 & 0 \\ 0 & 0 & \lambda_3 \end{pmatrix}\mathbf{T}^{-1}(k) = \mathbf{P}. \tag{3.9}$$

(f) Compute $\mathbf{P}^2$ and

$$\mathbf{T}(k)\begin{pmatrix} \lambda_1^2 & 0 & 0 \\ 0 & \lambda_2^2 & 0 \\ 0 & 0 & \lambda_3^2 \end{pmatrix}\mathbf{T}^{-1}(k)$$

and show that the two matrices are equal.

(g) Show that for a particular k

$$\frac{T_{kl}(k)}{|T(k)|} = \frac{1}{\prod_{\substack{m=1 \\ m \neq i}}^{3} (\lambda_l - \lambda_m)}, \qquad l = 1, 2, 3. \tag{3.14}$$

(h) Derive formulas for the n-step transition probabilities $p_{ij}(n)$.

12. *Continuation.* Work out problem 11 for

$$\mathbf{P} = \begin{pmatrix} .6 & .4 & 0 \\ .3 & .5 & .2 \\ 0 & .6 & .4 \end{pmatrix}.$$

13. In Example 1, Section 5

$$\mathbf{P}_4 = \begin{pmatrix} 0 & 1/3 & 2/3 \\ 1/2 & 1/4 & 1/4 \\ 1/2 & 1/2 & 0 \end{pmatrix},$$

$\lambda_1 = 1$, $\lambda_2 = -1/2$, and $\lambda_3 = -1/4$. Work out parts (d), (e), (f) and (g) in problem 11 for the matrix P_4.

14. Work out parts (d), (e), (f) and (g) in problem 11 for

$$\mathbf{P} = \begin{pmatrix} 1 - p_1 & p_1 \\ p_2 & 1 - p_2 \end{pmatrix}$$

15. Check the computation in Example 4, Section 5 of a four-state cyclical random walk.

CHAPTER 7

Renewal Processes

1. INTRODUCTION

In this chapter we will discuss repetitive occurrences of an event. We will be concerned with both the frequency of occurrence within a given time period and the length of time needed for a given number of occurrences. Time involved may be discrete as in the Markov chain, or continuous as in the stochastic processes described in subsequent chapters. Because of the wide range of applications of the theory, however, the renewal process is presented here as a separate topic.

By way of introduction, let us consider an infinite sequence of trials and an event E which may occur at any trial. Let t_1 be the number of trials up to and including the first occurrence of E; t_2, the number of trials following the first occurrence up to and including the second occurrence of E; etc. Generally, the behavior of an infinite sequence of random variables $\{t_r\}$ depends on the complexity of the underlying probability distribution. However, in many practical problems, processes start anew after an occurrence of an event so that a sequence of trials following an occurrence of E replicates any other sequence. Based on the concept of repetitive patterns, the theory of renewal processes treats renewal times, $t_1, t_2, \ldots$, as independent and identically distributed (i.i.d.) random variables with a common distribution. We shall see that taking this perspective of the problem greatly simplifies analysis of any sequence of random variables $\{t_r\}$. For example, the time required for r occurrences of E is the sum of r i.i.d. random variables, or

$$T_r = t_1 + t_2 + \ldots + t_r. \tag{1.1}$$

These can easily be studied using convolution or the central limit theorem.

Formally, we use the following two conditions to define a renewal process:

(1) The occurrence or nonoccurrence of E in any given sequence of trials is uniquely determined; and

(2) The sequence of trials following an occurrence of E is a complete replica of any other sequence.

It is the second condition which assures that $t_1, t_2, \ldots,$ are i.i.d. random variables. But before discussing theoretical aspects of the problem, let us illustrate the concept of renewal processes with a few examples.

Example 1. *Successes in Bernoulli Trials.* In a sequence of Bernoulli trials with a probability p of success and a probability $q = 1 - p$ of failure in a single trial, let E be a success. The result of a sequence of trials may appear as follows: FFFSFSSFFS..., so that event E occurs at the fourth, sixth, seventh, and tenth trials; or $t_1 = 4$, $t_2 = 2$, $t_3 = 1$, and $t_4 = 3$. Each renewal time t_r has the same geometric distribution:

$$\Pr\{t_r = n\} = q^{n-1}p, \qquad r = 1, 2, \ldots; \; n = 1, 2, \ldots. \tag{1.2}$$

For each r, the distribution of the sum T_r in (1.1) is the r-fold convolution of the distribution in (1.2) with itself. T_r has a negative binomial distribution as described in Section 4.3, Chapter 2. The probability that the r-th occurrence of E will take place at the n-th trial is

$$\Pr\{T_r = n\} = \binom{n-1}{r-1} q^{n-r}p^r, \qquad n = r, r+1, \ldots. \tag{1.3}$$

Example 2. *Return to Origin in a Random Walk.* Consider the (one-dimensional) random walk of a particle from the origin, having a probability p of moving one step to the right and a probability q of moving one step to the left. Let E be the event that the total displacement to the right equals the total displacement to the left so that E occurs when the particle returns to the origin. In the language of gambler's ruin, E occurs when gambler A's net gain is equal to zero. Starting from the origin, E may occur at the second, fourth, ..., moves: RL, LR, RRLL, LLRR, ... Let $p(n)$ be the probability that E occurs at the n-th move; we then have [cf., Chapter 4, equation (2.11)]

$$p(2n) = \binom{2n}{n} p^n q^n \qquad \text{and} \qquad p(2n+1) = 0, \qquad n = 1, 2, \ldots \tag{1.4}$$

Remark. The event "success" in Example 1 is a "single" event; its occurrence at a trial is independent of the preceding trials. In Example 2, RL, LR, RRLL, etc., describe a pattern; the occurrence of E at a particular trial is dependent on the outcomes of the preceding trials. Both problems satisfy the conditions underlying a renewal process nevertheless. Therefore, so far as occurrence of an event is concerned, trials need not be independent. Sequences of trials following occurrences of an event, however, are independent sequences.

Example 3. *Failure and Renewal.* When an electric bulb, an automobile tire, or a mechanical component fails, it is replaced with a new one. The renewal times, $t_1, t_2, \ldots$, of successive components, or their lengths of life, are assumed to have the same density function, $f(\tau)$. The distribution function

$$F(\tau) = \Pr\{t_r \le \tau\}, \qquad \text{for } r = 1, 2, \ldots, \tag{1.5}$$

is the probability that the rth item will fail in the time interval $(0, \tau)$. The complement,

$$\Pr\{t_r > \tau\}, \tag{1.6}$$

is sometimes called the *survival function*.

Example 4. *Pulse Rate.* Blood circulation in the human body is initiated by the pumping of the heart. Each pump sends fresh blood out of the left ventricle of the heart through the aorta to arteries and capillaries in the entire body. Pulse is felt at the radial artery as the blood passes through. As the heart muscle relaxes, old blood in the capillaries returns through veins and vena cava to the right atrium of the heart. The blood in the right atrium then passes through the right ventricle to the lungs for aeration and eventually with new oxygen returns to the left atrium and left ventricle for the next pumping. The process repeats. The interval between successive pulses, or pumpings of the heart, may be treated as a renewal time, and the whole circulatory process, a renewal process.

Example 5. *Rapid Transit.* The San Francisco Bay Area Rapid Transit (BART) system has a rigid schedule. During the period when the system is in service, the interval between the time a train arrives a station and the time the next train arrives is set at 12 minutes. Records show, however, that the actual waiting time deviates considerably from the expected 12 minutes. Once a train arrives at a station, the length of time (service time) required for passengers to get off or to get aboard also varies. The whole process is in effect a renewal process and each arrival of a train is an occurrence of a renewal event. The renewal times between successive arrivals, $t_1, t_2, \ldots,$ are independent and identically distributed random variables.

Example 6. *Nuclear Particle Counting.* A nuclear particle counting instrument is designed to count radioactive emissions by recording impulses. But each recorded impulse inactivates the instrument and creates a dead time during which the instrument is unresponsive to new impulses and subsequent emissions are lost. After a dead time, the instrument becomes free again to record new impulses. A second impulse creates another dead time, which is followed by another free period, and so on. Dead time and free period alternate in a nuclear particle counting process. Depending upon the effect of impulses that arrive unrecorded during a dead time, two types of counters are in use. In a type I counter, impulses arriving during a dead time are lost, but do not affect the instrument; in a type II counter, such impulses prolong dead time. Renewal processes have been used in devising counting instruments to reduce the number of lost emissions.

The theory of renewal processes was developed mainly by Feller in a series of papers ([1941] and [1949]) and in his well known volumes ([1968] and [1966]). Others who have contributed to renewal theory and renewal processes include Blackwell [1948], Cox [1962], Doob [1948], Pyke [1958], Smith [1957], Takács [1956], and others. In this chapter, we shall recount the renewal process for practical applications.

2. DISCRETE TIME RENEWAL PROCESSES

Discrete time renewal processes are analogous to Markov chains with two states, 1 and 0, defined by the occurrence or nonoccurrence of an event E. We shall follow the line of presenting Markov chains to discuss discrete time renewal processes.

2.1. Renewal Probability and Classification of Events.

Consider an infinite sequence of trials, an event E of interest, and the renewal time t as defined in Section 1. Define a sequence of random variables $\{X_n\}$, each corresponding to a particular trial, such that $X_n = 1$ if event E occurs at the n-th trial and $X_n = 0$ if event E does not occur at the n-th trial, for $n = 1, 2, \ldots$.

Let $f(n)$ be the (first) renewal probability:

$$f(n) = \Pr\{X_n = 1 \text{ and } X_m = 0;\ m = 1, \ldots, n-1 \mid X_0 = 1\}, \qquad n = 1, 2, \ldots. \tag{2.1}$$

Clearly $f(n)$ is the probability that the renewal time t assumes the value of n:

$$f(n) = \Pr\{t = n\}. \tag{2.2}$$

For convenience we define

$$f(0) = \Pr\{t = 0\} = 0. \tag{2.3}$$

The sum

$$\sum_{n=1}^{\infty} f(n) = f(\cdot) \tag{2.4}$$

is the probability that event E will eventually occur. An event E may be classified as one of several types depending on $f(\cdot) < 1$ or $f(\cdot) = 1$.

Transient events. A renewal event E is transient if $f(\cdot) < 1$. In this case, the difference

$$1 - f(\cdot) > 0 \tag{2.5}$$

is the probability that event E will not occur in a finite number of trials.

Recurrent events. A renewal event E is recurrent if $f(\cdot) = 1$.

For a recurrent event, the sequence $\{f(n)\}$ forms a proper probability distribution, and the expectation

$$\lambda = E(t) = \sum_{n=1}^{\infty} n f(n) \tag{2.6}$$

is the mean recurrent time.

Recurrent null events. A renewal event E is recurrent null if $f(\cdot) = 1$ and $\lambda = \infty$.

Recurrent non-null events. A renewal event E is recurrent non-null if $f(\cdot) = 1$ and $\lambda < \infty$.

Periodic events and aperiodic events. A renewal event E is periodic if there exists an integer $\alpha > 1$ such that E can occur only at trials $\alpha, 2\alpha, 3\alpha, \ldots$. The largest α with this property is the period of E. A renewal event which is not periodic is an aperiodic event.

Let t_r be the number of trials following the $(r - 1)$th occurrence up to and including the r-th occurrence. Since in a renewal process, each sequence of trials following an occurrence of E is a complete replica of the preceding sequence, the renewal times $t_1, t_2, \ldots$ are independent and identically distributed random variables with the common probability distribution

$$\Pr\{t_r = n\} = f(n), \qquad r, n = 1, 2, \ldots . \tag{2.7}$$

The sum

$$T_r = t_1 + t_2 + \ldots + t_r \tag{2.8}$$

is the number of trials up to and including the r-th occurrence of event E, and

$$\Pr\{T_r = n\} = f_r(n), \qquad n = r, r + 1, \ldots \tag{2.9}$$

is the probability that the r-th occurrence of E takes place at the n-th trial. The probability distribution $\{f_r(n)\}$ of T_r is the r-fold convolution of $\{f(n)\}$ with itself, or, using the notation introduced in Chapter 2,

$$\{f_r(n)\} = \{f(n)\}^{r*} \tag{2.10}$$

For $r = 2$, we have

$$\Pr\{T_2 = n\} = \sum_{l=1}^{n-1} \Pr\{t_1 = l\} \Pr\{t_2 = n - l\}, \qquad n = 2, 3, \ldots$$

or

$$f_2(n) = f(1)f(n - 1) + f(2)f(n - 2) + \ldots + f(n - 1)f(1), \tag{2.11}$$

and

$$\{f_2(n)\} = \{f(n)\} * \{f(n)\}. \tag{2.12}$$

Generally, for $r_1, r_2 \geq 1$ and $r_1 + r_2 = r$,

$$f_r(n) = \sum_{l=r_1}^{n-r_2} f_{r_1}(l) f_{r_2}(n - l) \tag{2.13}$$

and

$$\{f_r(n)\} = \{f_{r_1}(n)\} * \{f_{r_2}(n)\}. \tag{2.14}$$

For a given r, the sum

$$f_r(\cdot) = \sum_{n=1}^{\infty} f_r(n) \tag{2.15}$$

is the probability of at least r occurrences of E in an infinite sequence of trials. For a transient event E where $f(\cdot) < 1$, the probability $f_r(\cdot)$ of at least r occurrences of E tends to zero as r becomes large, whereas for a recurrent event, this probability tends to unity. This means that, in an infinite sequence of trials, a transient event occurs a finite number of times, while a recurrent event occurs infinitely often.

Example 7. The renewal time t has a geometric distribution

$$f(n) = \Pr\{t = n\} = q^{n-1}p. \tag{2.7a}$$

Using (2.10), the sum T_r has a negative binomial distribution,

$$f_r(n) = \Pr\{T_r = n\} = \binom{n-1}{r-1} q^{n-r} p^r. \tag{2.9a}$$

For $r = 2$,

$$\binom{n-1}{2-1} q^{n-2} p^2 = \sum_{l=1}^{n-1} [q^{l-1}p][q^{n-l-1}p], \tag{2.12a}$$

and generally for $r_1, r_2 \geq 1$ and $r_1 + r_2 = r$,

$$\binom{n-1}{r-1} q^{n-r} p^r = \sum_{l=r_1}^{n-r_2} \left[\binom{l-1}{r_1-1} q^{l-r_1} p^{r_1}\right] \times \left[\binom{n-l-1}{r_2-1} q^{n-l-r_2} p^{r_2}\right]. \tag{2.13a}$$

2.2. Probability of Occurrence of E.

There are two types of probabilities associated with occurrence of an event E at a particular trial. In addition to the renewal probability $f(n)$ discussed so far, there is a probability $p(n)$ that event E will occur at the n-th trial regardless of outcomes in the preceding trials. Formally, we define $p(n)$ as follows:

$$p(n) = \Pr\{X_n = 1 \mid X_0 = 1\}, \qquad n = 1, 2, \ldots, \tag{2.16}$$

with $p(0) = 1$. These two types of probabilities have a relationship similar to that between $f_{ii}(n)$ and $p_{ii}(n)$ in a Markov chain. Following the argument set forth in Section 4, Chapter 5, we find that

$$p(n) = \sum_{l=1}^{n} f(l)\, p(n-l). \tag{2.17}$$

Thus, given $f(n)$, we can successively compute the probabilities $p(n)$ from (2.17):

$$\begin{aligned} p(1) &= f(1), \\ p(2) &= f(1)\, p(1) + f(2)\, p(0), \\ P(3) &= f(1)\, p(2) + f(2)\, p(1) + f(3)\, p(0), \end{aligned} \tag{2.17a}$$

and so forth, where $p(0) = 1$. If, on the other hand, we know the values of $p(n)$, we use

$$f(n) = p(n) - \sum_{l=1}^{n-1} f(l)\, p(n-l) \tag{2.18}$$

successively to compute $f(n)$:

$$\begin{aligned} f(1) &= p(1), \\ f(2) &= p(2) - f(1)\, p(1), \\ f(3) &= p(3) - [f(1)\, p(2) + f(2)\, p(1)], \ldots \end{aligned} \tag{2.18a}$$

By repeated substitutions, starting with $n = 1$, we also find that

$$\begin{aligned} f(1) &= p(1), \\ f(2) &= p(2) - p^2(1), \\ f(3) &= p(3) - 2p(2)\, p(1) + p^3(1), \ldots . \end{aligned} \tag{2.18b}$$

From these we can easily derive a general formula expressing $f(n)$ as a function of $p(1)$, $p(2)$, ..., $p(n)$, but the notation is somewhat involved. The sum of $p(n)$ and the sum of $f(n)$, however, have an elegant relationship.

Theorem 1. *The sum of* $p(n)$ *and the sum*

$$\sum_{n=1}^{\infty} f(n) = f(\cdot) \tag{2.19}$$

are related by the formula

$$\sum_{n=0}^{\infty} p(n) = \frac{1}{1 - f(\cdot)}. \tag{2.20}$$

Proof. Summing both sides of (2.17) over n, recognizing that $p(0) = 1$, we find

$$\begin{aligned}\sum_{n=0}^{\infty} p(n) &= 1 + \sum_{n=1}^{\infty} \sum_{l=1}^{n} f(l) p(n-l) \\ &= 1 + \sum_{l=1}^{\infty} \sum_{n=l}^{\infty} f(l)\, p(n-l) \\ &= 1 + \sum_{l=1}^{\infty} f(l) \left[\sum_{n=l}^{\infty} p(n-l)\right] \\ &= 1 + \left[\sum_{l=1}^{\infty} f(l)\right]\left[\sum_{n=0}^{\infty} p(n)\right],\end{aligned} \tag{2.21}$$

from which formula (2.20) follows.

The probability $f(\cdot)$ can be expressed in terms of the sum of $p(n)$:

$$f(\cdot) = 1 - \frac{1}{\sum_{n=0}^{\infty} p(n)}. \tag{2.22}$$

Thus, $f(\cdot) = 1$, if the infinite sum $\sum_{n=0}^{\infty} p(n)$ diverges, and $f(\cdot) < 1$, if the infinite sum converges. Using equation (2.22), we can classify an event according to the convergence or divergence of the infinite sum of $p(n)$.

Corollary. *The event E is recurrent if*

$$\sum_{n=0}^{\infty} p(n) = \infty,$$

and is transient if

$$\sum_{n=0}^{\infty} p(n) < \infty.$$

Theorem 2. *If event E is recurrent non-null with period* α, *then*

$$\lim_{n\to\infty} p(\alpha n) = \frac{\alpha}{\lambda}, \tag{2.23}$$

where λ *is the mean renewal time. If E is recurrent non-null and aperiodic, then*

$$\lim_{n\to\infty} p(n) = \frac{1}{\lambda}. \tag{2.24}$$

If E is recurrent null or transient, then

$$p(n) \to 0$$

as $n\to\infty$.

Proof of Theorem 2 follows exactly the proof of Theorem 6, Chapter 5.

We illustrate the above findings with an example.

Example 8. Let E be success in an infinite sequence of Bernoulli trials, with the probability of success in a single trial being p. Then, as we found previously, $p(0) = 1$, $p(n) = p$, and

$$f(n) = q^{n-1}p. \tag{2.7a}$$

According to equation (2.17)

$$p = \sum_{l=1}^{n-1} [q^{l-1}p]\, p + q^{n-1}p,$$

which is obviously true. Furthermore, the infinite sum

$$\sum_{n=0}^{\infty} p(n) = \infty$$

and

$$f(\cdot) = \sum_{n=1}^{\infty} f(n) = \sum_{n=1}^{\infty} q^{n-1} p = 1$$

also satisfy equation (2.20) in Theorem 1. To verify equation (2.24) in Theorem 2, note that $p(n) = p$ is independent of n, so that

$$\lim_{n\to\infty} p(n) = p,$$

while the mean renewal time is

$$\begin{aligned}\lambda &= \sum_{n=1}^{\infty} n f(n)\\ &= \sum_{n=1}^{\infty} n q^{n-1} p\\ &= p \frac{d}{dq}\left[\sum_{n=1}^{\infty} q^n\right] = \frac{1}{p}.\end{aligned}$$

Thus, λ and p are reciprocal, as required by (2.24).

2.3. Probability Generating Functions of $\{f(n)\}$ and $\{p(n)\}$.

We can compute the probabilities $f(n)$ from $p(n)$ using (2.18) or $p(n)$ from $f(n)$ using (2.17). However, a more expeditious way to compute these probabilities is by means of probability generating functions. For $|s| \le 1$, let

$$P(s) = \sum_{n=0}^{\infty} s^n p(n) \tag{2.25}$$

and

$$F(s) = \sum_{n=1}^{\infty} s^n f(n)$$

be the p.g.f. of $p(n)$ and the p.g.f. of $f(n)$, respectively.

Theorem 3. *The probability generating functions $P(s)$ and $F(s)$ are related by the formula*

$$P(s) = \frac{1}{1 - F(s)} \tag{2.26}$$

or alternatively,

$$F(s) = 1 - \frac{1}{P(s)}. \tag{2.27}$$

Proof. The p.g.f. $P(s)$ may be written in two sums

$$P(s) = s^0 p(0) + \sum_{n=1}^{\infty} s^n p(n). \tag{2.28}$$

Substituting (2.17) in (2.28) gives

$$\begin{aligned} P(s) &= 1 + \sum_{n=1}^{\infty} s^n \sum_{l=1}^{n} f(l)\, p(n-l) \\ &= 1 + \sum_{l=1}^{\infty} \sum_{n=l}^{\infty} s^l f(l)\, s^{n-l} p(n-l) \\ &= 1 + \left[\sum_{l=1}^{\infty} s^l f(l)\right]\left[\sum_{n=0}^{\infty} s^n p(n)\right] \\ &= 1 + F(s)\, P(s), \end{aligned}$$

which, rearranged, yields (2.26) and (2.27).

2.4. An Application to Random Walk.

We have previously shown that in a random walk return to the origin can occur only on even moves, with $p(2n+1) = 0$ and

$$p(2n) = \binom{2n}{n} p^n q^n, \quad n = 1, 2, \ldots,$$

so that

$$p(2) = \binom{2}{1} pq, \quad p(4) = \binom{4}{2} p^2 q^2, \quad p(6) = \binom{6}{3} p^3 q^3, \quad \text{etc.}$$

Using (2.18b), we find the renewal probability $f(n)$,

$$f(2) = \binom{2}{1} pq,$$

$$f(4) = \left[\binom{4}{2} - \binom{2}{1}\binom{2}{1}\right] p^2 q^2,$$

and

$$f(6) = \left[\binom{6}{3} - 2\binom{4}{2}\binom{2}{1} + \binom{2}{1}^3\right] p^3 q^3.$$

The general formula for $f(n)$ is most easily derived using the probability generating functions. But first let us introduce the following lemma.

Lemma 1. *For any positive integer n,*

$$\binom{2n}{n} = (-4)^n \binom{-\frac{1}{2}}{n} \tag{2.29}$$

and

$$\binom{2n}{n} = -(-4)^n (2n-1) \binom{\frac{1}{2}}{n} \tag{2.30}$$

where

$$\binom{-\frac{1}{2}}{n} = \frac{(-\frac{1}{2})(-\frac{1}{2}-1)\dots(-\frac{1}{2}-n+1)}{n!}.$$

Proof. For $n = 1$, both sides of (2.29) are equal to 2. Assuming (2.29) is true for n, we shall prove that

$$\binom{2(n+1)}{n+1} = (-4)^{n+1} \binom{-\frac{1}{2}}{n+1}. \tag{2.31}$$

It is easy to verify that

$$\binom{2(n+1)}{n+1} = \frac{2(2n+1)}{(n+1)} \binom{2n}{n} \tag{2.32}$$

and

$$\binom{-\frac{1}{2}}{n} = (-1)\frac{2(n+1)}{(2n+1)} \binom{-\frac{1}{2}}{n+1}. \tag{2.33}$$

Substituting (2.29) in (2.32) and using (2.33), we recover (2.31). Proof of (2.30) is similar.

We now use (2.28) and (2.29) to write the probability generating function of $\{p(n)\}$:

$$\begin{aligned} P(s) &= \sum_{n=0}^{\infty} s^{2n} \binom{2n}{n} p^n q^n \\ &= \sum_{n=0}^{\infty} \binom{-\frac{1}{2}}{n} [-4pqs^2]^n \\ &= [1-4pqs^2]^{-1/2}. \end{aligned} \tag{2.34}$$

And substituting (2.34) in (2.27) gives us the p.g.f. of $\{f(n)\}$:

$$F(s) = 1 - [1 - 4pqs^2]^{1/2}$$
$$= 1 - \sum_{n=0}^{\infty} \binom{\frac{1}{2}}{n} (-4pqs^2)^n. \tag{2.35}$$

We identify $f(n)$ with the coefficient of s^n in (2.35) to obtain

$$f(0) = 0, \qquad f(2n+1) = 0, \qquad n = 1, \ldots,$$

and

$$f(2n) = -\binom{\frac{1}{2}}{n} (-4)^n p^n q^n, \qquad n = 1, \ldots. \tag{2.36}$$

Using (2.30) in (2.36), we can establish a relationship between $f(2n)$ and $p(2n)$ in this example.

$$f(2n) = \frac{1}{2n-1} \binom{2n}{n} p^n q^n$$
$$= \frac{1}{2n-1} p(2n), \qquad n = 1, 2, \ldots.$$

Thus, $f(2) = p(2)$ and $f(2n) < p(2n)$, for $n > 1$.

Whether return to origin in a random walk is a recurrent or a transient event depends upon the values of p and q. To ascertain this, we evaluate the generating function $F(s)$ at $s = 1$

$$f(\cdot) = 1 - [1 - 4pq]^{1/2}$$
$$= 1 - [(p-q)^2]^{1/2}$$
$$= 1 - |p - q|.$$

Thus $f(\cdot) = 1$ if and only if $p = q = \frac{1}{2}$. In this case, eventual return to the origin is certain, and the event is recurrent. If $p \neq q$, eventual return is not certain and the event is transient.

Where $p = q$, we find the mean renewal time

$$\lambda = \frac{d}{ds} F(s) \bigg|_{s=1} = \infty;$$

therefore, the event is recurrent null. According to Theorem 2, $p(n) \to 0$ as $n \to \infty$.

2.5. Delayed Renewal Processes.

In practical situations, often a first observation is made when a renewal process is already in progress: A particle in a random walk already has made a few moves, a light bulb has been in use for some time, a rapid transit train has left a station. Here the random variable t_1 has a probability distribution different from those of t_2, t_3, ... Let the probability distribution of t_1 be denoted by $k(n)$,

$$k(n) = \Pr\{t_1 = n\}, \qquad n = 1, 2, \ldots \tag{2.37}$$

and the common distribution of $t_2, t_3, \ldots$, by $f(n)$,

$$f(n) = \Pr\{t_r = n\}, \qquad r = 2, 3, \ldots; n = 1, 2, \ldots. \tag{2.7a}$$

Suppose that at the time of the first observation, n_0 trials have taken place since the last occurrence of E. Then $k(n)$ is the conditional probability that E will occur for the first time at the $(n_0 + n)^{\text{th}}$ trial given that E does not take place in the first n_0 trials. This means that $k(n)$ and $f(n)$ satisfy the equation

$$k(n) = \frac{f(n_0 + n)}{1 - \sum_{i=1}^{n_0} f(i)}. \tag{2.38}$$

The main feature of a delayed renewal process is the first occurrence of E. After the first occurrence, an ordinary renewal process returns. Let $q(n)$ be the probability of occurrence of E at the nth trial in a delayed renewal process and $p(n)$ be the corresponding probability in an ordinary renewal process, as defined in Section 2.1. We can establish a relationship among the three types of probabilities $q(n)$, $p(n)$, and $k(n)$ as follows. For an event E to occur at the nth trial, it must occur for the first time at the l-th trial with a probability $k(l)$ and occur again at the nth trial with a probability $p(n - l)$, for $l = 1, 2, \ldots, n$. Summing over all possible values of l yields

$$q(n) = k(n) + k(n-1)\,p(1) + k(n-2)\,p(2) + \ldots + k(1)\,p(n-1). \tag{2.39}$$

Formula (2.39) shows that the sequence $\{q(n)\}$ is a convolution of $\{k(n)\}$ and $\{p(n)\}$ or, in convolution notation,

$$\{q(n)\} = \{k(n)\} * \{p(n)\}. \tag{2.40}$$

When $k(n) = f(n)$, we have an ordinary renewal process and formula (2.39) reduces to formula (2.17) in Section 2.2.

3. CONTINUOUS TIME RENEWAL PROCESSES

The examples of failure and renewal of light bulbs and mechanical components, of pulse rate, and of rapid transit arrivals given in Section 1 are examples of continuous time renewal processes. In the failure and renewal problem, for example, as soon as a component fails, it is replaced by a new one. The lengths of life of the first, second, third, ... components, denoted by $t_1, t_2, t_3, \ldots$, are independent and identically distributed random variables assuming non-negative real numbers. The sequence $\{t_r\}$ forms an ordinary continuous renewal process. The common density function $f(\tau)$ or, more accurately, the product

$$f(\tau)\, d\tau = \Pr\{\tau < t_r \leq \tau + d\tau\}, \qquad r = 1, 2, \ldots, \tag{3.1}$$

is the probability that the r-th component will fail (for the first time) in interval $(\tau, \tau + d\tau)$. This density function $f(\tau)$ has a meaning similar to that of $f(n)$ in the discrete case. The distribution function of t_r, denoted by

$$F(\tau) = \int_0^\tau f(x)\, dx \tag{3.2}$$

is the probability that a component will fail prior to or at time τ.

The sum

$$T_r = t_1 + t_2 + \ldots + t_r \tag{3.3}$$

is the rth renewal time of a system. The density function and the distribution function of T_r denoted by $f_r(\tau)$ and $F_r(\tau)$, respectively, are defined by

$$f_r(\tau)d\tau = \Pr\{\tau < T_r \leq \tau + d\tau\} \tag{3.4}$$

and

$$F_r(\tau) = \int_0^\tau f_r(x)\, dx. \tag{3.5}$$

We can employ the method of convolution discussed in Chapter 3 to find the density function and the distribution function for the r-th renewal time T_r

$$f_r(\tau) = \int_0^\tau f_{r-1}(\tau - x) f(x)\, dx, \qquad r = 2, 3, \ldots, \tag{3.6}$$

$$F_r(\tau) = \int_0^\tau F_{r-1}(\tau - x)\, d F(x), \qquad r = 2, 3, \ldots. \tag{3.7}$$

Using the convolution notation, we write

$$\{f_r(\tau)\} = \{f_{r-1}(\tau)\} * \{f(\tau)\},$$

or

$$\{f_r(\tau)\} = \{f(\tau)\}^{r*}.$$

Delayed renewal process. If, at the initiation of a study, the first component is not new but has been in use for a period τ_0, then t_1 is the residual length of life of a component beyond "age" τ_0. We have a delayed, or a modified, renewal process. Let $k(\tau)$ be the density function of t_1 and $K(\tau)$, the distribution function. The distribution function $K(\tau)$ is the probability that a component will fail in the interval $(\tau_0, \tau_0 + \tau)$ given that it has survived to time τ_0, so that

$$K(\tau) = \frac{F(\tau_0 + \tau) - F(\tau_0)}{1 - F(\tau_0)}. \tag{3.8}$$

From the relation $k(\tau)\, d\tau = dK(\tau)$ we find the density function of t_1

$$k(\tau) = \frac{f(\tau_0 + \tau)}{1 - F(\tau_0)}. \tag{3.9}$$

Using convolutional formulas once again, we obtain the density function and distribution function of the second renewal time T_2

$$f_2(\tau) = \int_0^\tau k(\tau - x) f(x) dx \tag{3.10}$$

and

$$F_2(\tau) = \int_0^\tau K(\tau - x) d F(x), \tag{3.11}$$

and the density function and distribution function for the r-th renewal time T_r:

$$f_r(\tau) = \int_0^\tau f_{r-1}(\tau - x) f(x) dx, \qquad r = 2, 3, \ldots \tag{3.6a}$$

and

$$F_r(\tau) = \int_0^\tau F_{r-1}(\tau - x) dF(x), \qquad r = 2, 3, \ldots, \tag{3.7a}$$

where $f_1(\tau) = k(\tau)$ and $F_1(\tau) = K(\tau)$.

3.1. Some Specific Distributions.

(1) *Exponential Distribution*. Consider again the ordinary renewal process where each t_r has an exponential distribution with the density function

$$f(\tau) = \mu e^{-\mu\tau}, \tag{3.12}$$

the distribution function,

$$F(\tau) = \int_0^\tau \mu e^{-\mu x} dx$$

$$= 1 - e^{-\mu\tau}, \tag{3.13}$$

with the expectation and the variance

$$E(t_r) = \frac{1}{\mu} \quad \text{and} \quad V(t_r) = \frac{1}{\mu^2}, \qquad r = 1, 2, \ldots. \tag{3.14}$$

The parameter

$$\mu = \frac{f(t)}{1 - F(t)} \tag{3.15}$$

is known as the *force of mortality* in life table analysis and as the *failure rate* in reliability theory. The quantity $\mu\, d\tau$ is the probability that a component that works at time τ will fail in the time element $(\tau, \tau + d\tau)$.

The distribution of the second renewal time T_2 may be derived from (3.6) and (3.7) using (3.12):

$$f_2(\tau) = \int_0^\tau \mu e^{-\mu(\tau - x)} \mu e^{-\mu x} dx$$

$$= \mu^2 \tau e^{-\mu\tau}$$

and

$$F_2(\tau) = 1 - (1 + \mu\tau)\, e^{-\mu\tau}.$$

Generally, the rth renewal time has the density function

$$f_r(\tau) = \mu^r \frac{\tau^{r-1}}{\Gamma(r)} e^{-\mu\tau} \tag{3.16}$$

and the distribution function

$$\begin{aligned} F_r(t) &= \int_0^\tau \mu^r \frac{x^{r-1}}{\Gamma(r)} e^{-\mu x}\, dx \\ &= 1 - e^{-\mu\tau} \sum_{i=0}^{r-1} \frac{(\mu\tau)^i}{i!}, \end{aligned} \tag{3.17}$$

which is a gamma distribution with parameters μ and r.

In the delayed renewal process where t_1 is the residual length of life beyond τ_0, the distribution function of t_1, according to (3.8), is

$$\begin{aligned} K(\tau) &= \frac{[1 - e^{-\mu(\tau_0 + \tau)}] - [1 - e^{-\mu\tau_0}]}{1 - (1 - e^{-\mu\tau_0})} \\ &= 1 - e^{-\mu\tau} \\ &= F(\tau)\cdot \end{aligned} \tag{3.18}$$

The fact that the residual length of life t_1 has the same distribution as the total length of life is not entirely unexpected. Since in this case the failure rate μ is independent of the age of a component, the probability that a component will fail in a time element $(\tau, \tau + d\tau)$ remains the same regardless of the length of time it has been in use. Thus, a component that survives to time τ_0 will last as long as a new component. And equations (3.16) and (3.17) for the density function and the distribution function of the r-th renewal time hold for the delayed (modified) renewal process as well.

Suppose the force of mortality is a function of age; then the instantaneous probability of failure in $(\tau, \tau + d\tau)$ is $\mu(\tau)d\tau$. The distribution function of the total length of life takes the form

$$F(\tau) = 1 - e^{-\int_0^\tau \mu(x)dx}.$$

According to equation (3.8) the distribution function of the residual length of life beyond τ_0 is

$$K(\tau) = 1 - \exp\left\{-\int_{\tau_0}^{\tau_0+\tau} \mu(x)\,dx\right\}, \tag{3.19}$$

which differs from the distribution function of $F(\tau)$ given in (3.18).

(2) *Minimum length of life.* An electric circuit with light bulbs connected in a series fails as soon as one bulb burns out. A chain is broken when its weakest link fails. Generally, the failure time of a system, mechanical or otherwise, with k components operating concurrently is the shortest length of life among the k components. Suppose the lengths of life of k components have a common density function $h(\tau)$ and a distribution function $H(\tau)$:

$$H(\tau) = \int_0^{\tau} h(x)dx. \tag{3.20}$$

The joint density function of the lengths of life of k components is

$$h(\tau_1) \dots h(\tau_k). \tag{3.21}$$

Let $t_{(1)}$ be the shortest length of life among the k components. Then $t_{(1)}$ is the renewal time of a system. We shall use methods of order statistics to derive a formula for the density function $f_{(1)}(\tau)$ of $t_{(1)}$.

Let us arrange the observations on the length of life of k components in order of magnitude and use $t_{(1)}, t_{(2)}, \dots, t_{(k)}$ to denote these observations;

$$t_{(1)} \le t_{(2)} \le \dots \le t_{(k)} \tag{3.22}$$

so that the $t_{(1)}$ is the smallest random variable, $t_{(2)}$, the second smallest and $t_{(k)}$, the largest. Since any one of the k components may fail first, $t_{(1)}$ may be any one of the random variables $t_1, t_2, \dots, t_k$. Similarly, $t_{(k)}$ may be one of random variables $t_1, t_2, \dots, t_k$. The order statistics $t_{(1)}, \dots, t_{(k)}$, as a group, correspond to the original random variables $t_1, \dots, t_k$ in $k!$ possible ways. One of these is $t_{(1)} = t_1, \dots, t_{(k)} = t_k$. Therefore the joint density of $t_{(1)}, \dots, t_{(k)}$ is

$$f_{(1),\dots,(k)}(\tau_1, \dots, \tau_k) = k!h(\tau_1) \dots h(\tau_k). \tag{3.23}$$

We obtain the density function of $t_{(1)}$ from (3.23) by integrating over values of $t_{(2)}, \dots, t_{(k)}$:

$$f_{(1)}(\tau_1) = \int_{\tau_2=\tau_1}^{\infty} \cdots \int_{\tau_k=\tau_{k-1}}^{\infty} k!h(\tau_1) \dots h(\tau_k)d\tau_k \dots d\tau_2. \tag{3.24}$$

When the integration is effected, we find the density function of the renewal time of a system to be

$$f_{(1)}(\tau) = k\,[1 - H(\tau)]^{k-1}\,h(\tau), \tag{3.25}$$

where $H(\tau)$ is defined as (3.20). The distribution function of the renewal time of a system is obtained from

$$\begin{aligned} F_{(1)}(\tau) &= \int_0^{\tau} k\,[1 - H(x)]^{k-1}\,h(x)dx \\ &= 1 - [1 - H(\tau)]^{k}. \end{aligned} \tag{3.26}$$

The above results are subject to intuitive interpretation. The quantity

$$[1 - H(\tau)]^{k-1} \tag{3.27}$$

is the probability that $(k-1)$ components will survive to time τ, $h(\tau)d\tau$ is the probability that a component will fail in $(\tau, \tau + d\tau)$, and k is the number of ways of choosing one out of k. Thus the right hand side of (3.25) multiplied by $d\tau$ is the probability that the first failure of a system will occur in $(\tau, \tau + d\tau)$, which is $f(\tau)d\tau$. The last expression of (3.26) is the probability that at least one of the k components will fail, or that a system will fail, prior to or at time τ. This is exactly the definition of the distribution function $F_1(\tau)$.

Suppose the common distribution of k components is exponential, with

$$h(\tau) = \mu e^{-\mu\tau} \tag{3.28}$$

and

$$H(\tau) = 1 - e^{-\mu\tau}. \tag{3.29}$$

The density function of the renewal time of a system, as derived from (3.25) is

$$f_{(1)}(\tau) = k\mu e^{-k\mu\tau}. \tag{3.30}$$

The distribution function derived from (3.26) is

$$F_{(1)}(\tau) = 1 - e^{-k\mu\tau}, \tag{3.31}$$

and the expectation and the variance are

$$E\,[t_{(1)}] = \frac{1}{k\mu} \quad \text{and} \quad V(t_{(1)}) = \frac{1}{(k\mu)^2}. \tag{3.32}$$

Since (3.27) is the density function of an exponential distribution with parameter $k\mu$, we follow equations (3.16) and (3.17) to find the density function of the rth renewal time of the system, T_r

$$f_r(\tau) = (k\mu)^r \frac{\tau^{r-1}}{\Gamma(r)} e^{-k\mu\tau}, \tag{3.33}$$

the distribution function

$$F_r(\tau) = 1 - e^{-k\mu\tau} \sum_{i=0}^{r-1} \frac{(k\mu\tau)^i}{i!}, \tag{3.34}$$

and the expectation and the variance

$$E[T_r] = \frac{r}{k\mu} \quad \text{and} \quad V[T_r] = \frac{r}{(k\mu)^2}, \qquad r = 1, \ldots . \tag{3.35}$$

Note that since the parameter $k\mu$ is independent of the "age" of a component, formulas (3.33) through (3.35) hold also for delayed renewal processes.

(3) *Maximum length of life.* Consider again a system with k identical components operating concurrently as in the preceding case. The system is in operation as long as one or more of the components is working; the system fails when the component with the longest length of life fails. This means that the renewal time of the system is the maximum $t_{(k)}$ in the order statistics in (3.22). Let the common density function of k components be denoted by $h(\tau)$, and the distribution function by $H(\tau)$. We can obtain the distribution function of $t_{(k)}$ directly:

$$\begin{aligned} F_{(k)}(\tau) &= \Pr\{t_{(k)} \le \tau\} \\ &= \Pr\{\max(t_1, \ldots, t_k) \le \tau\} \\ &= \Pr\{t_1 \le \tau, \ldots, t_k \le \tau\} \\ &= \Pr\{t_1 \le \tau\} \ldots \Pr\{t_k \le \tau\} \\ &= [H(\tau)]^k. \end{aligned} \tag{3.36}$$

The density function $f_{(k)}(\tau)$ is the derivative of $F_{(k)}(\tau)$, or

$$f_{(k)}(\tau) = k[H(\tau)]^{k-1} h(\tau). \tag{3.37}$$

For an exponential distribution with

$$h(\tau) = e^{-\mu\tau}$$

and a distribution function

$$H(\tau) = 1 - e^{-\mu\tau},$$

the density and distribution functions of the renewal time of the system derived from (3.36) and (3.37) are

$$f_{(k)}(\tau) = k[1 - e^{-\mu\tau}]^{k-1}\mu e^{-\mu\tau} \tag{3.38}$$

and

$$F_{(k)}(\tau) = [1 - e^{-\mu\tau}]^{k}. \tag{3.39}$$

Simple computations give the expectation of the renewal time of the system:

$$\begin{aligned} E[t_{(k)}] &= \int_0^\infty \tau k[1 - e^{-\mu\tau}]^{k-1}\mu e^{-\mu\tau}\,d\tau \\ &= \left[\sum_{j=1}^{k}(-1)^{j-1}\binom{k}{j}\frac{1}{j}\right]\frac{1}{\mu} \\ &= \frac{1}{\mu}\left[1 + \frac{1}{2} + \ldots + \frac{1}{k}\right], \end{aligned} \tag{3.40}$$

and the variance

$$V[t_{(k)}] = \frac{1}{\mu^2}\left[1 + \frac{1}{2^2} + \ldots + \frac{1}{k^2}\right]. \tag{3.41}$$

We obtain the density function of the second renewal time T_2 from

$$\begin{aligned} f_2(\tau) &= \int_0^\tau f_{(k)}(x) f_{(k)}(\tau - x)\,dx \\ &= \int_0^\tau \{k[1 - e^{-\mu x}]^{k-1}\mu e^{-\mu x}\}\{k[1 - e^{-\mu(\tau-x)}]^{k-1}\mu e^{-\mu(\tau-x)}\}dx \\ &= \sum_{\substack{i=1 \\ i\neq j}}^{k}\sum_{j=1}^{k}(-1)^{i+j}\binom{k}{i}\binom{k}{j}\frac{ij\mu}{(i-j)}[e^{-j\mu\tau} - e^{-i\mu\tau}] \\ &\quad + \sum_{i=1}^{k}\binom{k}{i}^2 i^2\mu^2\tau\, e^{-i\mu\tau} \end{aligned} \tag{3.42}$$

and the distribution function from

$$F_2(\tau) = \int_0^\tau f_2(x)dx$$

$$= 1 + \sum_{i=1}^{k} \sum_{j=1}^{k} (-1)^{i+j} \binom{k}{i}\binom{k}{j} \frac{ij}{i-j} \left(\frac{1}{i} e^{-i\mu\tau} - \frac{1}{j} e^{-j\mu\tau}\right).$$

$$- \sum_{i=1}^{k} \binom{k}{i}^2 (1+i\mu\tau)\, e^{-i\mu\tau}, \qquad i \neq j. \tag{3.43}$$

The distribution of the r-th renewal time of the system T_r is complex for $r > 2$; but the expectation and variance of T_r is easily derived. Since T_r is the sum of r i.i.d. random variables,

$$T_r = t_{(k),1} + \dots + t_{(k),r}, \tag{3.44}$$

with the expectation and variance of $t_{(k)}$ given in (3.40) and (3.41), therefore,

$$E\,[T_r] = \frac{r}{\mu}\left[1 + \frac{1}{2} + \dots + \frac{1}{k}\right], \tag{3.45}$$

and

$$V\,[T_r] = \frac{r}{\mu^2}\left[1 + \frac{1}{2^2} + \dots + \frac{1}{k^2}\right]. \tag{3.46}$$

(4) *Erlang Process.* Imagine a system using k identical components consecutively; as soon as a component fails, it is replaced by a new component. The system fails when all k components have failed successively. Let the length of life of each component have a density function $h(\tau)$ and a distribution function $H(\tau)$. The density function of the renewal time of the system is the k-fold convolution of $h(\tau)$ with itself:

$$\{f(\tau)\} = \{h(\tau)\}^{k*}. \tag{3.47}$$

If the length of life of each component has an exponential distribution,

$$h(\tau) = \mu e^{-\mu\tau},$$

then the renewal time of the system has a gamma distribution with

$$f(\tau) = \mu^k \frac{\tau^{k-1}}{\Gamma(k)} e^{-\mu\tau} \tag{3.48}$$

and

$$F(\tau) = 1 - e^{-\mu\tau} \sum_{i=0}^{k-1} \frac{(\mu\tau)^i}{i!}. \tag{3.49}$$

The gamma distribution in (3.48) had been extensively used by A. K. Erlang in studies of telephone traffic (see Brockmeyer et al [1948]).

We know that the sum of independent gamma random variables with the same μ is a gamma random variable, the density function of the r-th renewal time of the system is

$$f_r(\tau) = \mu^{rk} \frac{\tau^{rk-1}}{\Gamma(rk)} e^{-\mu\tau}, \qquad r = 1, 2, \ldots \tag{3.50}$$

and the distribution function is

$$F_r(\tau) = 1 - e^{-\mu\tau} \sum_{i=0}^{rk-1} \frac{(\mu\tau)^i}{i!}, \qquad r = 1, 2, \ldots. \tag{3.51}$$

(5) *Non-identical components.* Consider again a system using k components consecutively. The system fails when all k components have failed successively, as in the Erlang Process. Suppose components are distinct and the length of life of the i-th component has a density function

$$h_i(\tau) = \lambda_i \mu(\tau) e^{-\lambda_i \int_0^\tau \mu(\xi) d\xi}, \qquad i = 1, \ldots, k, \tag{3.52}$$

where $\lambda_i \neq \lambda_j$, for $i \neq j$. What then are the formulas for the density function $f(x)$ and the distribution function $F(\tau)$ of the renewal time of the system? According to Theorem 4, Chapter 3,

$$f(\tau) = (-1)^{k-1} \lambda_1 \ldots \lambda_k \mu(\tau) \sum_{i=1}^{k} \frac{e^{-\lambda_i \int_0^\tau \mu(\xi) d\xi}}{\prod_{\substack{j=1 \\ j\neq i}}^{k} (\lambda_i - \lambda_j)}, \tag{3.53}$$

$$F(\tau) = (-1)^{k-1} \lambda_1 \ldots \lambda_k \sum_{j=1}^{k} \frac{1}{\prod_{\substack{j=1 \\ j\neq i}}^{k} (\lambda_i - \lambda_j)\lambda_i} [1 - e^{-\lambda_i \int_0^\tau \mu(\xi) d\xi}]. \tag{3.54}$$

If $\mu(\tau) = \mu$ is independent of time, (3.53) and (3.54) reduce to

$$f(\tau) = (-1)^{k-1}\lambda_1 \dots \lambda_k \mu \sum_{i=1}^{k} \frac{e^{-\lambda_i \mu \tau}}{\prod_{\substack{j=1 \\ j\neq i}}^{k} (\lambda_i - \lambda_j)}, \tag{3.55}$$

and

$$F(\tau) = (-1)^{k-1}\lambda_1 \dots \lambda_k \sum_{i=1}^{k} \frac{1}{\prod_{\substack{j=1 \\ j\neq i}}^{k} (\lambda_i - \lambda_j)\lambda_i} [1 - e^{-\lambda_i \mu \tau}]. \tag{3.56}$$

In this case, the expectation and the variance of the renewal time of the system are

$$E[T_1] = \frac{1}{\mu}\left[\frac{1}{\lambda_1} + \dots + \frac{1}{\lambda_k}\right] \tag{3.57}$$

and

$$V[T_1] = \frac{1}{\mu^2}\left[\frac{1}{\lambda_1^2} + \dots + \frac{1}{\lambda_k^2}\right] \tag{3.58}$$

respectively.

3.2. Number of Renewals In a Time Interval $(0,t]$.

Thus far we have dealt with the length of time $\{t_r\}$ or $\{T_r\}$ necessary for renewals to take place. Another aspect of renewal processes which is of considerable importance is the number of renewals $N(t)$ that will occur within a given time interval $(0,t]$. From this perspective of renewal processes, the time interval $(0,t]$ is fixed, while the number of renewals $N(t)$ is a random variable. The purpose of this section and the one that follows is to study various aspects of the distributions of $N(t)$ and their relationships with the distribution of the r-th renewal time T_r.

For a given interval $(0,t]$, let

$$\Pr\{N(t) = r\} = p_r(t), \qquad r = 1, 2, \dots . \tag{3.59}$$

It can be shown that

$$\sum_{r=0}^{\infty} \Pr\{N(t) = r\} = 1 \tag{3.60}$$

and hence $N(t)$ is a proper random variable.

Theorem 4. *The probability distribution and the expectation of $N(t)$ are related to the distribution function $F_r(t)$ of the rth renewal time T_r as follows:*

$$\Pr\{N(t) = 0\} = 1 - F_1(t), \tag{3.61}$$

$$\Pr\{N(t) = r\} = F_r(t) - F_{r+1}(t), \qquad r = 1, 2, \ldots \tag{3.62}$$

and

$$E[N(t)] = \sum_{r=1}^{\infty} F_r(t) \tag{3.63}$$

where $F_r(t)$ is the convolution between $F(t)$ and $F_{r-1}(t)$ and $F_1(t) = K(t)$ for delayed renewal processes.

Proof. If the number of renewals occurring within a time interval $(0,t]$ is greater than or equal to r, then the length of time required for r renewals must be less than or equal to t, and vice versa. In other words, the two events

$$N(t) \geq r \qquad \text{and} \qquad T_r \leq t$$

are equivalent, and the corresponding probabilities must be equal:

$$\begin{aligned} \Pr\{N(t) \geq r\} &= \Pr\{T_r \leq t\} \\ &= F_r(t). \end{aligned} \tag{3.64}$$

Therefore

$$\begin{aligned} \Pr\{N(t) = r\} &= \Pr\{N(t) \geq r\} - \Pr\{N(t) \geq r + 1\} \\ &= F_r(t) - F_{r+1}(t), \end{aligned}$$

proving (3.62). When $r = 0$, (3.62) implies (3.61). To find the expectation, we write

$$\begin{aligned} E[N(t)] &= \sum_{r=1}^{\infty} r \Pr\{N(t) = r\} \\ &= \sum_{r=1}^{\infty} r\,[F_r(t) - F_{r+1}(t)] \\ &= \sum_{r=1}^{\infty} F_r(t), \end{aligned}$$

thus completing the proof.

Theorem 5. *If in an ordinary renewal process the renewal time t_r has a finite expectation $E(t_r) = \lambda$ and a finite variance $\sigma_{t_r}^2 = \sigma^2$, then, as $t \to \infty$, the number of renewals $N(t)$ has an asymptotic normal distribution which has mean t/λ and variance $t\sigma^2/\lambda^3$. In other words,*

$$\lim_{t\to\infty} \Pr\left\{\frac{N(t) - t/\lambda}{\sqrt{t\sigma^2/\lambda^3}} < z\right\} = \frac{1}{\sqrt{2\pi}} \int_{-\infty}^{z} e^{-x^2/2}\, dx. \qquad (3.65)$$

Feller [1949] originally established the theorem for the discrete case where t is the number of trials. Takács [1956] proved the theorem for time continuous processes.

Proof. Since $E(t_r) = \lambda$ and $\sigma_{t_r}^2 = \sigma^2$, the sum $T_r = t_1 + \dots + t_r$ has an expectation

$$E(T_r) = r\lambda \qquad (3.66)$$

and a variance

$$\sigma_{T_r}^2 = r\sigma^2. \qquad (3.67)$$

According to the central limit theorem, for large r the random variable T_r has a normal distribution, with

$$\Pr\{T_r \le t\} = \Pr\left\{\frac{T_r - r\lambda}{\sigma\sqrt{r}} \le \frac{t - r\lambda}{\sigma\sqrt{r}}\right\}$$

$$\simeq \int_{-\infty}^{z} \frac{1}{\sqrt{2\pi}} e^{-x^2/2}\, dx, \qquad (3.68)$$

where

$$z = \frac{t - r\lambda}{\sigma\sqrt{r}}. \qquad (3.69)$$

Now let $r \to \infty$ and $t \to \infty$ in such a way that (3.69) holds for a fixed z, and recall the equality

$$\Pr\{N(t) \ge r\} = \Pr\{T_r \le t\}. \qquad (3.64)$$

The probability on the left may be rewritten as

$$\begin{aligned}\Pr\{N(t) \geq r\} &= \Pr\left\{\frac{\lambda N(t) - t}{\sigma\sqrt{r}} \geq \frac{\lambda r - t}{\sigma\sqrt{r}}\right\} \\ &= \Pr\left\{\frac{N(t) - t/\lambda}{\sigma\sqrt{r/\lambda}} \geq -z\right\} \\ &= \Pr\left\{\frac{N(t) - t/\lambda}{\sigma\sqrt{r/\lambda}}\sqrt{\frac{r\lambda}{t}} \geq -z\sqrt{\frac{r\lambda}{t}}\right\} \\ &= \Pr\left\{\frac{N(t) - t/\lambda}{\sqrt{t\sigma^2/\lambda^3}} \geq -z\sqrt{\frac{r\lambda}{t}}\right\}, \end{aligned} \tag{3.70}$$

which, due to (3.64) and (3.68), is also a normal probability. To evaluate the quantity on the right hand side of the last inequality sign, we rewrite equation (3.69) as

$$r\lambda + z\sigma\sqrt{r} - t = 0,$$

or as

$$\frac{r\lambda}{t} + \frac{z\sigma}{\sqrt{\lambda t}}\sqrt{\frac{r\lambda}{t}} - 1 = 0$$

to obtain

$$\sqrt{\frac{r\lambda}{t}} = \tfrac{1}{2}\left[-z\sigma/\sqrt{\lambda t} + \sqrt{z^2\sigma^2/\lambda t + 4}\right]. \tag{3.71}$$

Taking the limit of both sides of (3.71), we find that

$$\lim_{\substack{r\to\infty \\ t\to\infty}} \sqrt{\frac{r\lambda}{t}} = \frac{\sqrt{4}}{2} = 1. \tag{3.72}$$

Thus, as $r \to \infty$ and $t \to \infty$.

$$\begin{aligned}\Pr\{N(t) \geq r\} \to \Pr&\left\{\frac{N(t) - t/\lambda}{\sqrt{t\sigma^2/\lambda^3}} \geq -z\right\} \\ &= \int_{-z}^{\infty} \frac{1}{\sqrt{2\pi}} e^{-x^2/2} dx \\ &= \int_{-\infty}^{z} \frac{1}{\sqrt{2\pi}} e^{-x^2/2} dx. \end{aligned} \tag{3.73}$$

What we have found above is that the limiting distribution of $N(t)$ is normal and has an expectation t/λ and a variance $t\sigma^2/\lambda^3$. But since convergence of a distribution does not imply convergence of moments, we have not proven yet that

$$E[N(t)] \to \frac{t}{\lambda} \tag{3.74}$$

nor that

$$\text{Var}[N(t)] \to t\sigma^2/\lambda^3. \tag{3.75}$$

The convergence of the moments in (3.74) and (3.75) is nevertheless true, as stated in the following theorem.

Theorem 6. *If $E(t_r) = \lambda$ and $\sigma_{t_r}^2 = \sigma^2$ are finite, then we have*

$$\lim_{t\to\infty} \frac{E[N(t)]}{t} = \frac{1}{\lambda} \tag{3.76}$$

and

$$\lim_{t\to\infty} \frac{\text{Var}[N(t)]}{t} = \frac{\sigma^2}{\lambda^3}. \tag{3.77}$$

For proof of Theorem 6, the reader is referred to an excellent paper by Smith [1958].

3.3. Renewal Function and Renewal Density.

We have developed in (3.6a) and (3.7a) integral equations for $f_r(t)$ and $F_r(t)$ for a delayed renewal process. Similar equations exist for the expectation $U(t) = E[N(t)]$ and its derivative. The expectation $U(t)$ is known as the *renewal function*; its derivative $U'(t) = u(t)$ as the *renewal density*. According to Theorem 4,

$$U(t) = \sum_{r=1}^{\infty} F_r(t) \tag{3.63}$$

where $F_1(t) = K(t)$ and $F_r(t)$ is the convolution between $F(t)$ and $F_{r-1}(t)$. Taking the derivatives of both sides of (3.63) gives

$$u(t) = \sum_{r=1}^{\infty} f_r(t). \tag{3.78}$$

Since

$$f_r(t)\,dt = \Pr\{\text{the } r^{\text{th}} \text{ renewal will take place in } (t, t + dt)\};$$

therefore

$$u(t)\,dt = \Pr\{\text{a renewal will take place in } (t, t + dt)\} \tag{3.79}$$

and the term *renewal density* is appropriate for $u(t)$.

Theorem 7. *The renewal function $U(t)$ and the renewal density $u(t)$, respectively, satisfy the following integral equations*

$$U(t) = K(t) + \int_0^t U(t - \tau)\,dF(\tau) \tag{3.80}$$

and

$$u(t) = k(t) + \int_0^t u(t - \tau) f(\tau)\,d\tau. \tag{3.81}$$

Proof: We have from (3.63)

$$U(t) = K(t) + \sum_{r=1}^{\infty} F_{r+1}(t). \tag{3.82}$$

Introducing integral equation

$$F_{r+1}(t) = \int_0^t F_r(t - \tau)\,dF(\tau) \tag{3.7a}$$

in (3.82) yields

$$\begin{aligned} U(t) &= K(t) + \sum_{r=1}^{\infty} \int_0^t F_r(t - \tau)\,dF(\tau) \\ &= K(t) + \int_0^t \sum_{r=1}^{\infty} F_r(t - \tau)\,dF(\tau) \\ &= K(t) + \int_0^t U(t - \tau)\,dF(\tau) \end{aligned}$$

and equation (3.80). Formula (3.81) follows from (3.80) by taking the derivatives.

3.4. Illustrative Examples.

To appreciate the theorems in the preceding sections, we use the specific distributions in Section 3.1 as illustrative examples.

(1) *Exponential distribution.* For the exponential function in (3.12), we found the distribution function of the r-th renewal time T_r:

$$F_r(t) = 1 - e^{-\mu t} \sum_{i=0}^{r-1} \frac{(\mu t)^i}{i!}. \tag{3.17}$$

According to Theorem 4,

$$\Pr\{N(t) = r\} = F_r(t) - F_{r+1}(t). \tag{3.62}$$

Substituting (3.17) in (3.62) gives

$$\Pr\{N(t) = r\} = \frac{(\mu t)^r}{r!} e^{-\mu t}. \tag{3.83}$$

Therefore $N(t)$ has a Poisson distribution with parameter μt with

$$E[N(t)] = \mu t \qquad \text{and} \qquad \sigma^2_{N(t)} = \mu t. \tag{3.84}$$

In the exponential distribution in (3.12), the length of life of a component has an expectation

$$\lambda = E[t_r] = \int_0^\infty t\mu e^{-\mu t}\, dt = \frac{1}{\mu} \tag{3.85}$$

and a variance

$$\sigma^2_{t_r} = \sigma^2 = \int_0^\infty \left(t - \frac{1}{\mu}\right)^2 \mu e^{-\mu t}\, dt$$

$$= \frac{1}{\mu^2}. \tag{3.86}$$

According to Theorem 6,

$$E[N(t)] \to \frac{t}{\lambda} \tag{3.74}$$

and

$$\operatorname{Var}[N(t)] \to \frac{t\sigma^2}{\lambda^3}. \tag{3.75}$$

Substituting (3.85) and (3.86) in (3.74) and (3.75), we recover (3.84).

For the integral equation in Theorem 7,

$$U(t) = K(t) + \int_0^t U(t-\tau)\, dF(\tau), \tag{3.80}$$

we have

$$U(t) = \mu t, \tag{3.87}$$

$$K(t) = 1 - e^{-\mu t} \tag{3.13}$$

and

$$dF(\tau) = \mu e^{-\mu\tau}\, d\tau. \tag{3.12}$$

It is easy to show that (3.87), (3.13) and (3.12) satisfy the integral equation (3.80).

(2) *Minimum length of life.* When the initial distribution of each component is exponential with a constant force of mortality μ, the renewal time t_r also has an exponential distribution with a parameter $k\mu$, as shown in Section 3.1. Therefore, the number of renewals $N(t)$ also will have a Poisson distribution with

$$\Pr\{N(t) = r\} = \frac{(k\mu t)^r}{r!} e^{-k\mu t}, \qquad r = 0, 1, \ldots,$$

$$E\,[N(t)] = k\mu t, \qquad \text{and} \qquad \sigma^2_{N(t)} = k\mu t.$$

The validity of the theorems in the preceding sections for this case can be demonstrated in exactly the same way as for the exponential distribution.

(3) *Maximum length of life.* For the distribution of the order statistic $t_{(k)}$ where

$$f(\tau) = k\mu\,[1 - e^{-\mu\tau}]^{k-1} e^{-\mu\tau}, \tag{3.38}$$

the expectation of the renewal time is

$$\lambda = \frac{1}{\mu}\left[1 + \frac{1}{2} + \ldots + \frac{1}{k}\right] \tag{3.40}$$

and the variance is

$$\sigma^2 = \frac{1}{\mu^2}\left[1 + \frac{1}{2^2} + \ldots + \frac{1}{k^2}\right]. \tag{3.41}$$

Applying Theorem 6, we find the limiting values

$$\lim_{t\to\infty} \frac{E[N(t)]}{t} = \mu \left[1 + \frac{1}{2} + \dots + \frac{1}{k} \right]^{-1}$$

and

$$\lim_{t\to\infty} \frac{\operatorname{Var}[N(t)]}{t} = \mu \left[1 + \frac{1}{2} + \dots + \frac{1}{k} \right]^{-3} \left[1 + \frac{1}{2^2} + \dots + \frac{1}{k^2} \right].$$

(4) *The gamma distribution.* The gamma distribution,

$$f(\tau) = \mu^k \frac{\tau^{k-1}}{\Gamma(k)} e^{-\mu\tau}, \tag{3.48}$$

in Section 3.1, has an expectation

$$\lambda = \frac{k}{\mu}$$

and a variance

$$\sigma^2 = \frac{k}{\mu^2}.$$

The distribution function of the r-th renewal time T_r is

$$F_r(t) = 1 - e^{-\mu t} \sum_{i=0}^{rk-1} \frac{(\mu t)^i}{i!}, \qquad r = 0, 1, \dots . \tag{3.51}$$

Applying equation (3.62), we find

$$\Pr\{N(t) = r\} = e^{-\mu t} \sum_{i=rk}^{(r+1)k-1} \frac{(\mu t)^i}{i!}, \qquad r = 0, 1, \dots; \tag{3.88}$$

For $N(t) = 0$, for example,

$$\Pr\{N(t) = 0\} = e^{-\mu t} \left[1 + \frac{\mu t}{1!} + \frac{(\mu t)^2}{2!} + \dots + \frac{(\mu t)^{k-1}}{(k-1)!} \right].$$

Applying formulas (3.76) and (3.77), we find that, as $t \to \infty$,

$$\frac{E[N(t)]}{t} \to \frac{\mu}{k} \tag{3.89}$$

and

$$\frac{\operatorname{Var}[N(t)]}{t} \to \frac{\mu}{k^2}. \tag{3.90}$$

4. PROBLEMS FOR SOLUTION

1. Verify equation (2.13a)

$$\binom{n-1}{r-1} q^{n-r} p^r = \sum_{l=r_1}^{n-r_2} \left[\binom{l-1}{r_1-1} q^{l-r_1} p^{r_1} \right] \left[\binom{n-l-1}{r_2-1} q^{n-l-r_2} p^{r_2} \right], \tag{2.13a}$$

where $r = r_1 + r_2$.

2. Prove the following equality directly:

$$\sum_{n=1}^{\infty} n q^{n-1} p = \frac{1}{p}.$$

3. Prove the equality:

$$\binom{2n}{n} = -(-4)^n (2n-1) \binom{1/2}{n} \tag{2.30}$$

4. Let $F(x)$ be the distribution function of a continuous random variable X. Derive the distribution of $F(x)$.

5. Verify the following equality for the distribution function $F_r(\tau)$:

$$\int_0^\tau \mu^r \frac{x^{r-1}}{\Gamma(r)} e^{-\mu x} dx = 1 - e^{-\mu\tau} \sum_{i=0}^{r-1} \frac{(\mu\tau)^i}{i!}. \tag{3.17}$$

6. Derive the density function for the minimum length of life

$$f_{(1)}(\tau) = k\,[1 - H(\tau)]^{k-1} h(\tau) \tag{3.25}$$

by carrying out the integration in (3.24).

7. Show that

$$\int_0^\tau k\,[1 - H(x)]^{k-1} h(x)\,dx = 1 - [1 - H(\tau)]^k \tag{3.26}$$

8. Show that the expectation and the variance of the maximum life time $t_{(k)}$ are given respectively by

$$E\,[t_{(k)}] = \frac{1}{\mu}\left[1 + \frac{1}{2} + \dots + \frac{1}{k}\right] \tag{3.40}$$

and

$$V[t_{(k)}] = \frac{1}{\mu^2}\left[1 + \frac{1}{2^2} + \ldots + \frac{1}{k^2}\right]. \tag{3.41}$$

9. Verify the density function of the second renewal time of a system T_2 in (3.42).

10. Let $F_{(k)}(t)$ and $F_{(1)}(t)$ be the distribution function of the maximum and the minimum order statistics in a sample of k, and let $Y = F_{(k)}(t) - F_{(1)}(t)$. Find the density function of Y.

11. Derive the formulas for the expectation $E[T_1]$ and the variance $V[T_1]$ from the density function

$$f(\tau) = (-1)^{k-1}\lambda_1 \ldots \lambda_k \mu \sum_{i=1}^{k} \frac{e^{-\lambda_i \mu \tau}}{\prod_{\substack{j=1\\ j\neq i}}^{k} (\lambda_i - \lambda_j)} \tag{3.55}$$

12. Let $N(t)$ be the number of renewals in a time interval $(0, t]$. Show that

$$\sum_{r=0}^{\infty} Pr\{N(t) = r\} = 1. \tag{3.60}$$

13. Show that $U(t) = \mu t$, $K(t) = 1 - e^{-\mu t}$, and $dF(\tau) = \mu e^{-\mu\tau} d\tau$ satisfy the integral equation

$$U(t) = K(t) + \int_0^t U(t-\tau)\, dF(\tau). \tag{3.80}$$

14. Let the number of renewals in interval $(0, t]$ have a Poisson distribution with

$$\Pr\{N(t) = r\} = \frac{(k\mu t)^r}{r!} e^{-k\mu t}, \qquad r = 0, 1, \ldots$$

Verify Theorems 6 and 7 with this example.

15. Let the renewal time have a distribution function

$$F(\tau) = [1 - e^{-\mu\tau}]^k. \tag{3.39}$$

Use Theorem 6 to find $\lim_{t\to\infty} \frac{\mathrm{E}[\mathrm{N}(t)]}{t}$ and $\lim_{t\to\infty} \frac{\mathrm{Var}\,[\mathrm{N}(t)]}{t}$.

CHAPTER 8

Some Stochastic Models of Population Growth

1. INTRODUCTION

Since the early work of Kolmogorov [1931] and Feller [1936], the theory of stochastic processes has developed rapidly. It has been used to describe empirical phenomena and to solve many practical problems. Systematic treatments of the subject are given by Chung [1960], Doob [1953], Feller [1968], [1966], Harris [1963]; reference should also be made to Bartlett [1956], Bharucha-Reid [1960], Bailey [1964], Cox and Miller [1965], Karlin [1966], Kendall [1948], Parzen [1968], Prabhu [1965], and Takács [1960].

A stochastic process $\{X(t); t \varepsilon [0,\infty)\}$ is a family of random variables describing an empirical process whose development is governed by probabilistic laws. The parameter t, which is often interpreted as time, is real, but may be either discrete or continuous. The random variable $X(t)$ may be real-valued or complex-valued, or it may take the form of a vector. In diffusion processes, for example, both $X(t)$ and t are continuous variables, whereas in Markov chains $X(t)$ and t take on discrete values. In processes of population growth, time is a continuous parameter, but the random variable $X(t)$ has a discrete set of possible values, namely, the non-negative integers. Our main interest is the probability distribution

$$p_k(t) = \Pr\{X(t) = k\}, \qquad k = 0, 1, \ldots. \tag{1.1}$$

As with any attempt to describe empirical phenomena mathematically, the formulation of a practical problem in terms of stochastic processes necessarily involves some simplifying assumptions. On the other hand, such formulations often produce enlightening and useful solutions to problems. In this chapter we introduce a few simple, basic, but widely applicable stochastic processes that are commonly used as models of population growth.

2. THE POISSON PROCESS

In many practical problems the occurrence of a random event at a particular moment is independent of time and of the number of events that have already taken place. Examples of this kind are telephone calls coming into a switchboard, radioactive disintegrations, and accidents. Basic assumptions underlying the Poisson process are these: (1) For any $t \leq 0$, the probability that an event will occur during the time interval $(t, t + \Delta)$ is $\lambda\Delta + o(\Delta)$,[1] where the constant λ does not depend on t or on the number of events occurring in $(0, t)$; (2) the probability that more than one event will occur in $(t, t + \Delta)$ is $o(\Delta)$. Therefore, the probability of no change in $(t, t + \Delta)$ is $1 - \lambda\Delta - o(\Delta)$.

Let $X(t)$ be the total number of events that occur within the time interval $(0, t)$. In order to derive differential equations for the probabilities (1.1), we extend the interval $(0, t)$ to a point $t + \Delta$ to analyze the probability $p_k(t + \Delta)$ by enumerating all possibilities leading to the occurrence of k events during the interval $(0, t + \Delta)$. Consider then the two adjacent intervals $(0, t)$ and $(t, t + \Delta)$. The occurrence of exactly k events during the interval $(0, t + \Delta)$ can be realized in three mutually exclusive ways: (i) all k events will occur in $(0, t)$ and none in $(t, t + \Delta)$ with probability $p_k(t)\ [1 - \lambda\Delta - o(\Delta)]$; (ii) exactly $k - 1$ events will occur in $(0, t)$ and one event in $(t, t + \Delta)$ with probability $p_{k-1}(t)\ [\lambda\Delta + o(\Delta)]$; and (iii) exactly $k - j$ events will occur in $(0, t)$ and j events in $(t, t + \Delta)$, where $2 \leq j \leq k$, with probability $o(\Delta)$. Taking all these possibilities together and combining all quantities of order $o(\Delta)$, we have for $k \geq 1$

$$p_k(t + \Delta) = p_k(t)[1 - \lambda\Delta] + p_{k-1}(t)\lambda\Delta + o(\Delta) \tag{2.1}$$

and for $k = 0$

$$p_0(t + \Delta) = p_0(t)[1 - \lambda\Delta] + o(\Delta). \tag{2.2}$$

Transposing $p_k(t)$ to the left hand side of (2.1), dividing the resulting

---

[1]The standard notation $o(\Delta)$ represents any function of Δ which tends to 0 faster than Δ, i.e., any function such that $[o(\Delta)/\Delta] \to 0$ as $\Delta \to 0$.

equation through by Δ, and passing to the limit as $\Delta \to 0$, we find that the probabilities satisfy the system of differential equations[2]

$$\frac{d}{dt} p_k(t) = -\lambda p_k(t) + \lambda p_{k-1}(t), \qquad k \geq 1, \tag{2.3a}$$

and similarly that

$$\frac{d}{dt} p_0(t) = -\lambda p_0(t). \tag{2.3b}$$

We shall solve the differential equations in (2.3a) and (2.3b) by the method discussed in Section 7 of this chapter. Clearly the initial conditions are

$$p_0(0) = 1, \quad p_k(0) = 0, \qquad k \geq 1. \tag{2.4}$$

Integrating (2.3b) and using the condition $p_0(0) = 1$, we get

$$p_0(t) = e^{-\lambda t}. \tag{2.5}$$

Setting $k = 1$ in (2.3a) and multiplying through by $e^{\lambda t}$, we find

$$e^{\lambda t} \frac{d}{dt} p_1(t) + \lambda e^{\lambda t} p_1(t) = \frac{d}{dt} [e^{\lambda t} p_1(t)] = \lambda; \tag{2.6}$$

and the solution

$$p_1(t) = \lambda t e^{-\lambda t}. \tag{2.7}$$

Repeated applications of the same procedure for $k = 2, 3, \ldots$ yield the general formula

$$p_k(t) = \frac{e^{-\lambda t} (\lambda t)^k}{k!}, \qquad k = 0, 1, \ldots. \tag{2.8}$$

Equation (2.8) is, of course, a Poisson distribution with the parameter λt. Thus we see that the Poisson distribution, which is often derived as a limiting case of the binomial distribution, also arises as a consequence of reasonable assumptions about a simple stochastic process.

---

[2]This is a standard approach used in deriving differential equations in stochastic processes; it will be used repeatedly, but not necessarily explicitly, throughout this book.

2.1 The Method of Probability Generating Functions.

The recursive system of differential equations (2.3) was solved successively without difficulty. However, in many stochastic processes where the differential equations are quite complicated, such a direct approach is fruitless. In such cases, we resort to the method of p.g.f.'s: We first derive a differential equation for the p.g.f. of $X(t)$ and then solve it to obtain the p.g.f. Finally, the probability distribution is derived from the p.g.f. To illustrate the technique, let us reconsider the Poisson process.

Let the p.g.f. of the probability distribution $\{p_k(t)\}$ be defined, as in Chapter 2, by

$$G_X(s;t) = \sum_{k=0}^{\infty} p_k(t)s^k \qquad \begin{matrix} |s| \le 1 \\ 0 \le t < \infty. \end{matrix} \tag{2.9}$$

Differentiating (2.9) under the summation sign[3] and using (2.3) we obtain

$$\frac{\partial}{\partial t} G_X(s;t) = \sum_{k=0}^{\infty} \left[\frac{d}{dt} p_k(t) \right] s^k \tag{2.10}$$

$$= -\lambda \sum_{k=0}^{\infty} p_k(t)s^k + \lambda s \sum_{k=1}^{\infty} p_{k-1}(t)s^{k-1}. \tag{2.11}$$

The lower limit of the last summation is unity because of (2.3b). Since both of the last two summations are equal to the p.g.f. (2.9), we have the differential equation for the p.g.f.:

$$\frac{\partial}{\partial t} G_X(s;t) = -\lambda(1-s)\,G_X(s;t), \tag{2.12}$$

with the initial condition that, at $t = 0$,

$$G_X(s;0) = s^0 = 1. \tag{2.13}$$

If we rewrite (2.12) as

[3]Since $|p_k(t)s^k| < |s|^k$, each of the infinite series in (2.11) converges uniformly in t for $|s| < 1$; hence $\Sigma \frac{d}{dt} p_k(t)s^k$ converges uniformly in t and the term-by-term differentiation is justified for $|s| < 1$. Letting $s \to 1$, we have $\lim_{s\to 1} G_X(s;t) = G_X(1;t)$. Thus our argument applies also for $s = 1$. Justification for term-by-term differentiation in the remainder of this book is similar and will not be given explicitly.

$$\partial \log G_X(s;t) = -\lambda(1-s)\,\partial t, \tag{2.14}$$

direct integration gives

$$G_X(s;t) = c(s)e^{-\lambda t(1-s)}. \tag{2.15}$$

Setting $t = 0$ in (2.15) and using the initial condition (2.13), we determine that the constant of integration is $c(s) = 1$. Therefore

$$G_X(s;t) = e^{-\lambda t(1-s)} \tag{2.16}$$

which is the p.g.f. of the Poisson distribution given in (2.8).

2.2. Some Generalizations of the Poisson Process.

Generalizations of the Poisson process can be made in many ways; we shall consider two here.

(i) *Time dependent Poisson process.* We may replace the constant λ by a function of time $\lambda(t)$ in (2.1) and (2.2). Then (2.14) becomes

$$\partial \log G_X(s;t) = -\lambda(t)(1-s)\partial t$$

from which we derive the p.g.f.

$$G_X(s;t) = \exp\{-(1-s)\int_0^t \lambda(\tau)\,d\tau\}, \tag{2.17}$$

the probabilities

$$p_k(t) = \frac{\exp\left\{-\int_0^t \lambda(\tau)\,d\tau\right\}\left[\int_0^t \lambda(\tau)\,d\tau\right]^k}{k!}, \tag{2.18}$$

and the expectation

$$E[X(t)] = \int_0^t \lambda(\tau)\,d\tau. \tag{2.19}$$

We see that the generalization does not affect the form of the distribution, but allows variation to occur as determined by the function $\lambda(\tau)$.

(ii) *Weighted Poisson process.* The Poisson process describes the frequency of occurrence of an event to an individual with "risk" parameter λ. If we are sampling from a population of individuals, the variability of individuals with respect to this risk should be taken into account. Proneness to accidents, for example, varies throughout the population according to a density function $f(\lambda)$. Thus we interpret the probability distribution (2.8) as the conditional distribution $p_{k|\lambda}(t)$ of $X(t)$ given λ. The probability that an individual chosen at random from the population will experience k events in a time interval of length t is

$$p_k(t) = \int_0^\infty p_{k|\lambda}(t) f(\lambda)\, d\lambda = \int_0^\infty \frac{e^{-\lambda t}(\lambda t)^k}{k!} f(\lambda)\, d\lambda. \qquad (2.20)$$

Suppose, for example, that λ has a *gamma distribution*

$$\begin{aligned} f(\lambda) &= \frac{\beta^\alpha}{\Gamma(\alpha)} \lambda^{\alpha-1} e^{-\beta\lambda} \qquad && \lambda > 0, \alpha > 0, \beta > 0 \\ &= 0 && \lambda \leq 0 \end{aligned} \qquad (2.21)$$

where the gamma function $\Gamma(\alpha)$ is defined by

$$\Gamma(\alpha) = \int_0^\infty y^{\alpha-1} e^{-y}\, dy. \qquad (2.22)$$

Substituting (2.21) in (2.20), we get

$$\begin{aligned} p_k(t) &= \frac{\beta^\alpha t^k}{\Gamma(\alpha) k!} \int_0^\infty \lambda^{k+\alpha-1} e^{-\lambda(\beta+t)}\, d\lambda \\ &= \frac{\Gamma(k+\alpha)}{k!\Gamma(\alpha)} \beta^\alpha t^k (\beta+t)^{-(k+\alpha)}, \qquad k = 0, 1, \ldots. \end{aligned} \qquad (2.23)$$

Since the gamma function satisfies the recursion equation

$$\Gamma(\alpha+1) = \alpha\Gamma(\alpha), \qquad (2.24)$$

we may rewrite equation (2.23) as

$$p_k(t) = \binom{k+\alpha-1}{k} \left(\frac{t}{\beta+t}\right)^k \left(\frac{\beta}{\beta+t}\right)^\alpha, \qquad (2.25)$$

which is for each t a negative binomial distribution with parameters

$$r = \alpha, \qquad p = \frac{\beta}{\beta+t} \qquad (2.26)$$

(cf. Eq. (4.20) in Chapter 2). Thus we have the expected number of events occurring to a randomly chosen individual during the interval $(0, t)$:

$$E[X(t)] = \alpha \frac{t}{\beta}, \tag{2.27}$$

and the variance

$$\sigma^2_{X(t)} = \alpha \frac{t}{\beta}\left(1 + \frac{t}{\beta}\right). \tag{2.28}$$

In the original Poisson model with λ constant, the expectation and variance of $X(t)$ were both equal to λt. In the present generalization the expectation is still a linear function of t/β, but the variance is now a quadratic function of t/β. The present model which incorporates variability of risk has been found useful in studies of accident proneness (Bates and Neyman [1952]) and incidence of illness (Lundberg [1940], Chiang [1965]).

3. PURE BIRTH PROCESS

In the study of growth in a broad sense, "birth" may be liberally interpreted as an event whose probability is dependent upon the number of "parent" events already in existence. It may refer to a literal birth, to a new case in an epidemic, to the appearance of a new tumor cell in a tissue, etc. More precisely, we assume that, given $X(t) = k$, (i) the conditional probability that a new event will occur during $(t, t + \Delta)$ is $\lambda_k \Delta + o(\Delta)$, where λ_k is some function of k; and (ii) the conditional probability that more than one event will occur is $o(\Delta)$. Following the procedure used in the preceding section, we find that the probabilities $p_k(t)$ satisfy the system of differential equations

$$\frac{d}{dt} p_i(t) = -\lambda_i p_i(t) \tag{3.1a}$$

and

$$\frac{d}{dt} p_k(t) = -\lambda_k p_k(t) + \lambda_{k-1} p_{k-1}(t), \qquad k > i. \tag{3.1b}$$

Here $X(0) = i$, the number of events existing at $t = 0$, so that the initial conditions are

$$p_i(0) = 1 \qquad \text{and} \qquad p_k(0) = 0, \qquad \text{for } k \neq i. \tag{3.2}$$

The differential equations (3.1) have a recursive relation and can be solved successively. If the values of λ_i are all different, the solution is

$$p_k(t) = (-1)^{k-i}\lambda_i \dots \lambda_{k-1}\left[\sum_{j=i}^{k} \frac{e^{-\lambda_j t}}{\prod_{\substack{l=i\\ l\neq j}}^{k}(\lambda_j - \lambda_l)}\right]. \tag{3.3}$$

Inductive proof of (3.3) requires the following identity. For any distinct $\lambda_i, \dots, \lambda_k$,

$$\sum_{j=i}^{k} \frac{1}{\prod_{\substack{l=i\\ l\neq j}}^{k}(\lambda_j - \lambda_l)} = 0. \tag{3.4}$$

This identity is a special case of Lemma 2 in Section 2.1 of Chapter 6; the reader may refer to equation (2.16) in that chapter for verification.

We now prove (3.3) by induction. Equation (3.1a) has the solution

$$p_i(t) = e^{-\lambda_i t},$$

hence (3.3) is true for $k = i$. Suppose (3.3) is true for $k - 1$, i.e.,

$$p_{k-1}(t) = (-1)^{k-1-i}\lambda_i \dots \lambda_{k-2}\left[\sum_{j=i}^{k-1} \frac{e^{-\lambda_j t}}{\prod_{\substack{l=i\\ l\neq j}}^{k-1}(\lambda_j - \lambda_l)}\right]. \tag{3.5}$$

We shall derive (3.3) from (3.1b). Following the usual procedure for linear first-order differential equations, we multiply (3.1b) by $e^{\lambda_k t}$,

$$e^{\lambda_k t}\frac{d}{dt}p_k(t) + e^{\lambda_k t}\lambda_k p_k(t) = e^{\lambda_k t}\lambda_{k-1}p_{k-1}(t),$$

to obtain the exact equation

$$\frac{d}{dt}[e^{\lambda_k t}p_k(t)] = \lambda_{k-1}e^{\lambda_k t}p_{k-1}(t), \tag{3.6}$$

which upon substitution of (3.5) becomes

$$\frac{d}{dt}[e^{\lambda_k t}p_k(t)] = (-1)^{k-1-i}\lambda_i \ldots \lambda_{k-1}\left[\sum_{j=i}^{k-1} \frac{1}{\prod_{\substack{l=i \\ l\neq j}}^{k-1}(\lambda_i - \lambda_l)} e^{(\lambda_k - \lambda_j)t}\right]$$

$$= (-1)^{k-1-i}\lambda_i \ldots \lambda_{k-1}\left[\sum_{j=i}^{k-1} \frac{1}{\prod_{\substack{l=i \\ l\neq j}}^{k-1}(\lambda_j - \lambda_l)} \frac{\frac{d}{dt}e^{(\lambda_k - \lambda_j)t}}{(\lambda_k - \lambda_j)}\right].$$

Integrating both sides yields the general solution

$$e^{\lambda_k t}p_k(t) = (-1)^{k-i}\lambda_i \ldots \lambda_{k-1}\left[\sum_{j=i}^{k-1} \frac{1}{\prod_{\substack{l=i \\ l\neq j}}^{k}(\lambda_j - \lambda_l)} e^{(\lambda_k - \lambda_j)t} + c\right]. \tag{3.7}$$

At $t = 0$, $p_k(0) = 0$ for $k > i$. Using identity (3.4) we see that the constant c is given by

$$c = \frac{1}{\prod_{l=i}^{k-1}(\lambda_k - \lambda_l)}. \tag{3.8}$$

Substituting (3.8) in (3.7) and dividing the resulting equation through by $e^{\lambda_k t}$ yields (3.3), completing the inductive proof.

3.1. The Yule Process.

Suppose that all k individuals alive at time t have the same probability $\lambda\Delta + o(\Delta)$ of giving birth to another individual in the interval $(t, t + \Delta)$ and that individuals give birth independently of each other. Then the total number of births during $(t, t + \Delta)$ will have a binomial distribution:

$$\Pr\{j \text{ births during } (t, t+\Delta)\}$$

$$= \binom{k}{j}[\lambda\Delta + o(\Delta)]^j\,[1 - \lambda\Delta - o(\Delta)]^{k-j}.$$

It follows that the probability of exactly one birth among the k individuals in $(t, t+\Delta)$ is $k\lambda\Delta + o(\Delta)$ and the probability of more than one birth is $o(\Delta)$. Thus we have a simple birth process with $\lambda_k = k\lambda$. System (3.1) becomes

$$\frac{d}{dt} p_i(t) = -i\lambda p_i(t) \tag{3.9a}$$

and

$$\frac{d}{dt} p_k(t) = -k\lambda p_k(t) + (k-1)\lambda p_{k-1}(t), \qquad k > i \tag{3.9b}$$

with the initial conditions (3.2). Equations (3.9) are easily solved. For $k \geq i$

$$p_k(t) = \binom{k-1}{k-i} e^{-i\lambda t}(1 - e^{-\lambda t})^{k-i}. \tag{3.10}$$

We could use induction to prove equation (3.10), but we shall derive it from equation (3.3) instead.

The system of differential equations (3.9) is a special case of (3.1) where $\lambda_k = k\lambda$. Therefore (3.10) can be obtained from (3.3) by making the same substitution of $k\lambda$ for λ_k. This is demonstrated as follows. When $\lambda_k = k\lambda$, (3.3) becomes

$$p_k(t) = (-1)^{k-i}[i\lambda] \dots [(k-1)\lambda] \left[\sum_{j=i}^{k} \frac{e^{-j\lambda t}}{\prod_{\substack{l=i \\ l \neq j}}^{k} (j\lambda - l\lambda)} \right], \tag{3.11}$$

where

$$[i\lambda] \dots [(k-1)\lambda] = \lambda^{k-i} \binom{k-1}{k-i} (k-i)! \tag{3.12}$$

and

$$\prod_{\substack{l=i \\ l \neq j}}^{k} (j\lambda - l\lambda) = \lambda^{k-i}(-1)^{k-j} \binom{k-i}{j-i}^{-1} (k-i)!. \tag{3.13}$$

Therefore (3.11) can be rewritten as

$$p_k(t) = \binom{k-1}{k-i} e^{-i\lambda t}\left[\sum_{j=i}^{k}\binom{k-i}{j-i}(-e^{-\lambda t})^{j-i}\right]$$

$$= \binom{k-1}{k-i} e^{-i\lambda t}[1-e^{-\lambda t}]^{k-i}, \tag{3.14}$$

since

$$\sum_{j=i}^{k}\binom{k-i}{j-i}(-e^{-\lambda t})^{j-i} = [1-e^{-\lambda t}]^{k-i},$$

we recover (3.10).

This process was first considered by Yule in a mathematical study of evolution, with $X(t)$ representing the total number of species in some genus at time t. It is instructive to consider the number $Y(t)$ of new species generated in the interval $(0, t)$; that is, $Y(t) = X(t) - i$. From (3.10) we get the distribution of $Y(t)$,

$$\Pr\{Y(t) = k\} = p_{k+i}(t) = \binom{k+i-1}{k} e^{-\lambda ti}(1-e^{-\lambda t})^k, \tag{3.15}$$

which we easily recognize as a negative binomial distribution. Hence

$$E[X(t)] = i + E[Y(t)] = ie^{\lambda t}$$

and

$$\sigma^2_{X(t)} = \sigma^2_{Y(t)} = ie^{\lambda t}[e^{\lambda t} - 1].$$

From the form of the negative binomial p.g.f. (see equation (4.22) in Chapter 2), we see that $Y(t)$ is the sum of i independent and identically distributed random variables, which are the species generated by the i initial species.

3.2. Time Dependent Yule Process.

As with the Poisson process, we may generalize the Yule process by allowing λ to be a function of time, $\lambda(t)$. Then system (3.9) is replaced by

$$\frac{d}{dt}p_i(t) = -i\lambda(t)p_i(t) \tag{3.16a}$$

and

$$\frac{d}{dt}p_k(t) = -k\lambda(t)p_k(t) + (k-1)\lambda(t)p_{k-1}(t), \qquad k > i. \tag{3.16b}$$

Equations (3.16) could be solved successively. However we shall again use the method of the p.g.f. Let

$$G_X(s;t) = \sum_{k=i}^{\infty} p_k(t)\, s^k \tag{3.17}$$

with

$$G_X(s;0) = s^i. \tag{3.18}$$

Differentiating (3.17) term by term with respect to t and using (3.16b), we get

$$\frac{\partial}{\partial t} G_X(s;t) = \sum_{k=i}^{\infty} \frac{d}{dt} p_k(t)s^k$$

$$= -\lambda(t)s \sum_{k=i}^{\infty} kp_k(t)s^{k-1} + \lambda(t)s^2 \sum_{k=i+1}^{\infty} (k-1)p_{k-1}(t)s^{k-2}. \tag{3.19}$$

Each of the summations on the right is equal to the derivative of $G_X(s;t)$ with respect to s; hence

$$\frac{\partial}{\partial t} G_X(s;t) + \lambda(t)s(1-s)\frac{\partial}{\partial s} G_X(s;t) = 0. \tag{3.20}$$

To solve the partial differential equation (3.20), we use the standard approach as given in Section 7 of this chapter to write the auxiliary equations

$$\frac{dt}{1} = \frac{ds}{\lambda(t)s(1-s)} \quad \text{and} \quad dG_X(s;t) = 0. \tag{3.21}$$

From the first auxiliary equation we get

$$\frac{s}{1-s} \exp\left\{-\int_0^t \lambda(\tau)\, d\tau\right\} = \text{const.}, \tag{3.22}$$

and from the second

$$G_X(s;t) = \text{const.} \tag{3.23}$$

Therefore the general solution of (3.20) is

$$G_X(s;t) = \Phi\left\{\frac{s}{1-s} e^{-\int_0^t \lambda(\tau)d\tau}\right\}, \tag{3.24}$$

where Φ is an arbitrary differentiable function. To obtain the particular solution corresponding to the initial condition (3.18), we set $t = 0$ in (3.24) with the result

$$\Phi\left\{\frac{s}{1-s}\right\} = G_X(s;0) = s^i. \tag{3.25}$$

Equation (3.25) holds at least for all s with $|s| < 1$; hence for any θ such that $|\theta/(1+\theta)| < 1$,

$$\Phi\{\theta\} = \left\{\frac{\theta}{1+\theta}\right\}^i. \tag{3.26}$$

Letting

$$\theta = \frac{s}{1-s} e^{-\int_0^t \lambda(\tau)d\tau}$$

we obtain from (3.24) and (3.26) the solution to (3.20):

$$G_X(s;t) = s^i \left\{\frac{e^{-\int_0^t \lambda(\tau)d\tau}}{1 - s\left[1 - e^{-\int_0^t \lambda(\tau)d\tau}\right]}\right\}^i. \tag{3.27}$$

The second factor on the right-hand side is recognized as the p.g.f. of a negative binomial distribution with parameters i and $\exp\left\{-\int_0^t \lambda(\tau)d\tau\right\}$. The two factors inform us that $X(t)$ is the sum of a negative binomial random variable and the constant i. Hence the distribution and moments of $X(t)$ are exactly the same as for the simple Yule process, except that λt is replaced by $\int_0^t \lambda(\tau)d\tau$.

3.3. Joint Distribution in the Time Dependent Yule Process.

Consider two points t_1 and t_2 on the time axis, with $t_1 < t_2$. We wish to investigate the joint probability distribution of the corresponding random variables $X(t_1)$ and $X(t_2)$ in the case of the time-dependent simple birth process described in Section 3.2.

In deriving the equations for the birth process, we have treated $i = X(0)$ as a constant; however, we may regard the probabilities and p.g.f.'s as conditional on $X(0)$. Taking this approach, we define the bivariate p.g.f. as conditional expectation

$$G(s_1, s_2; t_1, t_2) = E\,[s_1^{X(t_1)} s_2^{X(t_2)} \mid X(0)]\,, \tag{3.28}$$

where

$$E\,[s_1^{X(t_1)} s_2^{X(t_2)} \mid X(0)] = E\,[s_1^{X(t_1)} E\,\{s_2^{X(t_2)} \mid X(t_1)\} \mid X(0)]\,. \tag{3.29}$$

The inner conditional expectation in the last expression is the p.g.f. of $X(t_2)$ given $X(t_1)$, which, in view of (3.27), is given by

$$E\{s_2^{X(t_2)} \mid X(t_1)\} = \left\{\frac{s_2 \exp\{-\int_{t_1}^{t_2} \lambda(\tau)\,d\tau\}}{1 - s_2(1 - \exp\{-\int_{t_1}^{t_2} \lambda(\tau)\,d\tau\})}\right\}^{X(t_1)}. \tag{3.30}$$

If we substitute (3.30) in (3.29) and introduce

$$z_1 = \frac{s_1 s_2 \exp\{-\int_{t_1}^{t_2} \lambda(\tau)\,d\tau\}}{1 - s_2(1 - \exp\{-\int_{t_1}^{t_2} \lambda(\tau)\,d\tau\})}, \tag{3.31}$$

(3.28) then becomes

$$G(s_2, s_2; t_1, t_2) = E\,[z_1^{X(t_1)} \mid X(0)]\,. \tag{3.32}$$

Since clearly $|z_1| < 1$, we can use (3.27) once again to obtain

$$G(s_1, s_2; t_1, t_2) = \left\{\frac{z_1 \exp\{-\int_0^{t_1} \lambda(\tau)\,d\tau\}}{1 - z_1(1 - \exp\{-\int_0^{t_1} \lambda(\tau)\,d\tau\})}\right\}^{X(0)}. \tag{3.33}$$

Substituting (3.31) in (3.33) and letting

$$\Pi_1 = \exp\{-\int_0^{t_1} \lambda(\tau)\,d\tau\} \quad \text{and} \quad \Pi_2 = \exp\{-\int_{t_1}^{t_2} \lambda(\tau)\,d\tau\}, \tag{3.34}$$

we have the desired form for the generating function

$$G(s_1 s_2; t_1, t_2) = \left\{\frac{s_1 \Pi_1 s_2 \Pi_2}{1 - s_1(1 - \Pi_1) s_2 \Pi_2 - s_2(1 - \Pi_2)}\right\}^{X(0)}. \tag{3.35}$$

Direct computations from (3.35) yield the covariance:

$$\operatorname{Cov}[X(t_1), X(t_2) \mid X(0)] = X(0) \exp\{\int_0^{t_2} \lambda(\tau)\,d\tau\}\,[\exp\{\int_0^{t_1} \lambda(\tau)\,d\tau\} - 1]\,. \tag{3.36}$$

The joint probability distribution of $X(t_1)$ and $X(t_2)$ may be obtained either from (3.35) or from the equation

$$\Pr\{X(t_1) = k_1, X(t_2) = k_2 | X(0) = k_0\}$$
$$= \Pr\{X(t_1) = k_1 | X(0) = k_0\} \Pr\{X(t_2) = k_2 | X(t_1) = k_1\}. \tag{3.37}$$

Using either approach, we find the probability

$$\Pr\{X(t_1) = k_1, X(t_2) = k_2 | X(0) = k_0\}$$
$$= \prod_{i=0}^{1} \binom{k_{i+1} - 1}{k_{i+1} - k_i} \exp\left\{-k_i \int_{t_i}^{t_{i+1}} \lambda(\tau)d\tau\right\}\left\{1 - \exp\left\{-\int_{t_i}^{t_{i+1}} \lambda(\tau)d\tau\right\}\right\}^{k_{i+1}-k_i}. \tag{3.38}$$

If we are concerned with a sequence of random variables $\{X(t_i)\}$ for which $0 < t_1 < t_2 < \ldots$, we will generate a chain of probability distributions which have the same form as (3.38), except that the upper limit of $(i + 1)$ will correspond to the last random variable of the sequence.

4. THE POLYA PROCESS

In our original formulation of the pure birth process, we assume the probability that a birth will occur in the time interval $(t, t + \Delta)$ to be $\lambda_k\Delta + o(\Delta)$. Suppose now that λ_k is a function of both k and t such that

$$\lambda_k(t) = \frac{\lambda + \lambda ak}{1 + \lambda at}, \tag{4.1}$$

where λ and a are non-negative constants. This assumption defines the Polya process. With $X(0) = i$, the differential equations for the probability distribution are

$$\frac{d}{dt} p_i(t) = -\frac{\lambda + \lambda ai}{1 + \lambda at} p_i(t) \tag{4.2a}$$

and

$$\frac{d}{dt} p_k(t) = -\frac{\lambda + \lambda ak}{1 + \lambda at} p_k(t) + \frac{\lambda + \lambda a(k-1)}{1 + \lambda at} p_{k-1}(t), \qquad k > i. \tag{4.2b}$$

We shall once again demonstrate the use of the p.g.f., although it is possible to solve equations (4.2a) and (4.2b) recursively. Let

$$G_X(s;t) = \sum_{k=i}^{\infty} p_k(t)s^k \tag{4.3}$$

with

$$G_X(s;0) = s^i, \tag{4.4}$$

and take the derivative of $G_X(s;t)$ with respect to t to obtain the partial differential equation

$$(1 + \lambda at)\frac{\partial}{\partial t} G_X(s;t) + \lambda as(1 - s)\frac{\partial}{\partial s} G_X(s;t) = -\lambda(1 - s)\, G_X(s;t). \tag{4.5}$$

The auxiliary equations are

$$\frac{dt}{1 + \lambda at} = \frac{ds}{\lambda as(1 - s)} = \frac{dG_X(s;t)}{-\lambda(1 - s)G_X(s;t)}. \tag{4.6}$$

We may write the first equation as

$$d \log (1 + \lambda at) = d \log \frac{s}{1 - s} \tag{4.7}$$

with the solution

$$\frac{1 - s}{s}(1 + \lambda at) = \text{const.} \tag{4.8}$$

From the second auxiliary equation we compute

$$\frac{1}{a} d \log s = -d \log G_X(s;t) \tag{4.9}$$

so that

$$G_X(s;t)s^{1/a} = \text{const.} \tag{4.10}$$

Hence the general solution of (4.5) is

$$G_X(s;t) = s^{-1/a}\Phi\left\{\left(\frac{1 - s}{s}\right)(1 + \lambda at)\right\} \tag{4.11}$$

where Φ is an arbitrary differentiable function.

For the particular solution corresponding to the initial condition (4.4), we set $t = 0$ in (4.11) and use (4.4) to write

$$s^{-1/a}\Phi\left\{\frac{1-s}{s}\right\} = s^i. \tag{4.12}$$

Equation (4.12) holds for all s such that $|s| < 1$; hence for any θ such that $|1/(1+\theta)| < 1$,

$$\Phi(\theta) = (1+\theta)^{-(i+1/a)}. \tag{4.13}$$

Now letting

$$\theta = \frac{1-s}{s}(1+\lambda at),$$

we have from (4.12) the required solution for the p.g.f.

$$G_X(s;t) = s^{-1/a}\left[1 + \frac{1-s}{s}(1+\lambda at)\right]^{-(i+1/a)}$$

$$= s^i\left\{\frac{\dfrac{1}{1+\lambda at}}{1 - s\dfrac{\lambda at}{1+\lambda at}}\right\}^{i+1/a}. \tag{4.14}$$

Except for the additive constant i, $X(t)$ is a negative binomial random variable (see equation (4.22), Chapter 2) with parameters

$$r = i + \frac{1}{a} \quad \text{and} \quad p = \frac{1}{1+\lambda at}.$$

If we rewrite (4.14) as

$$G_X(s;t) = \left\{\frac{s}{1+\lambda at - \lambda ats}\right\}^i [1 + \lambda at - \lambda ats]^{-1/a}, \tag{4.15}$$

t becomes clear that

$$\lim_{a\to 0} G_X(s;t) = s^i e^{-(1-s)\lambda t}. \tag{4.16}$$

Thus we see that as $a \to 0$ the Polya process (except for the additive constant i) approaches the Poisson process. This is natural in view of (4.1).

The situation is more surprising if we compare the Polya process with the weighted Poisson process in Section 2.2. In fact, the two processes are identical in the sense that, except for the additive constant

i, they are both negative binomial distributions where the parameter p is the inverse of a linear function of t. (The reader will recall that the Yule process also produced a negative binomial random variable, but with p being an exponential function of time.) In the Polya case, the risk of an event is allowed to depend both on time and on the past history of the process; in the weighted Poisson case, the risk is assumed to be independent of both. Thus we have two very different mechanisms on the "micro" level that give rise to the same system behavior on the "macro" level. This means that the two underlying mechanisms cannot be distinguished by observations of the random variables $X(t)$.

5. PURE DEATH PROCESS

The pure death process is exactly analogous to the pure birth process, except that in the pure death process $X(t)$ is decreased rather than increased by the occurrence of an "event". We specialize immediately to the case in which each member of a group of individuals alive at $t = 0$ is independently subject to the same risk of dying. In the usual applications this assumption is reasonable if t is interpreted as age (in this case the group is known as a *cohort*). Let $\mu(t)\Delta + o(\Delta)$ be the probability that an individual alive at age t will die in the interval $(t, t + \Delta)$; $\mu(t)$ is known as the *force of mortality, intensity of risk of dying,* or *failure rate.* If, at age t, the $X(t) = k$ individuals are independently subject to the force of mortality $\mu(t)$, then the probability of one death occurring in $(t, t + \Delta)$ is $k\mu(t)\Delta + o(\Delta)$, the probability of two or more deaths is $o(\Delta)$, and the probability of no deaths is $1 - k\mu(t)\Delta - o(\Delta)$. Following the steps outlined in Section 3, we can formulate the differential equations for the probabilities of $X(t)$ and then find the solution

$$\Pr\{X(t) = k \mid X(0) = i\} = p_k(t)$$

$$= \binom{i}{k} e^{-k\int_0^t \mu(\tau)d\tau}\left[1 - e^{-\int_0^t \mu(\tau)d\tau}\right]^{i-k}, \qquad k = 0, 1, \ldots, i. \tag{5.1}$$

But rather than repeat the same procedure used previously, we shall introduce a slightly different approach.

Since we assume the i individuals to be independently subject to the same force of mortality, we may start with $i = 1$ and then compute the i-fold convolution to obtain the required solution for $i > 1$. Let the continuous random variable T be the life span, so that the distribution function

$$F_T(t) = \Pr\{T \le t\} \tag{5.2}$$

is the probability that the individual will die prior to or at age t. Consider now the interval $(0, t + \Delta)$ and the corresponding distribution function $F_T(t + \Delta)$. For an individual to die prior to $t + \Delta$ he must die prior to t or else he must survive to t and die during the interval $(t, t + \Delta)$. Therefore the corresponding probabilities have the relationship:

$$F_T(t + \Delta) = F_T(t) + [1 - F_T(t)]\,[\mu(t)\Delta + o(\Delta)] \tag{5.3}$$

or

$$\frac{F_T(t + \Delta) - F_T(t)}{\Delta} = [1 - F_T(t)]\mu(t) + \frac{o(\Delta)}{\Delta}. \tag{5.4}$$

Taking the limits of both sides of (5.4) and $\Delta \to 0$, we have the differential equation

$$\frac{d}{dt} F_T(t) = [1 - F_T(t)]\mu(t) \tag{5.5}$$

with the initial condition

$$F_T(0) = 0. \tag{5.6}$$

Integrating (5.5) and using (5.6) yields the solution

$$1 - F_T(t) = e^{-\int_0^t \mu(\tau)\,d\tau}. \tag{5.7}$$

Equation (5.7) gives us the probability that one individual alive at age 0 will survive to age t. If there are i individuals alive at age 0, the number of those who will survive to age t is clearly a binomial random variable with the probability of success $1 - F_T(t)$. Consequently, $X(t)$ has the probability distribution (5.1), and the solution is complete.

The survival probability in (5.7) has been known to life table students for more than two hundred years.[4] Not until recently has it been given due recognition by investigators in statistics, although different forms of this function have appeared in various areas of research.

---

[4]E. Halley's famous table for the City of Breslau was published in the year 1693.

We shall mention a few below in terms of the probability density function of T,

$$f_T(t) = \frac{dF_T(t)}{dt} = \mu(t)e^{-\int_0^t \mu(\tau)\,d\tau} \qquad t \geq 0$$

$$= 0 \qquad t < 0. \tag{5.8}$$

(i) *Gompertz distribution.* In a celebrated paper on the law of human mortality, Benjamin Gompertz [1825] attributed death to either of two causes: chance, or deterioration of the power to withstand destruction. In deriving his law of mortality, however, he considered only deterioration, and assumed that man's power to resist death decreases at a rate proportional to the power itself. Since the force of mortality $\mu(t)$ is a measure of man's susceptibility to death, Gompertz used the reciprocal $1/\mu(t)$ as a measure of man's resistance to death and thus arrived at the formula

$$\frac{d}{dt}\left(\frac{1}{\mu(t)}\right) = -h\frac{1}{\mu(t)}, \tag{5.9}$$

or

$$\frac{d}{dt}\mu(t) = h\mu(t) \tag{5.10}$$

where h is a positive constant. Integrating (5.10) and letting $e^h = c$ yields the Gompertz law of mortality

$$\mu(t) = Bc^t. \tag{5.11}$$

The corresponding density function and distribution function are, respectively,

$$f_T(t) = Bc^t e^{-B[c^t-1]/\ln c} \tag{5.12}$$

and

$$F_T(t) = 1 - exp\left\{-\frac{B}{\ln c}(c^t - 1)\right\}. \tag{5.13}$$

(ii) *Makeham's distribution.* In 1860, W. M. Makeham suggested the modification

$$\mu(t) = A + B\,c^t, \tag{5.14}$$

to restore the missing component "chance" to the Gompertz formula. In this case,

$$f_T(t) = [A + Bc^t] \; exp\{-[At + B(c^t - 1)/ \ln c]\} \qquad (5.15)$$

and

$$F_T(t) = 1 - exp\{-[At + B(c^t - 1)/\ln c]\}. \qquad (5.16)$$

(iii) *Weibull distribution.* When the force of mortality (or failure rate) is assumed to be a power function of t, where $\mu(t) = \mu a t^{a-1}$,

$$f_T(t) = \mu a t^{a-1} e^{-\mu t^a} \qquad (5.17)$$

and

$$F_T(t) = 1 - e^{-\mu t^a}. \qquad (5.18)$$

This distribution, recommended by Weibull [1939] for studies of the life span of materials, is used extensively in reliability theory.

(iv) *Exponential distribution.* If $\mu(t) = \mu$ is a constant, then

$$f_T(t) = \mu e^{-\mu t},$$

and

$$F_T(t) = 1 - e^{-\mu t} \qquad (5.19)$$

which plays a central role in the problem of life testing (Epstein and Sobel [1953]).

(v) *Decreasing force of mortality.* It has been shown that the force of mortality for certain specific causes decreases, rather than increases, with age. In such cases, in contrast to Gompertz's formula, we have

$$\frac{d}{dt}\mu(t) = -\alpha\,\mu(t), \qquad \alpha > 0 \qquad (5.20)$$

so that

$$\mu(t) = \beta\, e^{-\alpha t}, \qquad \beta > 0. \qquad (5.21)$$

The corresponding density function and distribution functions are

$$f_T(t) = \beta\, e^{-\alpha t} e^{-(1-e^{-\alpha t})\beta/\alpha} \qquad (5.22)$$

and

$$F_T(t) = 1 - e^{-(1-e^{-\alpha t})\beta/\alpha}. \qquad (5.23)$$

As $t \to \infty$,

$$F_T(\infty) = 1 - e^{-\beta/\alpha} < 1; \tag{5.24}$$

therefore the distribution is improper.

6. MIGRATION PROCESSES

We have seen in Chapter 2 that the p.g.f. of the sum of independent random variables is the product of the p.g.f.'s of individual random variables. This relationship provides a convenient way to derive a probability distribution without carrying out lengthy routine computations. We shall illustrate this point with the migration process.

6.1. A Simple Immigration-Emigration Process.

A population's growth is subject to an immigration-emigration process with intensities η (immigration) and μ (emigration). Let $X(t)$ be the population size at time t, with $X(0) = i$. For every $t \geq 0$, the change in population size in the time element $(t, t + \Delta)$ is governed by the following conditional probabilities:

$$\begin{aligned} &\Pr\{X(t+\Delta) = k+1 | X(t) = k\} = \eta\Delta + o(\Delta), \\ &\Pr\{X(t+\Delta) \geq k+2 | X(t) = k\} = o(\Delta), \\ &\Pr\{X(t+\Delta) = k-1 | X(t) = k\} = k\mu\Delta + o(\Delta) \end{aligned} \tag{6.1}$$

and

$$\Pr\{X(t+\Delta) \leq k-2 | X(t) = k\} = o(\Delta). \tag{6.2}$$

Equations (6.1) and (6.2) also imply that

$$\Pr\{X(t+\Delta) = k | X(t) = k\} = 1 - (\eta + k\mu)\Delta - o(\Delta). \tag{6.3}$$

Let the probability distribution of the population size at time t be denoted by $\{p_k(t)\}$ so that

$$p_k(t) = \Pr\{X(t) = k | X(0) = i\}, \qquad k = 0, 1, \ldots \tag{6.4}$$

We are seeking explicit formulas for $p_k(t)$.

From the assumptions in (6.1), (6.2) and (6.3), we derive a system of differential equations for $p_k(t)$:

$$\frac{d}{dt} p_0(t) = -\eta p_0(t) + \mu p_1(t)$$

and

$$\frac{d}{dt} p_k(t) = -(\eta + k\mu) p_k(t) + \eta\, p_{k-1}(t) + (k+1)\mu p_{k+1}(t),$$

$$k = 1,2, \ldots, \tag{6.5}$$

with the initial conditions at $t = 0$

$$p_i(0) = 1, \qquad p_k(0) = 0, \qquad \text{for } k \neq i. \tag{6.6}$$

In each of the differential equations in (6.5), there are three unknown probabilities: $p_k(t)$, $p_{k-1}(t)$ and $p_{k+1}(t)$. Therefore these equations cannot be solved directly. We resort to the method of probability generating functions.

Denote the p.g.f. of $X(t)$ by $G_X(s;t)$; then

$$G_X(s;t) = \sum_{k=0}^{\infty} s^k p_k(t) \tag{6.7}$$

with the initial condition at $t = 0$

$$G_X(s;0) = s^i. \tag{6.8}$$

Taking the derivatives of (6.7) term by term and using (6.5) we find a partial differential equation for $G_X(s;t)$,

$$\frac{\partial}{\partial t} G_X(s;t) = \mu(1-s) \frac{\partial}{\partial s} G_X(s;t) - \eta\,(1-s)\, G_X(s;t) \tag{6.9}$$

and the corresponding auxiliary equations

$$\frac{dt}{-1} = \frac{ds}{\mu(1-s)} = \frac{d\, G_X(s;t)}{\eta(1-s)\, G_X(s;t)}. \tag{6.10}$$

Solving the first auxiliary equation in (6.10) yields

$$(1-s)\, e^{-\mu t} = c_1, \tag{6.11}$$

while the second yields

$$\exp\left\{-\frac{\eta}{\mu} s\right\} G_X(s;t) = c_2, \tag{6.12}$$

where c_1 and c_2 are constants of integration. Setting c_2 as a function of c_1, we arrive at the general solution:

$$G_X(s;t) = \exp\left\{\frac{\eta}{\mu} s\right\} \Phi\{(1-s)\, e^{-\mu t}\}, \tag{6.13}$$

where Φ is an arbitrary differentiable function of s and t. To determine Φ, we set $t = 0$ and use the initial condition (6.8) to write

$$\exp\left\{\frac{\eta}{\mu} s\right\} \Phi\{(1-s)\} = s^i \tag{6.14}$$

so that, for $|\theta| \le 1$,

$$\Phi\{\theta\} = (1-\theta)^i \exp\left\{-\frac{\eta}{\mu}(1-\theta)\right\}. \tag{6.15}$$

In the general solution (6.13)

$$\theta = (1-s)\, e^{-\mu t}. \tag{6.16}$$

We substitute (6.16) in (6.15) to obtain the required particular solution:

$$G_X(s;t) = [1-(1-s)e^{-\mu t}]^i \exp\left\{-(1-s)\frac{\eta}{\mu}(1-e^{-\mu t})\right\}. \tag{6.17}$$

In the above derivation of the generating function, we merely outlined the essential steps involved; the details for each step are ommitted. However, we can arrive at formula (6.17) quite simply by using a different approach.

6.1.1. An Alternative Derivation.

The population size at time t is the sum of two random variables

$$X(t) = Y(t) + Z(t), \tag{6.18}$$

where $Y(t)$ is the number of survivors of the initial i individuals and $Z(t)$ is the number of individuals who enter the population during the interval $(0, t)$ and are still living at time t. Obviously, $Y(t)$ and $Z(t)$ are independent random variables, so that the p.g.f. of $X(t)$ is the product of the p.g.f.'s of $Y(t)$ and $Z(t)$:

$$G_X(s;t) = g_Y(s;t) \times g_Z(s;t), \tag{6.19}$$

where, according to the death process in section 5,

$$g_Y(s;t) = [1-(1-s)e^{-\mu t}]^i. \tag{6.20}$$

To find the p.g.f. of $Z(t)$, let us consider a composite event: An individual will immigrate into the population in $(\tau, \tau + d\tau)$ with a probability $\eta d\tau$ and survive to t with probability $\exp\{-(t - \tau)\mu\}$, for $0 \le \tau \le t$. Therefore, the probability of the composite event is

$$[\eta d\tau]\, e^{-(t-\tau)\mu}. \tag{6.21}$$

Summing (6.21) over all possible values of τ, we find that

$$\int_0^t \eta e^{-(t-\tau)\mu} d\tau = \frac{\eta}{\mu}\,[1 - e^{-\mu t}]. \tag{6.22}$$

Now $Z(t)$, which is the total number of such composite events occurring in $(0, t)$, has a Poisson distribution with the expectation (6.22). This means that

$$g_Z(s;t) = \exp\left\{-(1-s)\frac{\eta}{\mu}\,[1 - e^{-\mu t}]\right\}. \tag{6.23}$$

Substituting (6.20) and (6.23) in (6.19) we recover the p.g.f. of $X(t)$ in (6.17).

Thus $X(t)$ is the sum of a binomial random variable $Y(t)$ in i "trials" with the probability of survival $e^{-\mu t}$, and a Poisson random variable $Z(t)$ with the parameter given in (6.22). It follows that

$$\Pr\{X(t) = k\} = \sum_{j=0}^{\min[i,k]} \Pr\{Y(t) = j\} \times \Pr\{Z(t) = k - j\} \tag{6.24}$$

where $\min[i, k]$ stands for the smaller of i and k;

$$\Pr\{Y(t) = j\} = \binom{i}{j} e^{-j\mu t}\,[1 - e^{-\mu t}]^{i-j}$$

and

$$\Pr\{Z(t) = j\} = \frac{\left(\dfrac{\eta}{\mu}\right)^j [1 - e^{-\mu t}]^j}{j!} \exp\left\{-\frac{\eta}{\mu}\,[1 - e^{-\mu t}]\right\}.$$

The expectation is

$$E[X(t)] = E[Y(t)] + E[Z(t)]$$

$$= i\,e^{-\mu t} + \frac{\eta}{\mu}\,[1 - e^{-\mu t}], \tag{6.25}$$

and the variance is

$$\text{Var}[X(t)] = i\,e^{-\mu t}[1 - e^{-\mu t}] + \frac{\eta}{\mu}\,[1 - e^{-\mu t}]. \tag{6.26}$$

If the migration intensities are functions of time, $\eta(t)$ and $\mu(t)$, then the binomial probability becomes

$$\exp\left\{-\int_0^t \mu(\tau)d\tau\right\} \tag{6.27}$$

and the Poisson parameter in (6.22) becomes

$$\int_0^t \eta(\tau)\,e^{-\int_\tau^t \mu(\xi)d\xi}\,d\tau. \tag{6.28}$$

Both (6.27) and (6.28) can be evaluated for specific functions of $\eta(t)$ and $\mu(t)$.

7. AN APPENDIX—FIRST ORDER DIFFERENTIAL EQUATIONS

Presented in this section is a brief but necessary introduction to the first order differential equations for a thorough understanding of the material in this book. The reader should also consult such excellent textbooks as Ford [1953], Miller [1965], Forsyth [1961], Kaplan [1958] and others for a full treatise on the subject.

7.1. Ordinary Differential Equations.

A *differential equation* is an equation which expresses a relationship among some independent variables, some functions (dependent variables) of these variables and their derivatives with respect to the independent variables. Differential equations are divided into classes according to the number of independent variables involved.

An *ordinary differential equation* contains a single independent variable so that the derivatives are ordinary derivatives. For example,

$$\frac{dy}{dx} = y \tag{7.1}$$

is an ordinary differential equation. Here y, the dependent variable, is a function of the independent variable, x.

A *partial differential equation,* on the other hand, contains two or more independent variables, so that the derivatives are partial derivatives. For example,

$$\frac{\partial z}{\partial x} + \frac{\partial z}{\partial y} = yz + xz \tag{7.2}$$

is a partial differential equation. Here z, the dependent variable, is a function of independent variables x and y.

A *first order differential equation* contains the derivatives of the first order only.

Solutions of differential equations. A relation $y = g(x)$ is a solution of the differential equation

$$\frac{dy}{dx} = f(x, y) \tag{7.3}$$

if the equation

$$\frac{d\,g(x)}{dx} = f\,[\mathrm{x}, g(x)] \tag{7.4}$$

holds identically in x. For example, the relation

$$y = c\,e^x$$

is a solution of the differential equation

$$\frac{dy}{dx} = y.$$

Methods of solutions: Variables separable. Consider the first order differential equation

$$\frac{dy}{dx} = f(x,y). \tag{7.3}$$

If it is possible to separate the variables so that the differential equation may be written as

$$M(x)dx + N(y)dy = 0, \tag{7.5}$$

where $M(x)$ is a function of x alone and $N(y)$ is a function of y alone, then integration gives the solution

$$\int M(x)\,dx + \int N(y)\,dy = c, \tag{7.6}$$

where c is the constant of integration.

Example. Find the solution of the equation

$$\frac{dy}{dx} = \frac{-2x}{3y + 4}. \tag{7.7}$$

Rewriting the equation as

$$2x\,dx + (3y + 4)\,dy = 0$$

and integrating yields the solution

$$x^2 + \frac{3}{2}y^2 + 4y = c. \tag{7.8}$$

A general solution of a differential equation contains an arbitrary constant. Therefore, a differential equation has infinitely many solutions depending on the values of the constant of integration.

A particular solution of a differential equation is a solution that corresponds to a particular value of the constant of integration.

Equation (7.8) is the general solution of the differential equation (7.7). If at $x = 0$, $y = -2$, and $c = -2$, then we have a particular solution

$$x^2 + \frac{3}{2}y^2 + 4y = -2.$$

Exact equation. A differential equation

$$M(x)\,dx + N(y)\,dy = 0 \tag{7.5}$$

is called an exact equation if there exists a function $z(x, y)$ such that

$$dz = M(x)\,dx + N(y)\,dy. \tag{7.9}$$

When (7.9) is true, equation (7.5) can be written as

$$dz = 0$$

and has the solution

$$z(x, y) = c.$$

Example. Find the general solution of the equation

$$\frac{dy}{dx} = -\frac{2x + y}{x}.$$

When we write the given equation in the form

$$ydx + xdy + 2xdx = 0, \tag{7.10}$$

we see that $ydx + xdy = dxy$ is an exact differential and the remaining term $2xdx = dx^2$ also is integrable. Therefore we can rewrite (7.10) as

$$d[xy + x^2] = 0 \tag{7.11}$$

to obtain the general solution

$$xy + x^2 = c.$$

Equations such as (7.10), which can be written as an exact equation (7.11), are easy to solve. In certain cases, the given equation is not an exact equation, but it can be made an exact equation by multiplying it by a factor. For example,

$$2ydx + xdy = 0 \tag{7.12}$$

is not an exact equation. However, when it is multiplied by x, (7.12) becomes an exact equation:

$$2xydx + x^2dy = d(x^2y) = 0.$$

The factor x is called an integrating factor of the equation.

Integrating factor. A non-zero function $z(x, y)$ is called an integrating factor of the equation

$$M(x)dx + N(y)dy = 0$$

if

$$z(x, y)[M(x)dx + N(y)dy] = 0$$

is an exact equation.

The importance of the integrating factor in solving differential equations is obvious. It should be noted, however, that the integrating factor of a given equation is not unique. For example, $1/xy$ is also an integrating factor of the differential equation (7.12) since

$$\frac{1}{xy}\,[2y\,dx + x\,dy] = d\,[2\ln x + \ln y].$$

Also $x^3 y$ is an integrating factor of (7.12):

$$x^3 y\,[2y\,dx + x\,dy] = d\left[\frac{x^4 y^2}{2}\right].$$

For a linear equation of first order, there is a simple way of finding an integrating factor.

Linear equations of the first order. The equation

$$\frac{dy}{dx} + Py + Q = 0 \tag{7.13}$$

where P and Q are functions of x only, has the function

$$e^{\int P\,dx} \tag{7.14}$$

as an integrating factor. Multiplying (7.13) by (7.14) gives

$$e^{\int P dx}\left[\frac{dy}{dx} + Py + Q\right]$$

$$= \frac{d}{dx}\,[y\,e^{\int P\,dx}] + Q\,e^{\int P\,dx} = 0 \tag{7.15}$$

which is an exact equation. Integrating (7.15) yields the general solution

$$y = e^{-\int P\,dx} \int Q\,e^{\int P\,dx}\,dx + c\,e^{-\int P\,dx}. \tag{7.16}$$

Bernoulli's equation. An equation of the form

$$\frac{dy}{dx} + Py = Qy^n, \tag{7.17}$$

where $n \geq 2$, can be transformed into a linear equation by the change of variables

$$z = y^{1-n}. \tag{7.18}$$

Substituting (7.18) in (7.17) gives

$$\frac{dz}{dx} + (1-n)\,P\,z = (1-n)\,Q, \tag{7.19}$$

which is linear in z.

7.2. Partial Differential Equations.

The partial differential equations encountered in this book are linear differential equations of the first order with two or more independent variables. They are known as *Lagrange's linear equations.* The typical equation involving two independent variables is

$$P\frac{\partial z}{\partial x} + Q\frac{\partial z}{\partial y} = R, \tag{7.20}$$

where P, Q, and R are functions of x, y, and z. Equation (7.20) can be solved quite elegantly. Corresponding to (7.20), there are two ordinary differential equations, known as auxiliary or subsidiary equations

$$\frac{dx}{P} = \frac{dy}{Q} = \frac{dz}{R}. \tag{7.21}$$

Any function $u(x, y, z) = a$ that satisfies (7.21) is also a solution of (7.20). Therefore, instead of solving the partial differential equation (7.20) directly, we may solve the ordinary differential equations (7.21). Justification is given in the following paragraphs. It should be noted that the discussion that follows holds true for equations involving three or more independent variables as well.

7.2.1. Preliminaries.

Let a dependent variable z be a function of two independent variables x and y

$$z = f(x, y). \tag{7.22}$$

For a fixed y, z will change as x changes. When x changes by an amount Δx, z will change by an amount Δz such that

$$\Delta z = f(x + \Delta, y) - f(x, y)$$

and

$$\frac{\Delta z}{\Delta x} = \frac{f(x + \Delta, y) - f(x, y)}{\Delta x}. \tag{7.23}$$

As $\Delta x \to 0$, the quotient in (7.23) may approach a limit. The limit, if it exists, is called the partial derivative of z with respect to x:

$$\frac{\partial z}{\partial x} = \lim_{\Delta x \to 0} \frac{f(x + \Delta x, y) - f(x, y)}{\Delta x}. \tag{7.24}$$

It is clear from this definition that the partial derivative in (7.24) is a function of y. Similarly the partial derivative of z with respect to y, defined as the limit

$$\frac{\partial z}{\partial y} = \lim_{\Delta y \to 0} \frac{f(x, y + \Delta y) - f(x, y)}{\Delta y}, \tag{7.25}$$

is a function of x.

We shall use the following symbols to denote the partial derivatives:

$$\frac{\partial}{\partial x} f, \quad f_x, \quad p \qquad \text{and} \qquad \frac{\partial}{\partial y} f, \quad f_y, \quad q.$$

Total differential. In the function

$$z = f(x, y),$$

if z changes by an amount Δz as a result of a change of Δx in x and a change of Δy in y, then

$$\Delta z = f(x + \Delta x, y + \Delta y) - f(x, y). \tag{7.26}$$

Writing (7.26) as

$$\Delta z = f(x + \Delta x, y + \Delta y) - f(x, y + \Delta y) + f(x, y + \Delta y) - f(x, y),$$

letting $\Delta x \to 0$ and $\Delta y \to 0$, and using (7.24) and (7.25), we arrive at the relation:

$$dz = \frac{\partial z}{\partial x} dx + \frac{\partial z}{\partial y} dy. \tag{7.27}$$

The total differential dz interpreted geometrically is the increment in z cut off by the tangent to the surface $z = f(x, y)$ at the point (x, y, z).

Function of functions. If x and y themselves are functions of a single variable s, then the total derivative of z with respect to s is

$$\frac{dz}{ds} = \frac{\partial z}{\partial x}\frac{dx}{ds} + \frac{\partial z}{\partial y}\frac{dy}{ds}. \tag{7.28}$$

Implicit functions. Let y be an implicit function of x by way of the equation $f(x, y) = 0$. Then the derivative of y with respect to x is

$$\frac{dy}{dx} = -\frac{\partial f/\partial x}{\partial f/\partial y}, \tag{7.29}$$

provided, of course, $\partial f/\partial y \neq 0$.

Direction numbers. The numbers that are proportional to the direction cosines of a line are direction numbers of the line.

Parallel and perpendicular lines. Let (a_1, b_1, c_1) and (a_2, b_2, c_2) be the direction numbers of lines L_1 and L_2, respectively. Two lines L_1 and L_2 are parallel if and only if their respective direction cosines are equal, or their direction numbers are proportional:

$$\frac{a_1}{a_2} = \frac{b_1}{b_2} = \frac{c_1}{c_2}. \tag{7.30}$$

Two lines L_1 and L_2 are perpendicular if and only if their direction numbers satisfy the relation

$$a_1 a_2 + b_1 b_2 + c_1 c_2 = 0. \tag{7.31}$$

Tangent plane to a surface. The equation of the plane tangent to the surface $F(x, y, z) = 0$ at a point $P:(x_0, y_0, z_0)$ on the surface may be written as

$$p_0(x - x_0) + q_0(y - y_0) - (z - z_0) = 0, \tag{7.32}$$

where p_0 and q_0 are the partial derivatives $\partial z/\partial x$ and $\partial z/\partial y$ evaluated at the point $P:(x_0, y_0, z_0)$.

Normal to a surface. The equations of the line N normal to the surface $F(x, y, z) = 0$ at a point $P:(x_0, y_0, z_0)$ on the surface may be written as

$$\frac{x - x_0}{p_0} = \frac{y - y_0}{q_0} = \frac{z - z_0}{-1}. \tag{7.33}$$

Example. Find the equation of the tangent plane and the equations of the normal line to the surface

$$x^2 + y^2 + z^2 = 14$$

at the point $P:(2, -1, 3)$.

Setting $F(x, y, z) = x^2 + y^2 + z^2 - 14$, we have the derivatives

$$p = -\frac{x}{z} \quad \text{and} \quad q = -\frac{y}{z}.$$

At the point P:(2, −1, 3),

$$p_0 = -\frac{2}{3} \qquad \text{and} \qquad q_0 = \frac{1}{3}.$$

Therefore, the equation for the tangent plane at P is

$$-\frac{2}{3}(x-2) + \frac{1}{3}(y+1) - (z-3) = 0,$$

or

$$2x - y + 3z - 14 = 0;$$

and the equations for the normal line at P are

$$-\frac{3(x-2)}{2} = 3(y+1) = -(z-3).$$

Intersection of surfaces. The intersection of two surface $F(x, y, z) = 0$ and $G(x, y, z) = 0$ generates a curve (space curve). The equations

$$F(x, y, z) = 0 \qquad \text{and} \qquad G(x, y, z) = 0,$$

considered simultaneously, represent the curve of intersection.

When a line T is tangent to the curve of intersection at the point P:(x, y, z), the differentials, dx, dy, dz at P may be taken as direction numbers of the tangent line.

7.2.2. Auxiliary Equations.

Consider a linear partial differential equation of the first order

$$p\,P(x, y, z) + q\,Q(x, y, z) = R(x, y, z) \tag{7.34}$$

where P, Q, R are functions of x, y, z and $p = \partial z/\partial x$ and $q = \partial z/\partial y$.

Suppose $z = f(x, y)$ is a particular solution of equation (7.34) and let a fixed point (x, y, z) be on the surface $z = f(x, y)$. We can give (7.34) a simple geometric interpretation. Since p, q, -1 are direction numbers of the normal N to the surface at the point (x, y, z), we see from (7.34) that the line N is perpendicular to a line L which passes through the point (x, y, z) with direction numbers P, Q, R. The two lines L and N define a plane that intersects the surface $z = f(x, y)$ in a curve C. The direction numbers of the curve C are dx, dy, dz.

Now the curve C and the line L have the same direction cosines and hence their direction numbers are proportional, i.e.,

$$\frac{dx}{P} = \frac{dy}{Q} = \frac{dz}{R}. \tag{7.35}$$

In conclusion, if $z = f(x, y)$ is a solution of the differential equation (7.34), then it also satisfies the auxiliary equations (7.35).

7.2.3 The General Solution.

Theorem 1. *Every function $u(x, y, z) = 0$ which satisfies*

$$\frac{dx}{P} = \frac{dy}{Q} = \frac{dz}{R} \tag{7.35}$$

is a solution of the partial differential equation

$$p\,P + q\,Q = R. \tag{7.34}$$

Proof. Suppose a function $u(x, y, z) = a$ satisfies (7.35). Taking the total derivative of $u(x, y, z) = a$, we find that [cf., (7.27)]

$$du = \frac{\partial u}{\partial x}\,dz + \frac{\partial u}{\partial y}\,dy + \frac{\partial u}{\partial z}\,dz = 0,$$

or

$$du = u_x dx + u_y dy + u_z dz = 0, \tag{7.36}$$

where u_x, u_y and u_z are partial derivatives of u. Denoting the common ratio in (7.35) by λ, then we have equations

$$dx = P\lambda, \qquad dy = Q\lambda, \qquad dz = R\lambda. \tag{7.37}$$

Substituting (7.37) in (7.36), we obtain the equation

$$u_x P\lambda + u_y Q\lambda + u_z R\lambda = 0,$$

or

$$-\frac{u_x}{u_z}P - \frac{u_y}{u_z}Q = R. \tag{7.38}$$

Now z is an implicit function of two independent variables x, y by means of the equation $u(x, y, z) = a$. Using (7.29) we can write the first partial derivatives of z with respect to x and y as

$$\frac{\partial z}{\partial x} = -\frac{u_x}{u_z} \quad \text{and} \quad \frac{\partial z}{\partial y} = -\frac{u_y}{u_z}. \tag{7.39}$$

Substituting (7.39) in (7.38) we recover the equation

$$p\,P + q\,Q = R. \tag{7.40}$$

Theorem 2. *Let u and v be two functions that both satisfy the differential equations*

$$\frac{dx}{P} = \frac{dy}{Q} = \frac{dz}{R} \tag{7.41}$$

and u and v are independent. Then any arbitrary function of u and v, say, $\Phi(u, v)$, is a solution of the differential equation

$$p\,P + q\,Q = R. \tag{7.42}$$

Proof: Differentiating $\Phi(u, v) = 0$ partially with respect to x and y, we have

$$\frac{\partial \phi}{\partial x} = \frac{\partial \phi}{\partial u}\frac{\partial u}{\partial x} + \frac{\partial \phi}{\partial u}\frac{\partial u}{\partial z}\frac{\partial z}{\partial x} + \frac{\partial \phi}{\partial v}\frac{\partial v}{\partial x} + \frac{\partial \phi}{\partial v}\frac{\partial v}{\partial z}\frac{\partial z}{\partial x}$$
$$= 0$$

or

$$\frac{\partial \phi}{\partial x} = \frac{\partial \phi}{\partial u}\,[u_x + u_z p] + \frac{\partial \phi}{\partial v}\,[v_x + v_z p] = 0, \tag{7.43}$$

and similarly,

$$\frac{\partial \phi}{\partial y} = \frac{\partial \phi}{\partial u}\,[u_y + u_z q] + \frac{\partial \phi}{\partial v}\,[v_y + v_z q] = 0. \tag{7.44}$$

These are two homogeneous equations in two unknowns, $\frac{\partial \phi}{\partial u}$ and $\frac{\partial \phi}{\partial v}$. A nontrivial solution exists if, and only if, the determinant of the coefficients vanishes. That is,

$$(u_x + u_z p)(v_y + v_z q) - (u_y + u_z q)(v_x + v_z p) = 0 \tag{7.45}$$

or

$$\frac{u_y v_z - u_z v_y}{u_x v_y - u_y v_x}\,p + \frac{u_z v_x - u_x v_z}{u_x v_y - u_y v_x}\,q = 1 \tag{7.46}$$

Now, u and v satisfy the auxiliary equations (7.41), and their first partial derivatives with respect to x, y and z have the relation in (7.38), or

$$-u_xP - u_yQ = u_zR \qquad \text{and} \qquad -v_xP - v_yQ = v_zR. \quad (7.47)$$

Solving the two equations in (7.47) for P and Q, we get

$$P = \frac{u_yv_z - u_zv_y}{u_xv_y - u_yv_x}R \qquad \text{and} \qquad Q = \frac{u_zv_x - u_xv_z}{u_xv_y - u_yv_x}R \quad (7.48)$$

and hence

$$\frac{u_yv_z - u_zv_y}{u_xv_y - u_yv_x} = \frac{P}{R} \qquad \text{and} \qquad \frac{u_zv_x - u_xv_z}{u_xv_y - u_yv_x} = \frac{Q}{R}. \quad (7.49)$$

Substituting (7.49) in (7.46) we recover the differential equation

$$\frac{P}{R}p + \frac{Q}{R}q = 1,$$

or

$$p\,P + q\,Q = R,$$

proving the theorem.

Therefore, given two independent integrals $u(x, y, z) = a$ and $v(x, y, z) = b$ of the auxiliary equations (7.35), any arbitrary function $\phi(u, v) = 0$ satisfies the linear partial differential equation (7.34). The solution $\phi(u, v) = 0$ is called the general solution of (7.34). Since ϕ is an arbitrary function, a partial differential equation is richer in solution than an ordinary differential equation.

8. PROBLEMS FOR SOLUTION

1. *Poisson Process.* Let $\{X(t)\}$ be a time dependent Poisson Process with the probability distribution given in (2.18). Find the joint probability distribution of $X(t)$ and $X(t + \tau)$ and their covariance.

2. *Continuation.* Solve the differential equations in (2.3a) to obtain $p_k(t)$ in terms $p_{k-1}(t)$.

3. The Child Health and Development Studies (CHDS) at the University of California, Berkeley, has collected longitudinal data on the health and development of a study population of some 19,000 children. Individual files have been maintained for the children from birth regarding clinic visits,

hospitalizations, dates of episodes, diagnoses, laboratory tests, therapeutic treatments, drug prescriptions, etc.

In the following table are frequency distributions according to clinic episodes during the first year of life of three categories of children: Children with severe congenital anomalies, with non-severe anomalies and with no congenital anomalies.

Table P3. Frequency distributions by the number of clinical episodes in the first year of life of three categories of children.

No. of Clinical Episodes	Children with Severe Congenital Anomalies	Children with Non-severe Congenital Anomalies	Children with No Congenital Anomalies
0	10	12	61
1	25	19	92
2	44	32	121
3	57	45	132
4	68	29	115
5	61	52	78
6	70	31	60
7	71	26	40
8	39	21	23
9	33	11	11
10	24	8	10
11	19	2	4
12	8	5	1
13	1	1	1
14	2	0	1
15+	2	2	0
Total	534	296	750

Source: Child Health and Development Studies, University of California, Berkeley, courtesy of Dr. Barbara J. van den Berg.

Let X be the number of clinical episodes a child has during the first year of life. Let the random variable X have a negative binomial distribution:

$$\Pr\{X = k\} = \frac{\Gamma(k+\alpha)}{k!\Gamma(\alpha)} \beta^{\alpha} (1+\beta)^{-(k+\alpha)}, \qquad k = 0, 1, \ldots .$$

(a) Find the expectation $E(X)$ and the variance $V(X)$ for the above distribution.

(b) Compute the sample mean $\overline{X}$ and sample variance S_X^2 from each of the frequency distributions in the table above, and use these values to estimate the corresponding α and β in the formula.

(c) For each distribution, compute the expected number of children F_k for each k and determine

$$X_0^2 = \sum \frac{(f_k - F_k)^2}{F_k}.$$

(d) Summarize your findings.

4. The Canadian Department of National Health and Welfare and the Dominion Bureau of Statistics conducted a sickness survey in 1950–1951 on a sample of approximately 10,000 households. Part of the published data has been fitted in a weighted Poisson distribution. The material in Table P4 was taken from Chiang [1965].

Table P4. Observed number of persons under 15 years of age by number of doctor's calls or clinic visits

Number of Doctors' Calls or Clinic Visits k	Observed Number of Persons f_k
0	2367
1	749
2	350
3	222
4	136
5	95
6	64
7	41
8	25
9	14
10	12
11	11
12	9
13	8
14	5
15+	8
Total	4116

(a) Find the mean and standard deviation of the frequency distribution.

(b) Fit a Poisson distribution to data and test for the goodness of fit.

(c) Fit a negative binomial distribution to the data and test for the goodness of fit.

(d) Which of the two distributions gives a better fit, the Poisson distribution or the negative binomial distribution? Explain.

(e) Summarize your findings.

5. *Yule process.* Solve the differential equations

$$\frac{d}{dt}p_k(t) = -k\lambda p_k(t) + (k-1)\lambda p_{k-1}(t), \qquad k \geq i$$

to obtain a general formula for the probability $p_k(t)$.

6. *Continuation.* Show that the p.g.f. in (3.27) satisfies the partial differential equation in (3.20).

7. *Continuation.* Derive the covariance of $X(t_1)$ and $X(t_2)$ in (3.36) (i) from the p.g.f. in (3.35), and (ii) by using the identity $E[X(t_1)\, X(t_2)|X(0)] = E[X(t_1) E\{X(t_2)|\, X(t_1)\}\,|\,X(0)]$.

8. *Continuation.* Find the correlation coefficient between $X(t_1)$ and $X(t_2)$ in Problem 7 and discuss it in view of the distance $t_2 - t_1$.

9. *Polya Process.* Derive the probability $p_k(t)$ by solving the differential equations in (4.2a) and (4.2b).

10. *Continuation.* Show that the p.g.f. in (4.15) satisfies the partial differential equation in (4.5).

11. *Continuation.* Let $X(t_1)$ and $X(t_2)$, with $t_1 < t_2$, be two random variables, each having the Polya distribution and satisfying the differential equations in (4.2).

(a) Derive the p.g.f. of the joint probability distribution of $X(t_1)$ and $X(t_2)$.

(b) Find from the p.g.f. in (a) the joint probability distribution of $X(t_1)$ and $X(t_2)$.

(c) Find the covariance and the correlation coefficient between $X(t_1)$ and $X(t_2)$.

12. *Pure death process.* Derive a system of differential equations for the probability distribution of the death process $\{X(t)\}$ defined in Section 5. Find from the differential equation the probability distribution in (5.1).

13. *Continuation.* Find the p.g.f. of $X(t)$.

14. *Continuation.* Consider a sequence of random variables $X(t_1), \ldots, X_w(t)$ defined at the points $0 \leq t_1 < \ldots < t_w$ on the time axis in the pure death process. Derive the p.g.f. for the joint distribution of $X(t_1), \ldots, X(t_w)$.

15. *Continuation.* Find from the p.g.f. in problem 14 the joint probability distribution of $X(t_1), \ldots, X_w(t)$.

16. *Continuation.* Let

$$p_i = \exp\left\{-\int_{t_i}^{t_{i+1}} \mu(\tau)\, d\tau\right\}$$

be the probability that an individual alive at time t_i will survive to time t_{i+1}.

(a) Derive the maximum likelihood estimators $\hat{p}_0, \hat{p}_1, \ldots, \hat{p}_{w-1}$ of the probabilities $p_0, p_1, \ldots, p_{w-1}$.

(b) Are these estimators unbiased?

17. *Continuation.* Find the variance of the maximum likelihood estimator $\hat{p}_i$.

18. *Continuation.* Derive the Cramér-Rao lower bound for an unbiased estimator. Find from the general formula the Cramér-Rao lower bound for an unbiased estimator for p_i.

19. *Continuation.* Let $\tilde{p}_i$ be any unbiased estimator of p_i. If $\tilde{p}_i$ is not equal to the maximum-likelihood estimator $\hat{p}_i$ in problem 16, then $V(\tilde{p}_i) > V(\hat{p}_i)$.

20. *Continuation.* Are the estimators $\hat{p}_i$ and $\hat{p}_j$, for $i \neq j$, in problem 16 correlated? Independent?

21. *Migration processes.* Show that both the general solution (6.13) and the particular solution (6.17) satisfy the differential equation in (6.9).

22. *Continuation.* Compute from the p.g.f. in (6.17)

(a) the probability $\Pr\{X(t) = k\}$,

(b) the expectation $E[X(t)]$, and

(c) the variance of $X(t)$.

CHAPTER 9

A General Birth Process, an Equality, and an Epidemic Model

1. INTRODUCTION

The stochastic processes discussed in Chapter 8 have been developed under different assumptions and using different approaches. We shall now introduce a general model of which these processes are special cases. We shall also present an equality of stochastic processes and apply it to an epidemic model to obtain explicit formulas for the corresponding probabilities.

The symbol $p_k(t)$ was introduced in Chapter 8 to denote the transition from $X(0) = i$ at $t = 0$ to $X(t) = k$ at t. This symbol is simple but inadequate insofar as it fails to include the initial time $t = 0$ and the initial value i. To remedy this inadequacy, in this chapter and in those that follow, we shall use symbols that will explicitly include the initial time and the initial value in a transition probability. Therefore we introduce $p_{i,k}(0, t)$ in place of $p_k(t)$:

$$p_{i,k}(0, t) = \Pr\{X(t) = k \mid X(0) = i\}, \tag{1.1}$$

and generally,

$$p_{i,k}(\tau, t) = \Pr\{X(t) = k \mid X(\tau) = i\}, \tag{1.2}$$

for $\tau \leq t$.

2. A GENERAL BIRTH PROCESS

Let $X(t)$ be the population size at time t, and let the change in the value of $X(t)$ be subject to the conditions

$$\Pr\{X(t+\Delta) = k+1 | X(t) = k\} = \lambda_k(t)\Delta + o(\Delta) \tag{2.1}$$

and

$$\Pr\{X(t+\Delta) \geq k+2 | X(t) = k\} = o(\Delta), \tag{2.2}$$

so that

$$\Pr\{X(t+\Delta) = k | X(t) = k\} = 1 - \lambda_k(t)\Delta + o(\Delta). \tag{2.3}$$

Following the enumeration of various possibilities leading to $X(t+\Delta) = k$ described in Chapter 8, we arrive at the following system of differential equations [cf., section 3, Chapter 8]:

$$\frac{d}{dt} p_{i,i}(0,t) = -\lambda_i(t) p_{i,i}(0,t) \tag{2.4a}$$

and

$$\frac{d}{dt} p_{i,k}(0,t) = -\lambda_k(t) p_{i,k}(0,t) + \lambda_{k-1}(t) p_{i,k-1}(0,t), \tag{2.4b}$$

for $k = i+1, \ldots,$ where i is the initial population size at $t = 0$ and $\lambda_k(t)$ is an integrable function of t. The initial conditions of the system described in (2.4) are

$$p_{i,i}(0,0) = 1 \quad \text{and} \quad p_{i,k}(0,0) = 0, \quad \text{for } k \neq i.$$

Equation (2.4a) has the solution

$$p_{i,i}(0,t) = \exp\left\{-\int_0^t \lambda_i(\tau)\,d\tau\right\}, \tag{2.5}$$

while (2.4b) leads to the recursive relation

$$p_{i,k}(0,t) = \int_0^t \exp\left\{-\int_\tau^t \lambda_k(\xi)\,d\xi\right\} \lambda_{k-1}(\tau) p_{i,k-1}(0,\tau)\,d\tau. \tag{2.6}$$

Therefore an explicit solution for $p_{i,k}(0,t)$ can be derived successively from (2.6) for any specific integrable function $\lambda_j(t)$ for every $j \geq i$.

The probabilities $p_{i,k}(0,t)$ will assume a simple form when $\lambda_j(t)$ is a product of two functions depending on j and t respectively; that is,

$$\lambda_j(t) = \lambda_j \beta(t). \tag{2.7}$$

Here $\beta(t)$ is an integrable function such that the integral

$$\int_0^t \beta(\tau)\,d\tau \to \infty, \qquad \text{as } t \to \infty, \tag{2.8}$$

and λ_j is any arbitrary function of j subject to the restriction that

$$\lambda_i \neq \lambda_j, \qquad \text{for } i \neq j. \tag{2.9}$$

Under these conditions, the differential equations (2.4) become

$$\frac{d}{dt} p_{i,i}(0, t) = -\lambda_i \beta(t) p_{i,i}(0, t) \tag{2.10}$$

and

$$\frac{d}{dt} p_{i,k}(0, t) = -\lambda_k \beta(t) p_{i,k}(0, t) + \lambda_{k-1} \beta(t) p_{i,k-1}(0, t), \qquad \text{for } k > i. \tag{2.11}$$

Equation (2.10) has the solution

$$p_{i,i}(0, t) = \exp\left\{-\lambda_i \int_0^t \beta(\tau)\,d\tau\right\}. \tag{2.12}$$

Solving the equations in (2.11) successively, we obtain the general formula

$$p_{i,k}(0, t) = (-1)^{k-i} \lambda_i \ldots \lambda_{k-1} \left[\sum_{j=i}^{k} \frac{\exp\left\{-\lambda_j \int_0^t \beta(\tau)\,d\tau\right\}}{\prod\limits_{\substack{l=i \\ l \neq j}}^{k} (\lambda_j - \lambda_l)} \right], \qquad k = i, i + 1, \ldots. \tag{2.13}$$

Formula (2.13) may be proven by induction in the same way as was formula (3.3) in section 3, Chapter 8. We leave the proof to the reader.

Formula (2.13) represents a general birth process where the population size increases with the occurrence of an event "birth". But it can be used to derive death processes as well. The following examples show how some processes may be derived from (2.13).

Example 1. *Birth process with immigration.* A plausible function for $\lambda_j(t)$ is linear in j such that,

$$\lambda_j(t) \beta(t) = j\lambda\beta(t) + \eta\beta(t), \tag{2.14}$$

where the linear term $j\lambda\beta(t)$ corresponds to birth, while the constant $\eta\beta(t)$ corresponds to immigration, and $\beta(t)$ is a function of time. Referring to formula (2.13), we compute

$$\lambda_i \dots \lambda_{k-1} = [i\lambda + \eta] \dots [(k-1)\lambda + \eta]$$

$$= \lambda^{k-i} \binom{k + \frac{\eta}{\lambda} - 1}{k - i} (k-i)! \tag{2.15}$$

and

$$\prod_{\substack{l=i \\ l \neq j}}^{k} (\lambda_j - \lambda_l) = \prod_{\substack{l=i \\ l \neq j}}^{k} [(j\lambda + \eta) - (l\lambda + \eta)]$$

$$= \lambda^{k-i}(-1)^{k-j} \binom{k-i}{k-j}^{-1} (k-i)!\,. \tag{2.16}$$

Substituting (2.15) and (2.16) in (2.13) yields

$$p_{i,k}(0, t) = \binom{k + \frac{\eta}{\lambda} - 1}{k - i} \sum_{j=i}^{k} (-1)^{j-i} \binom{k-i}{k-j}$$

$$\exp\left\{-(j\lambda + \eta) \int_0^t \beta(\tau)\, d\tau\right\}$$

$$= \binom{k + \frac{\eta}{\lambda} - 1}{k - i} \exp\left\{-\lambda\left(i + \frac{\eta}{\lambda}\right) \int_0^t \beta(\tau)\, d\tau\right\}$$

$$\times \sum_{j=i}^{k} \binom{k-i}{k-j} (-1)^{j-i} \exp\left\{-\lambda(j-i) \int_0^t \beta(\tau)\, d\tau\right\}$$

$$= \binom{k + \frac{\eta}{\lambda} - 1}{k - i} \left[\exp\left\{-\lambda \int_0^t \beta(\tau)\, d\tau\right\}\right]^{i + \eta/\lambda}$$

$$\times \left[1 - \exp\left\{-\lambda \int_0^t \beta(\tau)\, d\tau\right\}\right]^{k-i}. \tag{2.17}$$

The last expression in (2.17) shows that the difference $X - i$ has a negative binomial distribution with the parameters

$$i + \frac{\eta}{\lambda} \quad \text{and} \quad \exp\left\{-\lambda \int_0^t \beta(\tau)d\tau\right\}. \tag{2.18}$$

Therefore the expectation and variance of the distribution are given by

$$E[X(t)] = \left(i + \frac{\eta}{\lambda}\right)\left[\exp\left\{\lambda \int_0^t \beta(\tau)\,d\tau\right\} - 1\right] + i \tag{2.19}$$

and

$$\operatorname{Var}[X(t)] = \left(i + \frac{\eta}{\lambda}\right) \exp\left\{\lambda \int_0^t \beta(\tau)\,d\tau\right\}\left[\exp\left\{\lambda \int_0^t \beta(\tau)\,d\tau\right\} - 1\right]. \tag{2.20}$$

When $\beta(t) = 1$, we have the ordinary birth process with immigration. The probability function is

$$p_{i,k}(0, t) = \binom{k + \frac{\eta}{\lambda} - 1}{k - i} [e^{-\lambda t}]^{i + \eta/\lambda} [1 - e^{-\lambda t}]^{k-i}. \tag{2.21}$$

If there is no immigration so that $\eta = 0$, we have the Yule Process:

$$p_{i,k}(0, t) = \binom{k - 1}{k - i} e^{-i\lambda t} [1 - e^{-\lambda t}]^{k-i}, \qquad k = i, i + 1, \ldots . \tag{2.22}$$

Example 2. *A divergent process.* When $\lambda_j = j^2\lambda$ and $\beta(t)$ is a function of t, the probability function derived from (2.13) is

$$p_{i,k}(0, t) = \binom{k - 1}{k - i}^2 \sum_{j=i}^{k} (-1)^{j-i} \binom{k - i}{k - j}^2 \binom{2j - 1}{j - i}^{-1} \binom{k + j}{k - j}^{-1}$$
$$\times \exp\left\{-j^2\lambda \int_0^t \beta(\tau)\,d\tau\right\}, \qquad k = i, i + 1, \ldots . \tag{2.23}$$

A population whose development is governed by this probability function will experience a much more rapid rate of growth than those described in other processes. According to the function $\lambda_j = j^2\lambda$, the rate of growth in this model is proportionate to the square of the population size j. As a result, there is a positive probability

$$1 - \sum_{k=i} p_{i,k}(0, t) > 0$$

that, at least for large t, the population size will become infinitely large. The corresponding random variable $X(t)$ is therefore improper.

Example 3. *The death process.* The general model, as noted earlier, applies to both increasing processes and decreasing processes. To illustrate, we shall now derive the pure death process from the general formula (2.13). Let there be i individuals alive at time $t = 0$, and let the random variable $X(t)$ be the number of deaths occurring during the interval $(0, t)$, with $X(0) = 0$. The transition probability is defined by

$$p_{0,k}(0, t) = \Pr\{X(t) = k \,|\, X(0) = 0\}, \qquad k = 0, 1, \ldots, i. \tag{2.24}$$

Suppose that i individuals alive at time $t = 0$ are subject to the same force of mortality μ, and the events of death take place independently. Then, given $(i - j)$ survivors at time t, the quantities λ_j and $\beta(t)$ in (2.7) will be

$$\lambda_j = i - j \qquad \text{and} \qquad \beta(t) = \mu. \tag{2.25}$$

Therefore we find in formula (2.13) that

$$\begin{aligned} \lambda_0 \ldots \lambda_{k-1} &= (i - 0)(i - 1) \ldots (i - k + 1) \\ &= \binom{i}{k} k! \end{aligned} \tag{2.26}$$

and

$$\begin{aligned} \prod_{\substack{l=0 \\ l \neq j}}^{k} (\lambda_j - \lambda_l) &= \prod_{\substack{l=0 \\ l \neq j}}^{k} [(i - j) - (i - l)] \\ &= (-1)^j \binom{k}{j}^{-1} k!. \end{aligned} \tag{2.27}$$

Substituting (2.26), (2.27), and $\beta(t) = \mu$ in (2.13), we find the probability

$$p_{0,k}(0, t) = \binom{i}{k} \sum_{j=0}^{k} (-1)^{k-j} \binom{k}{j} e^{-(i-j)\mu t}$$

$$= \binom{i}{k} e^{-(i-k)\mu t} \sum_{j=0}^{k} \binom{k}{j} (-1)^{k-j} e^{-(k-j)\mu t}$$

$$= \binom{i}{k} e^{-(i-k)\mu t} [1 - e^{-\mu t}]^{k}, \qquad k = 0, 1, \ldots, i, \tag{2.28}$$

which is the same as that in the death process (cf., equations (5.1) in Chapter 8).

Example 4. *Poisson process.* While formula (2.13) holds only for cases where $\lambda_i \neq \lambda_j$, for $i \neq j$, the Poisson process may be derived from the general model as a limiting case as $\lambda_j \to \lambda$. That is, as $\lambda_j \to \lambda$, the probability

$$p_{0,k}(0, t) = (-1)^k \lambda_0 \ldots \lambda_{k-1} \left[\sum_{j=0}^{k} \frac{\exp\{-\lambda_j t\}}{\prod_{\substack{l=0 \\ l \neq j}}^{k} (\lambda_j - \lambda_l)} \right] \tag{2.29}$$

approaches

$$p_{0,k}(0, t) = \frac{(\lambda t)^k e^{-\lambda t}}{k!}, \qquad k = 0, 1, \ldots \tag{2.30}$$

We shall sketch the proof below.

According to Lemma 2 in section 2.1 of Chapter 6, for any distinct numbers $\varepsilon_0, \varepsilon_1, \ldots, \varepsilon_k$,

$$\sum_{j=0}^{k} \frac{\varepsilon_j^n}{\prod_{\substack{l=0 \\ l \neq j}}^{k} (\varepsilon_j - \varepsilon_l)} = 0, \qquad n = 0, 1, \ldots, (k-1),$$

$$= 1, \qquad n = k. \tag{2.31}$$

Let $\lambda_j = \lambda + \varepsilon_j$ in (2.29) with $\varepsilon_i \neq \varepsilon_j$, for $i \neq j$, and take the limit of the resulting expression as $\varepsilon_j \to 0$, for $j = 0, 1, \ldots, k$. Clearly,

$$\lim_{\substack{\varepsilon_j \to 0 \\ j=0,\ldots,k-1}} (\lambda + \varepsilon_0) \ldots (\lambda + \varepsilon_{k-1}) = \lambda^k. \tag{2.32}$$

To evaluate the sum inside the brackets in (2.29), we expand the exponential

$$e^{-(\lambda+\varepsilon_j)t} = e^{-\lambda t}\left[\sum_{n=0}^{\infty} \frac{\varepsilon_j^n(-t)^n}{n!}\right]$$

and write the sum as

$$\sum_{j=0}^{k} \frac{\exp\{-\lambda_j t\}}{\prod_{\substack{l=0\\ l\neq j}}^{k}(\lambda_j-\lambda_l)} = e^{-\lambda t}\sum_{j=0}^{k}\sum_{n=0}^{\infty} \frac{\varepsilon_j^n(-t)^n}{n!\prod_{\substack{l=0\\ l\neq j}}^{k}(\varepsilon_j-\varepsilon_l)}. \tag{2.33}$$

As $\varepsilon_j \to 0$, for $j = 0, 1, \ldots, k$, the ratio

$$\frac{\varepsilon_j^n}{\prod_{\substack{l=0\\ l\neq j}}^{k}(\varepsilon_j-\varepsilon_l)} \to 0$$

for every $n > k$, since in this case the numerator is of a smaller order of magnitude than the denominator. For every $n \le k$, we use the lemma and (2.31) to write

$$\sum_{j=0}^{k} \frac{\varepsilon_j^n}{\prod_{\substack{l=0\\ l\neq j}}^{k}(\varepsilon_j-\varepsilon_l)} = 0, \qquad n = 0, 1, \ldots, k-1$$

$$= 1, \qquad n = k.$$

Consequently,

$$\lim_{\substack{\varepsilon_j\to 0\\ j=0,\ldots,k}} e^{-\lambda t}\sum_{j=0}^{k}\sum_{n=0}^{\infty} \frac{\varepsilon_j^n(-t)^n}{n!\prod_{\substack{l=0\\ l\neq j}}^{k}(\varepsilon_j-\varepsilon_l)} = \frac{e^{-\lambda t}(-t)^k}{k!}. \tag{2.34}$$

Substituting (2.32) and (2.34) in (2.29), we recover (2.30).

Other processes described in Chapter 8 can be derived from the general formula (2.13) by specifying the functions λ_j and $\beta(t)$. Table 1 summarizes the relationships between the general birth process and the processes discussed in Chapter 8 and those in this chapter.

Table 1. The general birth process in (2.13) and other processes

Process	Formula	Chapter	λ_j	$\beta(t)$
Poisson Process	(2.8)	8	λ	1
Pure Birth Process	(3.3)	8	λ_j	1
Yule Process	(3.10)	8	$j\lambda$	1
	(3.27)*	8	j	$\lambda(t)$
Polya Processes	(4.14)*	8	$\lambda(1 + aj)$	$(1 + \lambda at)^{-1}$
Pure Death	(5.1)	8	$i - j$	$\mu(t)$
Process**	(2.28)	9	$i - j$	μ
Birth Process with immigration	(2.17)	9	$j\lambda + \eta$	$\beta(t)$
A divergent process	(2.23)	9	$j^2\lambda$	$\beta(t)$

*In terms of probability generating functions

**In the general formula (2.13), $X(t)$ is defined as the number of deaths occurring up to t among the original cohort of i.

3. AN EQUALITY IN STOCHASTIC PROCESSES

Explicit formulas of the transition probabilities $p_{i,k}(0, t)$ are needed in practical applications not only for the understanding of the problems at hand, but also for an appreciation of stochastic processes as an analytical tool. We have made an effort to obtain formulas in the problems discussed. We now introduce an equality to obtain explicit solutions in more complicated cases. Consider again the transition probability

$$p_{i,k}(0, t) = \Pr\{X(t) = k \mid X(0) = i\}. \tag{3.1}$$

Let j be an arbitrary but *fixed* integer $i \le j < k$. The transition $j \to j + 1$ must take place somewhere between 0 and t. Let it take place in $(\tau, \tau + d\tau)$; then we have a sequence of transitions: $i \to j \to j + 1 \to k$. The corresponding probability is

$$p_{i,j}(0, \tau)\lambda_j(\tau)d\tau\, p_{j+1,k}(\tau, t). \tag{3.2}$$

For different values of τ, the corresponding sequences are mutually independent. Addition theorem shows that the integral

$$\int_0^t p_{i,j}(0, \tau)\lambda_j(\tau)\, p_{j+1,k}(\tau, t)d\tau \tag{3.3}$$

is the probability that the sequence $i \to j \to j+1 \to k$ will occur during $(0, t)$. Since the random variable must assume value j before taking on value k at time t, the integral in (3.3) is identical to the probability in (3.1).

Theorem 1. *For every fixed integer j, where $i \leq j < k$, the probability in* (3.1) *satisfies the equality*

$$p_{i,k}(0, t) = \int_0^t p_{i,j}(0, \tau)\, \lambda_j(\tau) p_{j+1,k}(\tau, t)\, d\tau. \tag{3.4}$$

The argument that precedes the theorem is in effect a proof. We shall, however, present an analytic proof using the Riemann integral.[1]

Proof. Partition the closed interval $[0, t]$ into n disjoint closed intervals $\Delta_l = [t_l, t_{l+1}]$, where $0 = t_0 < t_1 < t_2 < \ldots < t_n = t$. The union of the n intervals is $[0, t]$. Let j be an arbitrary but fixed integer, $i \leq j < k$. Then the probability that the transition $j \to j + 1$ will occur within an interval $\Delta_l = [t_l, t_{l+1}]$ is, approximately,

$$p_{i,j}(0, t_l)\, \lambda_j(t_l) |\Delta_l|\, p_{j+1,k}(t_l, t). \tag{3.5}$$

The approximation improves as the length of the interval $|\Delta| \to 0$. Since the transition $j \to j + 1$ can occur within any interval Δ_l, for $l = 0, \ldots, n$, and since the Δ_l's are disjoint, we sum over l to obtain the approximate formula

$$p_{i,k}(0, t) \approx \sum_{l=0}^{n} p_{i,j}(0, t_l)\, \lambda_j(t_l)\, p_{j+1,k}(t_l, t) |\Delta_l|. \tag{3.6}$$

Let $\Delta = \max|\Delta_l|$; then as $n \to \infty$, $\Delta \to 0$. By definition of the Riemann integral, we have

$$\lim_{\substack{\Delta \to 0 \\ n \to \infty}} \sum_{l=0}^{n} p_{i,j}(0, t_l)\, \lambda_j(t_l)\, p_{j+1,k}(t_l, t) |\Delta_l| = \int_0^t p_{i,j}(0, \tau) \lambda_j(\tau) p_{j+1,k}(\tau, t)\, d\tau. \tag{3.7}$$

Formula (3.4) follows.

In deriving equation (3.4), we tacitly assumed that the process is increasing where the value of $X(t)$ is increased by the occurrence

[1] The author benefitted from a suggestion made by John Emerson.

of an event (for example, the pure birth process). It is easy to show by analogy that a similar equality can be derived for decreasing processes (for example, the pure death process). Applications of the equality are demonstrated in the following examples and in the problems at the end of this chapter.

Example 1. *The Poisson process.* In the nonhomogeneous case where $\lambda_j(\tau) = \lambda(\tau)$ is a function of time, the transition probability is

$$p_{i,k}(0, t) = \frac{\exp\left\{-\int_0^t \lambda(\xi)\,d\xi\right\}\left[\int_0^t \lambda(\xi)\,d\xi\right]^{k-i}}{(k-i)!}. \tag{3.8}$$

According to equality (3.4), the right-hand side of (3.8) is equal to

$$\int_0^t \left[\frac{\exp\left\{-\int_0^\tau \lambda(\xi)\,d\xi\right\}}{(j-i)!}\left(\int_0^\tau \lambda(\xi)d\xi\right)^{j-i}\right]$$
$$\times\, \lambda(\tau)\left[\frac{\exp\left\{-\int_\tau^t \lambda(\xi)\,d\xi\right\}}{(k-j-1)!}\left(\int_\tau^t \lambda(\xi)\,d\xi\right)^{k-j-1}\right]d\tau. \tag{3.9}$$

To evaluate the integral in (3.9), we introduce

$$\theta(\tau) = \frac{\int_0^\tau \lambda(\xi)d\xi}{\int_0^t \lambda(\xi)\,d\xi} \qquad \text{and} \qquad d\theta(\tau) = \frac{\lambda(\tau)d\tau}{\int_0^t \lambda(\xi)\,d\xi} \tag{3.10}$$

and rewrite (3.9) as

$$\frac{\exp\left\{-\int_0^t \lambda(\xi)d\xi\right\}}{(j-i)!(k-j-1)!}\left(\int_0^t \lambda(\xi)d\xi\right)^{k-i}\int_0^1 [\theta(\tau)]^{j-i}\,[1-\theta(\tau)]^{k-j-1}\,d\theta(\tau). \tag{3.11}$$

The last integral in (3.11) is a beta function with parameters $j-i$ and $k-j-1$, and the integral

$$\int_0^1 [\theta(\tau)]^{j-i}\,[1-\theta(\tau)]^{k-j-1}\,d\theta(\tau) = \frac{(j-i)!(k-j-1)!}{(k-i)!}. \tag{3.12}$$

Substituting (3.12) in (3.11), we recover (3.8).

Example 2. The Polya process is defined by the function

$$\lambda_j(t) = \frac{\lambda + \lambda a j}{1 + \lambda a t}. \tag{3.13}$$

The corresponding transition probability is

$$p_{i,k}(t_0, t) = \binom{k + \frac{1}{a} - 1}{k - i}\left[\frac{1 + \lambda a t_0}{1 + \lambda a t}\right]^{i+1/a}\left[1 - \frac{1 + \lambda a t_0}{1 + \lambda a t}\right]^{k-i}, \tag{3.14}$$

where t_0 is the initial time, λ and a are non-negative constants, and the combinatorial factor is defined, as usual, as

$$\binom{k + \frac{1}{a} - 1}{k - i} = \frac{\left(k + \frac{1}{a} - 1\right)\left(k + \frac{1}{a} - 2\right)\cdots\left(i + \frac{1}{a}\right)}{(k-i)!}. \tag{3.15}$$

Using the general formula (3.14) for the probabilities $p_{i,j}(0, t)$ and $p_{j+1,k}(\tau, t)$ in equality (3.4) we obtain

$$\int_{t_0}^{t} p_{i,j}(0, \tau)\lambda_j(\tau)p_{j+1,k}(\tau, t)\,d\tau$$

$$= \binom{j + \frac{1}{a} - 1}{j - i}\binom{k + \frac{1}{a} - 1}{k - j - 1}\int_{t_0}^{t}\left(\frac{1 + \lambda a t_0}{1 + \lambda a \tau}\right)^{i+1/a}\left(1 - \frac{1 + \lambda a t_0}{1 + \lambda a \tau}\right)^{j-i}$$

$$\times\left(\frac{\lambda + \lambda a j}{1 + \lambda a \tau}\right)\left(\frac{1 + \lambda a \tau}{1 + \lambda a t}\right)^{j+1+1/a}\left(1 - \frac{1 + \lambda a \tau}{1 + \lambda a t}\right)^{k-j-1} d\tau. \tag{3.16}$$

Here the integral is simply

$$\frac{(1+\lambda a t_0)^{i+1/a}}{(1+\lambda a t)^{k+1/a}}(\lambda a)^{k-i-1}(\lambda+\lambda a j)\int_{t_0}^{t}(\tau-t_0)^{j-i}(t-\tau)^{k-j-1}\,d\tau$$

$$=\left(\frac{1+\lambda a t_0}{1+\lambda a t}\right)^{i+1/a}\left(1-\frac{1+\lambda a t_0}{1+\lambda a t}\right)^{k-i}\left(j+\frac{1}{a}\right)\binom{k-i}{j-i}^{-1}(k-j)^{-1}.$$

(3.17)

When we substitute the last expression in (3.17) for the integral in (3.16), the right hand side of (3.16) reduces to that in (3.14), proving equality (3.4) for the Polya process.

4. A SIMPLE STOCHASTIC EPIDEMIC—McKENDRICK'S MODEL

In a simple stochastic epidemic model, a population consists of two groups of individuals: susceptibles and infectives. There are no removals, no deaths, no immunes, and no recoveries from infection. Suppose that at the initial time $t = 0$, there are N susceptibles and one infective. For each time t, for $t > 0$, let the number of infectives be denoted by $X(t)$ and the number of susceptibles be denoted by $N + 1 - X(t)$, so that the total population size remains unchanged. Our primary purpose is to derive an explicit solution for the probability distribution of the random variable $X(t)$:

$$p_{1,n}(0,t)=\Pr\{X(t)=n\,|\,X(0)=1\},\qquad \text{for } n=1,\ldots,N+1. \tag{4.1}$$

For each interval (τ, t), $0 \le \tau \le t < \infty$, and for each k, we assume that there is a non-negative continuous function $\lambda_k(\tau)$ such that

$$\left.\frac{\partial}{\partial t}p_{k,n}(\tau,t)\right|_{t=\tau}=\begin{cases}-\lambda_k(\tau) & \text{for } n=k\\ \lambda_k(\tau) & \text{for } n=k+1\\ 0 & \text{otherwise.}\end{cases} \tag{4.2}$$

Under the assumption of homogeneous mixing of the population, we let

$$\lambda_k(\tau)=k(N+1-k)\beta(\tau)=a_k\,\beta(\tau) \tag{4.3}$$

where

$$a_k=k(N+1-k). \tag{4.4}$$

The quantity $\beta(\tau)$, known as the *infection rate,* is a function of τ, such that the integral

$$\int_0^t \beta(\tau)\,d\tau = \theta(t) \tag{4.5}$$

tends to infinity as $t \to \infty$. We can show that, for each $t > 0$, the probability function $p_{1,n}\,(0,t)$ satisfies the system of differential equations

$$\frac{d}{dt}p_{1,1}(0, t) = -a_1\beta(t)p_{1,1}(0, t) \tag{4.6a}$$

$$\frac{d}{dt}p_{1,n}(0, t) = -a_n\beta(t)p_{1,n}(0, t) + a_{n-1}\beta(t)p_{1,n-1}(0, t) \tag{4.6b}$$

for $n = 2, \ldots, N + 1$. Equations (4.6a) and (4.6b) are essentially the same as (2.10) and (2.11) in the general birth process.

This epidemic model was originally formulated by A. M. McKendrick in 1926 in connection with the study of epidemics. It has since been studied extensively by Bailey [1963], Bartlett [1956], and Kendall [1956], among others. An important feature of this model is that the coefficient a_n in the differential equation (4.6b) is a quadratic function of n. As a result, a solution for the probability $p_{1,n}\,(0, t)$ is difficult to obtain by ordinary methods. For example, the differential equation for the probability generating function of $p_{1,n}\,(0, t)$ is of second order, which does not lend itself to easy solution. The Laplace transform does not provide an explicit solution either. The present method, which relies on equality (3.4) in Section 3, is based on a paper by Yang and Chiang [1971]. The original model of McKendrick studied by Bailey and others is time homogeneous in the sense that $\beta(t) = \beta$ is independent of time. This model is nonhomogeneous since $\beta(t)$ is time dependent. It allows the intensity of spreading of disease to vary with the "age" of an epidemic and is thus more realistic. The case where $\beta(t) = \beta$ will be discussed in section 4.2.

4.1 Solution for the Probability $p_{1,n}\,(0, t)$.

The formula for the probability depends upon whether $n \le (N + 1)/2$ or $n > (N + 1)/2$. When $1 \le n \le (N + 1)/2$, the constants $a_1, \ldots, a_n$ are all distinct, and equation (2.13) in the general birth process is directly applicable. In other words, the probability is given by

$$p_{1,n}(0, t) = (-1)^{n-1} a_1 \dots a_{n-1} \left[\sum_{i=1}^{n} \frac{e^{-a_i \theta(t)}}{\prod_{\substack{\alpha=1 \\ \alpha \neq i}}^{n} (a_i - a_\alpha)} \right],$$

$$\text{for } n = 1, \dots, \left[\frac{N+1}{2} \right], \tag{4.7}$$

where $[(N + 1)/2]$ designates the largest integer $\leq (N + 1)/2$. When $n = 1$, we assume that $a_0 = 1$ and that the product $\Pi(a_i - a_\alpha) = 1$, so

$$p_{1,1}(0, t) = e^{-a_1 \theta(t)}, \qquad \text{with} \qquad \theta(t) = \int_0^t \beta(\tau) d\tau. \tag{4.7a}$$

Formula (2.13) no longer applies when $n > (N + 1)/2$, since in this case, $a_1, \dots, a_n$ are not all distinct. In particular,

$$a_i = i(N + 1 - i) = a_{N+1-i}. \tag{4.8}$$

However, an explicit formula for the probability $p_{1n}(0, t)$ can be obtained by applying equality (3.4) in the preceding section:

$$p_{1,n}(0, t) = \int_0^t p_{1,k}(0, \tau) a_k \beta(\tau) p_{k+1,n}(\tau, t) d\tau. \tag{4.9}$$

The integer k in (4.9) must be chosen so that the a_i in the probability $p_{1,k}(0, \tau)$ are distinct and the a_i in $p_{k+1,n}(\tau, t)$ are also distinct. When N is even, $k = N/2$; when N is odd, $k = (N + 1)/2$.

With these values of k, we apply (4.7) to the two probabilities in the integrand in equation (4.9):

$$p_{1,k}(0, \tau) = (-1)^{k-1} a_1 \dots a_{k-1} \left[\sum_{i=1}^{k} \frac{\exp\{-a_i \theta(\tau)\}}{\prod_{\substack{\alpha=1 \\ \alpha \neq i}}^{k} (a_i - a_\alpha)} \right] \tag{4.10}$$

and

$$p_{k+1,n}(\tau, t) = (-1)^{n-k-1} a_{k+1} \dots a_{n-1} \left[\sum_{j=k+1}^{n} \frac{\exp\{-a_j [\theta(t) - \theta(\tau)]\}}{\prod_{\substack{\beta=k+1 \\ \beta \neq j}}^{n} (a_j - a_\beta)} \right]. \tag{4.11}$$

Substituting (4.10) and (4.11) in (4.9) gives us the basic formula

$$p_{1n}(0, t) = (-1)^n a_1 \dots a_{n-1}$$

$$\times \sum_{i=1}^{k} \sum_{j=k+1}^{n} \int_0^t \frac{\exp\{-a_i\theta(\tau)\} \exp\{-a_j[\theta(t) - \theta(\tau)]\}}{\prod_{\substack{\alpha=1 \\ \alpha \neq i}}^{k} (a_i - a_\alpha) \prod_{\substack{\beta=k+1 \\ \beta \neq j}}^{n} (a_j - a_\beta)} \beta(\tau)\, d\tau. \tag{4.12}$$

The integral in (4.12) depends on the values of a_i and a_j. According to the definition of $\theta(t)$ in (4.5),

$$\int_0^t \exp\{-a_i\theta(\tau)\} \exp\{-a_j[\theta(t) - \theta(\tau)]\}\beta(\tau)d\tau$$

$$= \frac{-1}{a_i - a_j}[\exp\{-a_i\theta(t)\} - \exp\{-a_j\theta(t)\}], \qquad \text{for } a_j \neq a_i, \tag{4.13}$$

and

$$\int_0^t \exp\{-a_i\theta(\tau)\} \exp\{-a_j[\theta(t) - \theta(\tau)]\}\beta(\tau)d\tau$$

$$= \theta(t)\exp\{-a_i\theta(t)\}, \qquad \text{for } a_j = a_i. \tag{4.14}$$

There are $(n - k)$ terms where $a_i = a_j$ with $i + j = N + 1$. They are

$$a_k = a_{k+1},\ a_{k-1} = a_{k+2},\ \dots,\ a_{2k-n+1} = a_n, \qquad \text{for } 2k = N$$

and

$$a_{k-1} = a_{k+1},\ a_{k-2} = a_{k+2},\ \dots,\ a_{2k-n} = a_n, \qquad \text{for } 2k = N+1.$$

Keeping in mind that when N is even, $k = N/2$, and when N is odd, $k = (N + 1)/2$, we can get from (4.12) the desired formula:

$$p_{1,n}(0, t) = (-1)^{n-1} a_1 \dots a_{n-1} \left[-\sum_{j=k+1}^{n} \frac{\theta(t)\exp\{-a_j\theta(t)\}}{\prod_{\substack{\beta=1 \\ a_\beta \neq a_j}}^{n} (a_j - a_\beta)} + \sum_{\substack{i=1 \\ a_i \neq a_j}}^{k} \sum_{j=k+1}^{n} \frac{\exp\{-a_i\theta(t)\} - \exp\{-a_j\theta(t)\}}{(a_i - a_j) \prod_{\substack{\alpha=1 \\ \alpha \neq i}}^{k} (a_i - a_\alpha) \prod_{\substack{\beta=k+1 \\ \beta \neq j}}^{n} (a_j - a_\beta)} \right], \quad (4.15)$$

for $n = k + 1, \dots, N + 1$.

4.2. Infection Time and Duration of an Epidemic.

The length of time elapsed up to the occurrence of the nth infection is a continuous random variable taking on non-negative real numbers. Let it be denoted by T_n, for $1 \leq n \leq N + 1$, with $T_1 = 0$. The duration of an epidemic is T_{N+1}, the length of time elapsed up to the infection of the last number of the population. The purpose of this section is to derive explicit formulas for the density function $f_n(t)$, the distribution $F_n(t)$, and the expectation and variance of T_n.

The density function $f_n(t)$ has a close relationship with the probability $p_{1,n}(t)$. By definition, $f_n(t)dt$ is the probability that the random variable T_n will take on values in $(t, t + dt)$. This means that at time t there are $n - 1$ infectives, and the nth infection takes place in the interval $(t, t + dt)$. The probability of the occurrence of these events is $p_{1,n-1}(0, t)a_{n-1}\beta(t)dt$. Therefore we have the density function

$$f_n(t)\,dt = p_{1,n-1}(0, t)a_{n-1}\beta(t)\,dt, \quad (4.16)$$

and the distribution function

$$F_n(t) = \int_0^t p_{1,n-1}(0, \tau)a_{n-1}\beta(\tau)\,d\tau, \qquad \text{for } n = 2, \dots, N + 1. \quad (4.17)$$

Using the formulas of the probabilities in the preceding section, we can write down explicit functions for $f_n(t)$ and $F_n(t)$ for each n. For example, for $n \leq (N + 1)/2$, we use formula (4.7) to obtain the density function

$$f_n(t)\,dt = (-1)^{n-2} a_1 \dots a_{n-1} \left[\sum_{i=1}^{n-1} \frac{\beta(t) \exp\{-a_i \theta(t)\}}{\prod_{\substack{\alpha=1 \\ \alpha \neq i}}^{n-1} (a_i - a_\alpha)} \right] dt \quad (4.18)$$

and the distribution function

$$F_n(t) = (-1)^{n-2} a_1 \dots a_{n-1} \sum_{i=1}^{n-1} \frac{1 - \exp\{-a_i \theta(t)\}}{\prod_{\substack{\alpha=1 \\ \alpha \neq i}}^{n-1} (a_i - a_\alpha) a_i}. \quad (4.19)$$

In this model, evidently the nth infection occurs within a finite time interval. Therefore, as $t \to \infty$, $f_n(t) \to 0$ and $F_n(t) \to 1$. This means that, since

$$\lim_{t\to\infty} \theta(t) = \lim_{t\to\infty} \int_0^t \beta(\tau)\,d\tau = \infty, \quad (4.5a)$$

we should have

$$F_n(\infty) = (-1)^{n-2} a_1 \dots a_{n-1} \sum_{i=1}^{n-1} \frac{1}{\prod_{\substack{\alpha=1 \\ \alpha \neq i}}^{n-1} (a_i - a_\alpha) a_i} = 1. \quad (4.20)$$

We can show that the last equality in (4.20) holds true by applying Lemma 2, Chapter 6. According to the lemma, for distinct $c_1, \dots, c_n$,

$$\sum_{i=1}^{n} \frac{1}{\prod_{\substack{\alpha=1 \\ \alpha \neq i}}^{n} (c_i - c_\alpha)} = 0$$

or

$$\sum_{i=1}^{n-1} \frac{1}{\prod_{\substack{\alpha=1 \\ \alpha \neq i}}^{n-1} (c_i - c_\alpha)(c_i - c_n)} = -\frac{1}{\prod_{\alpha=1}^{n} (c_n - c_\alpha)}. \quad (4.21)$$

When $c_n = 0$, (4.21) becomes

$$\sum_{i=1}^{n-1} \frac{1}{\prod_{\substack{\alpha=1 \\ \alpha \neq i}}^{n-1} (c_i - c_\alpha) c_i} = - \frac{1}{\prod_{\alpha=1}^{n-1} (-c_\alpha)}$$

$$= (-1)^{n-2} [c_1 \dots c_{n-1}]^{-1}, \qquad (4.22)$$

which implies (4.20).

The expectation and variance of T_n can be computed directly from the definitions

$$E(T_n) = \int_0^\infty t f_n(t) dt \qquad (4.23)$$

and

$$\mathrm{Var}(T_n) = \int_0^\infty [t - E(T_n)]^2 f_n(t) dt. \qquad (4.24)$$

Explicit formulas depend on the function $\beta(t)$. However, when the infection rate is independent of time with $\beta(t) = \beta$, an alternative approach proves somewhat simpler.

The length of time elapsed until the occurrence of the nth infection may be divided into two periods: A period of length T_{n-1} up to the occurrence of the $(n - 1)^{\text{th}}$ infection, and a period of length t_n between the occurrences of the $(n - 1)^{\text{th}}$ and the nth infections. The sum of the two periods is equal to the entire length of time:

$$T_n = T_{n-1} + t_n. \qquad (4.25)$$

When $\beta(t) = \beta$, T_{n-1} and t_n are independently distributed non-negative random variables, with their respective density functions being

$$f_{n-1}(t) = p_{1,n-2}(0, t) a_{n-2} \beta \qquad (4.26)$$

and

$$g_n(t) = p_{n-1,n-1}(0, t) a_{n-1} \beta. \qquad (4.27)$$

According to (4.25), the distribution of T_n is the convolution of the distributions of T_{n-1} and t_n, and the density functions satisfy the relationship

$$f_n(t) = \int_0^t f_{n-1}(\tau) g_n(t - \tau) d\tau. \qquad (4.28)$$

Now, the density function in (4.27) is exponential [cf., Equation (4.7a)],

$$g_n(t) = a_{n-1}\beta e^{-a_{n-1}\beta t}, \tag{4.29}$$

with the expectation

$$E(t_n) = \frac{1}{a_{n-1}\beta} \tag{4.30}$$

and the variance

$$\sigma^2_{t_n} = \frac{1}{a^2_{n-1}\beta^2}. \tag{4.31}$$

On the other hand, equation (4.25) can be extended so that

$$T_n = t_2 + \dots + t_n, \tag{4.32}$$

where $t_2, \dots, t_n$ are independently distributed random variables. It follows that the expectation and variance of T_n are

$$E(T_n) = \frac{1}{\beta}\sum_{i=1}^{n-1}\frac{1}{a_i} \quad \text{and} \quad \sigma^2_{T_n} = \frac{1}{\beta^2}\sum_{i=1}^{n-1}\frac{1}{a_i^2}, \qquad n = 2, \dots, N+1. \tag{4.33}$$

5. PROBLEMS FOR SOLUTION

1. Solve the differential equations for the transition probabilities in (2.10) and (2.11) successively to obtain the solution in (2.13).

2. Derive from the formula in (2.17) the p.g.f. for $p_{i,k}(0,t)$.

3. *Continuation.* Compute from $p_{i,k}(0,t)$ in equation (2.17) the expectation and variance of $X(t)$.

4. *Continuation.* Let two random variables $X(t_1)$ and $X(t_2)$ be defined at t_1 and t_2, respectively, for $0 \le t_1 < t_2$.

(a) Derive the joint probability distribution of the two random variables given $X(0) = i$.

(b) Find the expectations of $X(t_1)$ and $X(t_2)$ given $X(0) = i$.

(c) Find the variances and the covariance of $X(t_1)$ and $X(t_2)$.

5. *Polya Process.* When

$$\lambda_j = \lambda(1 + ja) \text{ and } \beta(t) = (1 + \lambda at)^{-1}$$

$p_{i,k}(0,t)$ in equation (2.13) becomes the transition probability in the Polya process. Find an explicit formula for $p_{i,k}(0,t)$.

6. Show that equation (3.4) holds true for the pure birth process with the transition probability

$$p_{i,k}(0,t) = (-1)^{k-i}\lambda_i \dots \lambda_{k-1} \sum_{j=i}^{k} \frac{\exp\left\{-\lambda_j \int_0^t \beta(\tau)\,d\tau\right\}}{\prod_{\substack{l=i \\ l \neq j}}^{k} (\lambda_j - \lambda_l)} \tag{2.13}$$

7. Show that the stochastic equality in (3.4) holds true for the transition probability in equation (2.17).

8. The equality in (3.4) may be extended for any number of intermediate values between $X(0)$ and $X(t)$. A simple example suffices to illustrate the idea. For every fixed integer j and k, $i \le j < k < l$, the probability

$$\mathrm{P}\{X(t) = l \mid X(0) = i\} = p_{i,l}(0,\,t)$$

satisfies the equality

$$p_{i,l}(0,\,t) = \int_0^t \int_0^{\tau_2} p_{i,j}(0,\,\tau_1)\,\lambda_j(\tau_1)\,p_{j+1,k}(\tau_1,\tau_2)\,\lambda_k(\tau_2)\,p_{k+1,l}(\tau_2,t)\,d\tau_1\,d\tau_2.$$

Prove the equality above.

9. The non-homogeneous death process has the transition probability

$$p_{i,l}(0,\,t) = \binom{i}{l}\left[e^{-\int_0^t \mu(\tau)d\tau}\right]^l \left[1 - e^{-\int_0^t \mu(\tau)d\tau}\right]^{i-l}.$$

Show that the above transition probability satisfies the equality

$$p_{i,l}(0,t) = \int_0^t p_{i,j}(0,\tau)\,j\,\mu(\tau)\,p_{j-1,l}(\tau,t)\,d\tau.$$

10. The Yule process has the transition probability

$$p_{ik}(0,t) = \binom{k-1}{k-i} e^{-i\lambda t}\left[1 - e^{-\lambda t}\right]^{k-i}.$$

Show that the above transition probability satisfies the equality in problem 8.

11. *Epidemic model.* Find the density function $f_n(t)$ and the distribution function $F_n(t)$ for the n-th infection time for $(N+1)/2 < n \le N+1$. Show that $f_n(t) \to 0$ and $F_n(t) \to 1$, as $t \to \infty$.

12. *Continuation.* When $\beta(t) = \beta$, the density function of the n-th infection time T_n in (4.18) reduces to

$$f_n(t)\,dt = (-1)^{n-2} a_1 \dots a_{n-1} \sum_{i=1}^{n-1} \frac{\beta e^{-a_i \beta t}}{\prod_{\substack{\alpha=1 \\ \alpha \neq i}}^{n-1} (a_i - a_\alpha)}$$

Find from this density function the expectation $E[T_n]$ and the variance $V[T_n]$.

13. *Continuation.* For $\beta(t) = \beta$, find the density function of the n-th infection time T_n for $(N + 1)/2 < n \le N + 1$. Derive from the density function the expectation $E[T_n]$ and the variance $V[T_n]$.

14. *Continuation.* Suppose $\beta(t) = Bc^t$. Find the density function and the distribution function of T_n, for $1 < n < (N + 1)/2$.

CHAPTER 10

Birth-Death Processes and Queueing Processes

1. INTRODUCTION

Most of the stochastic processes presented in Chapters 8 and 9 are either increasing processes or decreasing processes. In this chapter we shall consider processes that permit a population to grow as well as to decline. These are more relevant to biological and human populations in which both births and deaths occur. We shall discuss two models with a detailed application to queueing processes, and briefly describe some other models of practical interest in the exercises of this chapter.

Again we let $X(t)$ denote the size of a population at time t for $0 \leq t < \infty$, with the initial population $X(0) = i$ and the transition probability

$$p_{i,k}(0, t) = \Pr\{X(t) = k | X(0) = i\}, \qquad k = 0, 1, \ldots. \tag{1.1}$$

Using $\lambda_k(t)$ and $\mu_k(t)$ for the birth intensity and death intensity and following the enumeration process as in preceding chapters, we find that the probability $p_{i,k}(0, t + \Delta)$ may be expressed in the difference equation

$$\begin{aligned} p_{i,k}(0, t + \Delta) &= p_{i,k}(0, t)\,[1 - \lambda_k(t)\Delta - \mu_k(t)\Delta] \\ &\quad + p_{i,k-1}(0, t)\lambda_{k-1}(t)\Delta + p_{i,k+1}(0, t)\mu_{k+1}(t)\Delta + o(\Delta). \end{aligned} \tag{1.2}$$

This leads to the system of differential equations

$$\frac{d}{dt}p_{i,0}(0, t) = -[\lambda_0(t) + \mu_0(t)]\,p_{i,0}(0, t) + \mu_1(t)p_{i,1}(0, t)$$

$$\frac{d}{dt}p_{i,k}(0, t) = -[\lambda_k(t) + \mu_k(t)]\,p_{i,k}(0, t) + \lambda_{k-1}(t)p_{i,k-1}(0, t)$$

$$+ \mu_{k+1}(t)p_{i,k+1}(0, t). \tag{1.3}$$

System (1.3) and the initial conditions

$$p_{i,i}(0, 0) = 1 \qquad \text{and} \qquad p_{i,k}(0, 0) = 0 \qquad \text{for} \qquad k \neq i \tag{1.4}$$

completely determine the probability distribution $\{p_{i,k}(0, t)\}$. To obtain stochastic processes corresponding to empirical phenomena under study, we must make some assumptions regarding the functions $\lambda_k(t)$ and $\mu_k(t)$.

2. LINEAR GROWTH

Suppose both $\lambda_k(t)$ and $\mu_k(t)$ are independent of time but proportional to k,

$$\lambda_k(t) = k\lambda \qquad \text{and} \qquad \mu_k(t) = k\mu \tag{2.1}$$

where λ and μ are constant. The system of equations in (1.3) then becomes

$$\frac{d}{dt}p_{i,0}(0, t) = \mu p_{i,1}(0, t)$$

$$\frac{d}{dt}p_{i,k}(0, t) = -k(\lambda + \mu)p_{i,k}(0, t) + (k - 1)\lambda p_{i,k-1}(0, t)$$

$$+ (k + 1)\mu p_{i,k+1}(0, t), \qquad k = 1, 2, \ldots . \tag{2.2}$$

Since we cannot solve the equations in (2.2) directly, we shall use the method of the p.g.f. Let

$$G_X(s;t) = \sum_{k=0}^{\infty} s^k p_{i,k}(0, t). \tag{2.3}$$

It is easy to deduce from (2.2) that the p.g.f. satisfies the homogeneous partial differential equation

$$\frac{\partial}{\partial t}G_X(s; t) + (1 - s)(\lambda s - \mu)\frac{\partial}{\partial s}G_X(s; t) = 0 \tag{2.4}$$

with the initial condition at $t = 0$,

$$G_X(s; 0) = s^i. \tag{2.5}$$

According to the discussion on partial differential equations in section 7.2, Chapter 8, the auxiliary equations are

$$\frac{dt}{1} = \frac{ds}{(1-s)(\lambda s - \mu)} \quad \text{and} \quad dG_X(s; t) = 0. \tag{2.6}$$

In the case where $\lambda \neq \mu$ we may use partial fractions to rewrite the first auxiliary equation as

$$dt = \frac{\lambda}{(\lambda-\mu)(\lambda s-\mu)}ds + \frac{1}{(\lambda-\mu)(1-s)}ds \tag{2.7}$$

or

$$(\lambda - \mu)\,dt = d\ln\left\{\frac{\lambda s - \mu}{1-s}\right\}. \tag{2.8}$$

Integrating both sides of (2.8) gives the solution

$$\frac{1-s}{\lambda s - \mu}e^{(\lambda-\mu)t} = \text{const.} \tag{2.9}$$

The second auxiliary equation in (2.6) implies that

$$G_X(s; t) = \text{const.} \tag{2.10}$$

Therefore the general solution of (2.4) is

$$G_X(s; t) = \Phi\left\{\frac{1-s}{\lambda s-\mu}e^{(\lambda-\mu)t}\right\}, \tag{2.11}$$

where Φ is an arbitrary differentiable function. Using the initial condition in (2.5) we see from (2.11) that at $t = 0$

$$\Phi\left\{\frac{1-s}{\lambda s-\mu}\right\} = s^i \tag{2.12}$$

at least for all s with $|s| < 1$. Hence for all θ such that $|1 + \theta\mu| < |1 + \theta\lambda|$,

$$\Phi\{\theta\} = \left\{\frac{1+\theta\mu}{1+\theta\lambda}\right\}^i. \tag{2.13}$$

In formula (2.11), we have

$$\theta = \frac{1 - s}{\lambda s - \mu} e^{(\lambda - \mu)t}. \tag{2.14}$$

Therefore the particular solution for the case where $\mu \neq \lambda$ is

$$G_X(s;t) = \left\{ \frac{(\lambda s - \mu) + \mu(1 - s)e^{(\lambda-\mu)t}}{(\lambda s - \mu) + \lambda(1 - s)e^{(\lambda-\mu)t}} \right\}^i. \tag{2.15}$$

The p.g.f. in (6.18) may be rewritten in such a way that it can be expanded in a series in s. To achieve this, we let

$$\alpha(t) = \mu \frac{1 - e^{(\lambda-\mu)t}}{\mu - \lambda e^{(\lambda-\mu)t}} \quad \text{and} \quad \beta(t) = \frac{\lambda}{\mu}\alpha(t), \tag{2.16}$$

so that

$$G_X(s;t) = \left\{ \frac{\alpha(t) + [1 - \alpha(t) - \beta(t)]\, s}{1 - \beta(t)s} \right\}^i. \tag{2.17}$$

Now it is a simple matter of expanding the p.g.f. to obtain the probability distribution $\{p_{i,k}(0, t)\}$. The numerator in (2.17) is a binomial function:

$$\{\alpha(t) + [1 - \alpha(t) - \beta(t)]\, s\}^i = \sum_{j=0}^{i} \binom{i}{j} [\alpha(t)]^{i-j} [1 - \alpha(t) - \beta(t)]^j s^j.$$

And, since clearly $|\beta(t)s| < 1$, the inverse of the denominator

$$\{1 - \beta(t)s\}^{-i} = \sum_{j=0}^{\infty} \binom{-i}{j} (-1)^j [\beta(t)]^j s^j = \sum_{j=0}^{\infty} \binom{i+j-1}{j} [\beta(t)]^j s^j.$$

Hence the probability

$$p_{i,k}(0,t) = \sum_{j=0}^{\min[i,k]} \binom{i}{j} \binom{i+k-j-1}{k-j} [\alpha(t)]^{i-j} [\beta(t)]^{k-j} [1 - \alpha(t) - \beta(t)]^j \qquad k \geq 1, \tag{2.18}$$

and

$$p_{i,0}(0,\,t) = [\alpha(t)]^i. \tag{2.19}$$

When the initial population size is $i = 1$,

$$G_X(s;\,t) = \frac{\alpha(t) + [1 - \alpha(t) - \beta(t)]\,s}{1 - \beta(t)s}, \tag{2.20}$$

$$p_{1,k}(0,\,t) = [1 - \alpha(t)]\,[1 - \beta(t)]\,[\beta(t)]^{k-1}, \qquad k \ge 1, \tag{2.21}$$

and

$$p_{1,0}(0,\,t) = \alpha(t). \tag{2.22}$$

This shows that the i individuals reproduce and perish independently of one another and that the probability distribution $\{p_{i,k}(0,t)\}$ is the i-fold convolution of $\{p_{1,k}(0,t)\}$ with itself, or

$$\{p_{i,k}(0,t)\} = \{p_{1,k}(0,t)\}^{i*}. \tag{2.23}$$

Differentiating the p.g.f. in (2.17) with respect to s, we find the expectation and variance of $X(t)$:

$$E\,[X(t)] = i\frac{1 - \alpha(t)}{1 - \beta(t)} = ie^{(\lambda-\mu)t} \tag{2.24}$$

and

$$\begin{aligned}\sigma^2_{X(t)} &= i\frac{[1 - \alpha(t)]\,[\alpha(t) + \beta(t)]}{[1 - \beta(t)]^2} \\ &= i\left(\frac{\lambda + \mu}{\lambda - \mu}\right)e^{(\lambda-\mu)t}\,[e^{(\lambda-\mu)t} - 1].\end{aligned} \tag{2.25}$$

When $\lambda = \mu$, the partial fraction method in (2.7) fails and the above equations all become meaningless. In this case we start with the differential equation (2.4), which now becomes

$$\frac{\partial}{\partial t}G_X(s;t) - \lambda(1 - s)^2\frac{\partial}{\partial s}G_X(s;t) = 0. \tag{2.26}$$

Equation (2.26) is easy to solve; the solution is

$$G_X(s;t) = \left\{\frac{\lambda t + (1 - \lambda t)s}{1 + \lambda t - \lambda ts}\right\}^i, \tag{2.27}$$

and hence the probabilities are

$$p_{i,k}(0, t) = \sum_{j=0}^{\min[i,k]} \binom{i}{j}\binom{i+k-j-1}{k-j}\left(\frac{\lambda t}{1+\lambda t}\right)^{i+k-2j}\left(\frac{1-\lambda t}{1+\lambda t}\right)^{j} \qquad k \geq 1 \tag{2.28}$$

and

$$p_{i,0}(0,t) = \left\{\frac{\lambda t}{1+\lambda t}\right\}^{i}. \tag{2.29}$$

The expected value and variance of $X(t)$ are

$$E[X(t)] = i \qquad \text{and} \qquad \sigma^2_{X(t)} = 2k\lambda t. \tag{2.30}$$

Thus, when the birth rate is equal to the death rate, the population size has a constant expectation but an increasing variance.

Formulas (2.27) through (2.30) can be obtained from formulas (2.17), (2.18), (2.19), (2.24) and (2.25), respectively, by taking the limits as $\mu \to \lambda$. The reader is encouraged to verify this as an exercise.

Two terms have been suggested for the birth-death processes, depending upon the relative values of λ and μ. If $\lambda > \mu$, a birth-death process is called supercritical; if $\lambda < \mu$, subcritical.

The limiting behavior of the birth-death process is analogous to that encountered in branching processes. From (2.17) and (2.27) we see that, for $|s| < 1$,

$$\lim_{t\to\infty} G_X(s; t) = \left(\frac{\mu}{\lambda}\right)^{i}, \qquad \mu < \lambda$$

$$= 1, \qquad \mu \geq \lambda. \tag{2.31}$$

Now $G_X(0,t) = p_{i,0}(0,t)$ is the probability that the population will become extinct at time t. Thus, if $\mu \geq \lambda$ the probability of extinction tends to unity as $t \to \infty$, and the population is certain to die out eventually. On the other hand, if $\mu < \lambda$, the probability of ultimate extinction is $(\mu/\lambda)^i$. Furthermore, since the limiting p.g.f. is constant, the population will either eventually die out with probability $(\mu/\lambda)^i$, or increase without bound with probability $1 - (\mu/\lambda)^i$; no intermediate courses are possible.

The relative magnitude of λ and μ also influences the asymptotic value of the expectation and variance of $X(t)$. From (2.24), (2.25), and (2.29) we see that

$$\begin{aligned}\lim_{t\to\infty} E\,[X(t)] &= 0 \qquad \text{if } \mu > \lambda \\ &= i \qquad \text{if } \mu = \lambda \\ &= \infty \qquad \text{if } \mu < \lambda\end{aligned} \tag{2.32}$$

and

$$\begin{aligned}\lim_{t\to\infty} \sigma^2_{X(t)} &= 0 \qquad \text{if } \mu > \lambda \\ &= \infty \qquad \text{if } \mu \le \lambda.\end{aligned} \tag{2.33}$$

When $\lambda = \mu$ we have the interesting case in which the probability of extinction tends to unity, yet the expected population size tends to i. These seemingly contradictory facts may be intuitively explained by the large value of the variance. Although most populations will eventually become extinct, a few will attain huge sizes, so that the average size will be i.

3. A TIME-DEPENDENT GENERAL BIRTH-DEATH PROCESS

We may generalize the preceding model by letting both $\lambda = \lambda(t)$ and $\mu = \mu(t)$ be functions of time. The mathematics involved in deriving the probability distribution $p_{i,k}(0,t)$ is somewhat more complex than for linear growth, but we may follow the procedure in section 2 until we reach the partial differential equation analogous to (2.4),

$$\frac{\partial}{\partial t} G_X(s;t) + (1-s)\,[s\lambda(t) - \mu(t)]\,\frac{\partial}{\partial s} G_X(s;t) = 0, \tag{3.1}$$

and the corresponding auxiliary equations

$$\frac{dt}{1} = \frac{ds}{(1-s)\,[s\lambda(t) - \mu(t)]} \qquad \text{and} \qquad dG_X(s;t) = 0. \tag{3.2}$$

Since $\lambda(t)$ and $\mu(t)$ are functions of t, the method of partial fractions will not work here. Furthermore, the first equation in (3.2) is quadratic in s^2. Therefore we need to use the transformation discussed in Chapter 8, section 7, and introduce a new variable

$$z = (1-s)^{-1}. \tag{3.3}$$

Then the first equation in (3.2) becomes

$$\frac{dz}{dt} - [\lambda(t) - \mu(t)]\,z + \lambda(t) = 0, \tag{3.4}$$

which can be solved in the ordinary way. Letting

$$\gamma(t) = -\int_0^t [\lambda(\tau) - \mu(\tau)]\, d\tau \tag{3.5}$$

and multiplying (3.4) through by $e^{\gamma(t)}$, we find the equation

$$e^{\gamma(t)}\frac{dz}{dt} - [\lambda(t) - \mu(t)]\, ze^{\gamma(t)} + \lambda(t)e^{\gamma(t)} = 0$$

or

$$\frac{d}{dt}[ze^{\gamma(t)}] + \lambda(t)e^{\gamma(t)} = 0. \tag{3.6}$$

Integrating (3.6) and replacing z by $(1-s)^{-1}$ yields the equation

$$\frac{1}{1-s}e^{\gamma(t)} + \int_0^t \lambda(\tau)e^{\gamma(\tau)}\, d\tau = \text{const.} \tag{3.7}$$

Using (3.7) and the second auxiliary equation in (3.2), we obtain the general solution

$$G_X(s;t) = \Phi\left\{\frac{1}{1-s}e^{\gamma(t)} + \int_0^t \lambda(\tau)e^{\gamma(\tau)}d\tau\right\}. \tag{3.8}$$

For the initial population size $X(0) = i$,

$$G_X(s;0) = \Phi\left\{\frac{1}{1-s}\right\} = s^i, \tag{3.9}$$

at least for $|s| < 1$; hence for θ such that $|1 - \frac{1}{\theta}| < 1$,

$$\Phi(\theta) = \left\{1 - \frac{1}{\theta}\right\}^i. \tag{3.10}$$

Therefore the required formula for the p.g.f. is

$$G_X(s;t) = \left\{1 - \frac{1}{\dfrac{1}{1-s}e^{\gamma(t)} + \displaystyle\int_0^t \lambda(\tau)e^{\gamma(\tau)}d\tau}\right\}^i, \tag{3.11}$$

$$= \left\{1 - \frac{1-s}{e^{\gamma(t)} + \displaystyle\int_0^t \lambda(\tau)e^{\gamma(\tau)}d\tau - s\int_0^t \lambda(\tau)e^{\gamma(\tau)}d\tau}\right\}^i. \tag{3.12}$$

Letting

$$\alpha(t) = 1 - \frac{1}{e^{\gamma(t)} + \int_0^t \lambda(\tau) e^{\gamma(\tau)} d\tau} \tag{3.13}$$

and

$$\beta(t) = 1 - e^{\gamma(t)}[1 - \alpha(t)], \tag{3.14}$$

we may rewrite (3.12) as

$$G_X(s;t) = \left\{ \frac{\alpha(t) + [1 - \alpha(t) - \beta(t)]s}{1 - \beta(t)s} \right\}^i. \tag{3.15}$$

Except for the definitions of $\alpha(t)$ and $\beta(t)$, the p.g.f. here is of the same form as the one in (2.17); therefore the probability distribution $\{p_{ik}(0,t)\}$ is given by (2.18), with $\alpha(t)$ and $\beta(t)$ defined respectively as in (3.13) and (3.14).

The probability of extinction at time t may be obtained directly from (3.13) and (3.15)

$$p_{i,0}(0,t) = \left\{ 1 - \frac{1}{e^{\gamma(t)} + \int_0^t \lambda(\tau) e^{\gamma(\tau)} d\tau} \right\}^i. \tag{3.16}$$

Using the definition of $\gamma(t)$ in (3.5) we can write

$$e^{\gamma(t)} + \int_0^t \lambda(\tau) e^{\gamma(\tau)} d\tau = 1 + \int_0^t \mu(\tau) e^{\gamma(\tau)} d\tau \tag{3.17}$$

and

$$p_{i,0}(0,t) = \left\{ \frac{\int_0^t \mu(\tau) e^{\gamma(\tau) d\tau}}{1 + \int_0^t \mu(\tau) e^{\gamma(\tau)} d\tau} \right\}^i. \tag{3.19}$$

We see that in this case $p_{i,0}(0,t) \to 1$ as $t \to \infty$, if and only if the integral

$$\int_0^t \mu(\tau) e^{-\int_0^\tau [\lambda(\xi)-\mu(\xi)]\, d\xi} d\tau$$

diverges as $t \to \infty$. Obviously, the divergence occurs if $\mu(\tau) > \lambda(\tau)$ for every $\tau \geq 0$.

4. QUEUEING PROCESSES

A facility has s "stations" (or servers) for serving "customers". If all s stations are occupied, newly arriving customers must form a *queue,* or waiting line, until a station is available for service. The main problems to be dealt with in analytic studies of queueing are the length of queue, the waiting time, and the duration of service.

Queueing phenomena can be observed in many practical situations where congestion problems exist. Queueing is apparent in everyday business transactions, in communications, medicine, transportation, and industry. For example, shoppers wait in line at check-out counters; customers queue in banks, theaters, cafeterias, and clinics; planes circle in holding patterns over airports; telephone circuits handle incoming calls in order; and on an assembly line, bottles, for instance, are washed, filled, capped, and packaged in an orderly, single-file process. Even the early morning traffic approaching the San Francisco Bay Bridge illustrates the queueing process. The purposes of queueing are to resolve congestion, to optimize efficiency or safety, to minimize waiting time or inconvenience to customers, to speed production, or even to save lives.

The queueing concept was originally formulated by Erlang [1909] in his study of telephone network congestion problems. As advancements have been made in stochastic processes, queueing theory has also flourished. Mathematicians, statisticians, engineers, and investigators in many other disciplines have made contributions to the queueing theory and to resolving practical problems. Actual needs and the curiousity of theoretical investigators have elicited many variations of queueing problems. It has been observed, for example, that customers often arrive in groups of various sizes, rather than singly; unaccommodated incoming phone calls may be lost instead of waiting in a queue (balking); service time may vary from one station to another due to efficiency of servers (heterogeneous servers);

service provided in medical check-up, in assembly line, and others, consists of several phases, each phase requires a separate waiting line (tandem queues). Most of the problems have been resolved with great mathematical ingenuity, some beyond the level of this book. Still, we consider here those cases involving s stations having equal efficiency and one waiting line.

Generally, a queueing system is identified by (1) input process (arrivals may be random, planned, or patterned); (2) service time; and (3) number of stations; or simply by

Input distribution/service time/number of stations.

Symbolically, G stands for an arbitrary distribution; M for Poisson arrivals, exponential interarrival times, or exponential service times; D for constant interarrival times or service times. We can say, for example, that a queueing system with Poisson arrivals, an exponential service time and s stations will be denoted M/M/s, while a queue with arbitrary arrivals, a constant service time and one server will be denoted G/D/1.

The birth-death process discussed in section 2 is directly applicable to the queueing process with Poisson arrivals and exponential service times. We shall therefore discuss only M/M/s queues with $s = 1$ or $s > 1$. In section 4.1, we derive the differential equations for the number of customers at time t and for the limiting case when $t \to \infty$. In section 4.2, we discuss in some detail the number of customers, length of queue, waiting time, service time and their mutual relationships in terms of the M/M/1 queue. We extend our findings to M/M/s queues in section 4.3.

4.1 Differential Equations for an M/M/s Queue.

In this system, there are s stations (servers); the arrival of customers follows a Poisson process with parameter λ; service time has an exponential distribution with parameter μ; and the service discipline is first-come, first-served. When all the s stations are occupied at time t, there is a probability $s\mu\Delta + o(\Delta)$ that one of the stations will be free for service within the time element $(t, t + \Delta)$. Let $X(t)$ be the number of customers in the system at time t, including those being served and those in the waiting line, with $X(0) = i$. The transition probabilities

$$p_{i,k}(0,t) = \Pr\{X(t) = k | X(0) = i\}, \qquad k = 0, 1, \ldots, \tag{4.1}$$

satisfy the system of differential equations:

$$\frac{d}{dt}p_{i,0}(0,t) = -\lambda p_{i,0}(0,t) + \mu p_{i,1}(0,t)$$

$$\frac{d}{dt}p_{i,k}(0,t) = -(\lambda + k\mu)p_{i,k}(0,t) + \lambda p_{i,k-1}(0,t) + (k+1)\mu p_{i,k+1}(0,t), \qquad k = 1, \ldots, s-1,$$

$$\frac{d}{dt}p_{i,k}(0,t) = -(\lambda + s\mu)p_{i,k}(0,t) + \lambda p_{i,k-1}(0,t) + s\mu p_{i,k+1}(0,t), \qquad k = s, s+1, \ldots. \tag{4.2}$$

To obtain a solution for the system in (4.2) for any finite t requires mathematics beyond the scope of this book. But limiting probabilities can be derived.

Theorem 1. *If all states in a queueing process are communicative, then the limiting probabilities*

$$\lim_{t\to\infty} p_{i,k}(0,t) = \pi_k, \qquad i,k = 0, 1, \ldots \tag{4.3}$$

exist which are independent of the initial time and of the initial state i. The sum of the probabilities is unity

$$\sum_k \pi_k = 1. \tag{4.4}$$

Theorem 1 is similar to Theorem 11 in Chapter 5, section 7, regarding limiting probabilities in a Markov chain where all states are communicative. We shall not give the proof of Theorem 1, but merely use the theorem to derive formulas for the limiting probability distribution $\{\pi_k\}$. When $t \to \infty$, we let $X = X(\infty)$ and

$$\Pr\{X = k\} = \pi_k, \qquad k = 0, 1, \ldots. \tag{4.5}$$

Since the limiting probabilities are independent of time, their derivatives with respect to time vanish. Therefore, as $t \to \infty$, we get from (4.2) the following system of equations:

$$0 = -\lambda\pi_0 + \mu\pi_1$$

$$0 = -(\lambda + k\mu)\pi_k + \lambda\pi_{k-1} + (k+1)\mu\pi_{k+1}, \qquad k = 1, \ldots, s-1,$$

and

$$0 = -(\lambda + s\mu)\pi_k + \lambda\pi_{k-1} + s\mu\pi_{k+1}, \qquad k = s, s+1, \ldots. \tag{4.6}$$

We shall consider the two cases $s = 1$ and $s > 1$ separately in the following sections.

4.2 The M/M/1 Queue.

When there is a single station in a system, the equations in (4.6) become

$$0 = -\lambda\pi_0 + \mu\pi_1$$

and

$$0 = -(\lambda + \mu)\pi_k + \lambda\pi_{k-1} + \mu\pi_{k+1}, \qquad k = 1, 2, \dots . \tag{4.7}$$

Solving (4.7) successively, we obtain

$$\pi_k = \left(\frac{\lambda}{\mu}\right)^k \pi_0, \qquad k = 0, 1, \dots \tag{4.8}$$

or

$$\pi_k = \rho^k \pi_0, \qquad k = 0, 1, \dots, \tag{4.8a}$$

where

$$\rho = \frac{\lambda}{\mu} \tag{4.9}$$

is the *traffic intensity* of the system and π_0 is yet to be determined. According to Theorem 1, the limiting probabilities form a distribution. We introduce (4.8a) in (4.4) to derive a condition of π_0:

$$\sum_{k=0}^{\infty} \rho^k \pi_0 = 1, \tag{4.10}$$

or

$$\pi_0 = [1 + \rho + \rho^2 + \dots]^{-1}. \tag{4.11}$$

In order for the limiting distribution to exist, we must have a positive π_0 or a convergent infinite series

$$[1 + \rho + \rho^2 + \dots] < \infty. \tag{4.12}$$

Condition (4.12) implies that $\rho < 1$. From (4.11) we deduce that

$$\pi_0 = (1 - \rho). \tag{4.13}$$

Consequently,

$$\pi_k = \rho^k(1-\rho), \qquad k = 0, 1, \dots, \tag{4.14}$$

which is a geometric distribution with an expectation

$$E(X) = \sum_{k=0}^{\infty} k\rho^k(1-\rho) = \frac{\rho}{(1-\rho)} \tag{4.15}$$

and a variance

$$V(X) = \frac{\rho}{(1-\rho)^2}. \tag{4.16}$$

4.2.1 The Length of Queue.

Let $Q = Q(\infty)$ be the number of customers in a queue in the limiting case, and let $\{q_n\}$ be the probability distribution of Q,

$$q_n = \Pr\{Q = n\}, \qquad n = 0, 1, \dots. \tag{4.17}$$

We shall derive the formulas for q_n. When $Q = 0$, either there are no customers in the system ($X = 0$), or there is one customer ($X = 1$) who is being served. This means that

$$\Pr\{Q = 0\} = \Pr\{X = 0 \text{ or } X = 1\},$$

or

$$q_0 = (1-\rho) + (1-\rho)\rho = (1-\rho^2). \tag{4.18}$$

When Q assumes positive integers,

$$Q = X - 1. \tag{4.19}$$

Thus

$$q_n = \pi_{n+1} = \rho^{n+1}(1-\rho), \qquad n = 1, 2, \dots. \tag{4.20}$$

From (4.18) and (4.20) we find the expectation

$$E(Q) = \sum_{n=0}^{\infty} nq_n = \sum_{n=1}^{\infty} n\rho^{n+1}(1-\rho) = \frac{\rho^2}{1-\rho} \tag{4.21}$$

and the variance

$$V(Q) = \frac{\rho^2(1+\rho-\rho^2)}{(1-\rho)^2}. \tag{4.22}$$

Note that in (4.19) the simple relationship between the length of the queue and the total number of customers in the system holds only for $Q \geq 1$, and it does not hold for $Q = 0$. Therefore we should not expect a simple relationship between $E(X)$ and $E(Q)$ or between $V(X)$ and $V(Q)$.

4.2.2. Service Time and Waiting Time.

Let t be the length of time needed to render service to a customer. It is assumed in this model that t has an exponential distribution with a density function

$$h_t(\tau) = \mu e^{-\mu\tau}, \qquad \tau \geq 0, \tag{4.23}$$

an expectation

$$E(t) = \frac{1}{\mu}, \tag{4.24}$$

and a variance

$$V(t) = \frac{1}{\mu^2}. \tag{4.25}$$

Let W_n be the waiting time of the n-th person in the waiting line, or the length of time that the n-th person in the line has to wait before receiving service. Thus W_1 is the length of time that the first person in the line has to wait for service. If a customer arrives at the very moment the customer ahead of him begins to receive service, then it is clear that his waiting time W_1 will equal the service time t. However, in the present case, μ is independent of time; the process is time homogeneous. The waiting time W_1 has the same density function as the service time t regardless of when the preceding customer begins to receive service. In other words

$$f_{W_1}(\tau) = h_t(\tau) = \mu e^{-\mu\tau}. \tag{4.23}$$

When the station is free, the first person in the line begins to receive service, and the second person in the line moves up to the first position and waits for another period of W_1; his total waiting time is

$$W_2 = W_{11} + W_{12}. \tag{4.26}$$

Thus the distribution of W_2 is the two-fold convolution of $\{f_{W_1}(\tau)\}$ with itself:

$$\{f_{W_2}(\tau)\} = \{f_{W_1}(\tau)\} * \{f_{W_1}(\tau)\}, \tag{4.27}$$

and the density function of W_2 is given by

$$f_{W_2}(\tau) = \int_0^\tau [\mu e^{-\mu\xi}]\,[\mu e^{-\mu(\tau-\xi)}]\,d\xi$$
$$= \mu^2 \tau e^{-\mu\tau}. \tag{4.28}$$

In general, the waiting time W_n is the sum of n i.i.d. random variables W_1, or

$$W_n = W_{11} + W_{12} + \dots + W_{1n}. \tag{4.29}$$

The distribution of W_n is the n-fold convolution of $\{f_{W_1}(\tau)\}$ with itself:

$$\{f_{W_n}(\tau)\} = \{f_{W_1}(\tau)\}^{n*}, \tag{4.30}$$

or,

$$f_{W_n}(\tau) = \frac{\mu^n \tau^{n-1}}{(n-1)!} e^{-\mu\tau}, \qquad n = 1, 2, \dots . \tag{4.31}$$

Queueing phenomena is parallel to the delayed renewal process discussed in Chapter 7 in the sense that, at the time a new customer arrives and joins the queue, the person then being served has already been receiving service for some length of time; consequently, W_{11} in equations (4.26) and (4.29) is smaller than other W_{1i} in these equations. As we proved in section 3.1 of Chapter 7, when μ is independent of time, the distribution of the renewal time for the delayed renewal process is the same as that for the ordinary renewal process. For the same reason, equations (4.27) and (4.30) hold true for a time homogeneous queueing process. If the service intensity $\mu(\tau)$ is a function of time, then W_{11} in equation (4.26) and (4.29) has a density function different from the (common) density of other W_{1i}. To distinguish this, we replace W_{11} with W_{11}^*, and write

$$W_2 = W_{11}^* + W_{12} \tag{4.26a}$$

and

$$W_n = W_{11}^* + W_{12} + \dots + W_{1n}. \tag{4.29a}$$

It is apparent, then, that the queueing process is a renewal process; and, in fact, when $\mu(\tau) = \mu$, the density function of W_n in (4.31) is exactly the same as the density function of the *n-th renewal time* T_n in formula (3.16) of Chapter 7.

Let W be the length of time that an arriving customer has to wait before receiving service. The waiting time W obviously is a continuous random variable. However, because of the particular structure of the queueing process, W assumes the value zero with a positive probability. If, at the time of arrival of one customer, there is no one in the system ($X = 0$, with a probability π_0), the customer will receive service immediately; the waiting time is zero. Therefore

$$\Pr\{W = 0\} = \pi_0 = 1 - \rho. \tag{4.32}$$

If there are n people in the system ($X = n$, with a probability π_n), then the waiting time for a new arrival is W_n, with the density function given in (4.31). It follows that the density function of W is

$$f_W(\tau) = \sum_{n=1}^{\infty} \pi_n f_{W_n}(\tau), \tag{4.33}$$

$$= \sum_{n=1}^{\infty} \rho^n (1-\rho) \frac{\mu^n \tau^{n-1}}{(n-1)!} e^{-\mu\tau}$$

$$= \rho(1-\rho)\mu e^{-\mu\tau} \sum_{n=1}^{\infty} \frac{(\rho\mu\tau)^{n-1}}{(n-1)!}$$

$$= \rho(1-\rho)\mu e^{-(1-\rho)\mu\tau}, \qquad 0 < \tau < \infty. \tag{4.34}$$

The distribution function of W is calculated from (4.32) and (4.34):

$$\begin{aligned} F_w(\tau) &= \Pr\{W \le \tau\} \\ &= \Pr\{W = 0\} + \Pr\{0 < W \le \tau\} \\ &= \pi_0 + \int_0^\tau f_w(\xi)\, d\xi \\ &= (1-\rho) + \int_0^\tau \rho(1-\rho)\mu \exp\{-(1-\rho)\mu\xi\}\, d\xi \\ &= (1-\rho) + \rho\,[1 - \exp\{-(1-\rho)\mu\tau\}] \\ &= 1 - \rho \exp\{-(1-\rho)\mu\tau\}. \end{aligned} \tag{4.35}$$

As $\tau \to \infty$, $F_w(\tau) \to 1$. Therefore the waiting time W is a proper random variable with an expectation

$$E(W) = \int_0^\infty \tau\, dF_w(\tau)\, d\tau$$

$$= \frac{\rho}{\mu(1-\rho)} \tag{4.36}$$

and a variance

$$V(W) = \frac{\rho(2-\rho)}{\mu^2(1-\rho)^2}. \tag{4.37}$$

The total length of time T that a customer spends in a system is the sum of waiting time W and service time t:

$$T = W + t \tag{4.38}$$

with a density function $g_T(\tau)$ and a distribution function $G_T(\tau)$. Because W assumes a value of zero with a positive probability, the density function of T is not the simple convolution of the density functions of W and t [cf., Chapter 3, section 3]. In order to take the probability

$$\Pr\{W = 0\} = 1 - \rho$$

into account, we need first to derive the distribution function $G_T(\tau)$:

$$\begin{aligned} G_T(\tau) &= \int_0^\tau F_W(\xi)\,h(\tau-\xi)\,d\xi, \\ &= \int_0^\tau [1 - \rho\exp\{-(1-\rho)\mu\xi\}]\,\mu e^{-\mu(\tau-\xi)}\,d\xi \\ &= 1 - e^{-(1-\rho)\mu\tau}, \qquad 0 \le \tau < \infty. \end{aligned} \tag{4.39}$$

From (4.39) we then find the density function

$$\begin{aligned} g_T(\tau)\,d\tau &= dG_T(\tau) \\ &= (1-\rho)\mu e^{-(1-\rho)\mu\tau}, \end{aligned} \tag{4.40}$$

which is an exponential distribution with

$$E(T) = \frac{1}{(1-\rho)\mu} \tag{4.41}$$

and

$$V(T) = \frac{1}{(1-\rho)^2\mu^2}. \tag{4.42}$$

It is easy to see that

$$\frac{1}{(1-\rho)\mu} = \frac{\rho}{(1-\rho)\mu} + \frac{1}{\mu} \tag{4.43}$$

and

$$\frac{1}{(1-\rho)^2\mu^2} = \frac{\rho(2-\rho)}{(1-\rho)^2\mu^2} + \frac{1}{\mu^2},$$

so that the expectation

$$E(T) = E(W) + E(t) \tag{4.44}$$

and the variance

$$V(T) = V(W) + V(t), \tag{4.45}$$

as expected.

4.2.3 Interarrival Time and Traffic Intensity.

The length of the queue, the waiting time, and the queuing process itself are all dependent upon the intensity of incoming traffic, or the interarrival time between two consecutive customers. Let Y be the interarrival time, and let $K_Y(\tau)$ be the distribution function of Y. Then

$$1 - K_Y(\tau) = \Pr\{Y > \tau\} \tag{4.46}$$

is the probability of no new arrival during the interval $(0,\tau)$. This probability, in the Poisson model of arrivals, is given as

$$1 - K_Y(\tau) = e^{-\lambda\tau},$$

or

$$K_Y(\tau) = 1 - e^{-\lambda\tau}. \tag{4.47}$$

Therefore, the interarrival time Y has an exponential distribution with the mean interarrival time

$$E(Y) = \frac{1}{\lambda}. \tag{4.48}$$

The traffic intensity ρ has been defined as the ratio of λ to μ. But since λ gained a new meaning in (4.48), the traffic intensity ρ acquires a fresh interpretation:

$$\rho = \frac{\lambda}{\mu} = \frac{1/\mu}{1/\lambda} = \frac{\text{mean service time}}{\text{mean interarrival time}}. \tag{4.49}$$

Also, since a station is occupied whenever there are one or more customers in the system, we have still another interpretation of ρ:

$$\Pr\{\text{the station is busy}\} = \Pr\{X \geq 1\} = \rho. \tag{4.50}$$

4.3. The M/M/s Queue.

Let us consider again a queueing process with Poisson input, exponential service time, but having s stations to provide service. The s stations are equally efficient and have the same service time. In this case the limiting probabilities π_k satisfy the difference equations

$$\lambda\pi_0 = \mu\pi_1$$

$$(\lambda + k\mu)\pi_k = \lambda\pi_{k-1} + (k+1)\mu\pi_{k+1}, \qquad k = 1, \ldots, s-1,$$

and

$$(\lambda + s\mu)\pi_k = \lambda\pi_{k-1} + s\mu\pi_{k+1}, \qquad k = s, s+1, \ldots, \tag{4.6}$$

as given in section 4.1. Solving equations (4.6) successively beginning with π_1, we find that

$$\begin{aligned} \pi_k &= \frac{(s\rho)^k}{k!}\pi_0, \qquad k = 1, \ldots, s, \\ &= \rho^k \frac{s^s}{s!}\pi_0, \qquad k = s+1, \ldots, \end{aligned} \tag{4.51}$$

or

$$\pi_k = \rho^{k-s}\pi_s, \qquad k = s+1, \ldots, \tag{4.52}$$

where

$$\rho = \frac{\lambda}{s\mu} \tag{4.53}$$

is the traffic intensity. Substituting (4.51) in the restriction

$$\sum_{k=0}^{\infty} \pi_k = 1, \tag{4.4}$$

we find

$$\left[\sum_{k=0}^{s} \frac{(s\rho)^k}{k!}\pi_0 + \sum_{k=s+1}^{\infty} \frac{\rho^k s^s}{s!}\pi_0\right] = 1, \tag{4.54}$$

and hence

$$\pi_0 = \left[\sum_{k=0}^{s} \frac{(s\rho)^k}{k!} + \frac{(s\rho)^s}{s!} \sum_{k=s+1}^{\infty} \rho^{k-s} \right]^{-1}. \tag{4.55}$$

The geometric series in (4.55) must converge in order to have a positive π_0. This means that for the existence of the limiting probability distribution $\{\pi_k\}$, we must have $\rho < 1$. Under this condition the geometric series converges,

$$\sum_{k=s+1}^{\infty} \rho^{k-s} = \frac{\rho}{1-\rho},$$

and

$$\pi_0 = \left[\sum_{k=0}^{s} \frac{(s\rho)^k}{k!} + \frac{(s\rho)^s}{s!} \frac{\rho}{1-\rho} \right]^{-1}. \tag{4.56}$$

Substituting (4.56) in (4.52) gives the formulas for π_k in terms of s and ρ. But we shall retain formulas (4.51) and (4.52) in the sequel for simplicity. Thus the expected number of customers in the system is

$$E(X) = \left[\sum_{k=0}^{s} k \frac{(s\rho)^k}{k!} \pi_0 + \sum_{k=s+1}^{\infty} k\rho^{k-s} \pi_s \right]$$

$$= s\rho + \frac{\rho \pi_s}{(1-\rho)^2}, \tag{4.57}$$

and the variance is

$$V(X) = s\rho + \frac{\rho \pi_s}{(1-\rho)^3} [(1+\rho) + s(1-\rho)^2] - \frac{\rho^2 \pi_s^2}{(1-\rho)^4}. \tag{4.58}$$

4.3.1. The Length of Queue.

We again let the probability distribution of Q be denoted by $\{q_n\}$, with

$$q_n = \Pr\{Q = n\}, \qquad n = 0, 1, \ldots. \tag{4.59}$$

When there are s or fewer than s customers in the system, no one will be waiting in line, and hence

$$q_0 = \Pr\{X \le s\} = 1 - \frac{\rho}{1-\rho} \pi_s. \tag{4.60}$$

When there are $k = n + s$ customers in the system, for $k > s$, the length of queue is n, or

$$q_n = \Pr\{X = n + s\} = \rho^n \pi_s, \qquad n = 1, \ldots. \tag{4.61}$$

It is easy to verify that

$$\sum_{n=0}^{\infty} q_n = 1. \tag{4.62}$$

The expectation and variance of Q are computed from (4.60) and (4.61):

$$E(Q) = \sum_{n=1}^{\infty} n\rho^n \pi_s = \frac{\rho\pi_s}{(1-\rho)^2} \tag{4.63}$$

and

$$V(Q) = \frac{\rho(\rho+1)\pi_s}{(1-\rho)^3} - \frac{\rho^2\pi_s^2}{(1-\rho)^4} \tag{4.64}$$

where

$$\pi_s = \frac{(s\rho)^s}{s!}\pi_0.$$

4.3.2. Service Time and Waiting Time.

The length of time needed to render service to a customer is assumed to be the same for all s stations with the common density function

$$h_t(\tau) = \mu e^{-\mu\tau} \tag{4.66}$$

and the distribution function

$$H_t(\tau) = 1 - e^{-\mu\tau} \tag{4.67}$$

as in the M/M/1 queue. The waiting time for an M/M/s queue, however, is different from that for M/M/1 queue. Consider the first person in a queue and his waiting time W_1. Let $t_1, t_2, \ldots, t_s$, be the service times of the s stations, each having the distribution function as in (4.67). Since the first person in a queue will receive service as soon as one of the stations is free, the waiting time W_1 is the smallest of $t_1, t_2, \ldots, t_s$. To derive the density for W_1, we arrange the s service times in order of magnitude:

$$t_{(1)} \leq t_{(2)} \leq \ldots \leq t_{(s)}$$

where $t_{(1)}$ is the smallest service time and $t_{(s)}$ is the largest. With the same procedure used to arrive at equation (3.30) in the renewal process in Chapter 7, we find the density function

$$f_{W_1}(\tau) = f_{(1)}(\tau) = s\mu e^{-s\mu\tau} \tag{4.68}$$

and the distribution function

$$F_{W_1}(\tau) = 1 - e^{-s\mu\tau} \tag{4.69}$$

which is an exponential distribution with parameter $s\mu$. The waiting time of the nth person in a queue is the sum of n i.i.d. random variables W_1:

$$W_n = W_{11} + \ldots + W_{1n},$$

Hence, the density function of W_n is the n-fold convolution of the density function of W_1 with itself. That is,

$$f_{W_n}(\tau) = \{f_{W_1}(\tau)\}^{n*}.$$

Direct computations give

$$f_{W_n}(\tau) = (s\mu)^n \frac{\tau^{n-1}}{(n-1)!} e^{-s\mu\tau}. \tag{4.70}$$

Let W be the waiting time of an arriving customer. If there are less than s customers ahead of him in the system, he receives service immediately, W assumes a value of zero, and

$$\Pr\{W = 0\} = \sum_{k=0}^{s-1} \pi_k = 1 - \frac{\pi_s}{1-\rho}. \tag{4.71}$$

If there are $s + n - 1$ customers ahead of him, his waiting time is W_n. Therefore the density function of W is

$$f_W(\tau) = \sum_{n=1}^{\infty} \pi_{s+n-1} f_{W_n}(\tau). \tag{4.72}$$

Substituting (4.52) and (4.70) in (4.72), we find that

$$f_W(\tau) = \pi_s s\mu \exp\{-(1-\rho)s\mu\tau\}. \tag{4.73}$$

For the distribution function of W, we write

$$F_W(\tau) = \Pr\{W = 0\} + \Pr\{0 < W < \tau\}$$

$$= 1 - \frac{\pi_s}{1-\rho} + \int_0^\tau \pi_s s\mu \exp\{-(1-\rho)s\mu\xi\}\,d\xi$$

$$= 1 - \frac{\pi_s}{1-\rho} \exp\{-(1-\rho)s\mu\tau\}\,. \tag{4.74}$$

Simple computations yield the expectation

$$E(W) = \frac{\pi_s}{(1-\rho)^2 s\mu} \tag{4.75}$$

and the variance

$$V(W) = \frac{2\pi_s}{(1-\rho)^3(s\mu)^2} - \frac{\pi_s^2}{(1-\rho)^4(s\mu)^2}. \tag{4.76}$$

The total length of time a customer spends in the system is the sum of W and t:

$$T = W + t, \tag{4.77}$$

with a density function $g_T(t)$ and a distribution function $G_T(\tau)$. But the positive probability

$$\Pr\{W = 0\} = 1 - \frac{\pi_s}{1-\rho}$$

invalidates the convolutional relationship between the density functions of T and W and t. Once again we need to derive $g_T(\tau)$ from the distribution function $G_T(\tau)$. Expressing $G_T(\tau)$ as the convolution of $F_W(\tau)$ and $H_t(\tau)$,

$$G_T(\tau) = \int_0^\tau F_W(\xi)\,dH_t(\tau - \xi), \tag{4.78}$$

we find that

$$G_T(\tau) = \int_0^\tau \left[1 - \frac{\pi_s}{1-\rho}\exp\{-(1-\rho)s\mu\xi\}\right]\mu e^{-\mu(\tau-\xi)}\,d\xi$$

$$= 1 - e^{-\mu\tau} - \frac{\pi_s}{(1-\rho)[(1-\rho)s-1]}\left[e^{-\mu\tau} - e^{-(1-\rho)s\mu\tau}\right] \tag{4.79}$$

and the density function of T

$$g_T(\tau)\,d\tau = dG_T(\tau)$$

$$= \mu e^{-\mu\tau} + \frac{\pi_s \mu}{(1-\rho)\,[(1-\rho)s - 1]}\,[e^{-\mu\tau} - (1-\rho)se^{-(1-\rho)s\mu\tau}]\,. \tag{4.80}$$

Since $G_T(\infty) = 1$, the distribution function $G_T(\tau)$ is proper. From (4.80) we derive

$$E(T) = \int_0^\infty \tau g_T(\tau)\,d\tau$$

$$= \frac{\pi_s}{(1-\rho)^2 s\mu} + \frac{1}{\mu} \tag{4.81}$$

and

$$V(T) = \frac{2\pi_s}{(1-\rho)^3(s\mu)^2} - \frac{\pi_s^2}{(1-\rho)^4(s\mu)^2} + \frac{1}{\mu^2}. \tag{4.82}$$

Clearly (4.81) and (4.82) can be obtained also from (4.77). That is,

$$E(T) = E(W) + E(t)$$

and

$$V(T) = V(W) + V(t).$$

When $s = 1$, equations (4.79), (4.80), (4.81) and (4.82) reduce to equations (4.39), (4.40), (4.41) and (4.42), respectively.

A remark on the traffic intensity. We showed in the M/M/1 queue that the probability of the station being busy at a given moment is equal to ρ. A similar statement can be made for the M/M/s queue. Namely,

$$\Pr\{\text{a station will be busy at a given moment}\} = \rho\,.$$

If $X \geq s$, the probability that a station will be busy is one; if $X = k$, for $k < s$. the probability is $\frac{k}{s}$. Therefore the required probability is

$$\sum_{k=0}^{s-1} \pi_k \frac{k}{s} + \sum_{k=s}^{\infty} \pi_k = \rho\left[1 - \frac{\pi_s}{\rho(1-\rho)}\right] + \frac{\pi_s}{1-\rho}$$
$$= \rho. \tag{4.83}$$

5. PROBLEMS FOR SOLUTION

1. Show that, when $\lambda \neq \mu$,

$$\beta(t) = \lambda \frac{1 - e^{(\lambda-\mu)t}}{\mu - \lambda e^{(\lambda-\mu)t}}$$

is less than one.

2. Show that the p.g.f. $G_X(s;t)$ in (2.15) satisfies the differential equation in (2.4).

3. Derive the probability distribution $\{p_{i,k}(0,t)$ in (2.18) from the probability distribution $\{p_{1,k}(0,t)\}$ in (2.21) by means by convolution and induction.

4. Show that

$$p_{i,0}(0,t) = [\alpha(t)]^i$$

$$p_{i,k}(0,t) = \sum_{j=0}^{\min[i,k]} \binom{i}{j}\binom{i+k-j-1}{k-j}[\alpha(t)]^{i-j}[\beta(t)]^{k-j}[1-\alpha(t)-\beta(t)]^j$$

$$k \geq 1 \tag{2.18}$$

satisfy the differential equations in (2.2) for $i = 1$.

5. Find the expectation $E[X(t)]$ and the variance $V[X(t)$ from the probability distribution in (2.21).

6. Find the expectation $E[X(t)]$ and the variance $V[X(t)]$ from the probability distribution in (2.18).

7. Solve the partial differential equation in (2.26).

8. Derive from the p.g.f. in (2.27) the probabilities $p_{i,k}(0,t)$ for $k = 0, 1, \ldots$.

9. Derive each of the formulas in (2.27), (2.28), and (2.30) from the corresponding formulas in (2.15), (2.18), (2.24) and (2.25), respectively, by taking the limits as $\mu \to \lambda$.

10. Show that the p.g.f. in (2.15) tends to $(\mu/\lambda)^i$ for $\mu < \lambda$, and to unity for $\mu \geq \lambda$ as $t \to \infty$.

11. *The M/M/1 queue.* Find the expectation and the variance of W from the distribution function $F_W(\tau)$ in (4.35).

12. *Continuation.* Derive the distribution function $G_T(\tau)$ in (4.39) from

$$G_T(\tau) = \int_0^\tau h(\xi) F_W(\tau - \xi) d\xi$$

13. *The M/M/s queue.* Verify the formulas in (4.57) and (4.58) for the expectation $E(X)$ and the variance $V(X)$ in a $M/M/s$ queueing system.

14. *Continuation.* Derive the distribution function $G_T(\tau)$ in (4.79) from

$$G_T(\tau) = \int_0^\tau h_t(\xi) F_W(\tau - \xi) d\xi.$$

Find from $G_T(\tau)$ the density function $g_T(\tau)$.

15. *Continuation.* Compute $E(T)$ and $V(T)$ from the density function in (4.80).

16. *Continuation.* Show that in a $M/M/s$ queue system the probability of a station being busy at a given moment is ρ.

17. *A trunking problem.* A telephone system has an infinite number of trunks to accommodate the traffic. Suppose incoming calls follow a Poisson process with parameter λ and the length of a telephone conversation has an exponential distribution with parameter μ. Let $X(t)$ be the number of trunks that are engaged at time t. Derive a system of differential equations for the probability $\Pr\{X(t) = k\}$.

As $t \to \infty$, the probability $\Pr\{X(t) = k\} \to \pi_k$ and is independent of t. Find the limiting probability distribution $\{\pi_k\}$.

18. *Continuation.* Suppose the telephone system in problem 17 has s trunks, for a finite integer s. The system will accommodate incoming calls as long as there are free trunks available. If all the s trunks are engaged, incoming calls will be turned away and be lost to the system. Let $X(t)$ be the number of trunks that are engaged at time t, and assume again a Poisson incoming traffic and an exponential distribution for the length of a telephone conversation. Derive a system of differential equations for the probability $\Pr\{X(t) = k\}$, for $k = 0, 1, \ldots, s$. Investigate the limiting probability $\Pr\{X(t) = k\} \to \pi_k$ as $t \to \infty$.

19. *Continuation.* Consider a telephone system similar to that in Problem 18 and with the same general operating assumptions except that no unaccommodated calls will be turned away. When all the s trunks are engaged, incoming calls form a waiting line and will be served in the order of arrival (i.e., first-come first-served). Let $X(t)$ be the number of calls in the system at time t including those being served and those in the waiting line.

(a) Derive a system of differential equations for the probabilities $\Pr\{X(t) = k\}$, $k = 0, 1, \ldots$.

(b) Find the limiting probability distribution

$$\lim_{t \to \infty} \Pr\{X(t) = k\} = \pi_k.$$

20. *Continuation.* Solve problem 19 if the calls in the waiting line have the same probability of being served when a trunk becomes free for service.

21. *Continuation.* Solve problem 19 if the last-come first-served queue discipline is used.

22. *Servicing of machines* (C. Palm [1947]). A factory has m machines maintained by a single repairman. When a machine is in working condition at time t, there is a probability $\lambda\Delta + o(\Delta)$ that it will be out of order and need servicing during the interval $(t, t + \Delta)$. When a machine is being repaired at time t, there is a probability $\mu\Delta + o(\Delta)$ that it will be fully repaired and returned to working condition during the interval $(t, t + \Delta)$. Let $X(t)$ be the number of machines (out of m) not in working condition at time t.

(a) Derive a system of differential equations for the probabilities $P\{X(t) = k\}$, $k = 0, 1, \ldots, m$.

(b) Derive formulas for the limiting probabilities

$$\pi_k = \lim_{t \to \infty} \Pr\{X(t) = k\}, \quad k = 0, 1, \ldots, m.$$

23. *Continuation.* Solve problem 22 when the machines are maintained by s repairmen, for $s < m$.

24. *Continuation.* Solve parts (a) and (b) in problem 22 when the machines are maintained by s repairmen if $s > m$.

25. Suppose in a general $M/M/s$ queue, the incoming traffic parameters is $\lambda = .12$ (customers per a unit time interval) and the service time parameter is $\mu = .5$ so that the expected service time is $\mu^{-1} = 2$ units of time interval. Depending upon the number of servers in a system, the traffic intensity has the following values

No. of servers	s	1	2	3	4	5	6
Traffic intensity	ρ	.24	.12	.08	.06	.048	.04

For every number of servers

(a) Compute the probability π_k, $k = 0, 1, \ldots, s$.

(b) Find the expectation $E(X)$ and the variance $V(X)$.

(c) Compute the probability q_0 that there is no one in the waiting line.

(d) Compute the expected length of Q and the variance of Q.

(e) Give the formula for the density function $f_{W_n}(\tau)$ for $n = 1, 2, 3$, and the density function $f_W(\tau)$.

(f) Compute the expected waiting time $E(W)$ and the variance of the waiting time $V(W)$.

(g) Compute the expected value $E(T)$ and the variance $V(T)$.

26. *Continuation.* Do the computations in problem 24 if the incoming traffic intensity is doubled with $\lambda = .24$ and service efficiency remains unchanged with $\mu = .5$. Analyze the results that you have obtained in this problem and in problem 25.

27. *Continuation.* Do the computations in problem 25 when the service efficiency is doubled so that $\mu = 1.0$ and the incoming traffic remains unchanged with $\lambda = .12$. Analyze the results you have obtained in this problem and in problems 25 and 26.

28. Derive the p.g.f. of the limiting probability distribution $\{\pi_k\}$ for the $M/M/1$ queue. Find from the p.g.f. the expectation $E(X)$ and the variance $V(X)$.

29. Do problem 28 for the $M/M/s$ queue for $s > 1$.

30. Derive the p.g.f. of the probability distribution $\{q_n\}$ for the $M/M/1$ queue. Find from the p.g.f. the expectation $E(Q)$ and the variance $V(Q)$.

31. Do problem 30 for the $M/M/s$ queue for $s > 1$.

32. Derive the moment generating function (m.g.f.) for W_n, the waiting time of the n-th person in the waiting line in the $M/M/s$ queue

(a) For $s = 1$.

(b) For $s > 1$.

33. Derive the m.g.f. for the waiting time W for the $M/M/1$ queue

(a) Using the m.g.f. of W_n obtained in problem 32.

(b) Using the distribution function of W.

34. Find the expectation and variance of W from the m.g.f. obtained in problem 33.

35. Solve problems 33 and 34 for the $M/M/s$ queue, for $s > 1$.

36. Derive the m.g.f. for T, the total length of time that a customer spends in the $M/M/1$ queueing system. Find the expectation and the variance of T from the m.g.f.

37. Work out problem 36 for the $M/M/s$ queue for $s > 1$.

CHAPTER 11

A Simple Illness-Death Process —Fix-Neyman Process

1. INTRODUCTION

In this chapter we present a two-transient state Markov process with one or more absorbing states. While this model has applications in compartmental analysis, in survival analysis, in reliability theory, and in many other practical fields, we shall consider the human population as an example and use health condition and causes of death as criteria for defining states.

In discussing the pure death process in Chapter 8, we assumed that individuals have the same probability of dying within a given time interval regardless of their health condition. This assumption does not hold for the human population, as all individuals are not equally healthy; the chance of dying varies from one person to another. Since death is usually preceded by illness, a survival analysis is incomplete unless it takes illness into consideration. However, illness and death are distinct and different events. Illnesses are potentially concurrent, repetitive, and reversible, whereas death is an irreversible and absorbing state. Further complexity is introduced by competition among various causes of death: The probability of an individual dying from one cause is influenced by the presence of competition from other causes. In a mortality study one must be concerned with the probabilities of dying from a specific cause, both with and without competing risks.

A mathematical model of two transient states was first proposed by Du Pasquier [1913]. But it was Fix and Neyman [1951] who introduced the stochastic version and resolved many problems associated with the model. Sverdrop [1965] subsequently published his interesting work; some of his results are contained in the Fix-Neyman paper. A general illness-death stochastic model that can accommodate any finite number of transient states was presented by Chiang [1964]. In this general model, there are a finite number of health states and a finite number of death states. An individual is said to be in a particular health state if his health condition corresponds to the definition of that state; an individual is said to be in a particular death state if he dies of the corresponding cause. An individual also may leave a health state at any time through recovery, death, or by contracting other diseases; thus health states are transient. Death states, on the other hand, are absorbing states; having once entered a death state, an individual will remain there forever. In order to introduce basic concepts of the illness-death process, a simple model with two health states and a finite number of death states is presented in this chapter and in Chapters 12 and 13. A general model for any finite number of health states will be presented in Chapter 16.

Example 1. In a stochastic model of recovery, relapse, death and loss of cancer patients, Fix and Neyman [1951] considered two health states: The state of "leading a normal life" and the state of being under treatment for cancer; and two death states: Death from cancer or operative death, and death from other causes or cases lost to observation. The state of "leading a normal life" includes patients who have "recovered" from cancer, whether the recovery is real or only clinically apparent. A patient leaves the cancer state only if he dies from cancer or recovers; a patient "leading a normal life" can leave that state by having a recurrence of cancer, by dying from causes not connected with cancer, or by being lost to observation.

Example 2. A California mental hospital has different types of wards for patients with varying developmental disabilities, ranging from very mild to extremely severe. The ward to which a new patient is assigned depends on the severity of his case. A patient may be transferred from one ward to another when his condition improves or worsens; patients may also be discharged from the hospital, transferred to another hospital, or die. From the time of admission, a record is kept for each patient regarding treatments received, transfers between wards, time of transfers, and duration of stay in each ward. Data of this kind can be helpful in evaluating the progress of patients' health conditions, the effectiveness of treatments, the incidence and prevalence of mental illnesses in the general population, the need for hospital facilities and personnel, and the State's budget for mental health care.

Illness-death processes can be applied to many types of problems. A list of some other systems that can be described by a two-transient state model follows. (In the example of a woman's pregnancy, the probability of moving out of the pregnant state to the non-pregnant state depends on gestation; therefore, the process is a *semi-Markov process*. In this book we shall not discuss this process in any detail.)

	S_1	S_2
A person is	employed	unemployed
An elevator is	occupied	unoccupied
A telephone line is	engaged	free
A nuclear particle counting instrument is	free	in a dead period
An automobile is	working	out of order
A woman is	pregnant	not pregnant

2. HEALTH TRANSITION PROBABILITY $P_{\alpha\beta}(0, t)$ AND DEATH TRANSITION PROBABILITY $Q_{\alpha\delta}(0, t)$

Consider a population consisting of two health states, S_1 and S_2, and r death states, $R_1, \ldots, R_r$, for a finite positive integer r. Transitions are possible between the two health states S_1 and S_2 or from either one of the health states to a death state. In Figure 1, arrows show the possible transitions that may take place.

Let (τ, t) be a time interval with $0 \le \tau < t < \infty$. At time τ let an individual be in state S_α. During the interval (τ, t), the individual may travel continuously between S_α and S_β, for $\alpha, \beta = 1, 2$, and may reach a death state. Transitions from one state to another are governed by the intensities of illness $(\nu_{\alpha\beta})$ and intensities of death $(\mu_{\alpha\delta})$, which are defined as follows:

$$\nu_{\alpha\beta}\,\Delta + o(\Delta) = \Pr\{\text{an individual in state } S_\alpha \text{ at time } \xi \text{ will be in state } S_\beta \text{ at time } \xi + \Delta\}, \qquad \alpha \neq \beta;\ \alpha, \beta = 1, 2, \tag{2.1}$$

$$\mu_{\alpha\delta}\,\Delta + o(\Delta) = \Pr\{\text{an individual in state } S_\alpha \text{ at time } \xi \text{ will be in state } R_\delta \text{ at time } \xi + \Delta\}, \qquad \alpha = 1, 2;\ \delta = 1, \ldots, r, \tag{2.2}$$

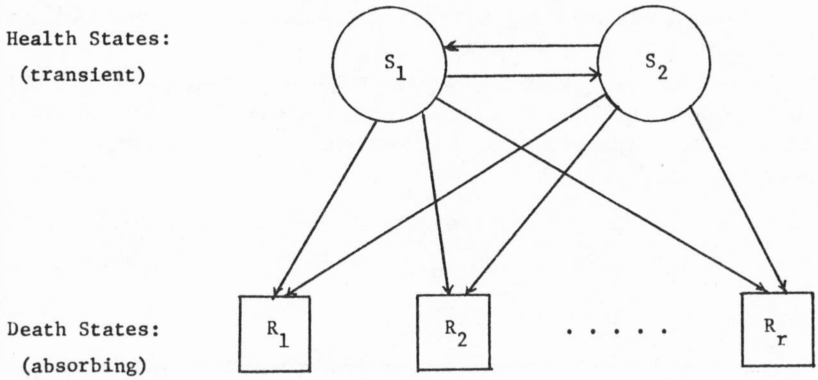

FIGURE 1

for each ξ, $\tau \le \xi \le t$. The intensities $\nu_{\alpha\beta}$ and $\mu_{\alpha\delta}$ are assumed to be independent of ξ for $\tau \le \xi \le t$; hence the process is time homogeneous. For notational convenience we define

$$\nu_{\alpha\alpha} = -\left[\nu_{\alpha\beta} + \sum_{\delta=1}^{r} \mu_{\alpha\delta}\right], \qquad \alpha \ne \beta;\ \alpha, \beta = 1, 2, \tag{2.3}$$

so that

$$\begin{aligned} 1 + \nu_{\alpha\alpha}\Delta + o(\Delta) = \Pr\{&\text{an individual in state } S_\alpha \text{ at time } \xi \\ &\text{will remain in } S_\alpha \text{ during the interval } (\xi, \xi + \Delta)\}. \end{aligned} \tag{2.4}$$

It is clear that $\nu_{\alpha\alpha} \le 0$. If $\nu_{\alpha\alpha} = 0$, then the state S_α would be an absorbing state, which we would treat as a death state. For this model we will assume that

$$\nu_{\alpha\alpha} < 0, \qquad \alpha = 1, 2. \tag{2.5}$$

We may regard state S_1 as a health state, and S_2 as an illness state, so that a transition from S_1 to S_2 means an illness or a relapse and a transition from S_2 to S_1 means recovery. But in the discussion that follows, we shall consider illness as a state of health and allow transitions $S_1 \to S_2$, $S_2 \to S_1$ to take place without specific designation. We shall also assume that

$$\sum_{\delta=1}^{r} \mu_{1\delta} > 0 \qquad \text{or} \qquad \sum_{\delta=1}^{r} \mu_{2\delta} > 0. \tag{2.6}$$

The case in which all $\mu_{\alpha\delta}$ vanish corresponds to a process with no absorbing states [cf., Chapter 13, section 6].

An individual in state S_α at time τ will be either in one of the health states S_β or in one of the death states R_δ at time t.[1] We will call the corresponding probabilities the *health transition probabilities*,

$$P_{\alpha\beta}(\tau, t) = \Pr\{\text{an individual in state } S_\alpha \text{ at } \tau \text{ will be in state } S_\beta \text{ at } t\},$$
$$\alpha, \beta = 1, 2, \tag{2.7}$$

and the *death transition probabilities*,

$$Q_{\alpha\delta}(\tau, t) = \Pr\{\text{an individual in state } S_\alpha \text{ at } \tau \text{ will be in state } R_\delta \text{ at } t\},$$
$$\alpha = 1, 2; \delta = 1, \ldots, r. \tag{2.8}$$

These probabilities satisfy the initial conditions

$$\begin{aligned} P_{\alpha\alpha}(\tau, \tau) &= 1, \qquad \alpha = 1, 2, \\ P_{\alpha\beta}(\tau, \tau) &= 0, \qquad \alpha \neq \beta; \alpha, \beta = 1, 2, \\ Q_{\alpha\delta}(\tau, \tau) &= 0, \qquad \alpha = 1, 2; \delta = 1, \ldots, r. \end{aligned} \tag{2.9}$$

First we derive expressions for the health transition probabilities; then we will use these to obtain the death transition probabilities.

Consider a time interval (τ, t), a fixed time ξ between τ and t, and an individual who is in state S_α at time τ. We assume that the future transitions of the individual are independent of the past transitions. It follows, then, that the probability that the individual will be in a particular state S_β at time ξ, and is in S_γ at time t, is

$$P_{\alpha\beta}(\tau, \xi) P_{\beta\gamma}(\xi, t), \qquad \alpha, \beta, \gamma = 1, 2. \tag{2.10}$$

Since, for different β, the events corresponding to (2.10) are mutually exclusive, we have

$$P_{\alpha\gamma}(\tau, t) = \sum_{\beta=1}^{2} P_{\alpha\beta}(\tau, \xi) P_{\beta\gamma}(\xi, t), \qquad \alpha, \gamma = 1, 2. \tag{2.11}$$

Equation (2.11) is a form of the Chapman-Kolmogorov equation, which we shall encounter again and discuss more generally in Chapter 14.

[1] In the discussion that follows, α may be equal to β; we will make the clarification whenever necessary.

The differential equations for $P_{\alpha\beta}(\tau, t)$ are obtained by considering two contiguous time intervals (τ, t) and $(t, t + \Delta)$, and the probabilities $P_{\alpha\beta}(\tau, t + \Delta)$. Using (2.11), (2.1), and (2.4), we find that, for $\alpha \neq \beta$,

$$P_{\alpha\alpha}(\tau, t + \Delta) = P_{\alpha\alpha}(\tau, t)[1 + \nu_{\alpha\alpha}\Delta] + P_{\alpha\beta}(\tau, t)\,\nu_{\beta\alpha}\Delta + o(\Delta),$$
$$P_{\alpha\beta}(\tau, t + \Delta) = P_{\alpha\alpha}(\tau, t)\,\nu_{\alpha\beta}\Delta + P_{\alpha\beta}(\tau, t)\,[1 + \nu_{\beta\beta}\Delta] + o(\Delta). \tag{2.12}$$

Rearranging (2.12) to form difference quotients and taking the limit as $\Delta \to 0$, we obtain the differential equations

$$\frac{\partial}{\partial t} P_{\alpha\alpha}(\tau, t) = P_{\alpha\alpha}(\tau, t)\,\nu_{\alpha\alpha} + P_{\alpha\beta}(\tau, t)\,\nu_{\beta\alpha},$$
$$\frac{\partial}{\partial t} P_{\alpha\beta}(\tau, t) = P_{\alpha\alpha}(\tau, t)\,\nu_{\alpha\beta} + P_{\alpha\beta}(\tau, t)\,\nu_{\beta\beta}, \qquad \alpha \neq \beta;\ \alpha, \beta = 1, 2. \tag{2.13}$$

This is a system of linear, homogenous first-order differential equations with constant coefficients. (Note that the resemblance of (2.13) to partial differential equations is only formal.) As is usual in solving such systems, we look for solutions of the form

$$P_{\alpha\alpha}(\tau, t) = c_{\alpha\alpha}\,e^{\rho t}, \qquad P_{\alpha\beta}(\tau, t) = c_{\alpha\beta}\,e^{\rho t}. \tag{2.14}$$

Substituting (2.14) in (2.13) gives us

$$\rho c_{\alpha\alpha}\,e^{\rho t} = c_{\alpha\alpha}\,e^{\rho t}\,\nu_{\alpha\alpha} + c_{\alpha\beta}\,e^{\rho t}\,\nu_{\beta\alpha}$$

and

$$\rho c_{\alpha\beta}\,e^{\rho t} = c_{\alpha\alpha}\,e^{\rho t}\,\nu_{\alpha\beta} + c_{\alpha\beta}\,e^{\rho t}\,\nu_{\beta\beta},$$

which reduce to

$$(\rho - \nu_{\alpha\alpha})\,c_{\alpha\alpha} - \nu_{\beta\alpha}\,c_{\alpha\beta} = 0$$

and

$$-\nu_{\alpha\beta}\,c_{\alpha\alpha} + (\rho - \nu_{\beta\beta})\,c_{\alpha\beta} = 0. \tag{2.15}$$

Since (2.15) is a linear homogeneous system, nontrivial solutions for $c_{\alpha\alpha}$ and $c_{\alpha\beta}$ can exist only if the determinant

$$\begin{vmatrix} \rho - \nu_{\alpha\alpha} & -\nu_{\beta\alpha} \\ -\nu_{\alpha\beta} & \rho - \nu_{\beta\beta} \end{vmatrix} = \rho^2 - (\nu_{\alpha\alpha} + \nu_{\beta\beta})\,\rho + (\nu_{\alpha\alpha}\,\nu_{\beta\beta} - \nu_{\alpha\beta}\,\nu_{\beta\alpha}) = 0. \tag{2.16}$$

Equation (2.16) is called the *characteristic equation* of the differential equations in (2.13). Equation (2.16) is symmetrical with respect to α and β; therefore, the roots are

$$\begin{aligned} \rho_1 &= \tfrac{1}{2}\,[\nu_{11} + \nu_{22} + \sqrt{(\nu_{11} - \nu_{22})^2 + 4\nu_{12}\nu_{21}}]\,, \\ \rho_2 &= \tfrac{1}{2}\,[\nu_{11} + \nu_{22} - \sqrt{(\nu_{11} - \nu_{22})^2 + 4\nu_{12}\nu_{21}}]\,. \end{aligned} \tag{2.17}$$

Thus ρ_1 and ρ_2 are the only values of ρ for which (2.14) is a valid solution of (2.13). Because

$$0 < \nu_{12} < |\nu_{11}| \qquad \text{and} \qquad 0 < \nu_{21} < |\nu_{22}|, \tag{2.18}$$

the discriminant is strictly positive, and

$$\sqrt{(\nu_{11} - \nu_{22})^2 + 4\nu_{12}\nu_{21}} < |\nu_{11} + \nu_{22}|.$$

Therefore, the roots ρ_1 and ρ_2 are real, distinct negative numbers.

For each ρ_i, the coefficients $c_{\alpha\alpha i}$ and $c_{\alpha\beta i}$ in equation (2.15) are related as follows:

$$\frac{c_{\alpha\alpha i}}{c_{\alpha\beta i}} = \frac{\nu_{\beta\alpha}}{\rho_i - \nu_{\alpha\alpha}} = \frac{\rho_i - \nu_{\beta\beta}}{\nu_{\alpha\beta}}. \tag{2.19}$$

(Note that the second equality is equivalent to equation (2.16)). Setting

$$k_i = \frac{c_{\alpha\alpha i}}{\rho_i - \nu_{\beta\beta}} = \frac{c_{\alpha\beta i}}{\nu_{\alpha\beta}}, \tag{2.20}$$

we have a pair of solutions for the original differential equations in (2.13):

$$P_{\alpha\alpha}(\tau, t) = k_i\,(\rho_i - \nu_{\beta\beta})\,e^{\rho_i t},$$

and

$$P_{\alpha\beta}(\tau, t) = k_i\,\nu_{\alpha\beta}\,e^{\rho_i t}, \qquad i = 1, 2. \tag{2.21}$$

Because the two roots ρ_1 and ρ_2 are distinct, the general solution is

$$P_{\alpha\alpha}(\tau, t) = \sum_{i=1}^{2} k_i(\rho_i - \nu_{\beta\beta})\, e^{\rho_i t},$$

$$P_{\alpha\beta}(\tau, t) = \sum_{i=1}^{2} k_i\, \nu_{\alpha\beta}\, e^{\rho_i t},$$

$$\alpha \neq \beta;\ \alpha, \beta = 1, 2. \qquad (2.22)$$

In order to determine the constants k_i, we let $t = \tau$ in equation (2.22) and use the initial conditions (2.9) to write

$$P_{\alpha\alpha}(\tau, \tau) = \sum_{i=1}^{2} k_i\,(\rho_i - \nu_{\beta\beta})\, e^{\rho_i \tau} = 1$$

and

$$P_{\alpha\beta}(\tau, \tau) = \sum_{i=1}^{2} k_i\, \nu_{\alpha\beta}\, e^{\rho_i \tau} = 0. \qquad (2.23)$$

Solving (2.23) for k_i gives us

$$k_i = \frac{1}{\rho_i - \rho_j}\, e^{-\rho_i \tau}, \qquad i \neq j;\ j = 1, 2. \qquad (2.24)$$

Substituting (2.24) in (2.22), we obtain the required formulas for the health transition probabilities,

$$P_{\alpha\alpha}(\tau, t) = \sum_{i=1}^{2} \frac{\rho_i - \nu_{\beta\beta}}{\rho_i - \rho_j}\, e^{\rho_i (t-\tau)}$$

and

$$P_{\alpha\beta}(\tau, t) = \sum_{i=1}^{2} \frac{\nu_{\alpha\beta}}{\rho_i - \rho_j}\, e^{\rho_i (t-\tau)},$$

$$j \neq i,\ \alpha \neq \beta;\ j, \alpha, \beta = 1, 2. \qquad (2.25)$$

The probabilities in (2.25) depend only on the difference $t - \tau$ but not on τ and t separately; thus the process is *homogeneous with respect to time* as pointed out earlier. We shall therefore let $\tau = 0$ and let t be the interval length, and write

$$P_{\alpha\alpha}(0, t) = \sum_{i=1}^{2} \frac{\rho_i - \nu_{\beta\beta}}{\rho_i - \rho_j} e^{\rho_i t}, \tag{2.26}$$

$$P_{\alpha\beta}(0, t) = \sum_{i=1}^{2} \frac{\nu_{\alpha\beta}}{\rho_i - \rho_j} e^{\rho_i t},$$

$$j \neq i, \alpha \neq \beta; j, \alpha, \beta = 1, 2. \tag{2.27}$$

The *death transition probability*, which we may now write as $Q_{\alpha\delta}(0, t)$, has a definite relationship with the health transition probabilities. The relationship can be established as follows: An individual in illness state S_α may reach the death state R_δ directly from S_α or by way of S_β, $\beta \neq \alpha$. Since an individual in R_δ at time t may have reached that state at any time before t, let us consider an infinitesimal time interval $(\tau, \tau + d\tau)$ for a fixed τ, $0 \le \tau < t$. The probability that an individual in state S_α at time 0 will reach the state R_δ in the interval $(\tau, \tau + d\tau)$ is

$$P_{\alpha\alpha}(0, \tau)\, \mu_{\alpha\delta}\, d\tau + P_{\alpha\beta}(0, \tau)\, \mu_{\beta\delta}\, d\tau,$$

$$\alpha \neq \beta; \alpha, \beta = 1, 2, \qquad \delta = 1, \ldots, r. \tag{2.28}$$

As τ varies over the interval $(0, t)$, the corresponding events, whose probabilities are given in (2.28), are mutually exclusive. Hence

$$Q_{\alpha\delta}(0, t) = \int_0^t P_{\alpha\alpha}(\tau)\, \mu_{\alpha\delta}\, d\tau + \int_0^t P_{\alpha\beta}(\tau)\, \mu_{\beta\delta}\, d\tau. \tag{2.29}$$

Now we substitute (2.26) and (2.27) in (2.29) and integrate the resulting expression to obtain the formula for the death transition probability,

$$Q_{\alpha\delta}(0, t) = \sum_{i=1}^{2} \frac{e^{\rho_i t} - 1}{\rho_i(\rho_i - \rho_j)} [(\rho_i - \nu_{\beta\beta})\, \mu_{\alpha\delta} + \nu_{\alpha\beta}\, \mu_{\beta\delta}]$$

$$j \neq i; \quad \alpha \neq \beta; \quad j, \alpha, \beta, = 1, 2, \quad \delta = 1, \ldots, r. \tag{2.30}$$

3. CHAPMAN-KOLMOGOROV EQUATIONS

The illness-death process described in this chapter is a Markov process in the sense that the transitions an individual might make in the future are independent of transitions made in the past. An important consequence of this property is the Chapman-Kolmogorov equation in (2.11). Since this process is homogeneous with respect to time, we may rewrite equation (2.11)

$$P_{\alpha\alpha}(0, t) = P_{\alpha\alpha}(0, \tau)P_{\alpha\alpha}(\tau, t) + P_{\alpha\beta}(0, \tau)P_{\beta\alpha}(\tau, t) \tag{3.1a}$$

and

$$P_{\alpha\beta}(0, t) = P_{\alpha\alpha}(0, \tau)P_{\alpha\beta}(\tau, t) + P_{\alpha\beta}(0, \tau)P_{\beta\beta}(\tau, t) \tag{3.1b}$$

for $0 \le \tau \le t$, $\alpha \neq \beta$; $\alpha, \beta = 1, 2$. We now verify that the transition probabilities in (2.26) and (2.27) satisfy equation (3.1a) and leave the verification of (3.1b) to the reader. Substituting (2.26) and (2.27) in (3.1a) yields

$$\sum_{i=1}^{2} \frac{\rho_i - \nu_{\beta\beta}}{\rho_i - \rho_j} e^{\rho_i t} = \left[\sum_{i=1}^{2} \frac{\rho_i - \nu_{\beta\beta}}{\rho_i - \rho_j} e^{\rho_i \tau}\right]\left[\sum_{i=1}^{2} \frac{\rho_i - \nu_{\beta\beta}}{\rho_i - \rho_j} e^{\rho_i (t-\tau)}\right]$$
$$+ \left[\sum_{i=1}^{2} \frac{\nu_{\alpha\beta}}{\rho_i - \rho_j} e^{\rho_i \tau}\right]\left[\sum_{i=1}^{2} \frac{\nu_{\beta\alpha}}{\rho_i - \rho_j} e^{\rho_i (t-\tau)}\right]. \tag{3.2}$$

We then simplify the right hand side of (3.2) to get

$$\sum_{i=1}^{2} \frac{(\rho_i - \nu_{\beta\beta})^2 + \nu_{\alpha\beta}\nu_{\beta\alpha}}{(\rho_i - \rho_j)^2} e^{\rho_i t} -$$
$$\frac{(\rho_1 - \nu_{\beta\beta})(\rho_2 - \nu_{\beta\beta}) + \nu_{\alpha\beta}\nu_{\beta\alpha}}{(\rho_1 - \rho_2)^2}\left[\sum_{\substack{i=1\\ j\neq i}}^{2} e^{\rho_i \tau + \rho_j (t-\tau)}\right]. \tag{3.3}$$

The numerator of the first term in (3.3) may be rewritten as

$$(\rho_i - \nu_{\beta\beta})^2 + \nu_{\alpha\beta}\nu_{\beta\alpha} = (\rho_i - \nu_{\beta\beta})(\rho_i - \rho_j),$$
$$i \neq j; \qquad i, j, = 1, 2, \tag{3.4}$$

whereas the second term vanishes because of

$$(\rho_1 - \nu_{\beta\beta})(\rho_2 - \nu_{\beta\beta}) + \nu_{\alpha\beta}\nu_{\beta\alpha} = 0. \tag{3.5}$$

When (3.4) and (3.5) are substituted in (3.3), we recover the left hand side of (3.2), verifying equation (3.2) and hence also equation (3.1a).

Chapman-Kolmogorov type equations can be established also for the transition probabilities leading to death. Consider an individual in illness state S_α at time 0. There is a probability $Q_{\alpha\delta}(0,t)$ that the individual will be in death state R_δ at time t. If we let τ be a fixed point in the interval $(0,t)$, the individual may reach state R_δ either before τ or after τ. The probability of the former event is $Q_{\alpha\delta}(0, \tau)$. For the latter event to occur, the individual must be in health state

S_α or S_β at time τ and enter R_δ during the interval (τ,t); the respective probabilities are $P_{\alpha\alpha}(0,\tau)Q_{\alpha\delta}(\tau,t)$ and $P_{\alpha\beta}(0,\tau)Q_{\beta\delta}(\tau,t)$. Taking these possibilities together, we have the equation

$$Q_{\alpha\delta}(0,t) = Q_{\alpha\delta}(0,\tau) + P_{\alpha\alpha}(0,\tau)Q_{\alpha\delta}(\tau,t) + P_{\alpha\beta}(0,\tau)Q_{\beta\delta}(\tau,t),$$
$$\alpha \neq \beta; \qquad \alpha, \beta = 1, 2. \tag{3.6}$$

4. EXPECTED DURATION OF STAY

In a study of human health, we need to determine the length of time a person is expected to be healthy. Similarly, in other studies we may inquire about the length of time an automobile is expected to be in working condition, a person is expected to be employed, or a telephone line is expected to be busy. These inquiries lead to an important concept in the illness-death process: That is *the expected duration of stay* in each of the states S_1, S_2, R_1, ..., R_r, within a time period of length t. This duration depends on the initial state and the corresponding transition probability. For an individual in state S_α at time 0, let

$$e_{\alpha\beta}(t) = \text{the expected duration of stay in } S_\beta \text{ on the interval } (0,t),$$
$$\beta = 1, 2, \tag{4.1}$$

and

$$\varepsilon_{\alpha\delta}(t) = \text{the expected duration of stay in } R_\delta \text{ in the interval } (0,t),$$
$$\delta = 1, \ldots, r. \tag{4.2}$$

To express $e_{\alpha\beta}(t)$ and $\varepsilon_{\alpha\delta}(t)$ mathematically, first consider an individual in S_α at time 0; then for each τ, $0 \le \tau \le t$, define indicator functions $I_{\alpha\beta}(\tau)$ and $J_{\alpha\delta}(\tau)$ such that

$$I_{\alpha\beta}(\tau) = \begin{cases} 1 & \text{if the individual is in } S_\beta \text{ at time } \tau \\ 0 & \text{otherwise} \end{cases} \tag{4.3}$$

and

$$J_{\alpha\delta}(\tau) = \begin{cases} 1 & \text{if the individual is in } R_\delta \text{ at time } \tau \\ 0 & \text{otherwise.} \end{cases} \tag{4.4}$$

The expectations are

$$E\,[I_{\alpha\beta}(\tau)] = P_{\alpha\beta}(0,\tau) \tag{4.5}$$

and

$$E[J_{\alpha\delta}(\tau)] = Q_{\alpha\delta}(0,\tau). \tag{4.6}$$

It is easy to see that

$$e_{\alpha\beta}(t) = E\int_0^t I_{\alpha\beta}(\tau)\,d\tau, \tag{4.7}$$

$$\varepsilon_{\alpha\delta}(t) = E\int_0^t J_{\alpha\delta}(\tau)\,d\tau. \tag{4.8}$$

By interchanging the expectation and the integral signs in these equations we get

$$e_{\alpha\beta}(t) = \int_0^t P_{\alpha\beta}(0,\tau)\,d\tau \tag{4.9}$$

and

$$\varepsilon_{\alpha\delta}(t) = \int_0^t Q_{\alpha\delta}(0,\tau)\,d\tau. \tag{4.10}$$

Using formulas (2.26), (2.27) and (2.30) for the transition probabilities $P_{\alpha\beta}(0,\tau)$ and $Q_{\alpha\delta}(0,\tau)$, we obtain the following explicit formulas:

$$e_{\alpha\alpha}(t) = \int_0^t \sum_{i=1}^{2} \frac{\rho_i - \nu_{\beta\beta}}{\rho_i - \rho_j} e^{\rho_i\tau}\,d\tau = \sum_{i=1}^{2} \frac{\rho_i - \nu_{\beta\beta}}{\rho_i(\rho_i - \rho_j)} (e^{\rho_i t} - 1), \tag{4.11}$$

$$e_{\alpha\beta}(t) = \int_0^t \sum_{i=1}^{2} \frac{\nu_{\alpha\beta}}{\rho_i - \rho_j} e^{\rho_i\tau}\,d\tau = \sum_{i=1}^{2} \frac{\nu_{\alpha\beta}}{\rho_i(\rho_i - \rho_j)} (e^{\rho_i t} - 1), \tag{4.12}$$

and

$$\varepsilon_{\alpha\delta}(t) = \int_0^t \sum_{i=1}^{2} \frac{e^{\rho_i\tau} - 1}{\rho_i(\rho_i - \rho_j)} [(\rho_i - \nu_{\beta\beta})\mu_{\alpha\delta} + \nu_{\alpha\beta}\mu_{\beta\delta}]\,d\tau$$

$$= \sum_{i=1}^{2} \left[\frac{1}{\rho_i}(e^{\rho_i t} - 1) - t\right] \frac{(\rho_i - \nu_{\beta\beta})\mu_{\alpha\delta} + \nu_{\alpha\beta}\mu_{\beta\delta}}{\rho_i(\rho_i - \rho_j)}. \tag{4.13}$$

The sum of the expected durations of stay over all states is equal to the entire length of the interval,

$$e_{\alpha 1}(t) + e_{\alpha 2}(t) + \varepsilon_{\alpha 1}(t) + \cdots + \varepsilon_{\alpha r}(t) = t, \qquad \alpha = 1, 2. \tag{4.14}$$

The reader can verify (4.14) using equations (4.11), (4.12), and (4.13).

5. POPULATION SIZES IN HEALTH STATES AND DEATH STATES

An individual in S_α at time 0 must be in one of the health states or in one of the death states at time t; consequently, the corresponding transition probabilities add to one:

$$\sum_{\beta=1}^{2} P_{\alpha\beta}(0,t) + \sum_{\delta=1}^{r} Q_{\alpha\delta}(0,t) = 1, \qquad \alpha = 1, 2. \tag{5.1}$$

Having derived explicit forms for the probabilities $P_{\alpha\beta}(0,t)$ and $Q_{\alpha\delta}(0,t)$, we can now verify equation (5.1) directly. We use (2.30) and (2.3) to write

$$\begin{aligned}\sum_{\delta=1}^{r} Q_{\alpha\delta}(0,t) &= \sum_{l=1}^{2} \frac{e^{\rho_l t}-1}{\rho_l(\rho_l-\rho_m)}\left[(\rho_l-\nu_{\beta\beta})\sum_{\delta=1}^{r}\mu_{\alpha\delta}+\nu_{\alpha\beta}\sum_{\delta=1}^{r}\mu_{\beta\delta}\right]\\ &= \sum_{l=1}^{2} \frac{e^{\rho_l t}-1}{\rho_l(\rho_l-\rho_m)}[-(\rho_l-\nu_{\beta\beta})(\nu_{\alpha\alpha}+\nu_{\alpha\beta})\\ &\qquad -\nu_{\alpha\beta}(\nu_{\beta\alpha}+\nu_{\beta\beta})]\\ &= \sum_{l=1}^{2} \frac{e^{\rho_l t}-1}{\rho_l(\rho_l-\rho_m)}[-\rho_l^2+\rho_l\nu_{\beta\beta}-\rho_l\nu_{\alpha\beta}],\end{aligned} \tag{5.2}$$

since ρ_l is a root of the characteristic equation (2.16). The last expression in (5.2) can be simplified to give

$$\sum_{\delta=1}^{r} Q_{\alpha\delta}(0,t) = 1 - \sum_{l=1}^{2} \frac{e^{\rho_l t}}{\rho_l-\rho_m}[(\rho_l-\nu_{\beta\beta})+\nu_{\alpha\beta}]. \tag{5.3}$$

And combining (5.3) with (2.26) and (2.27), we recover equation (5.1).

Equation (5.1) is used to derive the probability distribution of population sizes in states S_β and R_δ at any time t. At time $t = 0$, let there be i_1 individuals in state S_1 and i_2 individuals in state S_2, and let the sum

$$i = i_1 + i_2 \tag{5.4}$$

be the initial size of the population. Suppose that the i individuals travel independently from one state to another, and that at the end of the interval $(0,t)$, $X_\beta(t)$ individuals are in illness state S_β and $Y_\delta(t)$ individuals are in state R_δ. Obviously

$$i = X_1(t) + X_2(t) + Y_1(t) + \cdots + Y_r(t). \tag{5.5}$$

Each of the random variables on the right hand side of (5.5) is composed of two parts,

$$X_\beta(t) = X_{1\beta}(t) + X_{2\beta}(t), \qquad \beta = 1, 2, \tag{5.6}$$

where $X_{\alpha\beta}(t)$ is the number of those people in state S_β at time t who were in state S_α at time 0, and

$$Y_\delta(t) = Y_{1\delta}(t) + Y_{2\delta}(t), \qquad \delta = 1, \cdots, r, \tag{5.7}$$

where $Y_{\alpha\delta}(t)$ is the number of people in state R_δ at time t who were in state S_α at time 0. On the other hand, each of the i_α people in S_α at time 0 must be in one of the health states or in one of the death states at time t; therefore we have

$$i_\alpha = X_{\alpha 1}(t) + X_{\alpha 2}(t) + Y_{\alpha 1}(t) + \cdots + Y_{\alpha r}(t). \tag{5.8}$$

When summing (5.8) over $\alpha = 1, 2$, we get (5.5). Table 1 summarizes the population sizes of the states at time 0 and at time t.

Table 1: Distribution of Individuals in Health States S_β and Death States R_δ at time t According to Initial State S_α at time 0.

State at time 0	State at time t					Row Totals (initial population sizes)
	S_1	S_2	R_1	$\cdots$	R_r	
S_1	$X_{11}(t)$	$X_{12}(t)$	$Y_{11}(t)$	$\cdots$	$Y_{1r}(t)$	i_1
S_2	$X_{21}(t)$	$X_{22}(t)$	$Y_{21}(t)$	$\cdots$	$Y_{2r}(t)$	i_2
Column Totals (population sizes at time t)	$X_1(t)$	$X_2(t)$	$Y_1(t)$	$\cdots$	$Y_r(t)$	i

Equation (5.1) implies that, for each α, the random variables on the right hand side of (5.8) have a multinomial distribution with the p.g.f. given by

$$E\,[s_1^{X_{\alpha 1}(t)} s_2^{X_{\alpha 2}(t)} z_1^{Y_{\alpha 1}(t)} \ldots z_{r-1}^{Y_{\alpha,r-1}(t)} | i_\alpha]$$
$$= [s_1 P_{\alpha 1}(0,t) + s_2 P_{\alpha 2}(0,t) + z_1 Q_{\alpha 1}(0,t) + \ldots + z_r Q_{\alpha r}(0,t)]^{i_\alpha}, \tag{5.9}$$

where $z_r = 1$. Since the i_1 and i_2 people make their transitions independently of one another, the p.g.f. of the population sizes at time t is

$$E\,[s_1^{X_1(t)}\,s_2^{X_2(t)}\,z_1^{Y_1(t)}\ldots z_{r-1}^{Y_{r-1}(t)}|i_1,i_2]$$
$$=\prod_{\alpha=1}^{2}\,[s_1P_{\alpha 1}(0,t)+s_2P_{\alpha 2}(0,t)+z_1Q_{\alpha 1}(0,t)+\ldots+z_rQ_{\alpha r}(0,t)]^{i_\alpha}, \tag{5.10}$$

where $z_r = 1$. It follows that the expected population sizes of the states at time t are

$$E\,[X_\beta(t)|i_1,i_2]=i_1P_{1\beta}(0,t)+i_2P_{2\beta}(0,t) \tag{5.11}$$

and

$$E\,[Y_\delta(t)|i_1,i_2]=i_1Q_{1\delta}(0,t)+i_2Q_{2\delta}(0,t). \tag{5.12}$$

The corresponding variances are

$$\sigma^2_{X_\beta(t)}=\sum_{\alpha=1}^{2}i_\alpha P_{\alpha\beta}(0,t)\,[1-P_{\alpha\beta}(0,t)] \tag{5.13}$$

and

$$\sigma^2_{Y_\delta(t)}=\sum_{\alpha=1}^{2}i_\alpha Q_{\alpha\delta}(0,t)\,[1-Q_{\alpha\delta}(0,t)], \tag{5.14}$$

The population becomes extinct at time t if $X_1(t) = 0$ and $X_2(t) = 0$. We obtain the probability of extinction at time t from (5.10) by letting $s_1 = s_2 = 0$ and $z_1 = \ldots = z_r = 1$; and then using (5.3),

$$\Pr\{X_1(t)=0,\,X_2(t)=0|i_1,i_2\}=\prod_{\alpha=1}^{2}\,[Q_{\alpha 1}(0,t)+\ldots+Q_{\alpha r}(0,t)]^{i_\alpha}$$
$$=\prod_{\alpha=1}^{2}\left[1-\sum_{l=1}^{2}\frac{e^{\rho_l t}}{(\rho_l-\rho_m)}\,[(\rho_l-\nu_{\beta\beta})+\nu_{\alpha\beta}]\right]^{i_\alpha}, \tag{5.15}$$

where $m \neq l$, $m = 1, 2$.

5.1. The Limiting Distribution.

Since both ρ_1 and ρ_2 are negative, the transition probabilities in equations (2.26) and (2.27) approach zero as $t \to \infty$:

$$P_{\alpha\alpha}(0,\infty)=\lim_{t\to\infty}P_{\alpha\alpha}(0,t)=\lim_{t\to\infty}\sum_{l=1}^{2}\frac{\rho_l-\nu_{\beta\beta}}{\rho_l-\rho_m}\,e^{\rho_l t}=0, \tag{5.16}$$

$$P_{\alpha\beta}(0,\infty) = \lim_{t\to\infty} P_{\alpha\beta}(0,t) = \lim_{t\to\infty} \sum_{l=1}^{2} \frac{\nu_{\alpha\beta}}{\rho_l - \rho_m} e^{\rho_l t} = 0,$$
$$m \neq l,\ m = 1, 2$$
$$\alpha \neq \rho, \quad \alpha, \beta = 1, 2; \qquad (5.17)$$

and each of the death transition probabilities in (2.30) approaches a constant:

$$\begin{aligned} Q_{\alpha\delta}(0,\infty) &= \lim_{t\to\infty} Q_{\alpha\delta}(0,t) \\ &= \lim_{t\to\infty} \sum_{l=1}^{2} \frac{e^{\rho_l t} - 1}{\rho_l(\rho_l - \rho_m)} [(\rho_l - \nu_{\beta\beta})\mu_{\alpha\delta} + \nu_{\alpha\beta}\mu_{\beta\delta}] \\ &= \sum_{l=1}^{2} \frac{-[(\rho_l - \nu_{\beta\beta})\mu_{\alpha\delta} + \nu_{\alpha\beta}\mu_{\beta\delta}]}{\rho_l(\rho_l - \rho_m)}, \qquad \alpha = 1, 2, \\ &\qquad\qquad \delta = 1, \ldots, r, \quad (5.18) \end{aligned}$$

where

$$\sum_{\delta=1}^{r} Q_{\alpha\delta}(0,\infty) = 1. \qquad (5.19)$$

The limiting form of the p.g.f. (5.10) is

$$\prod_{\alpha=1}^{2} [z_1 Q_{\alpha 1}(0,\infty) + \ldots + z_r Q_{\alpha r}(0,\infty)]^{i_\alpha} \qquad (5.20)$$

where $z_\alpha = 1$. Thus, as $t \to \infty$, the initial populations i_1 and i_2 die out, the random variables $X_1(\infty)$ and $X_2(\infty)$ degenerate to a value of 0, and the limiting distribution is the convolution of two independent multinomial distributions with probabilities $Q_{\alpha 1}(0,\infty), \ldots, Q_{\alpha r}(0,\infty)$.

6. GENERATING FUNCTION OF POPULATION SIZES

As we pointed out before, in previous chapters we dealt exclusively with an entire population, while in this chapter we discuss a population that is divided into two groups, those in S_1 and those in S_2; and we allow people to travel from one state to another. In a later chapter, we shall consider a general case where a population is divided into a finite number of groups. In these cases, we are dealing only with living populations, and we use the probability generating function to derive the corresponding probability distributions. As a prelude to our discussion for the general model, let us treat the simple case in some detail.

Given initial population sizes i_1 and i_2 at time 0, let the probability function of the population sizes in states S_1 and S_2 at time t be denoted by $P(j_1, j_2; t)$

$$P(j_1, j_2;t) = \Pr\{X_1(t) = j_1, X_2(t) = j_2 | i_1, i_2\} \tag{6.1}$$

for $j_1, j_2 = 0, 1, \ldots, (i_1 + i_2)$. Using the intensity functions defined in section 2, we find that the probability function in (6.1) satisfies the following system of differential equations.

$$\begin{aligned}\frac{d}{dt}P(j_1, j_2;t) = P(j_1, j_2;t)(j_1\nu_{11} + j_2\nu_{22})\\ + P(j_1 + 1, j_2 - 1;t)(j_1 + 1)\nu_{12}\\ + P(j_1 - 1, j_2 + 1;t)(j_2 + 1)\nu_{21}\\ + P(j_1 + 1, j_2;t)(j_1 + 1)\mu_1\\ + P(j_1, j_2 + 1;t)(j_2 + 1)\mu_2,\end{aligned} \tag{6.2}$$

when $\mu_\alpha = \mu_{\alpha 1} + \ldots + \mu_{\alpha r}$. Let

$$G_{\mathbf{X}}(s_1, s_2;t) = E\,[s_1^{X_1(t)} s_2^{X_2(t)} | i_1, i_2] \tag{6.3}$$

be the p.g.f. of $X_1(t)$ and $X_2(t)$; the initial condition at $t = 0$ is

$$G_{\mathbf{X}}(s_1, s_2;0) = s_1^{i_1} s_2^{i_2}. \tag{6.4}$$

Taking the derivative of the p.g.f. in (6.3) with respect to t and substituting (6.2),we establish a partial differential equation for the p.g.f.:

$$\begin{aligned}\frac{\partial}{\partial t}G_{\mathbf{X}}(s_1, s_2;t) &= \nu_{11}s_1\frac{\partial}{\partial s_1}G_{X}(s_1, s_2;t) + \nu_{22}s_2\frac{\partial}{\partial s_2}G_{\mathbf{X}}(s_1, s_2;t)\\ &\quad + \nu_{12}s_2\frac{\partial}{\partial s_1}G_{\mathbf{X}}(s_1, s_2;t) + \nu_{21}s_1\frac{\partial}{\partial s_2}G_{\mathbf{X}}(s_1, s_2;t)\\ &\quad + \mu_1\frac{\partial}{\partial s_1}G_{\mathbf{X}}(s_1, s_2;t) + \mu_2\frac{\partial}{\partial s_2}G_{\mathbf{X}}(s_1, s_2;t)\\ &= [\nu_{11}s_1 + \nu_{12}s_2 + \mu_1]\frac{\partial}{\partial s_1}G_{\mathbf{X}}(s_1, s_2;t)\\ &\quad + [\nu_{21}s_1 + \nu_{22}s_2 + \mu_2]\frac{\partial}{\partial s_2}G_{\mathbf{X}}(s_1, s_2;t).\end{aligned} \tag{6.5}$$

The auxiliary equations are [cf., Chapter 8, section 7.2]

$$-\frac{dt}{1} = \frac{ds_1}{\nu_{11}s_1 + \nu_{12}s_2 + \mu_1} = \frac{ds_2}{\nu_{21}s_1 + \nu_{22}s_2 + \mu_2} = \frac{dG}{0}. \tag{6.6}$$

The last equation defines a solution

$$G_{\mathbf{X}}(s_1, s_2; t) = c_1(s_1, s_2) \tag{6.7}$$

where c_1 is independent of t but is a function of s_1 and s_2. The first two equations in (6.6) are to be solved simultaneously. Using the relation $\mu_\alpha = -[\nu_{\alpha 1} + \nu_{\alpha 2}]$ and changing variables s_α to $z_\alpha = 1 - s_\alpha$, the first two equations in (6.6) become

$$\left.\begin{aligned} \frac{dz_1}{dt} &= -\nu_{11}z_1 - \nu_{12}z_2 \\ \frac{dz_2}{dt} &= -\nu_{21}z_1 - \nu_{22}z_2 \end{aligned}\right\}. \tag{6.8}$$

Equations in (6.8) are essentially the same as equations (2.13), except for the transposition of ν_{12} and ν_{21}. Therefore we can follow the procedure used in Section 2 to arrive at a solution similar to that in (2.22).

$$\left.\begin{aligned} z_1 &= k_1\nu_{12}e^{-\rho_1 t} + k_2\nu_{12}e^{-\rho_2 t} \\ z_2 &= k_1(\rho_1 - \nu_{11})e^{-\rho_1 t} + k_2(\rho_2 - \nu_{11})e^{-\rho_2 t} \end{aligned}\right\}, \tag{6.9}$$

where ρ_1 and ρ_2 are given in (2.17). Solving (6.9) for k_1 and k_2 we obtain

$$\left.\begin{aligned} k_1 &= \frac{z_1(\rho_2 - \nu_{11}) - \nu_{12}z_2}{-\nu_{12}(\rho_1 - \rho_2)}e^{\rho_1 t} \\ k_2 &= \frac{z_1(\rho_1 - \nu_{11}) - \nu_{12}z_2}{\nu_{12}(\rho_1 - \rho_2)}e^{\rho_2 t} \end{aligned}\right\} \tag{6.10}$$

From (6.7) and (6.10) we find the general solution for the differential equation in (6.5),

$$\begin{aligned} G_{\mathbf{X}}(s_1, s_2; t) &= \Phi\{k_1, k_2\} \\ &= \Phi\left\{\frac{z_1(\rho_2 - \nu_{11}) - \nu_{12}z_2}{-\nu_{12}(\rho_1 - \rho_2)}e^{\rho_1 t}, \frac{z_1(\rho_1 - \nu_{11}) - \nu_{12}z_2}{\nu_{12}(\rho_1 - \rho_2)}e^{\rho_2 t}\right\} \end{aligned} \tag{6.11}$$

where Φ is an arbitrary function. To determine Φ we use the initial condition in (6.4) and write

$$G_{\mathbf{X}}(s_1, s_2;0) = \Phi\left\{\frac{z_1(\rho_2 - \nu_{11}) - \nu_{12}z_2}{-\nu_{12}(\rho_1 - \rho_2)}, \frac{z_1(\rho_1 - \nu_{11}) - \nu_{12}z_2}{\nu_{12}(\rho_1 - \rho_2)}\right\}$$
$$= (1 - z_1)^{i_1}(1 - z_2)^{i_2}. \tag{6.12}$$

Now let

$$k_{01} = \frac{z_1(\rho_2 - \nu_{11}) - \nu_{12}z_2}{-\nu_{12}(\rho_1 - \rho_2)}$$

and

$$k_{02} = \frac{z_1(\rho_1 - \nu_{11}) - \nu_{12}z_2}{\nu_{12}(\rho_1 - \rho_2)}, \tag{6.13}$$

and solve (6.13) for z_1 and z_2:

$$z_1 = \nu_{12}(k_{01} + k_{02})$$

and

$$z_2 = (\rho_1 - \nu_{11})k_{01} + (\rho_2 - \nu_{11})k_{02}, \tag{6.14}$$

where k_{01} and k_{02} are the values of k_1 and k_2 in (6.10) at $t = 0$. Thus we have established the function Φ; namely,

$$\Phi\{(k_{01}, k_{02}\} = (1 - z_1)^{i_1}(1 - z_2)^{i_2} \tag{6.15}$$

with z_1 and z_2 being given in (6.14). In general, for any given $t > 0$, we let

$$\xi_1 = \nu_{12}(k_1 + k_2)$$

and

$$\xi_2 = (\rho_1 - \nu_{11})k_1 + (\rho_2 - \nu_{11})k_2 \tag{6.16}$$

and use (6.15) to obtain the function

$$\Phi\{k_1, k_2\} = (1 - \xi_1)^{i_1}(1 - \xi_2)^{i_2}. \tag{6.17}$$

Substituting (6.10) in (6.16) and simplifying the resulting formulas yield

$$\xi_1 = \left[\frac{\rho_1 - \nu_{22}}{\rho_1 - \rho_2} e^{\rho_1 t} + \frac{\rho_2 - \nu_{22}}{\rho_2 - \rho_1} e^{\rho_2 t}\right] z_1 + \left[\frac{\nu_{12}}{\rho_1 - \rho_2} e^{\rho_1 t} + \frac{\nu_{12}}{\rho_2 - \rho_1} e^{\rho_2 t}\right] z_2$$
$$= P_{11}(0,t) z_1 + P_{12}(0,t) z_2 \tag{6.18}$$

and

$$\xi_2 = \left[\frac{\nu_{21}}{\rho_1 - \rho_2} e^{\rho_1 t} + \frac{\nu_{21}}{\rho_2 - \rho_1} e^{\rho_2 t}\right] z_1 + \left[\frac{\rho_1 - \nu_{11}}{\rho_1 - \rho_2} e^{\rho_1 t} + \frac{\rho_2 - \nu_{11}}{\rho_2 - \rho_1} e^{\rho_2 t}\right] z_2$$
$$= P_{21}(0,t) z_1 + P_{22}(0,t) z_2 \tag{6.19}$$

where $P_{\alpha\beta}(0,t)$ are the transition probabilities given in (2.26) and (2.27). Now, introducing (6.18) and (6.19) in (6.17), we obtain the p.g.f.

$$G_{\mathbf{X}}(s_1, s_2; t) = [1 - P_{11}(0,t) z_1 - P_{12}(0,t) z_2]^{i_1}$$
$$[1 - P_{21}(0,t) z_1 - P_{22}(0,t) z_2]^{i_2}. \tag{6.20}$$

Or, since $z_\alpha = 1 - s_\alpha$,

$$G_{\mathbf{X}}(s_1, s_2; t) = [Q_1(0,t) + P_{11}(0,t) s_1 + P_{12}(0,t) s_2]^{i_1}$$
$$\times [Q_2(0,t) + P_{21}(0,t) s_1 + P_{22}(0,t) s_2]^{i_2}, \tag{6.21}$$

where

$$Q_\alpha(0,t) = 1 - P_{\alpha 1}(0,t) - P_{\alpha 2}(0,t), \qquad \alpha = 1, 2, \tag{6.22}$$

is the probability of dying during $(0,t)$.

In (6.21) we have the p.g.f. of the convolution of two multinomial distributions, which is the same as the p.g.f. derived in (5.10) with $z_1 = \ldots = z_r = 1$ and

$$Q_{\alpha 1}(0,t) + \ldots + Q_{\alpha r}(0,t) = Q_\alpha(0,t).$$

7. SURVIVAL AND STAGES OF DISEASE

The development of many chronic conditions is characterized by stages. Generally, diseases advance with time from mild through intermediate stages to severe to death. The process often is irreversible but a patient may die while being in any one of the stages. In the development of diabetes, for example, the morbid process may progress from chemical diabetes to clinical diabetes to diabetes with complications. While this may not be the universal classification of diabetes and reversals may occur, the concept of staging of the disease is unquestioned. Evolution of cancer is almost always interrupted through intervention of therapy and surgery. However, in its natural progression, there are stages of the disease determined by the growth and size of the tumor and metastasis of cancer. Coma too can be classified by stages.

Birth order and child spacing are possible factors affecting a child's health and development. Here one begins with marriage to the time of birth of the first child, of the second child, etc. The time of transition (birth of a child) is well defined and easily determined. Clearly, the process is irreversible, and it terminates when a couple decides to stop having children. One is concerned with the waiting time between successive births and the length of time for the completion of the family.

In nuclear physics, high-energy electrons when passing through matter collide with atoms of the absorber. The collisions result in the radiation of photons. The emitted photons when charged with high energy may create pairs of electrons, which in turn may radiate further photons. A cascade process results.

We can find staging phenomena in many other areas; metamorphosis in biology, foraging process in wildlife, engagement-marriage-divorce in demography, etc. But we shall use chronic disease as an example for illustration. In this model we assume that the process is irreversible.

Denoting stages of a disease by $S_1, \ldots, S_k$ and the death state by R, we can describe the morbid process schematically as in the following diagram:

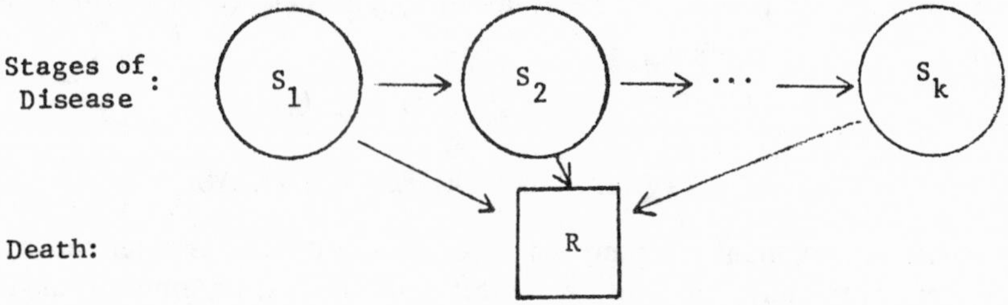

FIGURE 2

The arrows indicate the direction that transitions take place. From each stage s_i, for $i = 1, \ldots, k-1$, the disease process may enter the next stage s_{i+1} or the state of death R. From the final stage s_k, the process enters R. The final stage s_k is well defined in certain problems but not in others. Since a process may be terminated from any one of the transient states, a strict definition of the final stage is not always necessary. The purpose of this section is to propose a stochastic formulation of the morbid process, and to derive distribution of survival time. To obtain some of the results, we need the following lemma.

Lemma 1. *For distinct numbers* $\lambda_1, \ldots, \lambda_n$, *we have*

$$\sum_{i=1}^{n} \frac{1}{\prod_{\substack{j=1 \\ j \neq i}}^{n} (\lambda_i - \lambda_j)} = 0, \tag{7.1}$$

$$\sum_{i=1}^{n} \frac{1}{\prod_{\substack{j=1 \\ j \neq i}}^{n} (\lambda_i - \lambda_j)\lambda_i} = (-1)^{n-1} \frac{1}{\prod_{i=1}^{n} \lambda_i}, \tag{7.2}$$

$$\sum_{i=1}^{n} \frac{1}{\prod_{\substack{j=1 \\ j \neq i}}^{n} (\lambda_i - \lambda_j)\lambda_i^2} = (-1)^{n-1} \frac{1}{\prod_{i=1}^{n} \lambda_i} \left(\sum_{i=1}^{n} \frac{1}{\lambda_i} \right), \tag{7.3}$$

and

$$\sum_{i=1}^{n} \frac{1}{\prod_{\substack{j=1 \\ j \neq i}}^{n} (\lambda_i - \lambda_j)\lambda_i^3} = (-1)^{n-1} \frac{1}{\prod_{i=1}^{n} \lambda_i} \left(\sum_{j \geq i}^{n} \sum_{i=1}^{n} \frac{1}{\lambda_i \lambda_j} \right). \tag{7.4}$$

Proof. Identity (7.1) has been proven in Chapter 6, section 2.1. Now if $\lambda_1, \ldots, \lambda_{n+1}$ are distinct numbers, then (7.1) implies that

$$\sum_{i=1}^{n} \frac{1}{\prod_{\substack{j=1 \\ j \neq i}}^{n} (\lambda_i - \lambda_j)(\lambda_i - \lambda_{n+1})} + \frac{1}{\prod_{j=1}^{n} (\lambda_{n+1} - \lambda_j)} = 0. \tag{7.5}$$

When $\lambda_{n+1} = 0$, (7.5) reduces to (7.2).

To prove (7.3), we let x be any real number, so that $(\lambda_1 + x), \ldots, (\lambda_n + x)$ are distinct numbers. Replacing λ_i with $\lambda_i + x$ in (7.2), we find an identity in x,

$$\sum_{i=1}^{n} \frac{1}{\prod_{\substack{j=1 \\ j \neq i}}^{n} (\lambda_i - \lambda_j)(\lambda_i + x)} = (-1)^{n-1} \frac{1}{\prod_{i=1}^{n} (\lambda_i + x)}. \tag{7.6}$$

Differentiating both sides of (7.6) with respect to x and evaluating the derivatives at $x = 0$, we recover (7.3).

Replacing λ_i with $\lambda_i + x$ in (7.3), we find an identity in x,

$$\sum_{i=1}^{n} \frac{1}{\prod_{\substack{j=1 \\ j \neq i}}^{n} (\lambda_i - \lambda_j)(\lambda_i + x)^2} = (-1)^{n-1} \frac{1}{\prod_{i=1}^{n} (\lambda_i + x)} \left(\sum_{i=1}^{n} \frac{1}{\lambda_i + x} \right). \tag{7.7}$$

Differentiating both sides of (7.7) with respect to x and evaluating the derivatives at $x = 0$ and simplifying, we recover (7.4). Proof of the lemma is now complete.

7.1. Distribution of Survival Time.

For an individual in s_i at time τ, $0 \leq \tau < \infty$, let

$$\nu_{i,i+1}\,\theta(\tau)\,d\tau = \Pr\{\text{the individual will enter state } s_{i+1} \text{ in } (\tau, \tau + d\tau)\}, \tag{7.8}$$

and

$$\mu_i\,\theta(\tau)\,d\tau = \Pr\{\text{the individual will enter } R \text{ in } (\tau, \tau + d\tau)\} \tag{7.9}$$

and let

$$\nu_{ii}\,\theta(\tau) = -[\nu_{i,i+1}\,\theta(\tau) + \mu_i\,\theta(\tau)], \qquad i = 1, \ldots, k-1. \tag{7.10}$$

For an individual in the final stage s_k at time τ, we let

$$\mu_k\,\theta(\tau)\,d\tau = \Pr\{\text{the individual will enter } R \text{ in } (\tau, \tau + d\tau)\} \tag{7.11}$$

and

$$\nu_{kk}\,\theta(\tau) = -\mu_k\,\theta(\tau). \tag{7.12}$$

Each of the intensity functions in (7.8), (7.9) and (7.11), is a product of two factors: $\nu_{i,i+1}$ or μ_i is a function of the two stages involved, while $\theta(\tau)$ is a function of time τ at which the transition takes place. Regarding function $\theta(\tau)$, we assume that

$$\int_0^\infty \theta(\tau)\,d\tau = \infty.$$

While a disease develops continuously, the time of transition is somewhat restricted. Suppose the transition from stage s_i to stage s_{i+1} takes place during time interval $(\tau_i, \tau_i + d\tau_i)$, for $i = 1, 2, \ldots, k-1$. Then by the order of occurrences, we have $0 \le \tau_1 \le \tau_2 \le \ldots \le \tau_{k-1}$; or graphically:

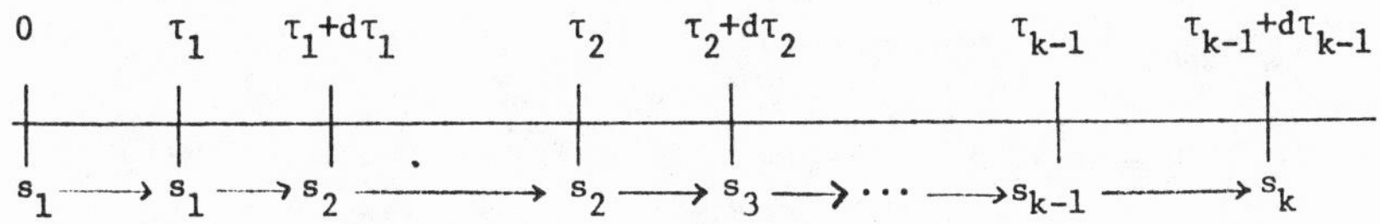

FIGURE 3

When death occurs during the interval $(t, t+dt)$, the individual must be in one of the stages $s_1, \ldots, s_k$ at time t. With this understanding, we can derive the density function $f_T(t)$ and the distribution function $F_T(t)$ of the length of life T of an individual who is in S_1 at the initial time 0.

By definition, $f_T(t)\,dt$ is the probability that an individual who is in S_1 at time 0, will die during the interval $(t, t+dt)$. Since he may be in one of k stages at time t, the density function is the sum of k terms:

$$f_T(t)dt = f_1(t)dt + f_2(t)dt + f_3(t)dt + \ldots + f_k(t)dt. \quad (7.13)$$

Each $f_j(t)dt$ in equation (8.13) corresponds to the sequence of transitions: $s_1 \to s_2 \to \ldots \to s_j \to R$. The first term $f_1(t)dt$, for example, is the probability of transition $s_1 \to R$ occurring in $(t, t+dt)$. It is easy to show that

$$\begin{aligned} f_1(t)dt &= \exp\{\nu_{11} \textstyle\int_0^t \theta(\tau)\,d\tau\}\,\mu_1\,\theta(t)\,dt \\ &= e^{\nu_{11}\beta(t)}\,\mu_1\,\theta(t)\,dt \end{aligned} \quad (7.14)$$

where

$$\beta(t) = \int_0^t \theta(\tau)\,d\tau. \tag{7.15}$$

The exponential function in (7.14) is the probability that an individual will remain in s_1 during the interval $(0, t)$, while the product $\mu_1\theta(t)\,dt$ is the probability of entering R from s_1 during the interval $(t, t+dt)$. Therefore, the right hand side quantity in (7.14) is the probability that an individual who is in s_1 at time 0 will enter R from s_1 during $(t, t+dt)$; that is, $f_1(t)\,dt$.

Function $f_2(t)$ represents the sequence of transitions $s_1 \to s_2 \to R$. For the transition $s_1 \to s_2$ to take place during a particular interval $(\tau_1, \tau_1 + d\tau_1)$, the probability of the sequence $s_1 \to s_2 \to R$ is

$$\exp\left\{\nu_{11}\int_0^{\tau_1}\theta(\tau)\,d\tau\right\}\nu_{12}\,\theta(\tau_1)\,d\tau_1 \exp\left\{\nu_{22}\int_{\tau_1}^{t}\theta(\tau)\,d\tau\right\}\mu_2\,\theta(t)\,dt \tag{7.16}$$

Integrating (7.16) from $\tau_1 = 0$ to $\tau_1 = t$ yields

$$f_2(t)\,dt = \nu_{12}\mu_2\theta(t)\left[\frac{1}{\nu_{11}-\nu_{22}}e^{\nu_{11}\beta(t)} + \frac{1}{\nu_{22}-\nu_{11}}e^{\nu_{22}\beta(t)}\right]dt. \tag{7.17}$$

For the sequence $s_1 \to s_2 \to s_3 \to R$, we consult Figure 2 and equations (7.8), (7.9) and (7.10) to find

$$\begin{aligned} f_3(t)\,dt &= \int_0^t\int_0^{\tau_2}\exp\left\{\nu_{11}\int_0^{\tau_1}\theta(\tau)\,d\tau\right\}\nu_{12}\,\theta(\tau_1)\,d\tau_1\exp\left\{\nu_{22}\int_{\tau_1}^{\tau_2}\theta(\tau)\,d\tau\right\} \\ &\quad\times \nu_{23}\,\theta(\tau_2)\,d\tau_2\exp\left\{\nu_{33}\int_{\tau_2}^{t}\theta(\tau)\,d\tau\right\}\mu_3\,\theta(\tau)\,dt \\ &= \nu_{12}\,\nu_{23}\,\mu_3\,\theta(t)\sum_{i=1}^{3}\frac{1}{\prod\limits_{\substack{l=1\\ l\neq i}}^{3}(\nu_{ii}-\nu_{ll})}e^{\nu_{ii}\beta(t)}\,dt. \end{aligned} \tag{7.18}$$

Generally, for the sequence $s_1 \to s_2 \to \ldots \to s_j \to R$,

$$f_j(t)\,dt = \nu_{12}\ldots\nu_{j-1,j}\mu_j\theta(t)\sum_{i=1}^{j}\frac{1}{\prod\limits_{\substack{l=1\\ l\neq i}}^{j}(\nu_{ii}-\nu_{ll})}e^{\nu_{ii}\beta(t)}\,dt, \qquad j = 2, \ldots, k. \tag{7.19}$$

Substituting (7.14) and (7.19) in (7.13), we obtain the density function of T,

$$f_T(t) = e^{\nu_{11}\beta(t)}\mu_1\theta(t) + \sum_{j=2}^{k}\left\{\nu_{12}\dots\nu_{j-1,j}\mu_j\theta(t)\sum_{i=1}^{j}\frac{1}{\prod\limits_{\substack{l=1\\l\neq i}}^{j}(\nu_{ii}-\nu_{ll})}e^{\nu_{ii}\beta(t)}\right\}. \tag{7.20}$$

The distribution function of T is derived directly from the relation

$$F_T(t) = \int_0^t f_T(\tau)\,d\tau. \tag{7.21}$$

Substituting (7.20) in (7.21) and integrating yield

$$F_T(t) = \frac{\mu_1}{\nu_{11}}[e^{\nu_{11}\beta(t)} - 1] + \sum_{j=2}^{k}\left\{\nu_{12}\dots\nu_{j-1,j}\mu_j\sum_{i=1}^{j}\frac{1}{\prod\limits_{\substack{l=1\\l\neq i}}^{j}(\nu_{ii}-\nu_{ll})\nu_{ii}}[e^{\nu_{ii}\beta(t)} - 1]\right\}. \tag{7.22}$$

As $t\to\infty$, $\beta(\infty)\to 0$, the exponential functions vanish and (7.22) becomes

$$F_T(\infty) = -\frac{\mu_1}{\nu_{11}} - \sum_{j=2}^{k}\left\{\nu_{12}\dots\nu_{j-1,j}\mu_j\sum_{i=1}^{j}\frac{1}{\prod\limits_{\substack{l=1\\l\neq i}}^{i}(\nu_{ii}-\nu_{ll})\nu_{ii}}\right\}. \tag{7.23}$$

Since an individual eventually dies, we expect

$$F_T(\infty) = 1. \tag{7.24}$$

To prove (7.24) directly from (7.23) we apply equality (7.2) in (7.23) to obtain

$$F_T(\infty) = -\frac{\mu_1}{\nu_{11}} - \sum_{j=2}^{k} \nu_{12} \ldots \nu_{j-1,j}\mu_j \frac{(-1)^{j-1}}{\prod_{i=1}^{j} \nu_{ii}}. \tag{7.25}$$

Because $-\mu_k = \nu_{kk}$ and $-(\mu_{k-1} + \nu_{k-1,k}) = \nu_{k-1,k-1,}$ we combine the last two terms in (7.25) to obtain

$$\begin{aligned}
&\frac{(-1)^{k-1}\nu_{12} \ldots \nu_{k-2,k-1}\mu_{k-1}}{\nu_{11} \ldots \nu_{k-1,k-1}} + \frac{(-1)^{k-1}\nu_{12} \ldots \nu_{k-2,k-1}\nu_{k-1,k}}{\nu_{11} \ldots \nu_{k-1,k-1}} \\
&= \frac{(-1)^{k-1}\nu_{12} \ldots \nu_{k-2,k-1}[\mu_{k-1} + \nu_{k-1,k}]}{\nu_{11} \ldots \nu_{k-1,k-1}} \\
&= \frac{(-1)^{k-2}\nu_{12} \ldots \nu_{k-2,k-1}}{\nu_{11} \ldots \nu_{k-2,k-2}}.
\end{aligned} \tag{7.26}$$

Combining (7.26) with the preceding term (the third term from the last) in (7.25) and recalling the equation $-(\mu_{k-2} + \nu_{k-2,k-1}) = \nu_{k-2,k-2}$, we find

$$\frac{(-1)^{k-2}\nu_{12} \ldots \nu_{k-3,k-2}\mu_{k-2}}{\nu_{11} \ldots \nu_{k-2,k-2}} + \frac{(-1)^{k-2}\nu_{12} \ldots \nu_{k-2,k-1}}{\nu_{11} \ldots \nu_{k-2,k-2}} = \frac{(-1)^{k-3}\nu_{12} \ldots \nu_{k-3,k-2}}{\nu_{11} \ldots \nu_{k-3,k-3}}. \tag{7.27}$$

Successively adding every last two terms together and simplifying, we reduce equation (7.25) to

$$F_T(\infty) = -\frac{\mu_1}{\nu_{11}} - \frac{\nu_{12}}{\nu_{11}} = \frac{-(\nu_1 + \nu_{12})}{\nu_{11}} = 1. \tag{7.28}$$

The expectation and variance of T are functions of $\theta(\tau)$. For the expectation we use the density function in (7.20) to obtain

$$\begin{aligned}
E[T] &= -\frac{\mu_1}{\nu_{11}} \int_0^\infty e^{\nu_{11}\beta(t)}\,dt \\
&\quad - \sum_{j=2}^{k} \nu_{12} \ldots \nu_{j-1,j}\ \mu_j \left\{ \sum_{i=1}^{j} \frac{1}{\prod_{\substack{l=1 \\ l \neq i}}^{j} (\nu_{ii} - \nu_{ll})\nu_{ii}} \int_0^\infty e^{\nu_{ii}\beta(t)}\,dt \right\}
\end{aligned} \tag{7.29}$$

where, according to the definition of $\beta(t)$ in (7.15),

$$\int_0^\infty e^{\nu_{ii}\beta(t)}\,dt = \int_0^\infty \exp\left\{\nu_{ii}\int_0^t \theta(\tau)\,d\tau\right\}dt$$

depends on function $\theta(\tau)$.

We summarize the above findings in the following theorem:[2]

Theorem 1. *If an individual is subject to k stages of a chronic disease with transitions as shown in Figure 1 and intensity functions as defined in equation* (7.8) *through* (7.12), *then survival time T has a density function in* (7.20), *a distribution function in* (7.22) *with* $F_T(\infty) = 1$, *and an expectation in* (7.29).

The above results are for cases where $\nu_{ii} \neq \nu_{jj}$ for $i \neq j$. Formulas will be much simpler if all ν_{ii} are equal.

When $\theta(\tau) = 1$, $\beta(t) = t$, the density function of survival time T reduces to

$$f_T(t) = \mu_1 e^{\nu_{11}t} + \sum_{j=2}^{k}\left\{\nu_{12}\cdots\nu_{j-1,j}\mu_j\sum_{i=1}^{j}\frac{e^{\nu_{ii}t}}{\prod\limits_{\substack{l=1\\l\neq i}}^{j}(\nu_{ii}-\nu_{ll})}\right\}, \tag{7.30}$$

the distribution function reduces to

$$F_T(t) = \frac{\mu_1}{\nu_{11}}(e^{\nu_{11}t}-1) + \sum_{j=2}^{k}\nu_{12}\cdots\nu_{j-1,j}\mu_j\sum_{i=1}^{j}\frac{(e^{\nu_{ii}t}-1)}{\prod\limits_{\substack{l=1\\l\neq i}}^{j}(\nu_{ii}-\nu_{ll})\nu_{ii}} \tag{7.31}$$

and the expectation of T becomes

$$E[T] = \frac{\mu_1}{\nu_{11}^2} + \sum_{j=2}^{k}\nu_{12}\cdots\nu_{j-1,j}\mu_j\sum_{i=1}^{j}\frac{1}{\prod\limits_{\substack{l=1\\l\neq i}}^{j}(\nu_{ii}-\nu_{ll})\nu_{ii}^2}. \tag{7.32}$$

---

[2] The reader may recognize the resemblance between $f_j(t)\,dt$ in equation (7.19) and the density function of the sum of consecutive random variations in equation (6.11), Chapter 3, and the density function of the duration of an epidemic in equation (4.18), Chapter 9.

The formula in (7.32) may be further simplified. As a result we find

$$E[T] = \frac{1}{-\nu_{11}} + \frac{\nu_{12}}{-\nu_{11}}\left(\frac{1}{-\nu_{22}}\right) + \frac{\nu_{12}}{-\nu_{11}}\frac{\nu_{23}}{-\nu_{22}}\left(\frac{1}{-\nu_{33}}\right) + \ldots + \prod_{i=1}^{k-1}\frac{\nu_{i,i+1}}{-\nu_{ii}}\left(\frac{1}{-\nu_{kk}}\right). \tag{7.33}$$

Each factor

$$\frac{\nu_{i,i+1}}{-\nu_{ii}} = \frac{\nu_{i,i+1}}{\nu_{i,i+1} + \mu_i} \tag{7.34}$$

in equation (7.33) is the conditional probability of the transition $s_i \rightarrow s_{i+1}$ given that a transition out of s_i takes place, while the factor $(-1/\nu_{i+1,i+1})$ is the expected duration of stay in stage s_{i+1}. Thus the expectation in equation (7.33) is the sum of expected durations of stay in $s_1, s_2, \ldots, s_k$.

The variance for the survival time T can be derived from the density function $f_T(t)$ in (7.30). The general formula is

$$V[T] = 2\left[\left(\frac{\mu_1}{-\nu_{11}}\right)\frac{1}{\nu_{11}^2} + \frac{\nu_{12}\mu_2}{\nu_{11}\nu_{22}}\sum_{j\geq i}^{2}\sum_{i=1}^{2}\frac{1}{\nu_{ii}\nu_{jj}} + \ldots + (-1)^k\left(\prod_{i=1}^{k-1}\frac{\nu_{i,i+1}}{\nu_{ii}}\right)\frac{\mu_k}{\nu_{kk}}\sum_{j\geq i}^{k}\sum_{i=1}^{k}\frac{1}{\nu_{ii}\nu_{jj}}\right] - [E(T)]^2 \tag{7.35}$$

where the expectation $E(T)$ is given in (7.33). For $k = 2$,

$$V[T] = \frac{1}{\nu_{11}^2} - \frac{\nu_{12}}{\nu_{11}}\left(\frac{1}{\nu_{22}^2}\right) + \frac{\nu_{12}\mu_1}{\nu_{11}\nu_{11}}\left(\frac{1}{\nu_{22}^2}\right). \tag{7.36}$$

7.2. Maximum-Likelihood Estimators.

A sample of n individuals initially in stage s_1 is observed for various lengths of time for survival and death and for the advancement of the disease under study. Let T_α be the period of observation of the α-th individual in the sample for $\alpha = 1, \ldots, n$. At the end of the period T_α, the individual either is living and is in stage s_j or has entered the death state R from s_j. We shall use the sample information to derive the maximum-likelihood estimators of the parameters in the model where $\theta(t) = 1$.

For the α-th individual in a sample, let $\varepsilon_{j\alpha}$ and $\delta_{j\alpha}$ be the indicators such that

$$\begin{aligned} \varepsilon_{j\alpha} &= 1 \quad \text{if the sequence } s_1 \to s_2 \to \ldots \to s_j \text{ occurs} \\ &= 0 \quad \text{otherwise,} \end{aligned} \tag{7.37}$$

$$\begin{aligned} \delta_{j\alpha} &= 1 \quad \text{if the sequence } s_1 \to s_2 \to \ldots \to s_j \to R \text{ occurs} \\ &= 0 \quad \text{otherwise,} \end{aligned} \tag{7.38}$$

for $j = 1, 2, \ldots, k$. We have for the α-th individual a vector with $2k$ components

$$(\varepsilon_{1\alpha}, \delta_{1\alpha}, \ldots, \varepsilon_{k\alpha}, \delta_{k\alpha})' \tag{7.39}$$

with the sum

$$\varepsilon_{1\alpha} + \delta_{1\alpha} + \ldots + \varepsilon_{k\alpha} + \delta_{k\alpha} = 1. \tag{7.40}$$

Let transition $s_i \to s_{i+1}$ occur during the interval $(\tau_{i\alpha}, \tau_{i\alpha} + d\tau_{i\alpha})$ and transition $s_j \to R$ occur in $(t_{j\alpha}, t_{j\alpha} + dt_{j\alpha})$. Then the likelihood function for the observations on the α-th individual is

$$L_\alpha = \prod_{j=1}^{k} \left[\prod_{i=1}^{j} e^{\nu_{ii}(\tau_{i\alpha} - \tau_{i-1,\alpha})} \nu_{i,i+1} \right]^{\varepsilon_{j\alpha}} \left[\prod_{i=1}^{j} e^{\nu_{ii}(\tau_{i\alpha} - \tau_{i-1,\alpha})} \nu_{i,i+1} \right]^{\delta_{j\alpha}} \tag{7.41}$$

where inside the brackets $[\quad]^{\varepsilon_{j\alpha}}$, $\tau_{0\alpha} = 0$, $\tau_{j\alpha} = T_\alpha$, and $\nu_{j,j+1} = 1$, while inside the brackets $[\quad]^{\delta_{j\alpha}}$, $\tau_{0\alpha} = 0$, $\tau_{j\alpha} = t_{j\alpha}$ and $\nu_{j,j+1} = \mu_j$. For the entire sample, the likelihood function is

$$L = \prod_{\alpha=1}^{n} L_\alpha. \tag{7.42}$$

Let

$$\sum_{\alpha=1}^{n} \left[\varepsilon_{1\alpha} T_\alpha + \delta_{1\alpha} t_{1\alpha} + \sum_{i=2}^{k} (\varepsilon_{i\alpha} + \delta_{i\alpha}) \tau_{1\alpha} \right] = \pi_1, \tag{7.43}$$

and

$$\sum_{\alpha=1}^{n} \Bigg[\varepsilon_{j\alpha}(T_\alpha - \tau_{j-1,\alpha}) + \delta_{j\alpha}(t_{j\alpha} - \tau_{j-1,\alpha}) + \sum_{i=j+1}^{k} (\varepsilon_{i\alpha} + \delta_{i\alpha})(\tau_{j\alpha} - \tau_{j-1,\alpha}) \Bigg] = \pi_j, \quad j = 2, \ldots k, \tag{7.44}$$

where π_j is the total length of time that n people stay in s_j, $j = 1, \ldots, k$. Let

$$X_j = \sum_{\alpha=1}^{n} \varepsilon_{j\alpha}, \qquad j = 1, \ldots, k, \tag{7.45}$$

be the number of individuals who are living and in s_j at the end of the study period, and let

$$Y_j = \sum_{\alpha=1}^{n} \delta_{j\alpha}, \qquad j = 1, \ldots, k, \tag{7.46}$$

be the number of people who enter death state R from s_j during the study period. The logarithm of the likelihood function in (7.42) may be written as

$$\ln L = \sum_{j=1}^{k} \pi_j \nu_{jj} + \sum_{j=1}^{k-1} \left\{ \sum_{i=j+1}^{k} (X_i + Y_i) \right\} \ln \nu_{j,j+1} + \sum_{j=1}^{k} Y_j \ln \mu_j . \tag{7.47}$$

Differentiating the logarithm of the likelihood function with respect to $\nu_{j,j+1}$ and μ_j yields equations

$$\frac{\partial}{\partial \nu_{j,j+1}} \ln L = -\pi_j + \frac{\sum_{i=j+1}^{k} (X_i + Y_i)}{\nu_{j,j+1}}, \qquad j = 1, \ldots, k-1 \tag{7.48}$$

and

$$\frac{\partial}{\partial \mu_j} \ln L = -\pi_j + \frac{Y_j}{\mu_j}, \qquad j = 1, \ldots, k. \tag{7.49}$$

Setting the derivatives equal to zero, we obtain the maximum-likelihood estimators

$$\hat{\nu}_{j,j+1} = \frac{\sum_{i=j+1}^{k} (X_j + Y_i)}{\pi_j} \qquad j = 1, \ldots, k = 1 \tag{7.50}$$

and

$$\hat{\mu}_j = \frac{Y_j}{\pi_j}, \qquad j = 1, \ldots, k. \tag{7.51}$$

The estimator of $\nu_{j,j}$ is obtained from

$$\hat{\nu}_{jj} = -[\hat{\nu}_{j,j+1} + \hat{\mu}_j], \qquad j = 1, \ldots, k \tag{7.52}$$

where $\nu_{k,k+1} = 0$.

Each estimator in equation (7.50) is the ratio of the number of transitions $s_j \rightarrow s_{j+1}$ to the total duration of stay in s_j by the n people in the sample, while each estimator in (7.51) is the ratio of transitions $s_j \rightarrow R$ to the total duration of stay in s_j.

Since every derivative in (7.48) or (7.49) contains only the parameter $\nu_{j,j+1}$ or μ_j, the asymptotic variances of the estimators are

$$V[\hat{\nu}_{j,j+1}] = \frac{1}{-E\left[\dfrac{\partial^2}{\partial \nu_{j,j+1}^2} \ln L\right]}, \qquad j = 1, \ldots, k-1, \tag{7.53}$$

and

$$V[\hat{\mu}_j] = \frac{1}{-E\left[\dfrac{\partial^2}{\partial \mu_j^2} \ln L\right]}, \qquad j = 1, \ldots, k, \tag{7.54}$$

where

$$\frac{\partial^2}{\partial \nu_{j,j+1}^2} \ln L = -\frac{\sum_{i=j+1}^{k} (X_i + Y_i)}{\nu_{j,j+1}^2}, \qquad j = 1, \ldots, k-1, \tag{7.55}$$

and

$$\frac{\partial^2}{\partial \mu_j^2} \ln L = -\frac{Y_j}{\mu_j^2}, \qquad j = 1, \ldots, k. \tag{7.56}$$

For making inferences with the observed data, we may substitute $\hat{\nu}_{j,j+1}$ and $\hat{\mu}_j$ for the corresponding parameters in (7.55) and (7.56) to obtain sample variances of the estimators

$$s^2(\hat{\nu}_{j,j+1}) = \frac{\sum_{i=j+1}^{k} (X_i + Y_i)}{\pi_j^2}, \qquad j = 1, \ldots, k-1,$$

and

$$s^2(\hat{\mu}_j) = \frac{Y_j}{\pi_j^2}, \qquad j = 1, \ldots, k.$$

The sample variance of $\hat{\nu}_{jj}$ is

$$s^2(\hat{\nu}_{jj}) = \frac{Y_j + \sum_{i=j+1}^{k} (X_i + Y_i)}{\pi_j^2}.$$

When sample size n is large, we can apply the central limit theorem to test hypotheses regarding the parameters or the distribution of survival time T.

8. PROBLEMS FOR SOLUTION

1. In a stochastic model for follow-up study of cancer patients, Fix and Neyman [1951] considered two illness states: S_1, the state of "leading a normal life" and S_2, the state of being under treatment for cancer; and two death states, R_1, death from other causes, and R_2, death from cancer. For illustration, they suggested the following two sets of numerical values for illness and death intensities:

(a) $\nu_{11} = -0.4$, $\nu_{12} = 0.2$, $\mu_{11} = 0.2$, $\mu_{12} = 0$,

$\nu_{21} = 2.7$, $\nu_{22} = -3.7$, $\mu_{21} = 0$, $\mu_{22} = 1.0$;

(b) $\nu_{11} = -0.5$, $\nu_{12} = 0.4$, $\mu_{11} = 0.1$, $\mu_{12} = 0$,

$\nu_{21} = 0.2$, $\nu_{22} = -0.4$, $\mu_{21} = 0$, $\mu_{22} = 0.2$.

For each set of data, compute the transition probabilities $P_{\alpha\beta}(0, t)$ and $Q_{\alpha\delta}(0, t)$ and the expected durations of stay $e_{\alpha\delta}(t)$ and $\varepsilon_{\alpha\delta}(t)$, for $\alpha, \beta, \delta = 1, 2$ and $t = 1$. Discuss briefly the numerical results.

2. *Transition probabilities.* If, instead of (2.20), we use

$$k_i = \frac{c_{\alpha\alpha i}}{\nu_{\beta\alpha}} = \frac{c_{\alpha\beta i}}{\rho_i - \nu_{\alpha\alpha}} \tag{2.20a}$$

then the general solution becomes

$$P_{\alpha\alpha}(0, t) = \sum_{i=1}^{2} k_i \nu_{\beta\alpha} e^{\rho_i t}$$

$$P_{\alpha\beta}(0, t) = \sum_{i=1}^{2} k_i (\rho_i - \nu_{\alpha\alpha}) e^{\rho_i t} \tag{2.22a}$$

Derive from (2.22a) the particular solution for the transition probabilities corresponding to the initial conditions (2.9).

3. *Continuation.* By taking the derivatives of the formulas on the right, verify that solution (2.25) satisfies the differential equations (2.13) and the initial condition (2.9).

4. *Chapman-Kolmogorov equation.* Verify that solution (2.27) satisfies the Chapman-Kolmogorov equation (3.1b).

5. Verify equations (3.4) and (3.5).

6. Substitute (2.27) and (2.30) for the transition probabilities $P_{\alpha\beta}(0,t)$ and $Q_{\alpha\delta}(0,t)$ in (3.6) and verify the resulting equation.

7. *Expected duration of stay.* Use (4.11), (4.12), and (4.13) to show that the sum of the expected durations of stay in the illness and death states during a time interval $(0,t)$ is equal to the length of the interval t.

8. *An alternative model.* Consider an illness-death process whose structure is similar to the one described in this chapter except that transition of an individual is possible only from health state S_1 to S_2 but not from S_2 to S_1, so that $\nu_{12} > 0$ and $\nu_{21} = 0$.

(a) Derive the transition probabilities $P_{\alpha\beta}(0,t)$ and $Q_{\alpha\delta}(0,t)$, $\alpha\ \beta = 1, 2$; $\delta = 1, \ldots, r$.

(b) Find the expected durations of stay $e_{\alpha\beta}(t)$ and $\varepsilon_{\alpha\delta}(t)$, α, $\beta = 1, 2$; $\delta = 1, \ldots, r$.

9. *Smoking habits.* A cigarette smoker wants to give up smoking. When he has an urge to smoke during a time interval $(t, t+\Delta)$, the probability of his refraining is $\nu_{12}\Delta + o(\Delta)$ and the probability of smoking is $1 + \nu_{11}\Delta + o(\Delta)$, with $\nu_{11} = -\nu_{12}$. After having given up the habit, he has the desire to smoke again; the probability of his resuming the habit in a time interval $(t, t+\Delta)$ is $\nu_{21}\Delta + o(\Delta)$ and of remaining a nonsmoker is $1 + \nu_{22}\Delta + o(\Delta)$, with $\nu_{22} = -\nu_{21}$. The transition probability $P_{12}(0,t)$ then is the probability that a person who smokes at the beginning of time interval $(0,t)$ will be a nonsmoker at time t. Derive the formulas for the transition probabilities $P_{\alpha\beta}(0,t)$, for $\alpha, \beta = 1, 2$. (The difference should be noted between a nonsmoker and a smoker who is not smoking at a particular moment.)

10. *Continuation.* Show that $P_{\alpha 1}(t) + P_{\alpha 2}(t) = 1$, for $\alpha = 1, 2$.

11. *Continuation.* Given a person who smokes at the beginning of a time interval, find the expected durations of time that he will be a smoker and a nonsmoker during the interval $(0,t)$.

12. *Continuation.* Compute the numerical results in problems 9, 10, and 11 for the interval $(0, 1)$ with

(a) $\nu_{12} = .1$ and $\nu_{21} = .4$
(b) $\nu_{12} = .2$ and $\nu_{21} = .4$
(c) $\nu_{12} = .3$ and $\nu_{21} = .4$
(d) $\nu_{12} = .4$ and $\nu_{21} = .4$

13. Solve the following equations for k_1 and k_2

$$z_1 = k_1(\rho_1 + \nu_{22})e^{-\rho_1 t} + k_2(\rho_2 + \nu_{22})e^{-\rho_2 t}$$

$$z_2 = -k_1\nu_{21}e^{-\rho_1 t} - k_2\nu_{21}e^{-\rho_2 t}$$

and use the solution to find the p.g.f. $G_X(s_1, s_2; t)$ in (6.11).

14. Use density function $f_T(t)$ in (7.30) to find the expectation $E[T]$ and the variance $V(t)$.

15. Derive the formula for the $\ln L$ in (7.47) from the likelihood function L_α in (7.41).

16. Find explicit formulas for the asymptotic variance $V[\hat{\nu}_{j,j+1}]$ in (7.53) and $V[\hat{\mu}_j]$ in (7.54).

NOTE: Problems 17 to 26 are related to an application of the illness-death model. They should be worked in the order they are presented.

AN APPLICATION TO STUDIES OF CHRONIC DISEASE

Statistical analysis of medical follow-up data is usually confined to survival and death of each member of a study population; health conditions of survivors and causes of death are not considered. However, when a study is designed to investigate a particular disease (or a group of diseases), such as coronary heart disease (CHD), either as a cause of death or for its incidence and prevalence, distinction should be made between survivors who are affected with the disease and those who are not, and between deaths from CHD and deaths from other causes.

The stochastic model discussed in this chapter provides an appropriate method of analysis of such data. For easy reference, coronary heart diseases are used as an example. Thus each individual in a study at any time may be in one of two transient states: In the "healthy" state S_1 if he is free from CHD, or in the "illness" state S_2 if he is affected with the disease. An individual may die from other causes (in R_1) or from CHD (in R_2). Transition between states is somewhat restricted. Inasmuch as CHD is not a reversible disease, transition from S_2 to S_1 is not allowed. Since a person cannot die from CHD without first having developed the disease, transition from S_1 to R_2 is also impossible.

Typically, a study consists of n_1 individuals who are free from the disease (in S_1) at the time of admission to the study. Each individual is observed for a period of time T_{1i}, which varies from one individual to another but is a fixed positive number for each i for $i = 1, \ldots, n$. Transitions taking place during the observation period and the end result at $T_{\alpha i}$ may be summarized as follows.

(1) remain free from CHD during the entire period $(0, T_{1i})$, $(S_1 \to S_1)$;

(2) develop the first symptoms of CHD at τ_{1i}, for $\tau_{1i} \le T_{1i}$, but still be alive at T_{1i}, $(S_1 \to S_2)$;

(3) die at t_{1i} from other causes, without ever having developed CHD, for $t_{1i} \le T_{1i}$, $(S_1 \to R_1)$;

(4) develop the first symptoms of CHD at τ_{1i} and die at t_{1i} from other causes $(S_1 \to S_2 \to R_1)$; or

(5) develop the first symptoms of CHD at τ_{1i} and die from the disease at t_{1i}, $(S_1 \to S_2 \to R_2)$.

For each individual, we introduce a vector of indicators corresponding to these sequences of transitions,

$$[\varepsilon_{11i}, \varepsilon_{12i}, \delta_{11\cdot 1i}, \delta_{11\cdot 2i}, \delta_{12i}]', \quad \text{for } i = 1, \ldots, n_1.$$

Each indicator takes on a value of one if the corresponding sequence of transitions takes place; a value of zero, if not, with

$$\varepsilon_{11i} + \varepsilon_{12i} + \delta_{11\cdot 1i} + \delta_{11\cdot 2i} + \delta_{12i} = 1.$$

The symbol ε is used to denote number living, and δ, number dying. In $\delta_{11\cdot 1i}$ and $\delta_{11\cdot 2i}$, the subscript 1 or 2 refers to the state S_1 or S_2 from which one enters R_1.

17. Using the two-transient state illness death model discussed in this chapter, find the expectations of the five indicators $E[\varepsilon_{11i}]$, $E[\varepsilon_{12i}]$, $E[\delta_{11\cdot 1i}]$, $E[\delta_{11\cdot 2i}]$ and $E[\delta_{12i}]$. Show that the sum of the expectations is equal to one.

18. *Continuation.* Derive for the i-th individual in the sample the likelihood function of the five indicators $[\varepsilon_{11i}, \varepsilon_{12i}, \delta_{11\cdot 1i}, \delta_{11\cdot 2i}, \delta_{12i}]$.

19. What is the physical meaning of the following quantities:

$$\pi_{11} = \sum_{i=1}^{n_1} (\varepsilon_{11i} T_{1i} + \varepsilon_{12i}\tau_{1i} + \delta_{11\cdot 1i} t_{1i} + \delta_{11\cdot 2i}\tau_{1i} + \delta_{12i}\tau_{1i}),$$

$$\pi_{12} = \sum_{i=1}^{n_1} [\varepsilon_{12i}(T_{1i} - \tau_{1i}) + (\delta_{11\cdot 2i} + \delta_{12i})(t_{1i} - \tau_{1i})],$$

$$X_{11} = \sum_{i=1}^{n_1} \varepsilon_{11i}, \qquad X_{12} = \sum_{i=1}^{n_1} \varepsilon_{12i}$$

$$Y_{11\cdot 1} = \sum_{i=1}^{n_1} \delta_{11\cdot 1i}, \qquad Y_{11\cdot 2} = \sum_{i=1}^{n_1} \delta_{11\cdot 2i}$$

$$Y_{12} = \sum_{i=1}^{n_1} \delta_{12i}.$$

Explain.

20. *Continuation.* Let L_1 be the likelihood function for the entire sample of n_1 individuals. The function contains four independent parameters ν_{12}, μ_{11}, μ_{21}, μ_{22} with $\nu_{11} = -[\nu_{12} + \mu_{11}]$ and $\nu_{22} = -[\mu_{21} + \mu_{22}]$. Show that the maximum likelihood estimators are

$$\hat{\nu}_{12} = (X_{12} + Y_{11\cdot 2} + Y_{12})/\pi_{11}, \qquad \hat{\mu}_{11} = Y_{11\cdot 1}/\pi_{11}$$

$$\hat{\mu}_{21} = Y_{11\cdot 2}/\pi_{12}, \qquad \hat{\mu}_{22} = Y_{12}/\pi_{12}.$$

21. Find the asymptotic variances of the estimators from

$$V(\hat{\nu}_{12}) = -\left\{E\left(\frac{\partial^2}{\partial \nu_{12}^2} \ln L_1\right]\right\}^{-1}$$

$$V(\hat{\mu}_{11}) = -\left\{E\left[\frac{\partial^2}{\partial \mu_{11}^2} \ln L_1\right]\right\}^{-1}$$

$$V(\hat{\mu}_{21}) = -\left\{E\left[\frac{\partial^2}{\partial \mu_{21}^2} \ln L_1\right]\right\}^{-1}$$

and

$$V(\hat{\mu}_{22}) = -\left\{E\left[\frac{\partial^2}{\partial \mu_{22}^2} \ln L_1\right]\right\}^{-1}.$$

22. Suppose that there are n_2 individuals who are afflicted with CHD at the time of admission to the study, and each is observed for a period of T_{2i} for $i = 1, \ldots, n_2$. For every individual in the group there are three possible sequences of transitions. An individual may

(1) remain ill, but alive at T_{2i}, $(S_2 \to S_2)$;

(2) die from other causes at t_{2i}, $t_{2i} < T_{2i}$ $(S_2 \to R_1)$; or

(3) die from CHD at t_{2i}, $t_{2i} < T_{2i}$ $(S_2 \to R_2)$.

The corresponding vector of indicators is $(\varepsilon_{22i}, \delta_{21i}, \delta_{22i})'$, so that each indicator is equal to one if the corresponding event occurs and is equal to zero otherwise, with

$$\varepsilon_{22i} + \delta_{21i} + \delta_{22i} = 1.$$

Find the expectation of each of the three indicators.

23. Derive the likelihood function L_2 for the sample of n_2 individuals. This function contains two independent parameters μ_{21} and μ_{22} with $\nu_{22} = -[\mu_{21} + \mu_{22}]$.

24. Derive the maximum likelihood estimator for μ_{21}, μ_{22} and ν_{22}.

25. When the two samples are combined, we have the likelihood function $L = L_1 \cdot L_2$. Find the maximum likelihood estimators of ν_{11}, ν_{12}, ν_{22}, μ_{11}, μ_{21} and μ_{22} from the likelihood function L.

26. Find the asymptotic variances of the estimators $\hat{\nu}_{1i}$, $\hat{\mu}_{11}$, $\hat{\mu}_{21}$, and $\hat{\mu}_{22}$ by using the formulas in problem 21.

27. *Illness-death Process.* A stochastic system has two transient states s_1 and s_2 and one absorbing state R with the intensity functions

$$\nu_{11} = -.3 \qquad \nu_{12} = .1 \qquad \mu_1 = .2$$

$$\nu_{21} = .4 \qquad \nu_{22} = -.6 \qquad \mu_2 = .2$$

(a) Derive differential equations for the transition probabilities $P_{\alpha\beta}(0,t)$ for α, $\beta = 1, 2$.

(b) Find from these equations the transition probabilities.

(c) Find the expected durations of stay $e_{\alpha\beta}(t)$, α, $\beta = 1, 2$.

(d) Compute $Q_\alpha(0,t)$ and show that for each α,

$$P_{\alpha 1}(0,t) + P_{\alpha 2}(0,t) + Q_\alpha(0,t) = 1 \qquad \alpha = 1, 2.$$

(e) Compute the expected duration of stay $\varepsilon_\alpha(0,t)$, $\alpha = 1, 2$.

28. *Continuation.* Work out the numerical result as in problem 27 for each of the following cases:

(i) $\nu_{11} = -.4 \qquad \nu_{12} = .2 \qquad \mu_1 = .2$

$\nu_{21} = .4 \qquad \nu_{22} = -.6 \qquad \mu_2 = .2$

(ii) $\nu_{11} = -.5 \qquad \nu_{12} = .3 \qquad \mu_1 = .2$

$\nu_{21} = .4 \qquad \nu_{22} = -.6 \qquad \mu_2 = .2$

(iii) $\nu_{11} = -.8 \qquad \nu_{12} = .6 \qquad \mu_1 = .2$

$\nu_{21} = .4 \qquad \nu_{22} = -.6 \qquad \mu_2 = .2$

CHAPTER 12

Multiple Transition Probabilities in the Simple Illness Death Process

1. INTRODUCTION

The transition probabilities $P_{\alpha\beta}(0,t)$ and $Q_{\alpha\delta}(0,t)$ presented in Chapter 11 describe the end result of an individual's movement over a given period of time, but they provide inadequate information regarding transitions that take place during an interval. For example, the probability that an individual who is healthy (in S_1) at the beginning of the interval $(0,t)$ will be healthy at the end of the interval is $P_{11}(0,t)$. But this probability provides no clue to changes in the individual's health during the interval. The person might become ill and recover a number of times during $(0,t)$, or remain healthy throughout the interval. The probability $P_{11}(0,t)$ does not distinguish one case from the other. Similarly, in the case of an automobile, $P_{11}(0,t)$ alone gives no information regarding the number of times it may have been serviced during a time interval. The other probabilities $P_{\alpha\beta}(0,t)$ and $Q_{\alpha\delta}(0,t)$ are not sufficient for describing an individual's health either. In order to present a more detailed picture of the health status of an individual (or the condition of an automobile) throughout an entire interval, we need to study the number of transitions the individual (or automobile) makes during the interval. This chapter is devoted to the derivation of explicit formulas for the multiple transition probabilities and to the discussion of related problems.

Consider a time interval $(0,t)$ and an individual in state S_α at the initial time 0. We are interested not only in the state the individual occupies at time t, but also in the number of transitions he or she makes during the interval $(0,t)$. For clarity, we shall use the term *renewal probability* when the ending state is the same as the initial state, and the term *passage probability* when the ending state is different from the initial state. We shall use $P_{\alpha\alpha}^{(m)}(0,t)$ to denote the m-th renewal probability and $P_{\alpha\beta}^{(m)}(0,t)$ for $\beta \neq \alpha$, the m-th passage probability. Formally, they are defined as follows:

$$\begin{aligned} P_{\alpha\alpha}^{(m)}(0,t) &= \Pr\{\text{an individual in state } S_\alpha \text{ at 0 will } \textit{leave } S_\alpha \\ &\qquad m \text{ times during } (0,t) \text{ and will be in } S_\alpha \text{ at } t\} \\ &= \Pr\{M_{\alpha\alpha}(0,t) = m\}, \end{aligned} \tag{1.1}$$

and

$$\begin{aligned} P_{\alpha\beta}^{(m)}(0,t) &= \Pr\{\text{an individual in } S_\alpha \text{ at 0 will } \textit{leave } S_\alpha \\ &\qquad m \text{ times during } (0,t) \text{ and will be in } S_\beta \text{ at } t\} \\ &= \Pr\{M_{\alpha\beta}(0,t) = m\}, \qquad \alpha \neq \beta; \alpha,\beta = 1,2 \\ &\qquad\qquad\qquad\qquad\qquad\qquad \text{m} = 0,1,\ldots. \end{aligned} \tag{1.2}$$

The random variable $M_{\alpha\beta}(0,t)$ corresponding to the probabilities $P_{\alpha\beta}^{(m)}(0,t)$ is the number of times the individual leaves S_α for S_β before reaching S_β at time t. Both the number of exits from S_α and the ending state S_β are subject to chance. Since the individual might not be in S_β at time t, $M_{\alpha\beta}(0,t)$ is an improper random variable (see section 4).

There are several ways to derive formulas for the multiple transition probabilities. In sections 2, 3, and 4 that follow, we describe three methods for formulating these probabilities using identities, differential equations, and the probability generating function.

2. IDENTITIES AND MULTIPLE TRANSITION PROBABILITIES

Consider the probability $P_{\alpha\beta}^{(m)}(0,t)$ that an individual who is in S_α at time 0 will leave S_α m times and be in S_β at time t. Let l be a fixed integer such that $0 \le l < m$. The probability that the $(l+1)$st transition from S_α to S_β will occur at a particular time τ (or, more precisely, during the infinitesimal time interval $(\tau, \tau + d\tau)$) and the remaining $m - l - 1$ transitions during the time interval (τ,t) is[1]

$$P_{\alpha\alpha}^{(l)}(0,\tau)\;[\nu_{\alpha\beta}(\tau)d\tau]\;P_{\beta\beta}^{(m-l-1)}(\tau,t). \tag{2.1}$$

[1] The intensity functions $\nu_{\alpha\beta}(\tau)$ have the same meaning as $\nu_{\alpha\beta}$ defined in (2.1), Chapter 11, except that they are functions of time τ.

Since for different τ, the events corresponding to (2.1) are mutually exclusive, we integrate (2.1) to obtain the identity

$$P_{\alpha\beta}^{(m)}(0,t) = \int_0^t P_{\alpha\alpha}^{(l)}(0,\tau)\,\nu_{\alpha\beta}(\tau)\,P_{\beta\beta}^{(m-l-1)}(\tau,t)\,d\tau,$$

$$l = 0, \ldots, m-1. \quad (2.2)$$

We obtain a different identity if we consider instead the first transition from S_β to S_α after the individual has left S_α l times. This consideration leads to the identity

$$P_{\alpha\beta}^{(m)}(0,t) = \int_0^t P_{\alpha\beta}^{(l)}(0,\tau)\,\nu_{\beta\alpha}(\tau)\,P_{\alpha\beta}^{(m-l)}(\tau,t)\,d\tau,$$

$$l = 1, \ldots, m-1. \quad (2.3)$$

Using similar reasoning we can find the two identities for $P_{\alpha\alpha}^{(m)}(0,t)$:

$$P_{\alpha\alpha}^{(m)}(0,t) = \int_0^t P_{\alpha\alpha}^{(l)}(0,\tau)\,\nu_{\alpha\beta}(\tau)\,P_{\beta\alpha}^{(m-l)}(\tau,t)\,d\tau,$$

$$l = 0, \ldots, m-1, \quad (2.4)$$

and

$$P_{\alpha\alpha}^{(m)}(0,t) = \int_0^t P_{\alpha\beta}^{(l)}(0,\tau)\,\nu_{\beta\alpha}(\tau)\,P_{\alpha\alpha}^{(m-l)}(\tau,t)\,d\tau,$$

$$l = 1, \ldots, m. \quad (2.5)$$

Identities for a time homogeneous process are obtained from equations (2.2) through (2.5) by replacing $\nu_{\alpha\beta}(\tau)$ with $\nu_{\alpha\beta}$:

$$P_{\alpha\beta}^{(m)}(0,t) = \int_0^t P_{\alpha\alpha}^{(l)}(0,\tau)\,\nu_{\alpha\beta}\,P_{\beta\beta}^{(m-l-1)}(\tau,t)\,d\tau,$$

$$l = 0, \ldots, m-1, \quad (2.2a)$$

$$P_{\alpha\beta}^{(m)}(0,t) = \int_0^t P_{\alpha\beta}^{(l)}(0,\tau)\,\nu_{\beta\alpha}\,P_{\alpha\beta}^{(m-l)}(\tau,t)\,d\tau,$$

$$l = 1, \ldots, m-1, \quad (2.3a)$$

$$P_{\alpha\alpha}^{(m)}(0,t) = \int_0^t P_{\alpha\alpha}^{(l)}(0,\tau)\nu_{\alpha\beta} P_{\beta\alpha}^{(m-l)}(\tau,t)\,d\tau,$$

$$l = 0, \ldots, m-1, \quad (2.4a)$$

$$P_{\alpha\alpha}^{(m)}(0,t) = \int_0^t P_{\alpha\beta}^{(l)}(0,\tau)\nu_{\beta\alpha} P_{\alpha\alpha}^{(m-l)}(\tau,t)\,d\tau,$$

$$l = 1, \ldots, m. \quad (2.5a)$$

Identities (2.1) through (2.5) are equivalent to the identity (3.4) in the general birth process in Chapter 9. They provide a convenient basis for formulating the multiple transition probabilities. Although several combinations of the identities can be used to derive the required formulas, identities (2.3) and (2.3a) are most suitable for this purpose.

2.1 Formula for the Multiple Passage Probability $P_{\alpha\beta}^{(m)}(0,t)$.

When $l = m-1$, identity (2.3) becomes a recursive equation expressing the probability $P_{\alpha\beta}^{(m)}(0,t)$ in terms of $P_{\alpha\beta}^{(m-1)}(0,t)$, or

$$P_{\alpha\beta}^{(m)}(0,t) = \int_0^t P_{\alpha\beta}^{(m-1)}(0,\tau)\,\nu_{\beta\alpha}(\tau)\,P_{\alpha\beta}^{(1)}(\tau,t)\,d\tau. \quad (2.6)$$

It may be successively used beginning with $m = 1$ to obtain the formula for $P_{\alpha\beta}^{(m)}(0,t)$.

We can easily show that the probability an individual will remain in the initial state S_α over an interval $(0,t)$ is

$$P_{\alpha\alpha}^{(0)}(0,t) = \exp\left\{\int_0^t \nu_{\alpha\alpha}(\tau)d\tau\right\}. \quad (2.7)$$

Introducing (2.7) in (2.2) for $m = 1$ and $l = 0$, we get the first passage probability,

$$P_{\alpha\beta}^{(1)}(0,t) = \int_0^t \exp\left\{\int_0^\tau \nu_{\alpha\alpha}(\xi)\,d\xi\right\}\nu_{\alpha\beta}(\tau)\exp\left\{\int_\tau^t \nu_{\beta\beta}(\xi)\,d\xi\right\}d\tau. \quad (2.8)$$

Substituting (2.8) in (2.6), and integrating the resulting expression, yields the second passage probability. A general formula can be derived.

For a time homogeneous process with $\nu_{\alpha\beta}(\tau) = \nu_{\alpha\beta}$, formulas (2.7) and (2.8) reduce to

$$P_{\alpha\alpha}^{(0)}(0,t) = e^{\nu_{\alpha\alpha}t} \quad (2.7a)$$

and

$$P_{\alpha\beta}^{(1)}(0,t) = \frac{\nu_{\alpha\beta}}{\nu_{\alpha\alpha} - \nu_{\beta\beta}} [e^{\nu_{\alpha\alpha}t} - e^{\nu_{\beta\beta}t}]. \tag{2.8a}$$

Now, if we substitute (2.8a) in (2.6), with $\nu_{\beta\alpha}(\tau) = \nu_{\beta\alpha}$, we obtain the second passage probability

$$P_{\alpha\beta}^{(2)}(0,t) = \frac{\nu_{\alpha\beta}^2 \nu_{\beta\alpha}}{\Delta^3} [-2(e^{\nu_{\alpha\alpha}t} - e^{\nu_{\beta\beta}t}) + \Delta t(e^{\nu_{\alpha\alpha}t} + e^{\nu_{\beta\beta}t})], \tag{2.9}$$

where $\Delta = \nu_{\alpha\alpha} - \nu_{\beta\beta}$. Repeated applications of (2.6) generate the formula for the mth passage probability.

Theorem 1. *For an individual in* S_α *at time* 0, *the* m-th *passage probability during interval* $(0,t)$ *is*

$$P_{\alpha\beta}^{(m)}(0,t) = \frac{\nu_{\alpha\beta}(-\nu_{\alpha\beta}\nu_{\beta\alpha})^{m-1}}{\Delta^{2m-1}} \sum_{k=0}^{m-1} \binom{2m-2-k}{m-1} \times \frac{(\Delta t)^k}{k!} [(-1)^k e^{\nu_{\alpha\alpha}t} - e^{\nu_{\beta\beta}t}]. \tag{2.10}$$

for $\alpha \neq \beta$; $m = 1, 2, \ldots$.

Deriving equation (2.10) in this fashion involves a lengthy process; however, an inductive proof requires only three simple equalities.

2.2 Three Equalities.

First, for any $V > 0$ and a non-negative integer k, the integral

$$\int_0^t \tau^k e^{-V\tau} d\tau = \frac{k!}{V^{k+1}} \left[1 - \sum_{i=0}^{k} \frac{(Vt)^i}{i!} e^{-Vt}\right]. \tag{2.11}$$

Letting $y = V\tau$ and $T = Vt$, we can rewrite the left hand side of (2.11) as:

$$\int_0^t \tau^k e^{-V\tau} d\tau = \frac{1}{V^{k+1}} \int_0^T y^k e^{-y} dy. \tag{2.12}$$

The last integral is an incomplete gamma function, which is given in equation (2.9) in Chapter 3:

$$\int_0^T y^k e^{-y} dy = k! \left[1 - \sum_{i=0}^{k} \frac{T^i}{i!} e^{-T}\right]. \tag{2.13}$$

The equality in (2.11) follows.

Second, for any finite sequence of numbers $\{a_{ik}\}$, depending on two indices, the following equality holds:

$$\sum_{k=0}^{m-1}\sum_{i=1}^{k+1} a_{ik} = \sum_{i=1}^{m}\sum_{k=i-1}^{m-1} a_{ik}. \tag{2.14}$$

Third, given two positive integers m and N, with $m < N$, we have

$$\binom{N}{m} = \binom{N-1}{m-1} + \binom{N-2}{m-1} + \ldots + \binom{m-1}{m-1}, \tag{2.15}$$

and also

$$\binom{2m}{m} = 2\left[\binom{2m-2}{m-1} + \binom{2m-3}{m-1} + \ldots + \binom{m-1}{m-1}\right]. \tag{2.16}$$

2.3. Inductive Proof of Formula for $P_{\alpha\beta}^{(m)}(0, t)$.

When $m = 1$, the right hand side of (2.10) is identical to (2.8a); therefore equation (2.10) is true for $m = 1$. Assuming (2.10) is true for m, we need to prove that it is true for $m + 1$; i.e., that

$$P_{\alpha\beta}^{(m+1)}(0,t) = \frac{\nu_{\alpha\beta}(-\nu_{\alpha\beta}\nu_{\beta\alpha})^m}{\Delta^{2m+1}} \sum_{k=0}^{m} \binom{2m-k}{m} \frac{(\Delta t)^k}{k!} [(-1)^k e^{\nu_{\alpha\alpha} t} - e^{\nu_{\beta\beta} t}]. \tag{2.17}$$

To prove (2.17), we introduce (2.8a) and (2.10) in

$$P_{\alpha\beta}^{(m+1)}(0, t) = \int_0^t P_{\alpha\beta}^{(m)}(0,\tau)\,\nu_{\beta\alpha}\,P_{\alpha\beta}^{(1)}(\tau, t)\,d\tau, \tag{2.18}$$

with the result that

$$P_{\alpha\beta}^{(m+1)}(0, t) = \frac{-\nu_{\alpha\beta}(-\nu_{\alpha\beta}\nu_{\beta\alpha})^m}{\Delta^{2m}} \sum_{k=0}^{m-1} \binom{2m-2-k}{m-1} \frac{\Delta^k}{k!}$$
$$\times \int_0^t \tau^k\,[(-1)^k e^{\nu_{\alpha\alpha}\tau} - e^{\nu_{\beta\beta}\tau}]\,[e^{\nu_{\alpha\alpha}(t-\tau)} - e^{\nu_{\beta\beta}(t-\tau)}]\,d\tau. \tag{2.19}$$

We use (2.11) to evaluate the integral:

$$\int_0^t \tau^k [(-1)^k e^{\nu_{\alpha\alpha}\tau} - e^{\nu_{\beta\beta}\tau}] [e^{\nu_{\alpha\alpha}(t-\tau)} - e^{\nu_{\beta\beta}(t-\tau)}] \, d\tau$$

$$= e^{\nu_{\alpha\alpha}t} \int_0^t [(-\tau)^k - \tau^k e^{-\Delta\tau}] \, d\tau + e^{\nu_{\beta\beta}t} \int_0^t [\tau^k - (-\tau)^k e^{\Delta\tau}] \, d\tau$$

$$= -e^{\nu_{\alpha\alpha}t}\left[\frac{(-t)^{k+1}}{k+1} + \frac{k!}{\Delta^{k+1}}\left(1 - \sum_{i=0}^{k} \frac{(\Delta t)^i}{i!} e^{-\Delta t}\right)\right]$$

$$+ e^{\nu_{\beta\beta}t}\left[\frac{t^{k+1}}{k+1} + \frac{k!}{\Delta^{k+1}}\left(1 - \sum_{i=0}^{k} \frac{(-\Delta t)^i}{i!} e^{\Delta t}\right)\right]. \tag{2.20}$$

Substituting (2.20) in (2.19) and rearranging terms yields

$$P_{\alpha\beta}^{(m+1)}(0, t) = \frac{\nu_{\alpha\beta}(-\nu_{\alpha\beta}\nu_{\beta\alpha})^m}{\Delta^{2m+1}}$$

$$\times \left[e^{\nu_{\alpha\alpha}t} \sum_{k=0}^{m-1} \binom{2m-2-k}{m-1} \left\{ 2 + \sum_{i=1}^{k+1} \frac{(-\Delta t)^i}{i!} \right\} \right.$$

$$\left. - e^{\nu_{\beta\beta}t} \sum_{k=0}^{m-1} \binom{2m-2-k}{m-1} \left\{ 2 + \sum_{i=1}^{k+1} \frac{(+\Delta t)^i}{i!} \right\} \right]. \tag{2.21}$$

Now we use equality (2.14) to rewrite the coefficient of exp $\{\nu_{\alpha\alpha}t\}$ in (2.21):

$$2\sum_{k=0}^{m-1} \binom{2m-2-k}{m-1} + \sum_{i=1}^{m} \sum_{k=i-1}^{m-1} \binom{2m-2-k}{m-1} \frac{(-\Delta t)^i}{i!}, \tag{2.22}$$

where, in view of (2.15) and (2.16),

$$2\sum_{k=0}^{m-1} \binom{2m-2-k}{m-1} = \binom{2m}{m} \tag{2.23}$$

and

$$\sum_{k=i-1}^{m-1} \binom{2m-2-k}{m-1} = \binom{2m-i}{m}. \tag{2.24}$$

Therefore, the coefficient of $\exp\{\nu_{\alpha\alpha}t\}$ in (2.21) is simply

$$\sum_{i=0}^{m} \binom{2m-i}{m} \frac{(-\Delta t)^i}{i!}. \tag{2.25}$$

Similarly, we can simplify the coefficient of $\exp\{\nu_{\beta\beta} t\}$ in (2.21) to get

$$\sum_{i=0}^{m} \binom{2m-i}{m} \frac{(\Delta t)^i}{i!}. \tag{2.26}$$

Substituting (2.25) and (2.26) in (2.21), we recover formula (2.17) and complete the inductive proof of (2.10).

The first passage probability in (2.8a) and the second passage probability in (2.9) are easily derived from (2.10).

2.4. Formula for the Multiple Renewal Probability $P_{\alpha\alpha}^{(m)}(0, t)$.

Theorem 2. *For an individual in state S_α at time 0, the m-th renewal probability during the interval* (0, *t*) *is*

$$P_{\alpha\alpha}^{(m)}(0, t) = \frac{(-\nu_{\alpha\beta}\nu_{\beta\alpha})^m}{\Delta^{2m}} \left[\sum_{k=0}^{m} \binom{2m-1-k}{m-1} \frac{(-\Delta t)^k}{k!} e^{\nu_{\alpha\alpha} t} - \sum_{k=0}^{m-1} \binom{2m-1-k}{m} \frac{(\Delta t)^k}{k!} e^{\nu_{\beta\beta} t} \right] \tag{2.27}$$

for $m = 1, 2, \ldots$.

Proof. When $l = m$, the identity in equation (2.5a) is

$$P_{\alpha\alpha}^{(m)}(0, \tau) = \int_0^t P_{\alpha\beta}^{(m)}(0, \tau)\, \nu_{\beta\alpha} P_{\alpha\alpha}^{(0)}(\tau, t)\, d\tau. \tag{2.28}$$

Substituting (2.10) in (2.28), integrating and simplifying the resulting expression yields the formula in (2.27).

When $m = 1$, (2.27) is the first renewal probability

$$P_{\alpha\alpha}^{(1)}(0, t) = \frac{\nu_{\alpha\beta}\nu_{\beta\alpha}}{\Delta^2} [\Delta t e^{\nu_{\alpha\alpha} t} - (e^{\nu_{\alpha\alpha} t} - e^{\nu_{\beta\beta} t})]\,; \tag{2.29}$$

when $m = 2$, it is the second renewal probability

$$P_{\alpha\alpha}^{(2)}(0, t) = \frac{(\nu_{\alpha\beta}\nu_{\beta\alpha})^2}{\Delta^4} \left[\frac{(\Delta t)^2}{2} e^{\nu_{\alpha\alpha} t} - \Delta t (2e^{\nu_{\alpha\alpha} t} + e^{\nu_{\beta\beta} t}) + 3(e^{\nu_{\alpha\alpha} t} - e^{\nu_{\beta\beta} t}) \right]. \tag{2.30}$$

The reader can prove that the probabilities $P_{\alpha\beta}^{(m)}(0, t)$ in (2.10) and $P_{\alpha\alpha}^{(m)}(0,t)$ in (2.27) satisfy the identities in (2.2a) through (2.5a).

3. DIFFERENTIAL EQUATIONS AND MULTIPLE TRANSITION PROBABILITIES

Differential equations for the probabilities $P_{\alpha\beta}^{(m)}(0, t)$ can be derived by considering two contiguous intervals $(0, t)$ and $(t, t + \Delta)$ and the probability that $M_{\alpha\beta}(0, t + \Delta) = m$:

$$P_{\alpha\alpha}^{(m)}(0, t + \Delta) = P_{\alpha\alpha}^{(m)}(0, t)\,[1 + \nu_{\alpha\alpha}\Delta] + P_{\alpha\beta}^{(m)}(0, t)\,\nu_{\beta\alpha}\Delta + o(\Delta) \tag{3.1}$$

and

$$P_{\alpha\beta}^{(m)}(0, t + \Delta) = P_{\alpha\alpha}^{(m-1)}(0, t)\,\nu_{\alpha\beta}\Delta + P_{\alpha\beta}^{(m)}(0, t)\,[1 + \nu_{\beta\beta}\Delta] + o(\Delta). \tag{3.2}$$

From (3.1) and (3.2) we obtain the differential equations

$$\frac{d}{dt} P_{\alpha\alpha}^{(m)}(0, t) = P_{\alpha\alpha}^{(m)}(0, t)\nu_{\alpha\alpha} + P_{\alpha\beta}^{(m)}(0, t)\nu_{\beta\alpha} \tag{3.3}$$

and

$$\frac{d}{dt} P_{\alpha\beta}^{(m)}(0, t) = P_{\alpha\alpha}^{(m-1)}(0, t)\nu_{\alpha\beta} + P_{\alpha\beta}^{(m)}(0, t)\nu_{\beta\beta},$$

$$\alpha \neq \beta \quad \alpha, \beta = 1, 2,$$

$$m = 1, 2, \ldots. \tag{3.4}$$

We solve these equations alternately beginning with equation (3.3) when $m = 0$.

When $m = 0$, equation (3.3) reduces to

$$\frac{d}{dt} P_{\alpha\alpha}^{(0)}(0, t) = P_{\alpha\alpha}^{(0)}(0, t)\nu_{\alpha\alpha}, \tag{3.5}$$

with the solution

$$P_{\alpha\alpha}^{(0)}(0, t) = e^{\nu_{\alpha\alpha} t}. \tag{3.6}$$

Now let $m = 1$, use (3.6) and rewrite (3.4) as

$$\frac{d}{dt} P_{\alpha\beta}^{(1)}(0, t) = e^{\nu_{\alpha\alpha} t} \nu_{\alpha\beta} + P_{\alpha\beta}^{(1)}(0, t)\, \nu_{\beta\beta}. \tag{3.7}$$

The solution of (3.7) is the first passage probability

$$P_{\alpha\beta}^{(1)}(0, t) = \frac{\nu_{\alpha\beta}}{\nu_{\alpha\alpha} - \nu_{\beta\beta}} \left[e^{\nu_{\alpha\alpha} t} - e^{\nu_{\beta\beta} t} \right]. \tag{3.8}$$

Substituting (3.8) in (3.3) for $m = 1$ and solving the resulting equation yield the first renewal probability

$$P_{\alpha\alpha}^{(1)}(0, t) = \frac{\nu_{\alpha\beta} \nu_{\beta\alpha}}{\nu_{\alpha\alpha} - \nu_{\beta\beta}} \left[t e^{\nu_{\alpha\alpha} t} - \frac{1}{\nu_{\alpha\alpha} - \nu_{\beta\beta}} \left(e^{\nu_{\alpha\alpha} t} - e^{\nu_{\beta\beta} t} \right) \right]. \tag{3.9}$$

Continuing this process of alternating substitutions and solving the successive differential equations yields the general formulas for the m-th passage probability in (2.10) and the m-th renewal probability in (2.27).

The reader is advised to solve equation (3.3) for the m-th renewal probability using equation (2.10) for the probability $P_{\alpha\beta}^{(m)}(0, t)$ and to solve equation (3.4) for the m-th passage probability using (2.27) for the probability $P_{\alpha\alpha}^{(m-1)}(0, t)$.

4. PROBABILITY GENERATING FUNCTIONS

In deriving formulas for a sequence of probabilities, normally the preferred approach is to use the probability generating function. This method often yields elegant solutions with a minimum amount of computation. Using the p.g.f. to obtain the multiple transition probabilities discussed in this chapter, however, generates formulas containing an infinite number of terms impractical for the purpose of application. Nevertheless, we will briefly review this method because it is basic to understanding the more general case we shall introduce in Chapter 16. The formulas of the p.g.f.'s also provide a convenient basis for computing the sums of probabilities, expectations, and other important quantities.

Let us then introduce p.g.f.'s of multiple renewal probabilities and multiple passage probabilities:

$$g_{\alpha\beta}(s; t) = \sum_{m=0}^{\infty} s^m P_{\alpha\beta}^{(m)}(t), \qquad \alpha, \beta = 1, 2. \tag{4.1}$$

Taking the derivatives of $g_{\alpha\beta}(s; t)$ in (4.1) with respect to t, and substituting the differential equations in (3.3) and (3.4), we obtain the differential equations for the p.g.f.'s

$$\frac{\partial}{\partial t} g_{\alpha\alpha}(s; t) = g_{\alpha\alpha}(s; t)\nu_{\alpha\alpha} + g_{\alpha\beta}(s; t)\nu_{\beta\alpha} \tag{4.2}$$

and

$$\frac{\partial}{\partial t} g_{\alpha\beta}(s; t) = g_{\alpha\alpha}(s; t)s\nu_{\alpha\beta} + g_{\alpha\beta}(s; t)\nu_{\beta\beta}, \qquad \alpha \neq \beta; \alpha, \beta = 1, 2. \tag{4.3}$$

Since $P_{\alpha\alpha}^{(0)}(0,0) = 1$, $P_{\alpha\beta}^{(0)}(0,0) = 0$, $P_{\alpha\alpha}^{(m)}(0,0) = 0$, and $P_{\alpha\beta}^{(m)}(0,0) = 0$, for $m > 0$, the initial conditions of (4.2) and (4.3) are

$$g_{\alpha\alpha}(s;0) = 1, \qquad g_{\alpha\beta}(s;0) = 0, \qquad \alpha \neq \beta; \alpha, \beta = 1, 2. \tag{4.4}$$

The differential equations in (4.2) and (4.3) can be solved in exactly the same way as equations in (2.13), Chapter 11. Here the characteristic equation is

$$\begin{vmatrix} (\rho - \nu_{11}) & -\nu_{21} \\ -s\nu_{12} & (\rho - \nu_{22}) \end{vmatrix} = \rho^2 - (\nu_{11} + \nu_{22})\rho + (\nu_{11}\nu_{22} - \nu_{12}\nu_{21}s) = 0 \tag{4.5}$$

with the roots

$$\rho_1 = \frac{1}{2}\left[(\nu_{11} + \nu_{22}) + \sqrt{(\nu_{11} - \nu_{22})^2 + 4\nu_{12}\nu_{21}s}\,\right]$$

and

$$\rho_2 = \frac{1}{2}\left[(\nu_{11} + \nu_{22}) - \sqrt{(\nu_{11} - \nu_{22})^2 + 4\nu_{12}\nu_{21}s}\,\right]. \tag{4.6}$$

Note that, except for the appearance of s, (4.5) and (4.6) are identical to the corresponding expressions in equations (2.17) in Chapter 11. The particular solutions of equations (4.2) and (4.3) corresponding to the initial conditions in (4.4) are

$$g_{\alpha\beta}(s;t) = \sum_{i=1}^{2} \frac{s\nu_{\alpha\beta}}{\rho_i - \rho_j} e^{\rho_i t} \tag{4.7}$$

and

$$g_{\alpha\alpha}(s;t) = \sum_{i=1}^{2} \frac{(\rho_i - \nu_{\beta\beta})}{\rho_i - \rho_j} e^{\rho_i t},$$

$$j \neq i;\ \alpha \neq \beta;\ \alpha, \beta = 1, 2. \tag{4.8}$$

To summarize, we state

Theorem 3. *The probability generating functions of multiple passage probabilities and multiple renewal probabilities are given in equations* (4.7) *and* (4.8).

4.1. Multiple Transition Probabilities.

Generally, we can obtain formulas for a probability distribution from the corresponding p.g.f. by taking the derivatives with respect to the quantity s. This approach is not appropriate in the present case because the p.g.f.'s in (4.7) and (4.8) have the quantity s in the roots ρ_1 and ρ_2, in the exponents, and under the square root signs. A more fruitful way is to expand the right hand side of equations in (4.7) and (4.8) in a power series in s and then identify the corresponding coefficients.

To achieve this, we let $\Delta = (\nu_{\alpha\alpha} - \nu_{\beta\beta})$ and

$$\sqrt{\cdot} = \sqrt{\Delta^2 + 4\nu_{\alpha\beta}\nu_{\beta\alpha}s}, \tag{4.9}$$

and use (4.6) to rewrite the equation in (4.7) as

$$g_{\alpha\beta}(s;t) = \frac{s\nu_{\alpha\beta}}{\sqrt{\cdot}} e^{(t/2)(\nu_{\alpha\alpha}+\nu_{\beta\beta})} [e^{(t/2)\sqrt{\cdot}} - e^{-(t/2)\sqrt{\cdot}}]. \tag{4.10}$$

Expanding the exponentials in a power series, we find that

$$\frac{1}{\sqrt{\cdot}} [e^{(t/2)\sqrt{\cdot}} - e^{-(t/2)\sqrt{\cdot}}] = 2\sum_{k=0}^{\infty} \frac{1}{(2k+1)!} \left(\frac{t}{2}\right)^{2k+1} (\sqrt{\cdot}\,)^{2k}, \tag{4.11}$$

where

$$(\sqrt{\cdot}\,)^{2k} = [\Delta^2 + 4\nu_{\alpha\beta}\nu_{\beta\alpha}s]^k = \sum_{n=0}^{k} \binom{k}{n} \Delta^{2(k-n)} (4\nu_{\alpha\beta}\nu_{\beta\alpha})^n s^n; \tag{4.12}$$

and hence, with an interchange of the summation signs, we get

$$\frac{1}{\sqrt{\cdot}}\left[e^{(t/2)\sqrt{\cdot}} - e^{-(t/2)\sqrt{\cdot}}\right]$$

$$= \frac{1}{\Delta^{2n+1}} \sum_{n=0}^{\infty} \sum_{k=n}^{\infty} \binom{k}{n} \frac{1}{(2k+1)!} \left(\frac{\Delta t}{2}\right)^{2k+1} (4\nu_{\alpha\beta}\nu_{\beta\alpha})^n s^n. \quad (4.13)$$

Substituting (4.13) in (4.10) and then letting $m = n + 1$, we obtain a power series in s,

$$g_{\alpha\beta}(s; t) = \sum_{m=0}^{\infty} P_{\alpha\beta}^{(m)}(0, t) s^m \quad (4.14)$$

where the coefficient of s^m is the desired probability

$$P_{\alpha\beta}^{(m)}(0, t) = \frac{2\nu_{\alpha\beta}}{\Delta^{2m-1}} (4\nu_{\alpha\beta}\nu_{\beta\alpha})^{m-1} e^{(t/2)(\nu_{\alpha\alpha}+\nu_{\beta\beta})}$$

$$\times \sum_{k=m-1}^{\infty} \binom{k}{m-1} \frac{1}{(2k+1)!} \left(\frac{\Delta t}{2}\right)^{2k+1} \quad (4.15)$$

for $m = 1, 2, \ldots; \alpha \neq \beta; \alpha, \beta = 1, 2$.

The equation in (4.8) can be expanded similarly:

$$g_{\alpha\alpha}(s; t) = \sum_{m=0}^{\infty} P_{\alpha\alpha}^{(m)}(0, t) s^m \quad (4.16)$$

where the coefficient is

$$P_{\alpha\alpha}^{(m)}(0, t) = \frac{1}{\Delta^{2m}} (4\nu_{\alpha\beta}\nu_{\beta\alpha})^m \exp\left\{\frac{t}{2}(\nu_{\alpha\alpha} + \nu_{\beta\beta})\right\}$$

$$\times \left[\sum_{k=m}^{\infty} \binom{k}{m} \left\{\frac{1}{(2k+1)!}\left(\frac{\Delta t}{2}\right)^{2k+1} + \frac{1}{(2k)!}\left(\frac{\Delta t}{2}\right)^{2k}\right\}\right] \quad (4.17)$$

for $m = 0, 1, \ldots; \alpha \neq \beta, \alpha, \beta = 1, 2$.

For fixed α, β, and t, the sum of the probabilities $P_{\alpha\beta}^{(m)}(0, t)$ over all possible values of m is the probability that an individual initially in S_α will be in S_β at time t, regardless of the number of transitions. This probability can be obtained directly from the corresponding p.g.f.

by setting $s = 1$. From equation (4.7), we know the passage probability is

$$\sum_{m=1}^{\infty} P_{\alpha\beta}^{(m)}(0, t) = P_{\alpha\beta}(0, t) = g_{\alpha\beta}(1; t)$$

$$= \sum_{i=1}^{2} \frac{\nu_{\alpha\beta}}{\rho_i - \rho_j} e^{\rho_i t}. \tag{4.18}$$

From the second equation, we know the renewal probability is

$$\sum_{m=0}^{\infty} P_{\alpha\alpha}^{(m)}(0, t) = P_{\alpha\alpha}(0, t) = g_{\alpha\alpha}(1; t)$$

$$= \sum_{i=1}^{2} \frac{\rho_i - \nu_{\beta\beta}}{\rho_i - \rho_j} e^{\rho_i t} \tag{4.19}$$

where $j \neq i$, $j = 1, 2$, and ρ_1 and ρ_2 are given in (4.6) with $s = 1$. Equations (4.18) and (4.19) are, of course, the same as equation (2.26) and (2.27) in Chapter 11.

An individual in state S_α at time 0 may be in S_α or in S_β at time t, or may even have left the population through death prior to time t; the probabilities given in (4.18) and (4.19) (and their sums) are less than one. Thus there is a positive probability that the random variables $M_{\alpha\beta}(t)$ will not take on any (finite) values at all; therefore, as noted earlier, they are improper random variables.

4.2. Equivalence of Formulas.

Formulas for multiple transition probabilities that are derived from probability generating functions are quite different in appearance from those derived in section 2 using identities. Before proceeding, it is imperative to note that the corresponding formulas are identical. Specifically, equations (4.15) and (4.17) are exactly equivalent to (2.10) and (2.17), respectively. Proof of the equalities appear in problems 15 and 18 of this chapter.

5. VERIFICATION OF THE STOCHASTIC IDENTITIES

In section 2, we presented four identities for the multiple transition probabilities. Formulas (4.15) and (4.17), which we derived from the probability generating functions can be used to affirm the validity of these identities. As preliminaries, we state three equalities that are needed in our verification. First.

$$\int_0^t \left(\frac{\tau}{2}\right)^{2i+1} \left(\frac{t-\tau}{2}\right)^{2j+1} d\tau = 2\left(\frac{t}{2}\right)^{2k+1} \frac{(2i+1)!(2j+1)!}{(2k+1)!}, \tag{5.1}$$

where $k = i + j + 1$. To prove the identity, we let $y = \tau/t$, then rewrite the left hand side of (5.1) as

$$2\left(\frac{t}{2}\right)^{2k+1} \int_0^1 y^{2i+1}(1-y)^{2j+1} dy = 2\left(\frac{t}{2}\right)^{2k+1} \frac{(2i+1)!(2j+1)!}{(2k+1)!}, \tag{5.2}$$

where the integral is a complete beta function. Equation (5.2) is a result of integration (cf. Problem 8, Chapter 3.)

Second, if $\{a_{ij}\}$ is an arbitrary sequence of numbers dependent upon two indices, then

$$\sum_{i=l-1}^{\infty} \sum_{j=m-l-1}^{\infty} a_{ij} = \sum_{k=m-1}^{\infty} \sum_{j=m-l-1}^{k-l} a_{k-j-1,j}. \tag{5.3}$$

Figure 1 shows a graphic illustration of equation (5.3) as an infinite grid of points (i, j). There are many ways to sum over the points in the grid. The left hand side of equation (5.3) represents the summation taken along the vertical $(j + 1)$ and then the horizontal (i) axes; the right hand side of (5.3) represents the summation taken first along the diagonal lines $k = i + j + 1 =$ constant, and then added over all the diagonals indicated. Equality (5.3) thus is readily apparent.

Figure 1

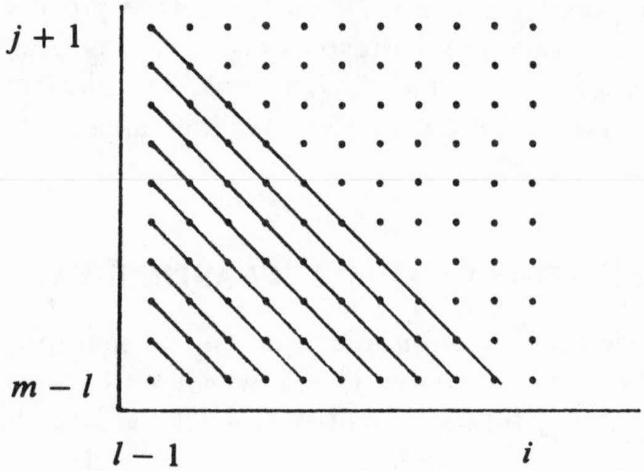

Third, we can prove the combinatorial equality

$$\sum_{j=n-l-1}^{k-l} \binom{k-j-1}{l-1}\binom{j}{m-l-1} = \binom{k}{m-1} \tag{5.4}$$

by expanding the identity

$$(1-c)^{-m} = (1-c)^{-l}(1-c)^{-(m-l)}, \tag{5.5}$$

where $|c| < 1$. Using Newton's binomial formula [cf., Chapter 2, equation (4.17)] to expand both sides of (5.5) and equating the coefficients of c^n yields

$$(-1)^n \binom{-m}{n} = \sum_{i=0}^{n} (-1)^n \binom{-l}{n-i}\binom{-(m-l)}{i}, \tag{5.6}$$

which we rewrite as

$$\binom{m+n-1}{m-1} = \sum_{i=0}^{n} \binom{l+n-i-1}{l-1}\binom{m-l+i-1}{m-l-1}. \tag{5.7}$$

Then making the substitutions of $m+n-1=k$ and $m-l+i-1=j$, we recover equality (5.4).

Using the three foregoing equalities we proceed to verify equation (2.3a). Substituting formula (4.15) for $P_{\alpha\beta}^{(m)}(0, t)$ in the right hand side of (2.3a) and using (5.1) to integrate the resulting expression, we obtain

$$\int_0^t P_{\alpha\beta}^{(l)}(0,\tau)\nu_{\beta\alpha}P_{\alpha\beta}^{(m-l)}(\tau, t)\,d\tau = \frac{1}{\Delta^{2m-1}}\, 2\nu_{\alpha\beta}(4\nu_{\alpha\beta}\nu_{\beta\alpha})^{m-1} e^{(t/2)(\nu_{\alpha\alpha}+\nu_{\beta\beta})}$$
$$\times\left[\sum_{i=l-1}^{\infty}\sum_{j=m-l-1}^{\infty}\binom{i}{l-1}\binom{j}{m-l-1}\left(\frac{\Delta t}{2}\right)^{2k+1}\frac{1}{(2k+1)!}\right], \tag{5.8}$$

where $k = i + j + 1$. Now (5.3) and (5.4) are used successively, the quantity inside the brackets is reduced to

$$\left[\sum_{k=m-1}^{\infty}\binom{k}{m-1}\left(\frac{\Delta t}{2}\right)^{2k+1}\frac{1}{(2k+1)!}\right]. \tag{5.9}$$

When (5.9) is substituted in (5.8), we recover the formula for $P_{\alpha\beta}^{(m)}(0, t)$ that was given in (4.15). Identity (2.3a) is verified.

The identities in equations (2.2a), (2.4a) and (2.5a) can be verified in the same manner.

6. CHAPMAN-KOLMOGOROV EQUATIONS

In the discussion of the multiple transition probabilities, we have implicitly assumed that the future transitions an individual may make are stochastically independent of past transitions. We now use this assumption to develop Chapman-Kolmogorov equations for the two transient states process. Consider an individual in S_α at time 0 and the probability $P_{\alpha\alpha}^{(m)}(0, t)$. For a given time τ, $0 \le \tau \le t$, we divide the interval $(0, t)$ into two subintervals: $(0, \tau)$ and (τ, t) and inquire as to the whereabouts of the individual at time τ. The individual is in S_α at time τ, having left S_α l times, and makes the remaining $m - l$ transitions during (τ, t). The probability corresponding to this sequence of transitions is

$$P_{\alpha\alpha}^{(l)}(0, \tau) P_{\alpha\alpha}^{(m-l)}(\tau, t), \qquad l = 0, 1, \dots, m.$$

Alternatively, the individual is in S_β at time τ, having left S_α l times and making the remaining $m - l + 1$ transitions from S_β to S_α during (τ, t). The probability corresponding to this sequence of transitions is

$$P_{\alpha\beta}^{(l)}(0, \tau) P_{\beta\alpha}^{(m-l+1)}(\tau, t), \qquad l = 1, 2, \dots, m.$$

The sequences of transitions for all possible values of m outlined above exhausts the possibilities for making m transitions from S_α to S_β and back to S_α with a stopover at τ; thus the equality

$$P_{\alpha\alpha}^{(m)}(0, t) = \sum_{l=0}^{m} P_{\alpha\alpha}^{(l)}(0, \tau) P_{\alpha\alpha}^{(m-l)}(\tau, t) + \sum_{l=1}^{m} P_{\alpha\beta}^{(l)}(0, \tau) P_{\beta\alpha}^{(m-l+1)}(\tau, t). \tag{6.1}$$

Using a similar interpretation for the multiple passage probability $P_{\alpha\beta}^{(m)}(0, t)$, we get the equality

$$P_{\alpha\beta}^{(m)}(0, t) = \sum_{l=0}^{m-1} P_{\alpha\alpha}^{(l)}(0, \tau) P_{\alpha\beta}^{(m-l)}(\tau, t) + \sum_{l=1}^{m} P_{\alpha\beta}^{(l)}(0, \tau) P_{\beta\beta}^{(m-l)}(\tau, t) \tag{6.2}$$

for $\alpha \ne \beta$; $\alpha, \beta = 1, 2$; $m = 1, 2, \dots$.

These equations are equivalent to the Chapman-Kolmogorov equations for the general stochastic process (cf., equation (1.6), Chapter 14), but they differ from the identities in equations (2.2a) through (2.5a) in three respects. First, in equations (2.2a) through (2.5a), the number l is fixed and the integral is taken over all possible values of τ in the interval $(0, t)$, whereas in the Chapman-Kolmogorov equations (6.1) and (6.2), the time τ is fixed and the sum is taken over all possible values of l from 0 to m. Second, the identities in section 2 require a transition to take place between τ and $\tau + d\tau$; no such transition is required in (6.1) and (6.2). Third, there is one integral in any one of equations (2.2a) and (2.5a), while each of the Chapman-Kolmogorov equations contains two different summations.

To verify (6.1), note that the sequence in the first term on the right hand side of the equality sign,

$$\sum_{l=0}^{m} P_{\alpha\alpha}^{(l)}(0, \tau) P_{\alpha\alpha}^{(m-l)}(\tau, t), \tag{6.3}$$

is the convolution of the two sequences $\{P_{\alpha\alpha}^{(m)}(0, \tau)\}$ and $\{P_{\alpha\alpha}^{(m)}(\tau, t)\}$; so that the p.g.f. of (6.3) is the product of the p.g.f.'s of $\{P_{\alpha\alpha}^{(m)}(0, \tau)\}$ and $\{P_{\alpha\alpha}^{(m)}(\tau, t)\}$, or

$$g_{\alpha\alpha}(s; \tau) g_{\alpha\alpha}(s; t - \tau). \tag{6.4}$$

Similarly, the p.g.f. of the sequence in the second sum in (6.1)

$$\sum_{l=1}^{m} P_{\alpha\beta}^{(l)}(0, \tau) P_{\beta\alpha}^{(m-l+1)}(\tau, t) \tag{6.5}$$

is the product of the p.g.f.'s of $\{P_{\alpha\beta}^{(m)}(0, \tau)\}$ and $\{P_{\beta\alpha}^{(m)}(\tau, t)\}$. Making adjustments for the power of s, we see that the p.g.f. of (6.5) is equal to

$$\frac{1}{s} g_{\alpha\beta}(s; \tau) g_{\beta\alpha}(s; t - \tau). \tag{6.6}$$

In order for equation (6.1) to hold for all $m = 0, 1, \ldots$, it is necessary and sufficient that the p.g.f. of the sequence $\{P_{\alpha\alpha}^{(m)}(0, t)\}$ in (6.1) equal the sum of the products in (6.4) and (6.6); i.e., that

$$g_{\alpha\alpha}(s; t) = g_{\alpha\alpha}(s; \tau) g_{\alpha\alpha}(s; t - \tau) + \frac{1}{s} g_{\alpha\beta}(s; \tau) g_{\beta\alpha}(s; t - \tau). \tag{6.7}$$

Substituting (4.7) and (4.8) for the p.g.f.'s in (6.7) gives

$$\sum_{i=1}^{2} \frac{\rho_i - \nu_{\beta\beta}}{\rho_i - \rho_j} e^{\rho_i t} = \left\{ \sum_{i=1}^{2} \frac{\rho_i - \nu_{\beta\beta}}{\rho_i - \rho_j} e^{\rho_i \tau} \right\} \left\{ \sum_{i=1}^{2} \frac{\rho_i - \nu_{\beta\beta}}{\rho_i - \rho_j} e^{\rho_i (t-\tau)} \right\}$$

$$+ \left\{ \sum_{i=1}^{2} \frac{\nu_{\alpha\beta}}{\rho_i - \rho_j} e^{\rho_i \tau} \right\} \left\{ \sum_{i=1}^{2} \frac{s\nu_{\beta\alpha}}{\rho_i - \rho_j} e^{\rho_i (t-\tau)} \right\}. \quad (6.8)$$

We can use the proof of equation (3.2), Chapter 11, to verify equation (6.8). Therefore, the multiple transition probabilities in (4.15) and (4.17), also those in (2.10) and (2.27), satisfy equation (6.1).

Likewise, for equation (6.2) to hold for all $m = 1, 2, \ldots$, it is necessary and sufficient that the corresponding p.g.f.'s satisfy the equation

$$g_{\alpha\beta}(s; t) = g_{\alpha\alpha}(s; \tau) g_{\alpha\beta}(s; t - \tau) + g_{\alpha\beta}(s; \tau) g_{\beta\beta}(s; t - \tau). \quad (6.9)$$

Verification of (6.9) is left to the reader.

7. CONDITIONAL PROBABILITY DISTRIBUTION OF THE NUMBER OF TRANSITIONS

If, in deriving multiple transition probabilities, we consider only those journeys having a specified ending state as well as a specified starting state, then the corresponding numbers of transitions are proper random variables. Let $\mathring{M}_{\alpha\beta}(0, t)$ be the number of transitions that a person makes from S_α to S_β during $(0, t)$, given that the individual starts in S_α at time 0 and ends in S_β at time t, and let

$$\Pr\{\mathring{M}_{\alpha\beta}(0, t) = m\} = \mathring{P}^{(m)}_{\alpha\beta}(0, t) \qquad m = 0, 1, \ldots, \quad (7.1)$$

be the corresponding probability. Because we assume that the individual will be in S_β at time t, (7.1) is a conditional probability for which

$$\mathring{P}^{(m)}_{\alpha\beta}(0, t) = P^{(m)}_{\alpha\beta}(0, t) / P_{\alpha\beta}(0, t), \quad (7.2)$$

and

$$\sum_{m=0}^{\infty} \mathring{P}^{(m)}_{\alpha\beta}(0, t) = 1. \quad (7.3)$$

Thus $\mathring{M}_{\alpha\beta}(0, t)$ is a proper random variable.

The probability $\mathring{P}^{(m)}_{\alpha\beta}(0, t)$ is the theoretical equivalent of the proportion of people, starting in S_α at 0 and ending in S_β at t, who make m transitions from S_α to S_β. The sum of the proportions for all possible values of m must equal one. It is meaningful here to determine the expected value and variance of $\mathring{M}_{\alpha\beta}(0, t)$. They are most easily obtained from the derivatives of the corresponding p.g.f.'s in (4.7) and (4.8). For example, the expected values are

$$E[\mathring{M}_{\alpha\beta}(0, t)] = 1 + \frac{\nu_{\alpha\beta}\nu_{\beta\alpha}t}{\rho_1 - \rho_2}\left\{\frac{e^{\rho_1 t} + e^{\rho_2 t}}{e^{\rho_1 t} - e^{\rho_2 t}}\right\} - \frac{2\nu_{\alpha\beta}\nu_{\beta\alpha}}{(\rho_1 - \rho_2)^2} \tag{7.4}$$

for $\alpha \neq \beta$, and

$$E[\mathring{M}_{\alpha\alpha}(0, t)] = \frac{\nu_{\alpha\beta}\nu_{\beta\alpha}t}{\rho_1 - \rho_2} + \frac{\nu_{\alpha\beta}\nu_{\beta\alpha}(\nu_{\alpha\alpha} - \nu_{\beta\beta})}{P_{\alpha\alpha}(0, t)(\rho_1 - \rho_2)^2} \times \left\{\left(1 - \frac{\rho_1 - \rho_2}{\nu_{\alpha\alpha} - \nu_{\beta\beta}}\right) te^{\rho_2 t} - \frac{e^{\rho_1 t} - e^{\rho_2 t}}{\rho_1 - \rho_2}\right\} \tag{7.5}$$

for $\beta = \alpha$, where ρ_1 and ρ_2 are as given in (4.6) with $s = 1$, and $P_{\alpha\alpha}(0, t)$ as in (4.19).

8. MULTIPLE TRANSITIONS LEADING TO DEATH

The probabilities for multiple transitions leading to death are defined by

$$Q_{\alpha\delta}^{(m)}(0, t) = \Pr\{\text{an individual in } S_\alpha \text{ at time 0 will leave } S_\alpha\ m \text{ times during } (0, t) \text{ and will be in } R_\delta \text{ at } t\}, \tag{8.1}$$

for $\alpha = 1, 2$; $\delta = 1, \ldots, r$; $m = 1, 2, \ldots$. The corresponding random variable, denoted by $D_{\alpha\delta}(t)$, is the number of times the individual leaves S_α before reaching R_δ sometime during $(0, t)$, so that

$$Q_{\sigma\delta}^{(m)}(0, t) = \Pr\{D_{\alpha\delta}(0, t) = m\}. \tag{8.2}$$

An individual in S_α may reach R_δ directly from S_α or by way of S_β during some interval $(\tau, \tau + d\tau)$, where $0 \leq \tau \leq t$. The corresponding probabilities are respectively

$$P_{\alpha\alpha}^{(m-1)}(0, \tau)\mu_{\alpha\delta}d\tau \qquad \text{and} \qquad p_{\alpha\beta}^{(m)}(0, \tau)\mu_{\beta\delta}d\tau.$$

For different values of τ, for $0 \leq \tau \leq t$, the corresponding sequences of events are distinct. The addition theorem implies that

$$Q_{\alpha\delta}^{(m)}(0, t) = \int_0^t P_{\alpha\alpha}^{(m-1)}(0, \tau)\mu_{\alpha\delta}d\tau + \int_0^t P_{\alpha\beta}^{(m)}(0, \tau)\mu_{\beta\delta}d\tau. \tag{8.3}$$

Explicit formulas for $Q_{\alpha\delta}^{(m)}(0, t)$ can be obtained by substituting into (8.3) equation (2.10) for $P_{\alpha\beta}^{(m)}(0, \tau)$ and equation (2.27) for $P_{\alpha\alpha}^{(m-1)}(0, \tau)$.

9. MULTIPLE ENTRANCE TRANSITION PROBABILITIES $P_{\alpha\beta}^{(n)}(0, t)$

The random variable $M_{\alpha\beta}(0, t)$ associated with the transition probabilities $P_{\alpha\beta}^{(m)}(0, t)$ is the number of times an individual *leaves* S_α during interval $(0, t)$. Alternatively, we may consider the number of times an individual *enters* S_β during $(0, t)$. We denote this random variable by $N_{\alpha\beta}(0, t)$ and its probability distribution by $p_{\alpha\beta}^{(n)}(0, t)$, i.e.,

$$\begin{aligned} p_{\alpha\beta}^{(n)}(0, t) &= \Pr\{N_{\alpha\beta}(0, t) = n\} \\ &= \Pr\{\text{an individual in } S_\alpha \text{ at 0 will } \textit{enter } S_\beta\ n \text{ times} \\ &\qquad \text{during } (0, t) \text{ and will be in } S_\beta \text{ at } t\}, \end{aligned} \tag{9.1}$$

$\alpha, \beta = 1, 2$; $n = 0, 1, \ldots$.

As the entrance transition into S_β is conceptually different from the exit transition out of S_α, generally the random variable $N_{\alpha\beta}(0, t)$ has a probability distribution different from $M_{\alpha\beta}(0, t)$, as we shall see in Chapter 16. In the case of two transient states, however, an individual who exits from one transient state must immediately enter another; therefore the number of exit transitions $M_{\alpha\beta}(0, t)$ and the number of entrance transitions $N_{\alpha\beta}(0, t)$ have the same probability distributions. In this section we derive the p.g.f.'s of $p_{\alpha\beta}^{(n)}(0, t)$ and show that they are the same as the p.g.f.'s of $P_{\alpha\beta}^{(m)}(0, t)$.

In section 3 we obtained differential equations for the exit transition probabilities $P_{\alpha\beta}^{(m)}(0, t)$ by considering the contiguous intervals $(0, t)$ and $(t, t + \Delta)$. While the same method applies to entrance transition probabilities here, we take a "backward" approach, considering the intervals $(0, \Delta)$ and $(\Delta, t + \Delta)$. Since the intensity functions $\nu_{\alpha\beta}$ are independent of time, the entrance probabilities $p_{\alpha\beta}^{(n)}(0, t)$ are also time homogeneous and

$$p_{\alpha\beta}^{(n)}(0 + \Delta, t + \Delta) = p_{\alpha\beta}^{(n)}(0, t) \tag{9.2}$$

whatever Δ may be. By enumerating all the possible events during the intervals $(0, \Delta)$ and $(\Delta, t + \Delta)$, we find that

$$p_{\alpha\beta}^{(n)}(0, t + \Delta) = (1 + \nu_{\alpha\alpha}\Delta)p_{\alpha\beta}^{(n)}(0, t) + \nu_{\alpha\beta}\Delta p_{\beta\beta}^{(n-1)}(0, t)$$

and

$$p_{\beta\beta}^{(n)}(0, t + \Delta) = \nu_{\beta\alpha}\Delta p_{\alpha\beta}^{(n)}(0, t) + (1 + \nu_{\beta\beta}\Delta)p_{\beta\beta}^{(n)}(0, t),$$

$$\alpha \neq \beta. \qquad (9.3)$$

Forming difference quotients and letting $\Delta \to 0$, we obtain from (9.3) the differential equations

$$\frac{d}{dt}p_{\alpha\beta}^{(n)}(0, t) = \nu_{\alpha\alpha}p_{\alpha\beta}^{(n)}(0, t) + \nu_{\alpha\beta}p_{\beta\beta}^{(n-1)}(0, t)$$

and

$$\frac{d}{dt}p_{\beta\beta}^{(n)}(0, t) = \nu_{\beta\alpha}p_{\alpha\beta}^{(n)}(0, t) + \nu_{\beta\beta}p_{\beta\beta}^{(n)}(0, t),$$

$$\alpha \neq \beta;\ \alpha, \beta = 1, 2. \qquad (9.4)$$

Introducing (9.4) into the derivatives of the p.g.f.'s

$$g_{\alpha\beta}(s; t) = \sum_{n=1}^{\infty} s^n p_{\alpha\beta}^{(n)}(0, t)$$

and

$$g_{\beta\beta}(s; t) = \sum_{n=0}^{\infty} s^n p_{\beta\beta}^{(n)}(0, t),$$

we find that the p.g.f.'s satisfy the partial differential equations

$$\frac{\partial}{\partial t}g_{\alpha\beta}(s; t) = \nu_{\alpha\alpha}g_{\alpha\beta}(s; t) + \nu_{\alpha\beta}sg_{\beta\beta}(s; t), \qquad (9.5)$$

and

$$\frac{\partial}{\partial t}g_{\beta\beta}(s; t) = \nu_{\beta\alpha}g_{\alpha\beta}(s; t) + \nu_{\beta\beta}g_{\beta\beta}(s; t) \qquad (9.6)$$

with the initial conditions at $t = 0$

$$g_{\alpha\beta}(s; 0) = 0$$

$$g_{\beta\beta}(s; 0) = 1. \qquad (9.7)$$

Proceeding as we did to solve the system in (4.2) and (4.3), we obtain the following solutions of equations (9.5) and (9.6):

$$g_{\alpha\beta}(s;\,t) = \sum_{i=1}^{2} \frac{s\nu_{\alpha\beta}}{\rho_i - \rho_j}\, e^{\rho_i t} \tag{9.8}$$

$$g_{\beta\beta}(s;\,t) = \sum_{i=1}^{2} \frac{\rho_i - \nu_{\alpha\alpha}}{\rho_i - \rho_j}\, e^{\rho_i t}, \qquad j \neq i; \quad \alpha \neq \beta;\ \alpha,\ \beta = 1,\ 2, \tag{9.9}$$

where ρ_1 and ρ_2 are given in (4.6). The formulas in (9.8) and (9.9) are identical to the corresponding p.g.f.'s of the multiple exit transition probabilities $P_{\alpha\beta}^{(m)}(0,\,t)$ in (4.7) and (4.8). Therefore, $N_{\alpha\beta}(0,\,t)$ has the same probability distribution as $M_{\alpha\beta}(0,\,t)$.

10. PROBLEMS FOR SOLUTION

1. Prove that given two integers m and N, with $m < N$, we have

$$\binom{N}{m} = \binom{N-1}{m-1} + \binom{N-2}{m-1} + \dots + \binom{m-1}{m-1} \tag{2.15}$$

and

$$\binom{2m}{m} = 2\left[\binom{2m-2}{m-1} + \binom{2M-3}{m-1} + \dots + \binom{m-1}{m-1}\right]. \tag{2.16}$$

2. Simplify the coefficient of $e^{\nu_{\beta\beta} t}$ in equation (2.21) as follows:

$$\sum_{k=0}^{m-1} \binom{2m-2-k}{m-1}\left\{2 + \sum_{i=1}^{k+1} \frac{(-\Delta t)^i}{i!}\right\} = \sum_{i=0}^{m} \binom{2m-i}{m} \frac{(\Delta t)^i}{i!}.$$

3. Derive the m-th multiple renewal probability from

$$P_{\alpha\alpha}^{(m)}(0,t) = \int_0^t P_{\alpha\beta}^{(m)}(0,\tau)\,\nu_{\beta\alpha}\,P_{\alpha\alpha}^{(0)}(\tau,t)\,d\tau \tag{2.28}$$

4. Use the formulas for the m-th passage probability in (2.10) and for the renewal probability in (2.27) to verify each of the following equations:

(a) $P_{12}^{(3)}(0,t) = \int_0^t P_{11}^{(1)}(0,\tau)\,\nu_{12}\,P_{22}^{(1)}(\tau,t)\,d\tau$

(b) $P_{12}^{(3)}(0,t) = \int_0^t P_{12}^{(2)}(0,\tau)\,\nu_{21}\,P_{12}^{(1)}(\tau,t)\,d\tau$

(c) $P_{11}^{(3)}(0,t) = \int_0^t P_{11}^{(1)}(0,\tau)\,\nu_{12}\,P_{21}^{(2)}(\tau,t)\,d\tau$

(d) $P_{22}^{(3)}(0,t) = \int_0^t P_{21}^{(2)}(0,\tau)\,\nu_{12}\,P_{22}^{(1)}(\tau,t)\,d\tau$

5. Solve the differential equation in (3.4) for $P_{\alpha\beta}^{(2)}(0,t)$ assuming the knowledge of $P_{\alpha\alpha}^{(1)}(0,t)$ in (3.9).

6. Solve the differential equation in (3.3) for $P_{\alpha\alpha}^{(2)}(0,t)$ assuming the knowledge of $P_{\alpha\beta}^{(2)}(0,t)$ derived in problem 5.

7. Solve the differential equation in (3.3) for the m-th renewal probability $P_{11}^{(m)}(0,t)$, assuming the formula in (2.10) for the m-th passage probability.

8. Solve the differential equation in (3.4) for the m-th passage probability $P_{12}^{(m)}(0,t)$, assuming the formula in (2.27) for the $(m-1)$th renewal probability.

9. Solve the partial differential equations in (4.2) and (4.3) for the p.g.f. $g_{12}(s;t)$ and $g_{11}(s;t)$.

10. Derive the formula for the m-th renewal probability in (4.17) from the p.g.f.

$$g_{\alpha\alpha}(s;t) = \sum_{i=1}^{2} \frac{(\rho_i - \nu_{\beta\beta})}{\rho_i - \rho_j} e^{\rho_i t}, \qquad j \neq i;\ \alpha \neq \beta;\ \alpha, \beta = 1, 2. \tag{4.8}$$

11. Show that the m-th passage probability in (2.10) satisfies the following equation

$$\sum_{m=1}^{\infty} P_{\alpha\beta}^{(m)}(0,t) = \sum_{i=1}^{2} \frac{\nu_{\alpha\beta}}{\rho_i - \rho_j} e^{\rho_i t}. \tag{4.18}$$

12. Show that the m-th renewal probability in (2.27) satisfies the following equation:

$$\sum_{m=0}^{\infty} P_{\alpha\alpha}^{(m)}(0,t) = \sum_{i=1}^{2} \frac{\rho_i - \nu_{\beta\beta}}{\rho_i - \rho_j} e^{\rho_i t}. \tag{4.19}$$

13. Let $m = 1$ in (4.15) and show that the resulting formula is the same as the first passage probability in (2.8a).

14. Let $m = 2$ in (4.15) and show that the resulting formula is the same as the second passage probability in (2.9).

15. Prove the equality of the two formulas in (2.10) and (4.15) for the m-th passage probability $P_{\alpha\beta}^{(m)}(0,t)$.

16. Let $m = 1$ in (4.17) and show that the resulting formula is the same as the first renewal probability in (2.29).

17. Let $m = 2$ in (4.17) and show that the resulting formula is the same as the second renewal probability in (2.30).

18. Prove the equality of the two formulas in (2.27) and (4.17) for the m-th renewal probability $P_{\alpha\alpha}^{(m)}(0,t)$.

19. Verify the equality in (5.2).

20. Use the three identifies in (5.1), (5.3) and (5.4) to show that the formulas for $P_{\alpha\beta}^{(m)}(0,t)$ in (4.15) and for $P_{\alpha\alpha}^{(m)}(0,t)$ in (4.17) satisfy each of the following identities:

(a) $$P_{\alpha\beta}^{(m)}(0,t)=\int_0^t P_{\alpha\alpha}^{(l)}(0,\tau)\,\nu_{\alpha\beta}\,P_{\beta\beta}^{(m-l-1)}(\tau,t)\,d\tau \qquad (2.2a)$$

(b) $$P_{\alpha\alpha}^{(m)}(0,t)=\int_0^t P_{\alpha\alpha}^{(l)}(0,\tau)\,\nu_{\alpha\beta}\,P_{\beta\alpha}^{(m-l)}(\tau,t)\,d\tau \qquad (2.4a)$$

(c) $$P_{\alpha\alpha}^{(m)}(0,t)=\int_0^t P_{\alpha\beta}^{(l)}(0,\tau)\,\nu_{\beta\alpha}\,P_{\alpha\alpha}^{(m-l)}(\tau,t)\,d\tau \qquad (2.5a)$$

21. Show that the formulas in (2.10) and (2.27) satisfy the equations:

(a) $$P_{\alpha\alpha}^{(1)}(0,t)=\sum_{l=0}^{1} P_{\alpha\alpha}^{(l)}(0,\tau)P_{\alpha\alpha}^{(1-l)}(\tau,t)+P_{\alpha\beta}^{(1)}(0,\tau)P_{\beta\alpha}^{(1)}(\tau,t)$$

(b) $$P_{\alpha\alpha}^{(2)}(0,t)=\sum_{l=0}^{2} P_{\alpha\alpha}^{(l)}(0,\tau)P_{\alpha\alpha}^{(2-l)}(\tau,t)+\sum_{l=1}^{2} P_{\alpha\beta}^{(l)}(0,\tau)P_{\beta\alpha}^{(3-l)}(\tau,t)$$

(c) $$P_{\alpha\alpha}^{(m)}(0,t)=\sum_{l=0}^{m} P_{\alpha\alpha}^{(l)}(0,\tau)P_{\alpha\alpha}^{(m-l)}(\tau,t)+\sum_{l=1}^{m} P_{\alpha\beta}^{(l)}(0,\tau)P_{\beta\alpha}^{(m-l+1)}(\tau,t).$$

(6.1)

22. Show that the formulas in (2.10) and (2.27) satisfy the equations

(a) $$P_{\alpha\beta}^{(1)}(0,t)=P_{\alpha\alpha}^{(0)}(0,\tau)P_{\alpha\beta}^{(1)}(\tau,t)+P_{\alpha\beta}^{(1)}(0,\tau)P_{\beta\beta}^{(0)}(\tau,t)$$

(b) $$P_{\alpha\beta}^{(2)}(0,t)=\sum_{l=0}^{1} P_{\alpha\alpha}^{(l)}(0,\tau)P_{\alpha\beta}^{(2-l)}(\tau,t)+\sum_{l=1}^{2} P_{\alpha\beta}^{(l)}(0,\tau)P_{\beta\beta}^{(2-l)}(\tau,t)$$

(c) $$P_{\alpha\beta}^{(m)}(0,t)=\sum_{l=0}^{m-1} P_{\alpha\alpha}^{(l)}(0,\tau)P_{\alpha\beta}^{(m-l)}(\tau,t)+\sum_{l=1}^{m} P_{\alpha\beta}^{(l)}(0,\tau)P_{\beta\beta}^{(m-l)}(\tau,t)$$

(6.2)

23. Find the expectation $E[\mathring{M}_{\alpha\beta}(0,t)]$ from the p.g.f. in (4.7).

24. Find the expectation $E[\mathring{M}_{\alpha\alpha}(0,t)]$ from the p.g.f. in (4.8).

25. Let $Q_{\alpha\delta\cdot\alpha}^{(m)}(0,t)$ be the probability that an individual who is in S_α at time 0 will leave S_α m times during the interval $(0,t)$ and enter the absorbing state R_δ from S_α. Derive this probability from

$$Q_{\alpha\delta\cdot\alpha}^{(m)}(0,t)=\int_0^t P_{\alpha\alpha}^{(m-1)}(0,\tau)\,\mu_{\alpha\delta}\,d\tau$$

where the $(m-1)$th renewal probability $P_{\alpha\alpha}^{(m-1)}(0,\tau)$ is given in (2.27).

26. Let $Q_{\alpha\delta\cdot\beta}^{(m)}(0,t)$ be the probability that an individual who is in S_α at time 0 will leave S_α m times during the interval $(0,t)$ and enter R_δ from S_β. Derive this probability from

$$Q^{(m)}_{\alpha\delta\cdot\beta}(0,t) = \int_0^t P^{(m)}_{\alpha\beta}(0,\tau)\mu_{\beta\delta}\,d\tau$$

where the m-th passage probability $P^{(m)}_{\alpha\beta}(0,\tau)$ is given in (2.10).

27. Let the p.g.f.'s of $Q^{(m)}_{\alpha\delta\cdot\alpha}(0,t)$ and $Q^{(m)}_{\alpha\delta\cdot\beta}(0,t)$ be defined by

$$h_{\alpha\delta\cdot\alpha}(s;t) = \sum_{m=1}^{\infty} s^m Q^{(m)}_{\alpha\delta\cdot\alpha}(0,t)$$

and

$$h_{\alpha\delta\cdot\beta}(s;t) = \sum_{m=1}^{\infty} s^m Q^{(m)}_{\alpha\delta\cdot\beta}(0,t)$$

Derive explicit formulas for the two p.g.f.'s.

28. Interpret the following two sums of probabilities:

$$Q_{\alpha\delta\cdot\alpha}(0,t) = \sum_{m=1}^{\infty} Q^{(m)}_{\alpha\delta\cdot\alpha}(0,t)$$

and

$$Q_{\alpha\delta\cdot\beta}(0,t) = \sum_{m=1}^{\infty} Q^{(m)}_{\alpha\delta\cdot\alpha}(0,t).$$

Find these probabilities.

29. Derive four identities similar to (2.2a), (2.3a), (2.4a), and (2.5a) for the multiple entrance transition in formula (9.1).

30. Derive the probabilities $P^{(0)}_{\alpha\alpha}(0,t)$ and the m-th passage probability $P^{(m)}_{\alpha\beta}(0,t)$ using the identity

$$P^{(m)}_{\alpha\beta}(0,t) = \int_0^t P^{(l)}_{\alpha\beta}(0,\tau)\nu_{\beta\alpha}P^{(m-l)}_{\alpha\beta}(\tau,t)\,d\tau$$

for $\alpha \neq \beta$, $\alpha, \beta = 1, 2$ for each of the following sets of intensity functions

(i) $\nu_{11} = -.3$, $\nu_{12} = .1$; $\nu_{21} = .4$, and $\nu_{22} = -.6$

(ii) $\nu_{11} = -.4$, $\nu_{12} = .2$; $\nu_{21} = .4$, and $\nu_{22} = -.6$

(iii) $\nu_{11} = -.5$, $\nu_{12} = .3$; $\nu_{21} = .4$, and $\nu_{22} = -.6$

(iv) $\nu_{11} = -.8$, $\nu_{12} = .6$; $\nu_{21} = .4$, and $\nu_{22} = -.6$.

Show that the sums

$$\sum_{m=0}^{\infty} P^{(m)}_{\alpha\alpha}(0,t) = P_{\alpha\alpha}(0,t), \qquad \alpha = 1, 2,$$

are equal to the corresponding probabilities obtained in problems 27 and 28 in Chapter 11.

31. Derive the m-th renewal probability $P_{\alpha\alpha}^{(m)}(0,t)$ using the identity

$$P_{\alpha\alpha}^{(m)}(0,t) = \int_0^t P_{\alpha\alpha}^{(1)}(0,\tau)\,\nu_{\alpha\beta}\,P_{\beta\alpha}^{(m-1)}(\tau,t)\,d\tau$$

for $\alpha \neq \beta$; α, $\beta = 1, 2$, for each of the four sets of intensity functions in problem 30. Show that the sums

$$\sum_{m=0}^{\infty} P_{\alpha\alpha}^{(m)}(0,t) = P_{\alpha\alpha}(0,t), \qquad \alpha = 1, 2$$

are equal to the corresponding probabilities obtained in problem 27 and 28 in Chapter 11.

32. Solve the following system of differential equations for each of the four sets of intensity functions in problem 30,

$$\frac{d}{dt} P_{11}^{(m)}(0,t) = P_{11}^{(m)}(0,t)\,\nu_{11} + P_{12}^{(m)}(0,t)\,\nu_{21}$$

$$\frac{d}{dt} P_{12}^{(m)}(0,t) = P_{11}^{(m-1)}(0,t)\,\nu_{12} + P_{12}^{(m)}(0,t)\,\nu_{22}.$$

33. Solve the following system of differential equations for each of the four sets of intensity functions in problem 30,

$$\frac{d}{dt} P_{22}^{(m)}(0,t) = P_{22}^{(m)}(0,t)\,\nu_{22} + P_{21}^{(m)}(0,t)\,\nu_{12}$$

$$\frac{d}{dt} P_{21}^{(m)}(0,t) = P_{22}^{(m-1)}(0,t)\,\nu_{21} + P_{21}^{(m)}(0,t)\,\nu_{11}.$$

34. Solve the following system of partial differential equations for the p.g.f.'s for each of the four sets of intensity functions in problem 30,

$$\frac{\partial}{\partial t} g_{11}(s;t) = g_{11}(s;t)\,\nu_{11} + g_{12}(s;t)\,\nu_{21}$$

$$\frac{\partial}{\partial t} g_{12}(s;t) = g_{11}(s;t)\,s\nu_{12} + g_{12}(s;t)\,\nu_{22}.$$

Compute from the p.g.f.'s the probabilities $P_{11}^{(m)}(0,t)$, $P_{12}^{(m)}(0,t)$, $P_{11}(0,t)$, and $P_{12}(0,t)$.

35. Solve the following system of partial differential equations for the p.g.f.'s for each of the four sets of intensity functions in problem 30.

$$\frac{\partial}{\partial t} g_{22}(s;t) = g_{22}(s;t)\nu_{22} + g_{21}(s;t)\nu_{12}$$

$$\frac{\partial}{\partial t} g_{21}(s;t) = g_{22}(s;t)s\nu_{21} + g_{21}(s;t)\nu_{11}.$$

Compute from the p.g.f.'s the probabilities $P_{21}^{(m)}(0,t)$, $P_{22}^{(m)}(0,t)$, $P_{21}(0,t)$ and $P_{22}(0,t)$.

36. Show that the multiple transition probabilities obtained in problems 30 through 35 satisfy the Chapman-Kolmogorov equations in (6.1).

37. Show that the multiple transition probabilities obtained in problems 30 through 35 satisfy the Chapman-Kolmogorov equations in (6.2).

38. For each of the following four sets of intensity functions and using the multiple transition probabilities obtained in problems 30 and 31 compute the probabilities $Q_\alpha^{(m)}(0,t)$ in equation (8.3),

(i) $\nu_{11} = -.3$, $\nu_{12} = .1$, $\mu_1 = .2$; $\nu_{21} = .4$, $\nu_{22} = -.6$ and $\mu_2 = .2$

(ii) $\nu_{11} = -.4$, $\nu_{12} = .2$, $\mu_1 = .2$; $\nu_{21} = .4$, $\nu_{22} = -.6$ and $\mu_2 = .2$

(iii) $\nu_{11} = -.5$, $\nu_{12} = .3$, $\mu_1 = .2$; $\nu_{21} = .4$, $\nu_{22} = -.6$ and $\mu_2 = .2$

(iv) $\nu_{11} = -.8$, $\nu_{13} = .6$, $\mu_1 = .2$; $\nu_{21} = .4$, $\nu_{22} = -.6$ and $\mu_2 = .2$

Verify that for each set of values, the sum

$$\sum_{m=0}^{\infty} Q_\alpha^{(m)}(0,t) = Q_\alpha(0,t) \qquad \alpha = 1, 2$$

is equal to the probability $Q_\alpha(0,t)$ obtained in problems 27 and 28 in Chapter 11.

Discuss the numerical results in problems from 30 to 38 according to the increasing values of ν_{12}: .1, .2, .3, and .6.

CHAPTER 13

Multiple Transition Time in the Simple Illness-Death Process—An Alternating Renewal Process

1. INTRODUCTION

In the discussion of multiple transition probabilities in Chapter 12, we treated the number of transitions as a random variable and the length of time as a constant. Our findings acquire new significance when we consider the length of time required for a given number of transitions as a random variable. While the two approaches are conceptually related, the perspective of the process given in this chapter has practical importance. In evaluating the prognosis of an illness, for example, we might inquire how long it takes a patient to return to good health, or how long before a second episode occurs. Clearly, in such investigations, the length of time interval is a random variable.

In a time homogeneous illness-death process where the intensity functions are independent of time, transitions from one health state to another and back to the original state constitute a renewal. For example, starting from S_1, a sequence of transitions $S_1 \to S_2 \to S_1$ constitutes a renewal because after returning to S_1 the system starts afresh. The sequence $S_1 \to S_2 \to S_1 \to S_2 \to S_1$ is also a renewal, which also embeds a renewal $S_2 \to S_1 \to S_2$. Generally, renewals of the types $S_1 \to S_2 \to S_1$ and $S_2 \to S_1 \to S_2$ alternate in a sequence of transitions. Therefore the process is called an alternating renewal process. A process terminates as soon as the system enters an absorbing state.

The difference between the present model and the ordinary renewal process is the number of states. In the ordinary (time continuous) renewal process, there is only one state; immediately after leaving the state, the system re-enters the same state and the process starts all over again. In the present alternating renewal process with two transient states, once the system leaves a state, it must enter the other state, or an absorbing state; only a change of states is considered a transition. This version of the model is a special case of the general Markov renewal process where there is a countable number of states and a sequence of transitions from one state to another form a Markov chain. For a comprehensive description of the general model and some theoretical findings, the reader may consult Pike [1961a, 1961b], Chung [1960], and Takács [1954].

In the first part of this chapter, we shall be concerned with the model having two transient states S_1 and S_2 and a given number of absorbing states $R_1, \ldots, R_r$. The intensity functions, as before, are $\nu_{12}(S_1 \to S_2)$, $\nu_{21}(S_2 \to S_1)$, $\mu_{1\delta}$ $(S_1 \to R_\delta)$ and $\mu_{2\delta}$ $(S_2 \to R_\delta)$; and again

$$\nu_{11} = -(\nu_{12} + \mu_{11} + \ldots + \mu_{1r})$$

and

$$\nu_{22} = -(\nu_{21} + \mu_{21} + \ldots + \mu_{2r}). \tag{1.1}$$

In Section 6 we shall study alternating renewals in a two-state model with no absorbing states.

2. DENSITY FUNCTIONS OF MULTIPLE TRANSITION TIMES

Consider an individual in state S_α at time $t = 0$. Let a random variable $T_{\alpha\alpha}^{(m)}$ be the length of time up to the m-th renewal of the type $S_\alpha \to S_\beta \to S_\alpha$, and let $T_{\alpha\beta}^{(m)}$ be the length of time up to the m-th transition $S_\alpha \to S_\beta$. For every $m = 0, 1, \ldots$, $T_{\alpha\alpha}^{(m)}$ and $T_{\alpha\beta}^{(m)}$ take on non-negative real numbers. We will call $T_{\alpha\alpha}^{(m)}$ the m-th renewal time and $T_{\alpha\beta}^{(m)}$ the m-th passage time. A simple example is $m = 1$: $T_{\alpha\alpha}^{(1)}$ is the first renewal time and $T_{\alpha\beta}^{(1)}$ is the first passage time. If S_1 stands for the healthy state and S_2 for the illness state, then $T_{12}^{(1)}$ is the length of time a person enjoys good health before an illness occurs, and $T_{21}^{(1)}$ is the time needed to recover from an illness. In this chapter we shall assume in all the formulas that $\alpha \neq \beta$.

Let $f_{\alpha\alpha}^{(m)}(t)$ and $f_{\alpha\beta}^{(m)}(t)$ be the density functions of $T_{\alpha\alpha}^{(m)}$ and $T_{\alpha\beta}^{(m)}$ respectively. They can be derived from the multiple transition probabilities presented in Chapter 12. For the m-th renewal time $T_{\alpha\alpha}^{(m)}$, let us consider two contiguous time intervals $(0, t)$ and $(t, t + dt)$.

By the definition of a density function,

$$f_{\alpha\alpha}^{(m)}(t)dt = \Pr\{t < T_{\alpha\alpha}^{(m)} \le t + dt\}. \tag{2.1}$$

On the other hand, an individual starting in state S_α at time 0 will make m transitions from S_α to S_β during the interval $(0, t)$ and then will exit from S_β and re-enter S_α within the interval $(t, t + dt)$. The probability corresponding to this sequence of transitions is

$$P_{\alpha\beta}^{(m)}(0, t)\nu_{\beta\alpha}dt. \tag{2.2}$$

The random variable $T_{\alpha\alpha}^{(m)}$ takes on values in the interval $(t, t + dt)$ if, and only if, the m-th return to S_α occurs in $(t, t + dt)$. Therefore, the two probabilities in (2.1) and (2.2) are equal; that is,

$$f_{\alpha\alpha}^{(m)}(t)dt = P_{\alpha\beta}^{(m)}(0, t)\nu_{\beta\alpha}dt. \tag{2.3}$$

Similarly, the density function of the m-th passage time has the following relationship with the $(m - 1)$-th renewal probability:

$$f_{\alpha\beta}^{(m)}(t)dt = P_{\alpha\alpha}^{(m-1)}(0, t)\nu_{\alpha\beta}dt. \tag{2.4}$$

Substituting equations (2.10) and (2.27) in Chapter 12 for $P_{\alpha\beta}^{(m)}(0, t)$ and $p_{\alpha\alpha}^{(m)}(0,t)$ in (2.3) and (2.4) respectively we get the density functions.

Theorem 1. *In a two transient state process, the density function of the m-th renewal time $T_{\alpha\alpha}^{(m)}$ and the density function of the m-th passage time $T_{\alpha\beta}^{(m)}$ are*

$$f_{\alpha\alpha}^{(m)}(t) = \frac{-(-\nu_{\alpha\beta}\nu_{\beta\alpha})^m}{\Delta^{2m-1}} \sum_{k=0}^{m-1} \binom{2m-k-2}{m-1} \frac{(\Delta t)^k}{k!} [(-1)^k e^{\nu_{\alpha\alpha} t} - e^{\nu_{\beta\beta} t}] \tag{2.5}$$

and

$$f_{\alpha\beta}^{(m)}(t) = \frac{(-\nu_{\alpha\beta}\nu_{\beta\alpha})^{m-1}\nu_{\alpha\beta}}{\Delta^{2m-2}} \left[\sum_{k=0}^{m-1} \binom{2m-k-3}{m-2} \frac{(-\Delta t)^k}{k!} e^{\nu_{\alpha\alpha} t} - \sum_{k=0}^{m-2} \binom{2m-k-3}{m-1} \frac{(\Delta t)^k}{k!} e^{\nu_{\beta\beta} t}\right]$$

$$\alpha \ne \beta;\ \alpha, \beta = 1, 2;\ m = 2, \ldots, \tag{2.6}$$

where $\Delta = \nu_{\alpha\alpha} - \nu_{\beta\beta}$.

When $m = 1$, we have the density functions of the first renewal time

$$f_{\alpha\alpha}^{(1)}(t) = \frac{\nu_{\alpha\beta}\nu_{\beta\alpha}}{\nu_{\alpha\alpha} - \nu_{\beta\beta}} [e^{\nu_{\alpha\alpha}t} - e^{\nu_{\beta\beta}t}], \tag{2.7}$$

and of the first passage time

$$f_{\alpha\beta}^{(1)}(t) = \nu_{\alpha\beta} e^{\nu_{\alpha\alpha}t}. \tag{2.8}$$

When $m = 2$, we have

$$f_{\alpha\alpha}^{(2)}(t) = \frac{(\nu_{\alpha\beta}\nu_{\beta\alpha})^2}{\Delta^3} [-2(e^{\nu_{\alpha\alpha}t} - e^{\nu_{\beta\beta}t}) + \Delta t(e^{\nu_{\alpha\alpha}t} + e^{\nu_{\beta\beta}t})] \tag{2.9}$$

and

$$f_{\alpha\beta}^{(2)}(t) = \frac{\nu_{\alpha\beta}^2\nu_{\beta\alpha}}{\Delta^2} [\Delta t e^{\nu_{\alpha\alpha}t} - (e^{\nu_{\alpha\alpha}t} - e^{\nu_{\beta\beta}t})]. \tag{2.10}$$

3. CONVOLUTION OF MULTIPLE TRANSITION TIME

It is intuitively clear that the sum of the first passage times $T_{\alpha\beta}^{(1)}$ and $T_{\beta\alpha}^{(1)}$ is equal to the first renewal time $T_{\alpha\alpha}^{(1)}$,

$$T_{\alpha\alpha}^{(1)} = T_{\alpha\beta}^{(1)} + T_{\beta\alpha}^{(1)}. \tag{3.1}$$

The two random variables on the right hand side of (3.1) are independently distributed. Therefore, the density function $f_{\alpha\alpha}^{(1)}(t)$ of $T_{\alpha\alpha}^{(1)}$ is a convolution of the density functions $f_{\alpha\beta}^{(1)}(t)$ and $f_{\beta\alpha}^{(1)}(t)$, or

$$f_{\alpha\alpha}^{(1)}(t) = \int_0^t f_{\alpha\beta}^{(1)}(\tau) f_{\beta\alpha}^{(1)}(t - \tau)\, d\tau. \tag{3.2}$$

Substituting (2.8) in (3.2), we obtain

$$\begin{aligned} f_{\alpha\alpha}^{(1)}(t) &= \int_0^t \nu_{\alpha\beta} e^{\nu_{\alpha\alpha}\tau} \nu_{\beta\alpha} e^{\nu_{\beta\beta}(t-\tau)}\, d\tau \\ &= \frac{\nu_{\alpha\beta}\nu_{\beta\alpha}}{\nu_{\alpha\alpha} - \nu_{\beta\beta}} [e^{\nu_{\alpha\alpha}t} - e^{\nu_{\beta\beta}t}]. \end{aligned} \tag{3.3}$$

Similarly, since

$$T_{\alpha\alpha}^{(2)} = T_{\alpha\alpha}^{(1)} + T_{\alpha\alpha}^{(1)}, \tag{3.4}$$

the convolutional relationship holds true:

$$f_{\alpha\alpha}^{(2)}(t) = \int_0^t f_{\alpha\alpha}^{(1)}(\tau) f_{\alpha\alpha}^{(1)}(t-\tau)\, d\tau, \tag{3.5}$$

or,

$$\{f_{\alpha\alpha}^{(2)}(t)\} = \{f_{\alpha\alpha}^{(1)}(t)\} * \{f_{\alpha\alpha}^{(1)}(t)\}. \tag{3.6}$$

In general, $T_{\alpha\alpha}^{(m)}$ is the sum of m first renewal times,

$$T_{\alpha\alpha}^{(m)} = T_{\alpha\alpha}^{(1)} + \ldots + T_{\alpha\alpha}^{(1)}, \tag{3.7}$$

so that $\{f_{\alpha\alpha}^{(m)}(t)\}$ is the m-fold convolution of $\{f_{\alpha\alpha}^{(1)}(t)\}$ with itself,

$$\{f_{\alpha\alpha}^{(m)}(t)\} = \{f_{\alpha\alpha}^{(1)}(t)\}^{m*}, \tag{3.8}$$

and formula (2.5) is the m-fold convolution of (2.7) with itself. In view of (3.2), we also have

$$\{f_{\alpha\alpha}^{(m)}(t)\} = [\{f_{\alpha\beta}^{(1)}(t)\} * \{f_{\beta\alpha}^{(1)}(t)\}]^{m*}. \tag{3.9}$$

Also for any fixed number l between 0 and m, the length of time $T_{\alpha\alpha}^{(m)}$ may be divided into two periods: $T_{\alpha\alpha}^{(l)}$ and $T_{\alpha\alpha}^{(m-l)}$. In each case,

$$f_{\alpha\alpha}^{(m)}(t) = \int_0^t f_{\alpha\alpha}^{(l)}(\tau) f_{\alpha\alpha}^{(m-l)}(t-\tau)\, d\tau. \tag{3.10}$$

Substituting (2.3) in (3.10) yields the equality

$$P_{\alpha\beta}^{(m)}(0, t) = \int_0^t P_{\alpha\beta}^{(l)}(0, \tau)\, \nu_{\beta\alpha} P_{\alpha\beta}^{(m-l)}(\tau, t)\, d\tau,$$

$$l = 1, \ldots, m-1, \tag{3.11}$$

which is the same as the identity in equation (2.3a), Chapter 12. Alternatively, one might decompose $T_{\alpha\alpha}^{(m)}$ as:

$$T_{\alpha\alpha}^{(m)} = T_{\alpha\beta}^{(l+1)} + T_{\beta\alpha}^{(m-l)} \tag{3.12}$$

with the corresponding density functions satisfying the equation

$$f_{\alpha\alpha}^{(m)}(t) = \int_0^t f_{\alpha\beta}^{(l+1)}(\tau) f_{\beta\alpha}^{(m-l)}(t-\tau)\, d\tau. \tag{3.13}$$

Substituting (2.3) and (2.4) in (3.13) yields

$$P_{\alpha\beta}^{(m)}(0, t) = \int_0^t P_{\alpha\alpha}^{(l)}(0, \tau)\nu_{\alpha\beta} P_{\beta\beta}^{(m-l-1)}(\tau, t)\,d\tau, \tag{3.14}$$

which is the same as the identity in equation (2.2a), Chapter 12.

The length of time $T_{\alpha\beta}^{(m)}$ also can be decomposed into its constituent parts in any meaningful way. For example, for every l, $0 \le l < m$,

$$T_{\alpha\beta}^{(m)} = T_{\alpha\alpha}^{(l)} + T_{\alpha\beta}^{(m-l)}, \tag{3.15}$$

so that

$$f_{\alpha\beta}^{(m)}(t) = \int_0^t f_{\alpha\alpha}^{(l)}(\tau) f_{\alpha\beta}^{(m-l)}(t-\tau)\,d\tau, \tag{3.16}$$

which leads to the identity

$$P_{\alpha\alpha}^{(m-1)}(t) = \int_0^t P_{\alpha\beta}^{(l)}(0, \tau)\nu_{\beta\alpha} P_{\alpha\alpha}^{(m-l-1)}(\tau, t)\,d\tau, \tag{3.17}$$

as in equation (2.5a), Chapter 12.

Also,

$$T_{\alpha\beta}^{(m)} = T_{\alpha\alpha}^{(m-1)} + T_{\alpha\beta}^{(1)}; \tag{3.18}$$

hence

$$f_{\alpha\beta}^{(m)}(t) = \int_0^t f_{\alpha\alpha}^{(m-1)}(\tau) f_{\alpha\beta}^{(1)}(t-\tau)\,d\tau. \tag{3.19}$$

Therefore, the density function $f_{\alpha\beta}^{(m)}(t)$ of the m-th passage time can be derived from the density function $f_{\alpha\alpha}^{(m-1)}(t)$. On the other hand

$$T_{\alpha\alpha}^{(m)} = T_{\alpha\beta}^{(m)} + T_{\beta\alpha}^{(1)}, \tag{3.20}$$

and

$$f_{\alpha\alpha}^{(m)}(t) = \int_0^t f_{\alpha\beta}^{(m)}(\tau) f_{\beta\alpha}^{(1)}(t-\tau)\,d\tau. \tag{3.21}$$

Therefore, the density function $f_{\alpha\alpha}^{(m)}(t)$ of the m-th renewal time may be derived from $f_{\alpha\beta}^{(m)}(t)$. This shows that, starting with $f_{\alpha\beta}^{(1)}(t)$ in (2.8) one may use alternately (3.19) and (3.21) to obtain explicit formulas for the density functions of $T_{\alpha\alpha}^{(m)}$ and $T_{\alpha\beta}^{(m)}$.

4. DISTRIBUTION FUNCTIONS OF MULTIPLE TRANSITION TIMES

Before discussing the distribution functions, we first must establish two identities.

Lemma 1. *For any two non-zero real numbers p and q, with $p + q = 1$, and any positive integer m,*

$$\sum_{k=0}^{m-1} \binom{2m-k-2}{m-1} \left(\frac{1}{p^{k+1}} + \frac{1}{q^{k+1}} \right) = \frac{1}{p^m q^m}, \tag{4.1}$$

and

$$\sum_{k=0}^{m-1} \binom{2m-k-3}{m-2} \frac{1}{p^{k+1}} + \sum_{k=0}^{m-2} \binom{2m-k-3}{m-1} \frac{1}{q^{k+1}} = \frac{1}{p^m q^{m-1}}. \tag{4.2}$$

Proof. Formula (4.1) is obviously true for $m = 1$. Assuming it is true for m, we need to show that

$$\sum_{k=0}^{m} \binom{2m-k}{m} \left(\frac{1}{p^{k+1}} + \frac{1}{q^{k+1}} \right) = \frac{1}{p^{m+1} q^{m+1}}. \tag{4.3}$$

Let us rewrite (4.1) as follows:

$$\sum_{k=0}^{m-1} \binom{2m-k-2}{m-1} [p^{m-k-1} q^m + p^m q^{m-k-1}] = 1. \tag{4.4}$$

Equation (4.4) is assumed to hold for every p, therefore we can differentiate (4.4) with respect to p to obtain the equation

$$\sum_{k=0}^{m-1} \binom{2m-k-2}{m-1} [(m-k-1)p^{m-k-2} q^m - mp^{m-k-1} q^{m-1}$$
$$+ mp^{m-1} q^{m-k-1} - (m-k-1)p^m q^{m-k-2}] = 0. \tag{4.5}$$

Since

$$\binom{2m-k-2}{m-1} (m-k-1) = m \binom{2m-k-2}{m},$$

for $k = 0, 1, \ldots, m-2$, equation (4.5) becomes

$$\sum_{k=0}^{m-2}\binom{2m-k-2}{m}[p^{m-k-2}q^m - p^m q^{m-k-2}]$$
$$+\sum_{k=0}^{m-1}\binom{2m-k-2}{m-1}[p^{m-1}q^{m-k-1} - p^{m-k-1}q^{m-1}] = 0. \quad (4.6)$$

Equation (4.4) implies that

$$\sum_{k=0}^{m-1}\binom{2m-k-2}{m-1}p^{m-1}q^{m-k-1} = p^{-1} - \sum_{k=0}^{m-1}\binom{2m-k-2}{m-1}p^{m-k-2}q^m, \quad (4.7)$$

therefore we can also rewrite the second summation in (4.6)

$$p^{-1} - \sum_{k=0}^{m-1}\binom{2m-k-2}{m-1}[p^{m-k-2}q^m + p^{m-k-1}q^{m-1}]$$
$$= p^{-1} - \sum_{k=0}^{m-1}\binom{2m-k-2}{m-1}p^{m-k-2}q^{m-1}$$
$$= p^{-1} - \sum_{k=0}^{m-2}\left\{\binom{2m-k-1}{m} - \binom{2m-k-2}{m}\right\}q^{m-1} - p^{m-1}q^{m-1}$$
$$= p^{-1} - \sum_{k=0}^{m-1}\binom{2m-k-1}{m}p^{m-k-2}q^{m-1} + \sum_{k=0}^{m-2}\binom{2m-k-2}{m}p^{m-k-2}q^{m-1}$$
$$= p^{-1} - \sum_{k=1}^{m}\binom{2m-k}{m}p^{m-k-1}q^{m-1} + \sum_{k=2}^{m}\binom{2m-k}{m}p^{m-k}q^{m-1}$$
$$= p^{-1} - \binom{2m-1}{m}p^{m-2}q^{m-1}$$
$$- \sum_{k=2}^{m}\binom{2m-k}{m}[p^{m-k-1}q^{m-1} - p^{m-k}q^{m-1}]. \quad (4.8)$$

Substituting the last expression in (4.8) for the second summation in (4.6), and multiplying the resulting equation through by p, we find that

$$\sum_{k=2}^{m}\binom{2m-k}{m}[p^{m-k+1}q^m - p^{m+1}q^{m-k} - p^{m-k}q^{m-1} + p^{m-k+1}q^{m-1}]$$
$$+ 1 - \binom{2m-1}{m}p^{m-1}q^{m-1} = 0, \quad (4.9)$$

where

$$[p^{m-k+1}q^m - p^{m+1}q^{m-k} - p^{m-k}q^{m-1} + p^{m-k+1}q^{m-1}]$$
$$= -p^{m-k}q^{m+1} - p^{m+1}q^{m-k}$$

and

$$\binom{2m-1}{m}p^{m-1}q^{m-1} = \binom{2m}{m}[p^m q^{m+1} + p^{m+1}q^m]$$
$$+\binom{2m-1}{m}[p^{m-1}q^{m+1} + p^{m+1}q^{m-1}].$$

Equation (4.9) thus reduces to

$$-\sum_{k=0}^{m}\binom{2m-k}{m}[p^{m-k}q^{m+1} + p^{m+1}q^{m-k}] + 1 = 0, \quad (4.10)$$

which may be rewritten as (4.3). The inductive proof of equation (4.1) is complete.

Proof of (4.2) is similar.

4.1. Distribution Function of the *m*-th Renewal Time.

Theorem 2. *The distribution function of the m-th renewal time $T_{\alpha\alpha}^{(m)}$ is*

$$F_{\alpha\alpha}^{(m)}(t) = \frac{-(-\nu_{\alpha\beta}\nu_{\beta\alpha})^m}{\Delta^{2m}}\sum_{k=0}^{m-1}\binom{2m-k-2}{m-1}$$
$$\times\left[\left(\frac{\Delta}{\nu_{\alpha\alpha}}\right)^{k+1}\left\{\sum_{i=0}^{k}\frac{(-\nu_{\alpha\alpha}t)^i}{i!}e^{\nu_{\alpha\alpha}t} - 1\right\}\right.$$
$$\left.+\left(\frac{-\Delta}{\nu_{\beta\beta}}\right)^{k+1}\left\{\sum_{i=0}^{k}\frac{(-\nu_{\beta\beta}t)^i}{i!}e^{\nu_{\beta\beta}t} - 1\right\}\right], \quad (4.11)$$

where $\Delta = \nu_{\alpha\alpha} - \nu_{\beta\beta}$. As $t \to \infty$,

$$F_{\alpha\alpha}^{(m)}(\infty) = \left[\frac{\nu_{\alpha\beta}\nu_{\beta\alpha}}{\nu_{\alpha\alpha}\nu_{\beta\beta}}\right]^m, \quad (4.12)$$

which is less than 1. Therefore $T_{\alpha\alpha}^{(m)}$ is an improper random variable.

Proof. We can obtain the formula in (4.11) directly from the density function $f_{\alpha\alpha}^{(m)}(t)$ as derived in (2.5). To prove the second part of the theorem, we let $t \to \infty$ to get

$$F_{\alpha\alpha}^{(m)}(\infty) = \frac{(-\nu_{\alpha\beta}\nu_{\beta\alpha})^m}{\Delta^{2m}} \sum_{k=0}^{m-1} \binom{2m-k-2}{m-1} \left[\left(\frac{\Delta}{\nu_{\alpha\alpha}}\right)^{k+1} + \left(\frac{-\Delta}{\nu_{\beta\beta}}\right)^{k+1} \right]. \tag{4.13}$$

Formula (4.13) can be further simplified. We let

$$p = \frac{\nu_{\alpha\alpha}}{\Delta} \quad \text{and} \quad q = \frac{-\nu_{\beta\beta}}{\Delta}$$

and apply identity (4.1) to find the summation

$$\sum_{k=0}^{m-1} \binom{2m-k-2}{m-1} \left[\left(\frac{\Delta}{\nu_{\alpha\alpha}}\right)^{k+1} + \left(\frac{-\Delta}{\nu_{\beta\beta}}\right)^{k+1} \right] = \left(\frac{\Delta}{\nu_{\alpha\alpha}}\right)^m \left(\frac{-\Delta}{\nu_{\beta\beta}}\right)^m. \tag{4.14}$$

Substituting (4.14) in (4.13) yields the formula in (4.12). Proof of Theorem 2 is complete.

The difference

$$1 - F_{\alpha\alpha}^{(m)}(\infty) = 1 - \left[\frac{\nu_{\alpha\beta}\nu_{\beta\alpha}}{\nu_{\alpha\alpha}\nu_{\beta\beta}}\right]^m \tag{4.15}$$

is the probability that a system starting in S_α at time 0 will not return to S_α in m transitions within a finite length of time.

When $m = 1$

$$F_{\alpha\alpha}^{(1)}(t) = \frac{\nu_{\alpha\beta}\nu_{\beta\alpha}}{\nu_{\alpha\alpha}\nu_{\beta\beta}} + \frac{\nu_{\alpha\beta}\nu_{\beta\alpha}}{\Delta} \left[\frac{1}{\nu_{\alpha\alpha}} e^{\nu_{\alpha\alpha}t} - \frac{1}{\nu_{\beta\beta}} e^{\nu_{\beta\beta}t} \right]. \tag{4.16}$$

Inasmuch as the m-th renewal presupposes the realization of the $(m-1)$th renewal, the random variable $T_{\alpha\alpha}^{(m)}$ is stochastically greater than the random variable $T_{\alpha\alpha}^{(m-1)}$ in the sense that, for every t in the interval $[0, \infty)$,

$$\Pr\{T_{\alpha\alpha}^{(m)} < t\} < \Pr\{T_{\alpha\alpha}^{(m-1)} < t\}. \tag{4.17}$$

In other words, the sequence of random variables $\{T_{\alpha\alpha}^{(m)}\}$ increases with m. We can verify inequality (4.17) directly from the distribution function $F_{\alpha\alpha}^{(m)}(t)$ given in (4.11). As $t \to \infty$, it is obvious from equation (4.12) that

$$F_{\alpha\alpha}^{(m)}(\infty) < F_{\alpha\alpha}^{(m-1)}(\infty), \qquad m = 1, 2, \ldots. \tag{4.18}$$

Consequently,

$$\lim_{m\to\infty} F_{\alpha\alpha}^{(m)}(\infty) = \lim_{m\to\infty} \left[\frac{\nu_{\alpha\beta}\nu_{\beta\alpha}}{\nu_{\alpha\alpha}\nu_{\beta\beta}}\right]^m = 0. \tag{4.19}$$

Thus, as m becomes infinitely large, the probability that the m-th renewal will take place within a finite interval of time approaches zero. We hasten to add that this assertion holds true for an alternating renewal process only when there are absorbing states $R_1, \ldots, R_r$, and

$$\nu_{\alpha\alpha} = -[\nu_{\alpha\beta} + \mu_{\alpha 1} + \ldots + \mu_{\alpha r}] \tag{1.1a}$$

is greater in absolute value than $\nu_{\alpha\beta}$ for $\alpha = 1$ or $\alpha = 2$. If there is no absorbing state, then $\nu_{\alpha\alpha} = -\nu_{\alpha\beta}$, and $F_{\alpha\alpha}^{(m)}(\infty) = 1$ for every m. We shall discuss the latter case in more detail in Section 6.

4.2 Distribution function of the m-th passage time.

Theorem 3. *The distribution function of the m-th passage time $T_{\alpha\beta}^{(m)}$ is*

$$F_{\alpha\beta}^{(m)}(t) = \frac{\nu_{\alpha\beta}(-\nu_{\alpha\beta}\nu_{\beta\alpha})^{m-1}}{\Delta^{2m-1}} \left[\sum_{k=0}^{m-1} \binom{2m-k-3}{m-2} \left(\frac{\Delta}{\nu_{\alpha\alpha}}\right)^{k+1} \times \left\{\sum_{i=0}^{k} \frac{(-\nu_{\alpha\alpha}t)^i}{i!} e^{\nu_{\alpha\alpha}t} - 1\right\}\right.$$

$$\left. + \sum_{k=0}^{m-2} \binom{2m-k-3}{m-1} \left(\frac{-\Delta}{\nu_{\beta\beta}}\right)^{k+1} \left\{\sum_{i=0}^{k} \frac{(-\nu_{\beta\beta}t)^i}{i!} e^{\nu_{\beta\beta}t} - 1\right\}\right]. \tag{4.20}$$

As $t \to \infty$,

$$F_{\alpha\beta}^{(m)}(\infty) = \left(\frac{-\nu_{\alpha\beta}}{\nu_{\alpha\alpha}}\right)^m \left(\frac{-\nu_{\beta\alpha}}{\nu_{\beta\beta}}\right)^{m-1} \tag{4.21}$$

which is less than 1. *Therefore $T_{\alpha\beta}^{(m)}$ is an improper random variable.*

Proof. We obtain the formula in (4.20) directly from the density function $f_{\alpha\beta}^{(m)}(t)$ as derived in equation (2.6). To prove the second part of the theorem, we let $t \to \infty$ and find that

$$F_{\alpha\beta}^{(m)}(\infty) = \frac{-\nu_{\alpha\beta}(-\nu_{\alpha\beta}\nu_{\beta\alpha})^{m-1}}{\Delta^{2m-1}}\left[\sum_{k=0}^{m-1}\binom{2m-k-3}{m-2}\left(\frac{\Delta}{\nu_{\alpha\alpha}}\right)^{k+1} + \sum_{k=0}^{m-2}\binom{2m-k-3}{m-1}\left(\frac{-\Delta}{\nu_{\beta\beta}}\right)^{k+1}\right]. \tag{4.22}$$

The right hand side of (4.22) may be further simplified by using identity (4.2) in lemma 1. Letting

$$p = \frac{\nu_{\alpha\alpha}}{\Delta} \quad \text{and} \quad q = \frac{-\nu_{\beta\beta}}{\Delta}$$

and applying identity (4.2) yields

$$\sum_{k=0}^{m-1}\binom{2m-k-3}{m-2}\left(\frac{\Delta}{\nu_{\alpha\alpha}}\right)^{k+1} + \sum_{k=0}^{m-2}\binom{2m-k-3}{m-1}\left(\frac{-\Delta}{\nu_{\beta\beta}}\right)^{k+1} = \left(\frac{\Delta}{\nu_{\alpha\alpha}}\right)^{m}\left(\frac{-\Delta}{\nu_{\beta\beta}}\right)^{m-1}, \tag{4.23}$$

and hence,

$$F_{\alpha\beta}^{(m)}(\infty) = \left(\frac{-\nu_{\alpha\beta}}{\nu_{\alpha\alpha}}\right)^{m}\left(\frac{-\nu_{\beta\alpha}}{\nu_{\beta\beta}}\right)^{m-1}. \tag{4.24}$$

The sequence $\{F_{\alpha\beta}^{(m)}(\infty)\}$ also is monotonically decreasing and, as $m \to \infty$,

$$\lim_{m\to\infty} F_{\alpha\beta}^{(m)}(\infty) = 0. \tag{4.25}$$

When $m = 1$,

$$F_{\alpha\beta}^{(1)}(t) = -\frac{\nu_{\alpha\beta}}{\nu_{\alpha\alpha}}(1 - e^{\nu_{\alpha\alpha}t}). \tag{4.26}$$

For each m, $T_{\alpha\alpha}^{(m)}$ is stochastically greater than $T_{\alpha\beta}^{(m)}$, so that for every $t > 0$,

$$\Pr\{T_{\alpha\alpha}^{(m)} < t\} < \Pr\{T_{\alpha\beta}^{(m)} < t\}. \tag{4.27}$$

On the other hand $T_{\alpha\beta}^{(m)}$ is stochastically greater than $T_{\alpha\alpha}^{(m-1)}$ with

$$\Pr\{T_{\alpha\beta}^{(m)} < t\} < \Pr\{T_{\alpha\alpha}^{(m-1)} < t\}. \tag{4.28}$$

Inequalities (4.27) and (4.28) are quite evident as $t \to \infty$, since equations in (4.12) and (4.24) make it clear that

$$F_{\alpha\alpha}^{(m)}(\infty) = \left(\frac{\nu_{\alpha\beta}\,\nu_{\beta\alpha}}{\nu_{\alpha\alpha}\,\nu_{\beta\beta}}\right)^m < \left(\frac{-\nu_{\alpha\beta}}{\nu_{\alpha\alpha}}\right)^m \left(\frac{-\nu_{\beta\alpha}}{\nu_{\beta\beta}}\right)^{m-1} = F_{\alpha\beta}^{(m)}(\infty) \quad (4.29)$$

and

$$F_{\alpha\beta}^{(m)}(\infty) = \left(\frac{-\nu_{\alpha\beta}}{\nu_{\alpha\alpha}}\right)^m \left(\frac{-\nu_{\beta\alpha}}{\nu_{\beta\beta}}\right)^{m-1} < \left(\frac{\nu_{\alpha\beta}\,\nu_{\beta\alpha}}{\nu_{\alpha\alpha}\,\nu_{\beta\beta}}\right)^{m-1} = F_{\alpha\alpha}^{(m-1)}(\infty). \quad (4.30)$$

5. SURVIVAL TIME

Given an individual is in S_α let $t_{\alpha\delta}^{(m)}$ be the length of time elapsed before the individual enters a death (absorbing) state R_δ after having left S_α m times. We interpret the quantity $t_{\alpha\delta}^{(m)}$ as the survival time of an individual who is initially in S_α. Depending on the state from which the individual enters R_δ, the survival time may be decomposed into $t_{\alpha\delta\cdot\alpha}^{(m)}$, if a transition $S_\alpha \to R_\delta$ takes place, and $t_{\alpha\delta\cdot\beta}^{(m)}$, if a transition $S_\beta \to R_\delta$ takes place. The corresponding density function $h_{\alpha\delta\cdot\alpha}^{(m)}(t)$ and $h_{\alpha\delta\cdot\beta}^{(m)}(t)$ have definite relationships with the multiple transition probabilities. Specifically,

$$h_{\alpha\delta\cdot\alpha}^{(m)}(t) = P_{\alpha\alpha}^{(m-1)}(0,t)\mu_{\alpha\delta} \quad (5.1)$$

and

$$h_{\alpha\delta\cdot\beta}^{(m)}(t) = P_{\alpha\beta}^{(m)}(0,t)\mu_{\beta\delta}, \quad (5.2)$$

where $P_{\alpha\alpha}^{(m-1)}(0,t)$ and $P_{\alpha\beta}^{(m)}(0,t)$ are given in equations (2.27) and (2.10) in Chapter 12, respectively. On substituting these formulas in (5.1) and (5.2), we find that

$$h_{\alpha\delta\cdot\alpha}^{(m)}(t) = \frac{(-\nu_{\alpha\beta}\nu_{\beta\alpha})^{m-1}\mu_{\alpha\delta}}{\Delta^{2m-2}}\left[\sum_{k=0}^{m-1}\binom{2m-k-3}{m-2}\frac{(-\Delta t)^k}{k!}e^{\nu_{\alpha\alpha}t} - \sum_{k=0}^{m-2}\binom{2m-k-3}{m-1}\frac{(\Delta t)^k}{k!}e^{\nu_{\beta\beta}t}\right] \quad (5.3)$$

and

$$h_{\alpha\delta\cdot\beta}^{(m)}(t) = \frac{(-\nu_{\alpha\beta}\nu_{\beta\alpha})^{m-1}\nu_{\alpha\beta}\mu_{\beta\delta}}{\Delta^{2m-1}}\sum_{k=0}^{m-1}\binom{2m-k-2}{m-1}\frac{(\Delta t)^k}{k!}[(-1)^k e^{\nu_{\alpha\alpha}t} - e^{\nu_{\beta\beta}t}].$$

The density function of $t_{\alpha\delta}^{(m)}$ is the sum

$$h_{\alpha\delta}^{(m)}(t) = h_{\alpha\delta\cdot\alpha}^{(m)}(t) + h_{\alpha\delta\cdot\beta}^{(m)}(t). \tag{5.5}$$

Distribution functions can be derived, as usual, from

$$H_{\alpha\delta\cdot\alpha}^{(m)}(t) = \int_0^t h_{\alpha\delta\cdot\alpha}^{(m)}(\xi)d\xi \tag{5.6}$$

and

$$H_{\alpha\delta\cdot\beta}^{(m)}(t) = \int_0^t h_{\alpha\delta\cdot\beta}^{(m)}(\xi)d\xi. \tag{5.7}$$

We should also note that $h_{\alpha\delta\cdot\alpha}^{(m)}(t)$ in (5.3) and the density function $f_{\alpha\beta}^{(m)}(t)$ in (2.6) are related as follows:

$$h_{\alpha\delta\cdot\alpha}^{(m)}(t) = \frac{\mu_{\alpha\delta}}{\nu_{\alpha\beta}} f_{\alpha\beta}^{(m)}(t). \tag{5.8}$$

Therefore the corresponding distribution functions also have the same relationship:

$$H_{\alpha\delta\cdot\alpha}^{(m)}(t) = \frac{\mu_{\alpha\delta}}{\nu_{\alpha\beta}} F_{\alpha\beta}^{(m)}(t). \tag{5.9}$$

Similarly,

$$h_{\alpha\delta\cdot\beta}^{(m)}(t) = \frac{\mu_{\beta\delta}}{\nu_{\alpha\beta}} f_{\alpha\alpha}^{(m)}(t) \tag{5.10}$$

and

$$H_{\alpha\delta\cdot\beta}^{(m)}(t) = \frac{\mu_{\beta\delta}}{\nu_{\beta\alpha}} F_{\alpha\alpha}^{(m)}(t). \tag{5.11}$$

Therefore the general formulas for $H_{\alpha\delta\cdot\alpha}^{(m)}(t)$ and $H_{\alpha\delta\cdot\beta}^{(m)}(t)$ can be derived from $F_{\alpha\beta}^{(m)}(t)$ and $F_{\alpha\alpha}^{(m)}(t)$, respectively. For $m = 1$, they are

$$H_{\alpha\delta\cdot\alpha}^{(1)}(t) = \frac{-\mu_{\alpha\delta}}{\nu_{\alpha\alpha}}(1 - e^{\nu_{\alpha\alpha}t}), \tag{5.12}$$

$$H_{\alpha\delta\cdot\beta}^{(1)}(t) = \frac{-\nu_{\alpha\beta}\mu_{\beta\delta}}{\nu_{\alpha\alpha} - \nu_{\beta\beta}}\left[\frac{1}{\nu_{\alpha\alpha}}(1 - e^{\nu_{\alpha\alpha}t}) - \frac{1}{\nu_{\beta\beta}}(1 - e^{\nu_{\beta\beta}t})\right] \tag{5.13}$$

and the distribution functions of $t_{\alpha\delta}^{(1)}$ is

$$H_{\alpha\delta}^{(1)}(t) = H_{\alpha\delta\cdot\alpha}^{(1)}(t) + H_{\alpha\delta\cdot\beta}^{(1)}(t). \tag{5.14}$$

As $t \to \infty$, the limiting distribution functions become

$$H_{\alpha\delta\cdot\alpha}^{(m)}(\infty) = -\left(\frac{\nu_{\alpha\beta}\nu_{\beta\alpha}}{\nu_{\alpha\alpha}\nu_{\beta\beta}}\right)^{m-1} \frac{\mu_{\alpha\delta}}{\nu_{\alpha\alpha}} < 1, \tag{5.15}$$

$$H_{\alpha\delta\cdot\beta}^{(m)}(\infty) = \left(\frac{\nu_{\alpha\beta}\nu_{\beta\alpha}}{\nu_{\alpha\alpha}\nu_{\beta\beta}}\right)^{m} \frac{\mu_{\beta\delta}}{\nu_{\beta\alpha}} < 1, \tag{5.16}$$

and

$$H_{\alpha\delta}^{(m)}(\infty) = \left(\frac{\nu_{\alpha\beta}\nu_{\beta\alpha}}{\nu_{\alpha\alpha}\nu_{\beta\beta}}\right)^{m-1} \left(\frac{\nu_{\alpha\beta}\mu_{\beta\delta} - \nu_{\beta\beta}\mu_{\alpha\delta}}{\nu_{\alpha\alpha}\nu_{\beta\beta}}\right) < 1. \tag{5.17}$$

Thus, for any given $m = 1, 2, \ldots$, the survival time $t_{\alpha\delta}^{(m)}$ is an improper random variable. However, starting from any state S_α, an individual will eventually be in one of the absorbing states R_δ. This means that

$$\sum_{\delta=1}^{r} \sum_{m=1}^{\infty} H_{\alpha\delta}^{(m)}(\infty) = 1, \tag{5.18}$$

or, in view of (5.17),

$$\sum_{\delta=1}^{r} \sum_{m=1}^{\infty} \left(\frac{\nu_{\alpha\beta}\nu_{\beta\alpha}}{\nu_{\alpha\alpha}\nu_{\beta\beta}}\right)^{m-1} \left(\frac{\nu_{\alpha\beta}\mu_{\beta\delta} - \nu_{\beta\beta}\mu_{\alpha\delta}}{\nu_{\alpha\alpha}\nu_{\beta\beta}}\right) = 1. \tag{5.19}$$

Equation (5.19) is easily verified.

6. A TWO-STATE STOCHASTIC PROCESS

As an epilogue to the simple illness-death process, let us consider a stochastic system where there are only two transient states S_1 and S_2 and no absorbing states. Transitions take place only between the two states, with the intensity functions ν_{12} and ν_{21} as defined before. The functions ν_{11} and ν_{22}, however, we now define as

$$\nu_{11} = -\nu_{12} \quad \text{and} \quad \nu_{22} = -\nu_{21}. \tag{6.1}$$

Most of the formulas derived heretofore either remain unchanged with the exception of the new definitions of ν_{11} and ν_{22} in (6.1), or else can be further simplified. For easy reference, though at the expense of repetition, we will restate some of the formulas.[1]

Consider first the transition probability $P_{\alpha\beta}(0, t)$ that a system which is in S_α at time 0 will be in S_β at time t. Formulas for the transition probabilities may be derived from equations (2.26) and (2.27), Chapter 11. In a two-state process discussed here,

$$\rho_1 = \nu_{11} + \nu_{22} \qquad \text{and} \qquad \rho_2 = 0. \tag{6.2}$$

For every $t > 0$, the probabilities are

$$P_{\alpha\alpha}(0, t) = \frac{\nu_{\alpha\alpha}}{\nu_{\alpha\alpha} + \nu_{\beta\beta}} e^{(\nu_{\alpha\alpha} + \nu_{\beta\beta})t} + \frac{\nu_{\beta\beta}}{\nu_{\alpha\alpha} + \nu_{\beta\beta}} \tag{6.3}$$

and

$$P_{\alpha\beta}(0, t) = \frac{-\nu_{\alpha\alpha}}{\nu_{\alpha\alpha} + \nu_{\beta\beta}} e^{(\nu_{\alpha\alpha} + \nu_{\beta\beta})t} + \frac{\nu_{\alpha\alpha}}{\nu_{\alpha\alpha} + \nu_{\beta\beta}}, \tag{6.4}$$

with the obvious relationship

$$P_{\alpha\alpha}(0, t) + P_{\alpha\beta}(0, t) = 1. \tag{6.5}$$

As $t \to \infty$,

$$P_{\alpha\alpha}(0, \infty) = \frac{\nu_{\beta\beta}}{\nu_{\alpha\alpha} + \nu_{\beta\beta}} \tag{6.6}$$

and

$$P_{\alpha\beta}(0, \infty) = \frac{\nu_{\alpha\alpha}}{\nu_{\alpha\alpha} + \nu_{\beta\beta}}. \tag{6.7}$$

Equations (6.6) and (6.7) are equivalent to the limiting probabilities π_1 and π_2 in the two-state Markov chain in section 5, Chapter 6.

6.1. Multiple Transition Probabilities.

Given a system in S_α at time 0, we again let $M_{\alpha\beta}(0, t)$ be the number of times the system will leave S_α during the interval $(0, t)$ so that it ends in S_β at time t. The random variable $M_{\alpha\alpha}(0, t)$ is the number of alternating renewals of the type $S_\alpha \to S_\beta \to S_\alpha$, and $M_{\alpha\beta}(0, t)$ is the number of passages $S_\alpha \to S_\beta$ that occur during

[1]Note that the model described in this section is the counterpart of a two-state Markov chain in Chapter 6, section 5, example 2.

$(0, t)$. For any positive integer m, the corresponding probabilities are given in equations (2.27) and (2.10), Chapter 12 with $\nu_{\alpha\beta} = -\nu_{\alpha\alpha}$:

$$P_{\alpha\alpha}^{(m)}(0,t) = \frac{(-\nu_{\alpha\alpha}\nu_{\beta\beta})^m}{\Delta^{2m}}\left[\sum_{k=0}^{m}\binom{2m-k-1}{m-1}\frac{(-\Delta t)^k}{k!}e^{\nu_{\alpha\alpha}t} - \sum_{k=0}^{m-1}\binom{2m-k-1}{m}\frac{(\Delta t)^k}{k!}e^{\nu_{\beta\beta}t}\right] \quad (6.8)$$

and

$$P_{\alpha\beta}^{(m)}(0,t) = \frac{-\nu_{\alpha\alpha}(-\nu_{\alpha\alpha}\nu_{\beta\beta})^{m-1}}{\Delta^{2m-1}}\sum_{k=0}^{m-1}\binom{2m-k-2}{m-1}\frac{(\Delta t)^k}{k!}\left[(-1)^k e^{\nu_{\alpha\alpha}t} - e^{\nu_{\beta\beta}t}\right]. \quad (6.9)$$

We can show that

$$\sum_{m=0}^{\infty} P_{\alpha\alpha}^{(m)}(0,t) = P_{\alpha\alpha}(0,t) < 1$$

and

$$\sum_{m=1}^{\infty} P_{\alpha\beta}^{(m)}(0,t) = P_{\alpha\beta}(0,t) < 1,$$

where $P_{\alpha\alpha}(0,t)$ and $P_{\alpha\beta}(0,t)$ are as given in (6.3) and (6.4) respectively. Therefore $M_{\alpha\alpha}(0,t)$ and $M_{\alpha\beta}(0,t)$ also are improper random variables. If we consider instead the conditional probabilities

$$P_{\alpha\alpha}^{(m)}(0,t)/P_{\alpha\alpha}(0,t) \quad (6.10)$$

and

$$P_{\alpha\beta}^{(m)}(0,t)/P_{\alpha\beta}(0,t) \quad (6.11)$$

as we did in section 7 in Chapter 12, then the corresponding random variables, denoted by $\mathring{M}_{\alpha\alpha}(0,t)$ and $\mathring{M}_{\alpha\beta}(0,t)$, are proper. We can compute their expectations and higher order moments. For example, the expectation of $\mathring{M}_{\alpha\alpha}(0,t)$,

$$E[\mathring{M}_{\alpha\alpha}(0,t)] = \sum_{m=0}^{\infty} m P_{\alpha\alpha}^{(m)}(0,t)/P_{\alpha\alpha}(0,t),$$

may be derived from formula (7.4) in Chapter 12. From that formula and equations (6.1) through (6.3) we find that

$$E[\mathring{M}_{\alpha\alpha}(0,t)] = \frac{\nu_{\alpha\alpha}\nu_{\beta\beta}t}{\nu_{\alpha\alpha}+\nu_{\beta\beta}} + \frac{\nu_{\alpha\alpha}\nu_{\beta\beta}(\nu_{\alpha\alpha}-\nu_{\beta\beta})}{(\nu_{\alpha\alpha}+\nu_{\beta\beta})[\nu_{\alpha\alpha}e^{(\nu_{\alpha\alpha}+\nu_{\beta\beta})t}+\nu_{\beta\beta}]}$$
$$\times\left\{\frac{-2\nu_{\beta\beta}t}{\nu_{\alpha\alpha}-\nu_{\beta\beta}} - \frac{e^{(\nu_{\alpha\alpha}+\nu_{\beta\beta})t}-1}{\nu_{\alpha\alpha}+\nu_{\beta\beta}}\right\}. \quad (6.12)$$

6.2. Multiple Transition Time.

Let $T_{\alpha\alpha}^{(m)}$ be the m-th renewal time and $T_{\alpha\beta}^{(m)}$ the m-th passage time of a system as defined in section 2. Their density functions are

$$f_{\alpha\alpha}^{(m)}(t) = \frac{-(-\nu_{\alpha\alpha}\nu_{\beta\beta})^m}{\Delta^{2m-1}}\sum_{k=0}^{m-1}\binom{2m-k-2}{m-1}\frac{(\Delta t)^k}{k!}[(-1)^k e^{\nu_{\alpha\alpha}t} - e^{\nu_{\beta\beta}t}]$$
$$(6.13)$$

and

$$f_{\alpha\beta}^{(m)}(t) = \frac{-(-\nu_{\alpha\alpha}\nu_{\beta\beta})^{m-1}\nu_{\alpha\alpha}}{\Delta^{2m-2}}\left[\sum_{k=0}^{m-1}\binom{2m-k-3}{m-2}\frac{(-\Delta t)^k}{k!}e^{\nu_{\alpha\alpha}t}\right.$$
$$\left.-\sum_{k=0}^{m-2}\binom{2m-k-3}{m-1}\frac{(\Delta t)^k}{k!}e^{\nu_{\beta\beta}t}\right] \quad (6.14)$$

where $\Delta = \nu_{\alpha\alpha} - \nu_{\beta\beta}$. The distribution functions $F_{\alpha\alpha}^{(m)}(t)$ and $F_{\alpha\beta}^{(m)}(t)$ also have the same expressions as those in (4.11) and (4.20). As $t \to \infty$, equations (4.12) and (4.21) show that

$$F_{\alpha\alpha}^{(m)}(\infty) = 1 \quad \text{and} \quad F_{\alpha\beta}^{(m)}(\infty) = 1. \quad (6.15)$$

Therefore both random variables $T_{\alpha\alpha}^{(m)}$ and $T_{\alpha\beta}^{(m)}$ are proper. We can use the density functions to compute their expectations and variances. For example, the expected length of time needed to make m alternating renewals $S_\alpha \to S_\beta \to S_\alpha$ is determined from

$$E[T_{\alpha\alpha}^{(m)}] = \int_0^\infty t f_{\alpha\alpha}^{(m)}(t)dt. \quad (6.16)$$

The computations involved can be much simplified, however, if we recall from section 3 that

$$T_{\alpha\alpha}^{(1)} = T_{\alpha\beta}^{(1)} + T_{\beta\alpha}^{(1)} \quad (3.1)$$
$$T_{\alpha\alpha}^{(m)} = T_{\alpha\alpha}^{(1)} + \dots + T_{\alpha\alpha}^{(1)}, \quad (3.7)$$

and

$$T_{\alpha\beta}^{(m)} = T_{\alpha\alpha}^{(m-1)} + T_{\alpha\beta}^{(1)}, \tag{3.18}$$

and that all the random variables are independently distributed. Starting with $m = 1$, we find the density function of $T_{\alpha\beta}^{(1)}$ to be

$$f_{\alpha\beta}^{(1)}(t) = -\nu_{\alpha\alpha} e^{\nu_{\alpha\alpha} t},$$

and hence the expectation

$$E\,[T_{\alpha\beta}^{(1)}] = -\frac{1}{\nu_{\alpha\alpha}} \tag{6.17}$$

and the variance

$$V\,[T_{\alpha\beta}^{(1)}] = \frac{1}{\nu_{\alpha\alpha}^2}. \tag{6.18}$$

Using the relationships in (3.1), (3.7), and (3.18), we find the expectations

$$E\,[T_{\alpha\alpha}^{(m)}] = -\left[\frac{m}{\nu_{\alpha\alpha}} + \frac{m}{\nu_{\beta\beta}}\right] \quad \text{and} \quad E\,[T_{\alpha\beta}^{(m)}] = -\left[\frac{m}{\nu_{\alpha\alpha}} + \frac{m-1}{\nu_{\beta\beta}}\right] \tag{6.19}$$

and the variances

$$V\,[T_{\alpha\alpha}^{(m)}] = \frac{m}{\nu_{\alpha\alpha}^2} + \frac{m}{\nu_{\beta\beta}^2} \quad \text{and} \quad V\,[T_{\alpha\beta}^{(m)}] = \frac{m}{\nu_{\alpha\alpha}^2} + \frac{m-1}{\nu_{\beta\beta}^2}. \tag{6.20}$$

6.3. Number of Renewals and Renewal Time.

The alternating renewal process discussed in this section complies with the conditions underlying the general renewal theory given in Chapter 7. Therefore the relationship between the number of renewals and the renewal time should also conform to the theory presented in the renewal process. We shall state two general theorems for the alternating renewal process.

Theorem 4. *The probability distributions of the number of transitions $M_{\alpha\alpha}(0, t)$ and $M_{\alpha\beta}(0, t)$ and the distribution function $F_{\alpha\alpha}^{(m)}(t)$ and $F_{\alpha\beta}^{(m)}(t)$ are related as follows*

$$P_{\alpha\alpha}^{(m)}(0, t) = F_{\alpha\alpha}^{(m)}(t) - F_{\alpha\beta}^{(m+1)}(t) \tag{6.21}$$

and

$$P^{(m)}_{\alpha\beta}(0,t) = F^{(m)}_{\alpha\beta}(t) - F^{(m)}_{\alpha\alpha}(t) \tag{6.22}$$

for $\alpha \neq \beta$; $\alpha, \beta = 1,2$.

Proof. The validity of (6.21) and (6.22) rests on the following two assertions. First

$$T^{(m)}_{\alpha\alpha} \le t \qquad \text{if and only if} \qquad M_{\alpha\alpha}(0,t) \ge m \text{ or } M_{\alpha\beta}(0,t) \ge m+1,$$

so that the corresponding probabilities satisfy the equation

$$F^{(m)}_{\alpha\alpha}(t) = \sum_{n=m}^{\infty} P^{(n)}_{\alpha\alpha}(0,t) + \sum_{n=m+1}^{\infty} P^{(n)}_{\alpha\beta}(0,t); \tag{6.23}$$

and second,

$$T^{(m)}_{\alpha\beta} \le t \qquad \text{if and only if} \qquad M_{\alpha\alpha}(0,t) \ge m \text{ or } M_{\alpha\beta}(0,t) \ge m,$$

so that

$$F^{(m)}_{\alpha\beta}(t) = \sum_{n=m}^{\infty} P^{(n)}_{\alpha\alpha}(0,t) + \sum_{n=m}^{\infty} P^{(n)}_{\alpha\beta}(0,t). \tag{6.24}$$

We can obtain equation (6.21) by subtracting (6.24) from (6.23), and obtain equation (6.22) by subtracting (6.23) from (6.24).

The reader may verify these equations by using the explicit formulas for the probabilities $P^{(m)}_{\alpha\alpha}(0,t)$ and $P^{(m)}_{\alpha\beta}(0,t)$ and the distribution functions $F^{(m)}_{\alpha\alpha}(t)$ and $F^{(m)}_{\alpha\beta}(t)$. We shall demonstrate the validity of Theorem 4 for $m = 1$.

When $m = 1$, we recall formulas in equations (4.16), (4.26) and (4.20) for $m = 2$, to compute the differences in equations (6.21) and (6.22):

$$\begin{aligned}
F^{(1)}_{\alpha\alpha}(t) - F^{(2)}_{\alpha\beta}(t) &= \left[1 + \frac{\nu_{\alpha\alpha}\nu_{\beta\beta}}{\Delta}\left(\frac{1}{\nu_{\alpha\alpha}} e^{\nu_{\alpha\alpha}t} - \frac{1}{\nu_{\beta\beta}} e^{\nu_{\beta\beta}t}\right)\right] \\
&\quad - \frac{\nu^2_{\alpha\alpha}\nu_{\beta\beta}}{\Delta^3}\left[\frac{-\Delta}{\nu_{\alpha\alpha}}(1 - e^{\nu_{\alpha\alpha}t}) - \left(\frac{\Delta}{\nu_{\alpha\alpha}}\right)^2 \{1 - (1 - \nu_{\alpha\alpha}t)e^{\nu_{\alpha\alpha}t}\}\right. \\
&\qquad \left. + \frac{\Delta}{\nu_{\beta\beta}}(1 - e^{\nu_{\beta\beta}t})\right] \\
&= \frac{-\nu_{\alpha\alpha}\nu_{\beta\beta}}{\Delta^2}\left[(1 - \Delta t)e^{\nu_{\alpha\alpha}t} - e^{\nu_{\beta\beta}t}\right], \qquad (6.25)
\end{aligned}$$

where $\nu_{\alpha\alpha} = -\nu_{\alpha\beta}$ and $\Delta = \nu_{\alpha\alpha} - \nu_{\beta\beta}$. We recognize the last expression in (6.25) as the probability $P_{\alpha\alpha}^{(1)}(0,t)$ [c.f., equation (3.9), Chapter 12]. Equation (6.21) follows.

As for the equation in (6.22), we find the difference

$$F_{\alpha\beta}^{(1)}(t) - F_{\alpha\alpha}^{(1)}(t) = [1 - e^{\nu_{\alpha\alpha}t}] - \left[1 + \frac{\nu_{\alpha\alpha}\nu_{\beta\beta}}{\Delta}\left\{\frac{1}{\nu_{\alpha\alpha}}e^{\nu_{\alpha\alpha}t} - \frac{1}{\nu_{\beta\beta}}e^{\nu_{\beta\beta}t}\right\}\right]$$

$$= -\frac{\nu_{\alpha\alpha}}{\Delta}[e^{\nu_{\alpha\alpha}t} - e^{\nu_{\beta\beta}t}], \tag{6.26}$$

which is the formula for $P_{\alpha\beta}^{(1)}(0,t)$ [cf., equation (3.8), Chapter 12]. The verification is complete.

Theorem 5. *As $t \to \infty$, the expectations and the variances of the number of renewals of $\mathring{M}_{\alpha\alpha}(0,t)$ and of the first renewal time $T_{\alpha\alpha}^{(1)}$ are related as follows:*

$$\lim_{t\to\infty} \frac{E[\mathring{M}_{\alpha\alpha}(0,t)]}{t} = \frac{1}{E[T_{\alpha\alpha}^{(1)}]} \tag{6.27}$$

and

$$\lim_{t\to\infty} \frac{\operatorname{Var}[\mathring{M}_{\alpha\alpha}(0,t)]}{t} = \frac{\operatorname{Var}[T_{\alpha\alpha}^{(1)}]}{\{E[T_{\alpha\alpha}^{(1)}]\}^3}. \tag{6.28}$$

Theorem 5 is equivalent to Theorem 6 in Chapter 7 on renewal processes.

Proof. For notational clarity, let us consider the case $\alpha = 1$. The expectation and variance of the first renewal time $T_{11}^{(1)}$ are

$$E[T_{11}^{(1)}] = -\frac{\nu_{11} + \nu_{22}}{\nu_{11}\nu_{22}} \tag{6.19a}$$

and

$$\operatorname{Var}[T_{11}^{(1)}] = \frac{\nu_{11}^2 + \nu_{22}^2}{\nu_{11}^2\nu_{22}^2}. \tag{6.20a}$$

The p.g.f. of the number of renewals $M_{11}(0,t)$ is

$$g_{11}(s;t) = \frac{\rho_1 - \nu_{22}}{\rho_1 - \rho_2} e^{\rho_1 t} + \frac{\rho_2 - \nu_{22}}{\rho_2 - \rho_1} e^{\rho_2 t}, \tag{6.29}$$

where

$$\rho_1, \rho_2 = \frac{1}{2}\left[(\nu_{11} + \nu_{22}) \pm \sqrt{(\nu_{11} - \nu_{22})^2 + 4\nu_{11}\nu_{22}s}\right]. \tag{6.30}$$

When $s = 1$, $\rho_1 = \nu_{11} + \nu_{22}$ and $\rho_2 = 0$. As $t \to \infty$,

$$g_{11}(1;\infty) = P_{11}(0,\infty) = \frac{\nu_{22}}{\nu_{11} + \nu_{22}}, \tag{6.6a}$$

as derived in (6.6).

Taking the first derivative of $g_{11}(s;t)$ with respect to s, we find the limit

$$\lim_{t\to\infty} \frac{1}{t} \frac{\partial}{\partial s} g_{11}(s;t)\Big|_{s=1} = -\frac{\nu_{11}\nu_{22}^2}{(\nu_{11} + \nu_{22})^2}. \tag{6.31}$$

Therefore, for the expectation of the properized random variable $\mathring{M}_{11}(0,t)$ the limit is

$$\lim_{t\to\infty} \frac{E\mathring{M}_{11}(0,t)}{t} = \lim_{t\to\infty} \frac{1}{tP_{11}(0,t)} \frac{\partial}{\partial s} g_{11}(s;t)\Big|_{s=1}$$

$$= -\frac{\nu_{11}\nu_{22}}{\nu_{11} + \nu_{22}}, \tag{6.32}$$

which is the inverse of $E[T_{11}^{(1)}]$, proving (6.27).

For the second part of Theorem 5, we compute the limit from the p.g.f.:

$$\lim_{t\to\infty} \frac{\mathrm{Var}[\mathring{M}_{11}(0,t)]}{t} = \lim_{t\to\infty} \left[\frac{1}{t\,P_{11}(0,t)} \frac{\partial^2}{\partial s^2} g_{11}(s;t)\Big|_{s=1} + \frac{E\mathring{M}_{11}(0,t)}{t} - \frac{[E\,\mathring{M}_{11}(0,t)]^2}{t}\right] \tag{6.33}$$

where[2]

---

[2]To show the computation in some detail, we display equations (6.34) and (6.35) separately.

$$\lim_{t\to\infty} \frac{1}{t\,P_{11}(0,t)} \frac{\partial^2}{\partial s^2} g_{11}(s;t)\bigg|_{s=1}$$
$$= \lim_{t\to\infty} \frac{\nu_{11}^2 \nu_{22}}{(\nu_{11}+\nu_{22})^3} [(\nu_{11}+\nu_{22})\,\nu_{22}\,t + 4\,\nu_{22} - 2\nu_{11}], \quad (6.34)$$

and

$$\lim_{t\to\infty} \frac{[E\,\mathring{M}_{11}(0,t)]^2}{t} = \lim_{t\to\infty} \frac{\nu_{11}^2 \nu_{22}}{(\nu_{11}+\nu_{22})^3} [(\nu_{11}+\nu_{22})\nu_{22}t - 2(\nu_{11}-\nu_{22})]. \quad (6.35)$$

Substituting (6.32), (6.34) and (6.35) in (6.33), we get

$$\lim_{t\to\infty} \frac{V[\mathring{M}_{11}(0,t)]}{t} = \frac{-\nu_{11}\nu_{22}}{(\nu_{11}+\nu_{22})^3} [\nu_{11}^2 + \nu_{22}^2]$$
$$= \frac{V[T_{11}^{(1)}]}{\{E[T_{11}^{(1)}]\}^3}, \quad (6.36)$$

thus completing the proof of Theorem 5.

7. PROBLEMS FOR SOLUTION

1. *Convolution in terms of density functions.* Derive the density function of the third renewal time from

(a) $f_{\alpha\alpha}^{(3)}(t) = \int_0^t f_{\alpha\alpha}^{(2)}(\tau) f_{\alpha\alpha}^{(1)}(t-\tau)\,d\tau$

(b) $f_{\alpha\alpha}^{(3)}(t) = \int_0^t f_{\alpha\beta}^{(2)}(\tau) f_{\beta\alpha}^{(2)}(t-\tau)\,d\tau$

when $f_{\alpha\alpha}^{(1)}(t)$, $f_{\alpha\alpha}^{(2)}(t)$, and $f_{\alpha\beta}^{(2)}(t)$ are given in (2.7), (2.9), and (2.10), respectively.

2. *Continuation.* Derive the density function of the third passage time from

(a) $f_{\alpha\beta}^{(3)}(t) = \int_0^t f_{\alpha\beta}^{(2)}(\tau) f_{\beta\beta}^{(1)}(t-\tau)\,d\tau$

(b) $f_{\alpha\beta}^{(3)}(t) = \int_0^t f_{\alpha\alpha}^{(2)}(\tau) f_{\alpha\beta}^{(1)}(t-\tau)\,d\tau.$

3. *Continuation.* Derive the density function of the m-th passage time from

$$f_{\alpha\beta}^{(m)}(t)=\int_0^t f_{\alpha\alpha}^{(m-1)}(\tau)f_{\alpha\beta}^{(1)}(t-\tau)\,d\tau. \tag{3.19}$$

4. *Continuation.* Derive the density function of the m-th renewal time from

$$f_{\alpha\alpha}^{(m)}(t)=\int_0^t f_{\alpha\beta}^{(m)}(\tau)f_{\beta\alpha}^{(1)}(t-\tau)\,d\tau \tag{3.21}$$

5. Prove by induction the identity in (4.2).

6. *Convolution in terms of distribution functions.* Verify the following convolutional relationship

$$F_{\alpha\alpha}^{(1)}(t)=\int_0^t F_{\alpha\beta}^{(1)}(t-\tau)\,dF_{\beta\alpha}^{(1)}(\tau)$$

where the distribution functions $F_{\alpha\beta}^{(1)}(t)$ and $F_{\alpha\alpha}^{(1)}(t)$ are given in (4.26) and (4.16), respectively.

7. *Continuation.* Derive the distribution function of the second passage time from

(a) $F_{\alpha\beta}^{(2)}(t)=\int_0^t F_{\alpha\alpha}^{(1)}(t-\tau)\,dF_{\alpha\beta}^{(1)}(\tau)$

(b) $F_{\alpha\beta}^{(2)}(t)=\int_0^t F_{\alpha\beta}^{(1)}(t-\tau)\,dF_{\beta\beta}^{(1)}(\tau)$.

8. *Continuation.* Derive the distribution function of the second renewal time from

(a) $F_{\alpha\alpha}^{(2)}(t)=\int_0^t F_{\alpha\alpha}^{(1)}(t-\tau)\,dF_{\alpha\alpha}^{(1)}(\tau)$

(b) $F_{\alpha\alpha}^{(2)}(t)=\int_0^t F_{\alpha\beta}^{(2)}(t-\tau)\,dF_{\beta\alpha}^{(1)}(\tau)$

(c) $F_{\alpha\alpha}^{(2)}(t)=\int_0^t F_{\alpha\beta}^{(1)}(t-\tau)\,dF_{\beta\alpha}^{(2)}(\tau)$

9. *Continuation.* List, with some justification, as many convolutional formulas as you can to derive the distribution function of the third passage time, $F_{\alpha\beta}^{(3)}(t)$. Use one of the formulas to find it.

10. *Continuation.* List, with some justification, as many convolutional formulas as you can to derive the distribution function of the third renewal time, $F_{\alpha\alpha}^{(3)}(t)$. Use one of the formulas to find it.

11. *Continuation.* Verify the following convolutional relationships using the distribution functions in (4.11) and (4.20)

(a) $F_{\alpha\beta}^{(m)}(t) = \int_0^t F_{\alpha\alpha}^{(m-1)}(t-\tau)\,dF_{\alpha\beta}^{(1)}(\tau)$

(b) $F_{\alpha\beta}^{(m)}(t) = \int_0^t F_{\alpha\beta}^{(m-1)}(t-\tau)\,dF_{\beta\beta}^{(1)}(\tau)$

(c) $F_{\alpha\beta}^{(m)}(t) = \int_0^t F_{\alpha\beta}^{(1)}(t-\tau)\,dF_{\beta\beta}^{(m-1)}(\tau)$

(d) $F_{\alpha\beta}^{(m)}(t) = \int_0^t F_{\alpha\alpha}^{(1)}(t-\tau)\,dF_{\alpha\beta}^{(m-1)}(\tau).$

12. *Continuation.* Verify the following convolutional relationships using the distributions functions in (4.11) and (4.20).

(a) $F_{\alpha\alpha}^{(m)}(t) = \int_0^t F_{\alpha\beta}^{(m)}(t-\tau)\,dF_{\beta\alpha}^{(1)}(\tau)$

(b) $F_{\alpha\alpha}^{(m)}(t) = \int_0^t F_{\alpha\alpha}^{(m-1)}(t-\tau)\,dF_{\alpha\alpha}^{(1)}(\tau)$

(c) $F_{\alpha\alpha}^{(m)}(t) = \int_0^t F_{\alpha\beta}^{(1)}(t-\tau)\,dF_{\beta\alpha}^{(m)}(\tau)$

(d) $F_{\alpha\alpha}^{(m)}(t) = \int_0^t F_{\alpha\alpha}^{(1)}(t-\tau)\,dF_{\alpha\alpha}^{(m-1)}(\tau)$

NOTE: The above exercises show that the density functions and the distribution functions of the m-th renewal time and the m-th passage time can be derived directly without the aid of the transition probabilities in Chapter 12.

13. *"Properized" passage time distributions.* The limiting distribution function

$$F_{\alpha\beta}^{(1)}(\infty) = -\frac{\nu_{\alpha\beta}}{\nu_{\alpha\alpha}}$$

shows that the first passage time $T_{\alpha\beta}^{(1)}$ is an improper random variable and the density function

$$f_{\alpha\beta}^{(1)}(t) = \nu_{\alpha\beta}\,e^{\nu_{\alpha\alpha}t} \tag{2.8}$$

is an improper density function. However, we may generate from $T_{\alpha\beta}^{(1)}$ a proper random variable $\mathring{T}_{\alpha\beta}^{(1)}$ with the density function

$$\mathring{f}^{(1)}_{\alpha\beta}(t) = \frac{f^{(1)}_{\alpha\beta}(t)}{F^{(1)}_{\alpha\beta}(\infty)}$$

$$= -\nu_{\alpha\alpha}\, e^{\nu_{\alpha\alpha} t}.$$

Find the expectation $E[\mathring{T}^{(1)}_{\alpha\beta}]$ and the variance $V[\mathring{T}^{(1)}_{\alpha\beta}]$.

14. *Continuation.* Consider a random variable $\mathring{T}^{(2)}_{\alpha\beta}$, a properized second passage time, with the density function [cf., equation (2.10)]

$$\mathring{f}^{(2)}_{\alpha\beta}(t) = \frac{f^{(2)}_{\alpha\beta}}{F^{(2)}_{\alpha\beta}(\infty)}$$

$$= \frac{\nu^2_{\alpha\alpha}\nu_{\beta\beta}}{\Delta^2}\,[e^{\nu_{\alpha\alpha} t} - e^{\nu_{\beta\beta} t} - \Delta\, t\, e^{\nu_{\alpha\alpha} t}] \tag{2.10a}$$

where $\Delta = \nu_{\alpha\alpha} - \nu_{\beta\beta}$. Find the expectation $E[\mathring{T}^{(2)}_{\alpha\beta}]$ and the variance $V[\mathring{T}^{(2)}_{\alpha\beta}]$.

15. *"Properized" renewal time distribution.* Find the expectation and the variance of the properized first renewal time $\mathring{T}^{(1)}_{\alpha\alpha}$ from the density function

$$\mathring{f}^{(1)}_{\alpha\alpha}(t) = \frac{\nu_{\alpha\alpha}\nu_{\beta\beta}}{\nu_{\alpha\alpha} - \nu_{\beta\beta}}\,[e^{\nu_{\alpha\alpha} t} - e^{\nu_{\beta\beta} t}]. \tag{2.7a}$$

16. *Continuation.* Find the expectation and the variance of the properized second renewal time $\mathring{T}^{(2)}_{\alpha\alpha}$ with the density function

$$\mathring{f}^{(2)}_{\alpha\alpha}(t) = \frac{(\nu_{\alpha\alpha}\nu_{\beta\beta})^2}{\Delta^3}\,[-2(e^{\nu_{\alpha\alpha} t} - e^{\nu_{\beta\beta} t}) + \Delta\, t\,(e^{\nu_{\alpha\alpha} t} + e^{\nu_{\beta\beta} t})]. \tag{2.9}$$

17. *Relative magnitude of renewal time and passage time.* It is intuitively clear that the second passage time is stochastically greater than the first renewal time, and the second renewal time is stochastically greater than the second passage time. This means that whatever may be $0 \le t \le \infty$, we have

(a) $\Pr\{T^{(2)}_{\alpha\beta} < t\} < \Pr\{T^{(1)}_{\alpha\alpha} < t\}$

(b) $\Pr\{T^{(2)}_{\alpha\alpha} < t\} < \Pr\{T^{(2)}_{\alpha\beta} < t\}$.

Prove these inequalities.

18. *Continuation.* Show that whatever may be $0 \le t < \infty$,

(a) $\Pr\{T^{(3)}_{\alpha\beta} < t\} < \Pr\{T^{(2)}_{\alpha\alpha} < t\}$

(b) $\Pr\{T^{(3)}_{\alpha\alpha} < t\} < \Pr\{T^{(3)}_{\alpha\beta} < t\}$.

19. *Continuation.* Generally, we have the following inequalities regarding the passage times and renewal times

(a) $\Pr\{T_{\alpha\beta}^{(m)} < t\} < \Pr\{T_{\alpha\alpha}^{(m-1)} < t\}$

(b) $\Pr\{T_{\alpha\alpha}^{(m)} < t\} < \Pr\{T_{\alpha\beta}^{(m)} < t\}$

(c) $\Pr\{T_{\alpha\alpha}^{(m)} < t\} < \Pr\{T_{\alpha\alpha}^{(m-1)} < t\}$

(d) $\Pr\{T_{\alpha\beta}^{(m)} < t\} < \Pr\{T_{\alpha\beta}^{(m-1)} < t\}$ (4.17)

for $0 \le t < \infty$. Prove each of these inequalities.

20. *Survival time.* Find the density function of $\tau_{\alpha\delta}^{(m)}$,

$$h_{\alpha\delta}^{(m)}(t) = h_{\alpha\delta\cdot\alpha}^{(m)}(t) + h_{\alpha\delta\cdot\beta}^{(m)}(t) \tag{5.5}$$

and the distribution function of $\tau_{\alpha\delta}^{(m)}$,

$$H_{\alpha\delta}^{(m)} = H_{\alpha\delta\cdot\alpha}^{(m)}(t) + H_{\alpha\delta\cdot\beta}^{(m)}(t)$$

for $m = 1, 2$.

21. *Continuation.* Derive the propertized density function of $\mathring{\tau}_{\alpha\delta}^{(m)}$

$$\mathring{h}_{\alpha\delta}^{(m)}(t) = \frac{h_{\alpha\delta}^{(m)}(t)}{H_{\alpha\delta}^{(m)}(\infty)}$$

for $m = 1, 2$, and show that the density function obtained is proper.

22. *Continuation.* Find the expectation and the variance of $\mathring{\tau}_{\alpha\delta}^{(m)}$ for $m = 1, 2$.

23. *Continuation.* Let $\tau_{\alpha\delta}$ be the survival time of an individual who is initially in S_α before dying from risk R_δ. The density function of $\tau_{\alpha\delta}$ is

$$h_{\alpha\delta}(t) = \sum_{m=1}^{\infty} h_{\alpha\delta}^{(m)}(t)$$

where $h_{\alpha\delta}^{(m)}(t)$ is given in (5.5). The distribution function of $\tau_{\alpha\delta}$ is

$$H_{\alpha\delta}(t) = \int_0^t h_{\alpha\delta}(\tau)\,d\tau.$$

(a) Derive explicit formulas for $h_{\alpha\delta}(t)$ and $H_{\alpha\delta}(t)$, and show that $H_{\alpha\delta}(\infty) < 1$.

(b) Let $\mathring{\tau}_{\alpha\delta}$ be the properized random variable of $\tau_{\alpha\delta}$ with the density function

$$\mathring{h}_{\alpha\delta}(t) = \frac{h_{\alpha\delta}(t)}{H_{\alpha\delta}(\infty)}.$$

The expectation $E(\mathring{\tau}_{\alpha\delta})$ is the average survival time before an individual dies from R_δ. Find this expected value.

(c) Find the variance of $\mathring{\tau}_{\alpha\delta}$.

24. *Continuation.* Verify the equation in (5.19)

25. *Two-state process—multiple transition probabilities.* Show that the sums of the multiple transition probabilities in (6.8) and (6.9) are $P_{\alpha\alpha}(0,t)$ and $P_{\alpha\beta}(0,t)$ in (6.3) and (6.4), or

$$\sum_{m=0}^{\infty} P_{\alpha\alpha}^{(m)}(0,t) = \frac{\nu_{\alpha\alpha}}{\nu_{\alpha\alpha}+\nu_{\beta\beta}} e^{(\nu_{\alpha\alpha}+\nu_{\beta\beta})t} + \frac{\nu_{\beta\beta}}{\nu_{\alpha\alpha}+\nu_{\beta\beta}}$$

$$\sum_{m=1}^{\infty} P_{\alpha\beta}^{(m)}(0,t) = \frac{-\nu_{\alpha\alpha}}{\nu_{\alpha\alpha}+\nu_{\beta\beta}} e^{(\nu_{\alpha\alpha}+\nu_{\beta\beta})t} + \frac{\nu_{\alpha\alpha}}{\nu_{\alpha\alpha}+\nu_{\beta\beta}}.$$

26. *Continuation.* Compute the expected number of renewals in (6.12) from the probability distribution in (6.10).

27. *Continuation.* Compute the expected number of passages $E[\mathring{M}_{\alpha\beta}(0,t)]$ from the probability distribution in (6.11).

28. *Multiple transition times.* Compute the expectation and the variance of the m-th return time $T_{\alpha\alpha}^{(m)}$ from the density function in (6.13).

29. *Continuation.* Compute the expectation and the variance of the m-th passage time $T_{\alpha\beta}^{(m)}$ from the density function in (6.14).

30. Derive formulas for the distribution functions $F_{\alpha\alpha}^{(2)}(t)$ from (6.13), and $F_{\alpha\beta}^{(2)}(t)$ and $F_{\alpha\beta}^{(3)}(t)$ from (6.14).

31. Use the results obtained in Problem 30 to prove the following identities between renewal probability, passage probability and the distribution functions of renewal time and passage time

(a) $P_{\alpha\alpha}^{(2)}(0,t) = F_{\alpha\alpha}^{(2)}(t) - F_{\alpha\beta}^{(3)}(t)$

(b) $P_{\alpha\beta}^{(2)}(0,t) = F_{\alpha\beta}^{(2)}(t) - F_{\alpha\alpha}^{(2)}(t)$.

32. Use formulas (4.20), (4.22) and (6.8) to prove the following identity

$$P_{\alpha\alpha}^{(m)}(0,t) = F_{\alpha\alpha}^{(m)}(t) - F_{\alpha\beta}^{(m+1)}(t). \tag{6.21}$$

33. Use formula (4.20), (4.22) and (6.9) to prove the following identity

$$P_{\alpha\beta}^{(m)}(0,t) = F_{\alpha\beta}^{(m)}(t) - F_{\alpha\alpha}^{(m)}(t). \tag{6.22}$$

34. Derive the quantity in (6.31) from the generating function $g_{11}(s;t)$ in (6.29).

35. Derive the quantity in (6.34) from the generating function $g_{11}(s;t)$ in (6.29).

36. Using the results in (6.32), (6.34) and (6.35) to find the limit:

$$\lim_{t\to\infty} \frac{V[\mathring{M}_{11}(0,t)]}{t}. \tag{6.36}$$

37. Derive the density functions $f_{\alpha\beta}^{(1)}(t)$ and $f_{\alpha\alpha}^{(1)}(t)$ for each of the following sets of intensity functions

(i) $\nu_{11} = -.3,\quad \nu_{12} = .1;\quad \nu_{21} = .4$ and $\nu_{22} = -.6$

(ii) $\nu_{11} = -.4,\quad \nu_{12} = .2;\quad \nu_{21} = .4$ and $\nu_{22} = -.6$

(iii) $\nu_{11} = -.5,\quad \nu_{12} = .3;\quad \nu_{21} = .4$ and $\nu_{22} = -.6$

(iv) $\nu_{11} = -.8,\quad \nu_{12} = .6;\quad \nu_{21} = .4$ and $\nu_{22} = -.6$

38. Derive the density functions $f_{\alpha\alpha}^{(m)}(t)$ from the convolutional relationship

$$f_{\alpha\alpha}^{(m)}(t) = \int_0^t f_{\alpha\alpha}^{(1)}(\tau) f_{\alpha\alpha}^{(m-1)}(t-\tau)\,d\tau$$

for $\alpha = 1, 2$ for each of four sets of intensity functions in problem 37.

39. Derive the density functions $f_{\alpha\beta}^{(m)}(t)$ from the convolutional relationship

$$f_{\alpha\beta}^{(m)}(t) = \int_0^t f_{\alpha\alpha}^{(m-1)}(\tau) f_{\alpha\beta}^{(1)}(t-\tau)\,d\tau$$

for $\alpha \neq \beta$; $\alpha, \beta = 1, 2$, for each of the four sets of intensity functions in problem 37.

40. Find the distribution functions $F_{\alpha\alpha}^{(m)}(t)$ and $F_{\alpha\beta}^{(m)}(t)$ for the density functions obtained in problems 37 through 39.

41. Derive density functions of the survival time $h_{\alpha\delta}^{(m)}(t)$ in (5.5) for each of the four sets of intensity functions in problem 37 assuming $\mu_1 = .2$ and $\mu_2 = .2$ in each case.

(a) Derive the corresponding distribution functions $H_{\alpha\delta}^{(m)}(t)$.

(b) Discuss briefly the numerical findings from problems 37 to 41 according to the increasing values of ν_{12}: .1, .2, .3, .6.

42. In a two-state process, we consider four sets of intensity functions

(i) $\nu_{11} = -.2,\quad \nu_{12} = .2;\quad \nu_{21} = .6$ and $\nu_{22} = -.6$

(ii) $\nu_{11} = -.3,\quad \nu_{12} = .3;\quad \nu_{21} = .6$ and $\nu_{22} = -.6$

(iii) $\nu_{11} = -.4,\quad \nu_{12} = .4;\quad \nu_{21} = .6$ and $\nu_{22} = -.6$

(iv) $\nu_{11} = -.5,\quad \nu_{12} = .5;\quad \nu_{21} = .6$ and $\nu_{33} = -.6$

For each of the four sets of intensity functions

(a) Compute the probabilities $P_{\alpha\beta}(0,t)$, $\alpha, \beta = 1, 2$.

(b) Compute the multiple renewal probabilities $P_{\alpha\alpha}^{(m)}(0,t)$ and check that the sums

$$\sum_{m=0}^{\infty} P_{\alpha\alpha}^{(m)}(0,t) = P_{\alpha\alpha}(0,t), \qquad \alpha = 1, 2,$$

are equal to the corresponding probabilities obtained in (a).

(c) Compute the multiple passage probabilities $P_{\alpha\beta}^{(m)}(0,t)$ and check that the sums

$$\sum_{m=1}^{\infty} P_{\alpha\beta}^{(m)}(0,t) = P_{\alpha\beta}(0,t) \qquad \alpha \neq \beta;\, \alpha, \beta = 1, 2$$

are equal to the corresponding probabilities obtained in (a).

(d) Compute the density functions $f_{\alpha\alpha}^{(m)}(t)$ and the distribution function $F_{\alpha\alpha}^{(m)}(t)$ for the m-th renewal time $T_{\alpha\alpha}^{(m)}$ and show that for each m

$$F_{\alpha\alpha}^{(m)}(t) < F_{\alpha\alpha}^{(m-1)}(t).$$

(e) Compute the density function $f_{\alpha\beta}^{(m)}(t)$ and the distribution function $F_{\alpha\beta}^{(m)}(t)$ for the m-th passage time $T_{\alpha\beta}^{(m)}$, and show that, for each m,

$$F_{\alpha\beta}^{(m)}(t) < F_{\alpha\beta}^{(m-1)}(t).$$

(f) Show that, for each m,

$$F_{\alpha\alpha}^{(m)}(t) < F_{\alpha\beta}^{(m)}(t) \quad \text{and} \quad F_{\alpha\beta}^{(m)}(t) < F_{\alpha\alpha}^{(m-1)}(t).$$

(g) Show that $F_{\alpha\beta}^{(m)}(\infty) = 1$ for every $m \geq 1$ and $\alpha, \beta = 1, 2$.

(h) Compute the expectation $E[T_{\alpha\alpha}^{(1)}]$ and the variance $V[T_{\alpha\alpha}^{(1)}]$ of the first renewal time.

(i) Compute the expectation $E[T_{\alpha\alpha}^{(m)}]$ and the variance $V[T_{\alpha\alpha}^{(m)}]$ of the m-th renewal time $T_{\alpha\alpha}^{(m)}$ from the density function $f_{\alpha\alpha}^{(m)}(t)$.

(j) Compute the expectation $E[T_{\alpha\beta}^{(m)}]$ and the variance $V[T_{\alpha\beta}^{(m)}]$ of the m-th passage time $T_{\alpha\beta}^{(m)}$ from the density function $f_{\alpha\beta}^{(m)}(t)$.

(k) Use the numerical results obtained above to verify for each m and for every $\alpha \neq \beta$, $\alpha, \beta = 1, 2$, the identities

$$P_{\alpha\alpha}^{(m)}(0,t) = F_{\alpha\alpha}^{(m)}(t) - F_{\alpha\beta}^{(m+1)}(t)$$

and

$$P_{\alpha\beta}^{(m)}(0,t) = F_{\alpha\beta}^{(m)}(t) - F_{\alpha\alpha}^{(m)}(t).$$

(l) Compute the expectation $E[\mathring{M}_{\alpha\alpha}(0,t)]$ and the variance $V[\mathring{M}_{\alpha\alpha}(0,t)]$ of the properized number of renewals, for $\alpha = 1, 2$.

(m) Use the numerical values that you have obtained in (h) and (l) to verify equation (6.27) and (6.28) in Theorem 5.

(n) Discuss briefly your numerical results according to the increasing values of ν_{12}: .2, .3, .4, .5.

CHAPTER 14

The Kolmogorov Differential Equations and Finite Markov Processes

1. MARKOV PROCESSES AND THE CHAPMAN-KOLMOGOROV EQUATION

So far we have been concerned with specific stochastic processes. We will now present a general formulation that will include these processes as special cases. Consider a system that can be in any one of a finite or denumerable number of states 1, 2, ... For each $t \in [0, \infty)$, we define a discrete random variable $X(t)$ whose value indicates the state of the system at time t, i.e., the event "$X(t) = j$" is the same as the event "the system is in state j at time t." In the population growth models in Chapter 8, for example, the state of the system is the population size, and $X(t)$ has an infinite number of possible values. In the illness-death process as Chapter 11, the state of the system is the health or death state of one individual, and the system has $r + 2$ possible states.

In Chapters 8, 9, and 10 we made a rather restrictive assumption that, within a small time element $(t, t + \Delta)$, a population size may increase (or decrease) by only one with an appreciable probability. We now remove this restriction, allowing a system to move from any non-absorbing state to any other state. We use $P_{ij}(\tau, t)$ to denote the transition (or conditional) probability that the system will be in state j at time t, given that it was in state i at time τ; that is, for $\tau < t$; $\tau, t \in [0, \infty)$,

$$P_{ij}(\tau, t) = \Pr\{X(t) = j \mid X(\tau) = i\}, \qquad i, j = 1, 2, \ldots. \qquad (1.1)$$

For arbitrary $\tau < t$, the transition probability in equation (1.1) indicates the stochastic dependence of $X(t)$ on $X(\tau)$. Two forms of dependence that are particularly important are defined below.

Definition 1. A discrete-valued stochastic process $\{X(t): t \varepsilon [0, \infty)\}$ is a *Markov process* if, for any $t_0 < t_1 < \dots < t_i < \dots < t_j$, and any integers $k_0, k_1, \dots, k_j$,

$$\begin{aligned} \Pr\{X(t_j) = k_j | X(t_0) = k_0, X(t_1) = k_1, \dots, X(t_i) = k_i\} \\ = \Pr\{X(t_j) = k_j | X(t_i) = k_i\}. \end{aligned} \tag{1.2}$$

Thus, in a Markov process as in a Markov chain, given $X(t_i)$ (present), the conditional probability distribution of $X(t_j)$ (future) is independent of $X(t_0), \dots, X(t_{i-1})$ (past). In this book discussion is confined exclusively to Markov processes.

Definition 2. A Markov process $\{X(t); t \varepsilon [0, \infty)\}$ is said to be *homogeneous with respect to time,* or *time homogeneous,* if the transition probability (1.1) depends only on the difference $t - \tau$ but not on τ or t separately. In such cases, we may write

$$P_{ij}(0, t - \tau) = \Pr\{X(t) = j | X(\tau) = i\}, \qquad i, j = 1, 2, \dots. \tag{1.3}$$

The simple Poisson process and the illness-death process are examples of homogeneous processes, whereas the Polya process is non-homogeneous.

1.1. The Chapman-Kolmogorov Equation.

The Markov property stated in equation (1.2) implies important relationships among the transition probabilities $P_{ij}(\tau, t)$. If we let ξ be a fixed point in the interval (τ, t), so that $\tau < \xi < t$, and let $X(\tau)$, $X(\xi)$, and $X(t)$ be the corresponding random variables, then, because of equation (1.2), we have the conditional probability

$$\begin{aligned} \Pr\{X(t) = k | X(\tau) = i, X(\xi) = j\} \\ = \Pr\{X(t) = k | X(\xi) = j\} = P_{jk}(\xi, t), \end{aligned}$$

and therefore,

$$\Pr\{X(\xi) = j \text{ and } X(t) = k | X(\tau) = i\} = P_{ij}(\tau, \xi) P_{jk}(\xi, t). \tag{1.4}$$

The last expression is the probability that a passage will occur from $X(\tau) = i$ to $X(t) = k$ by way of a particular state j at time ξ. At time ξ, the event $[X(\xi) = 1 \text{ or } X(\xi) = 2 \text{ or } \dots]$ is a sure event and

$$\Pr\{X(\xi) = 1 \text{ or } X(\xi) = 2 \text{ or } \dots\} = 1.$$

Therefore, the transition probability $\Pr\{X(t) = k | X(\tau) = i\}$ can be written as

$$\begin{aligned}
&\Pr\{X(t) = k | X(\tau) = i\} = \\
&\Pr\{X(t) = k \text{ and } [X(\xi) = 1 \text{ or } X(\xi) = 2 \text{ or } \dots] | X(\tau) = i\} \\
&\qquad = \Pr\{[X(\xi) = 1 \text{ and } X(t) = k] \text{ or } \\
&\qquad\qquad [X(\xi) = 2 \text{ and } X(t) = k] \text{ or } \dots | X(\tau) = i\} \\
&\qquad = \sum_j \Pr\{X(\xi) = j \text{ and } X(t) = k | X(\tau) = i\}. \qquad (1.5)
\end{aligned}$$

Substituting (1.4) in (1.5) yields the equation

$$P_{ik}(\tau, t) = \sum_j P_{ij}(\tau, \xi) P_{jk}(\xi, t), \qquad i, k = 1, 2, \dots; \quad \tau < \xi < t. \tag{1.6}$$

Equation (1.6), which is known as the *Chapman-Kolmogorov equation,* is the starting point for our general discussion of Markov processes. In the case of a time-homogeneous process, equation (1.6) is replaced by

$$P_{ik}(0, \tau + t) = \sum_j P_{ij}(0, \tau) p_{jk}(0, t). \tag{1.7}$$

2. THE KOLMOGOROV DIFFERENTIAL EQUATIONS

Kolmogorov in 1931 derived two systems of differential equations for the transition probabilities $p_{ij}(\tau, t)$: The *forward differential equations* when the differentiation of $P_{ij}(\tau, t)$ is taken with respect to t, and the *backward differential equations* when the differentiation is taken with respect to τ. When the transition probabilities $P_{ij}(\tau, t)$ satisfy certain regularity conditions, both systems may be derived from the Chapman-Kolmogorov equation in (1.6). Following Kolmogorov, Chung [1960], Doob [1953], Feller [1940], and others have discussed theoretical aspects of these different equations in detail. Feller, for example, has shown that, if $\sum_j P_{ij}(\tau, t) = 1$, then there always exists a unique solution $P_{ij}(\tau, t)$ that satisifes both the forward and the backward differential equations as well as the Chapman-Kolmogorov equation. In this chapter we shall present explicit solutions for the individual transition probabilities $P_{ij}(\tau, t)$. But first let us discuss regularity assumptions that underlie Markov processes.

Assumption 1. For every integer i, there exists a continuous function $\nu_{ii}(\tau) \leq 0$ such that

$$\lim_{\Delta \to 0} \frac{1 - P_{ii}(\tau, \tau + \Delta)}{\Delta} = -\nu_{ii}(\tau). \tag{2.1}$$

Assumption 2. For every pair of integers $i \neq j$, there exists a continuous function $\nu_{ij}(\tau) \geq 0$ such that

$$\lim_{\Delta \to 0} \frac{P_{ij}(\tau, \tau + \Delta)}{\Delta} = \nu_{ij}(\tau); \tag{2.2}$$

furthermore, for fixed j the passage in (2.2) is uniform with respect to i.

The functions $\nu_{ij}(\tau)$ are called *intensity functions.* If we require that

$$P_{ij}(\tau, \tau) = \delta_{ij}, \tag{2.3}$$

where δ_{ij} is the Kronecker delta,[1] then it becomes clear from (2.1) and (2.2) that

$$\nu_{ij}(\tau) = \frac{\partial}{\partial t} P_{ij}(\tau, t)\bigg|_{t=\tau} \qquad i, j = 1, 2, \ldots . \tag{2.4}$$

The probabilistic meaning of the intensity functions emerges when we write (2.1) and (2.2) as

$$P_{ii}(\tau, \tau + \Delta) = 1 + \nu_{ii}(\tau)\Delta + o(\Delta) \tag{2.5}$$

and

$$P_{ij}(\tau, \tau + \Delta) = \nu_{ij}(\tau)\Delta + o(\Delta). \tag{2.6}$$

Note that, if

$$\sum_j P_{ij}(\tau, t) = 1, \tag{2.7}$$

whatever may be the values of $\tau < t$, then

[1] The Kronecker delta δ_{ij} is defined as follows: $\delta_{ii} = 1$ and $\delta_{ij} = 0$, *for* $j \neq i$.

$$\nu_{ii}(\tau) = -\sum_{j \neq i} \nu_{ij}(\tau). \tag{2.8}$$

2.1. Derivation of the Kolmogorov Differential Equations.

We now use the above assumptions to derive Kolmogorov's differential equations. Let us consider three points, $\tau < t < t + \Delta$, on the time axis and use the Chapman-Kolmogorov equation (1.6) to write

$$P_{ik}(\tau, t + \Delta) = P_{ik}(\tau, t)P_{kk}(t, t + \Delta) + \sum_{j \neq k} P_{ij}(\tau, t)P_{jk}(t, t + \Delta). \tag{2.9}$$

By substituting (2.5) and (2.6) for the probabilities $P_{kk}(t, t + \Delta)$ and $P_{jk}(t, t + \Delta)$ respectively, and transposing the term $P_{ik}(\tau, t)$, we can rewrite (2.9) as

$$\frac{P_{ik}(\tau, t + \Delta) - P_{ik}(\tau, t)}{\Delta} = P_{ik}(\tau, t)\,\nu_{kk}(t) + \sum_{j \neq k} P_{ij}(\tau, t)\frac{P_{jk}(t, t + \Delta)}{\Delta} + \frac{o(\Delta)}{\Delta}. \tag{2.10}$$

According to Assumption 2, as $\Delta \to 0$, the term $P_{jk}(t, t + \Delta)/\Delta \to \nu_{jk}(t)$ uniformly in j, therefore the right hand side of (2.10) tends to a limit; hence the left hand side also tends to a limit. Therefore, the transition probability $P_{ik}(\tau, t)$ satisifes the differential equation

$$\frac{\partial}{\partial t} P_{ik}(\tau, t) = \sum_{j} P_{ij}(\tau, t)\,\nu_{jk}(t), \qquad i, k = 0, 2, \ldots . \tag{2.11}$$

Equation (2.11) describes the system of Kolmogorov forward differential equations with the initial conditions set forth in (2.3). We should note that, since τ is regarded as being fixed, in spite of the appearance of a partial derivative sign, (2.11) may be treated as a system of ordinary differential equations.

To derive the backward differential equations, we keep t fixed and consider the transition probability $P_{ik}(\tau, t)$ as a function of τ. We start with the Chapman-Kolmogorov equation in the form

$$P_{ik}(\tau - \Delta, t) = P_{ii}(\tau - \Delta, \tau)P_{ik}(\tau, t) + \sum_{j \neq i} P_{ij}(\tau - \Delta, \tau)P_{jk}(\tau, t). \tag{2.12}$$

By substituting (2.5) and (2.6) for the probabilities $P_{ii}(\tau - \Delta, \tau)$ and $P_{ij}(\tau - \Delta, \tau)$, we can rewrite (2.12) as

$$\frac{P_{ik}(\tau - \Delta, t) - P_{ik}(\tau, t)}{-\Delta} = -\nu_{ii}(\tau - \Delta)P_{ik}(\tau, t) + \sum_{j \neq i} \frac{P_{ij}(\tau - \Delta, \tau)}{-\Delta} P_{jk}(\tau, t) + o(\Delta). \tag{2.13}$$

Passing to the limit as $\Delta \to 0$, and applying Assumption 2, we obtain a system of Kolmogorov backward differential equations

$$\frac{\partial}{\partial \tau} P_{ik}(\tau, t) = -\sum_{j} \nu_{ij}(\tau)P_{jk}(\tau, t), \qquad i, k = 1, 2, \ldots. \tag{2.14}$$

Again we have a system of ordinary differential equations for the transition probabilities. In this case, however, t is fixed and the initial conditions are

$$P_{ik}(t, t) = \delta_{ik}. \tag{2.15}$$

Let us summarize the results obtained so far in the following theorem.

Theorem 1. *Let $P_{ik}(\tau, t)$ be the transition probabilities of a Markov process defined in equation* (1.1), *and suppose that Assumptions 1 and 2 hold. Then the transition probabilities satisfy the system of forward differential equations* (2.11) *and the system of backward differential equations in* (2.14), *with the initial conditions given in* (2.3) *and* (2.15) *respectively.*

In general, the solution $P_{ik}(\tau, t)$ is non-homogeneous with respect to time; however, if the intensity functions $\nu_{ij}(t) = \nu_{ij}$ are independent of time, then the process is time homogeneous. In this case, the two systems of differential equations become

$$\frac{d}{dt} P_{ik}(0, t) = \sum_{j} P_{ij}(0, t)\nu_{jk} \tag{2.16}$$

and

$$\frac{d}{dt} P_{ik}(0, t) = \sum_j \nu_{ij} P_{jk}(0, t), \tag{2.17}$$

with common initial conditions

$$P_{ik}(0, 0) = \delta_{ik}. \tag{2.18}$$

Kolmogorov's differential equations are more compactly represented in matrix notation. Let

$$\mathbf{P}(\tau, t) = \begin{pmatrix} P_{11}(\tau, t) & P_{12}(\tau, t) & \cdots \\ P_{21}(\tau, t) & P_{22}(\tau, t) & \cdots \\ \cdot & \cdot & \cdot \\ \cdot & \cdot & \cdot \end{pmatrix} \tag{2.19}$$

be the *transition probability matrix* and

$$\mathbf{V}(t) = \begin{pmatrix} \nu_{11}(t) & \nu_{12}(t) & \cdots \\ \nu_{21}(t) & \nu_{22}(t) & \cdots \\ \cdot & \cdot & \cdot \\ \cdot & \cdot & \cdot \end{pmatrix} \tag{2.20}$$

the *intensity function matrix.* Then the Chapman-Kolmogorov equation (1.6) is of the form

$$\mathbf{P}(\tau, t) = \mathbf{P}(\tau, \xi)\,\mathbf{P}(\xi, t). \tag{2.21}$$

The forward differential equations in (2.11) can be written as

$$\frac{\partial}{\partial t} \mathbf{P}(\tau, t) = \mathbf{P}(\tau, t)\mathbf{V}(t), \tag{2.22}$$

with the initial condition

$$\mathbf{P}(\tau, \tau) = \mathbf{I}. \tag{2.23}$$

The backward differential equations in (2.14) can be written as

$$\frac{\partial}{\partial \tau} \mathbf{P}(\tau, t) = -\mathbf{V}(\tau)\,\mathbf{P}(\tau, t), \tag{2.24}$$

with the initial condition

$$\mathbf{P}(t, t) = \mathbf{I}. \tag{2.25}$$

The symbol **I** denotes an $s \times s$ unit matrix.

We will conclude this section by restating some stochastic processes in terms of this new formulation.

2.2. Examples.

Example 1: In a *Poisson process* the intensity matrix is

$$\mathbf{V} = \begin{pmatrix} -\lambda & \lambda & 0 & 0 & \cdot & \cdot \\ 0 & -\lambda & \lambda & 0 & \cdot & \cdot \\ 0 & 0 & -\lambda & \lambda & \cdot & \cdot \\ \cdot & \cdot & \cdot & \cdot & \cdot & \cdot \end{pmatrix}. \tag{2.26}$$

The Kolmogorov differential equations are

$$\frac{\partial}{\partial t} P_{ij}(\tau, t) = P_{ij}(\tau, t)(-\lambda) + P_{i, j-1}(\tau, t)\lambda$$

and

$$\frac{\partial}{\partial \tau} P_{ij}(\tau, t) = \lambda P_{ij}(\tau, t) - \lambda P_{i+1, j}(\tau, t). \tag{2.27}$$

Example 2: In the *pure death process* the intensity matrix is

$$\mathbf{V}(t) = \begin{pmatrix} 0 & 0 & 0 & 0 & \cdot & \cdot \\ \mu(t) & -\mu(t) & 0 & 0 & \cdot & \cdot \\ 0 & 2\mu(t) & -2\mu(t) & 0 & \cdot & \cdot \\ 0 & 0 & 3\mu(t) & -3\mu(t) & \cdot & \cdot \\ \cdot & \cdot & \cdot & \cdot & \cdot & \cdot \end{pmatrix}. \tag{2.28}$$

The Kolmogorov differential equations are

$$\frac{\partial}{\partial t} P_{ij}(\tau, t) = P_{ij}(\tau, t)\,[-j\mu(t)] + P_{i, j+1}(\tau, t)(j+1)\mu(t)$$

and

$$\frac{\partial}{\partial \tau} P_{ij}(\tau, t) = i\mu(\tau) P_{ij}(\tau, t) - i\mu(\tau) P_{i-1, j}(\tau, t). \tag{2.29}$$

Example 3: In the *general birth-death process* the intensity matrix is

$$\mathbf{V}(t) = \begin{pmatrix} 0 & 0 & 0 & 0 & \cdot & \cdot \\ \mu(t) & -[\lambda(t)+\mu(t)] & \lambda(t) & 0 & \cdot & \cdot \\ 0 & 2\mu(t) & -2[\lambda(t)+\mu(t)] & 2\lambda(t) & \cdot & \cdot \\ \cdot & \cdot & \cdot & \cdot & \cdot & \cdot \\ \cdot & \cdot & \cdot & \cdot & \cdot & \cdot \end{pmatrix}. \quad (2.30)$$

The two systems of equations are

$$\frac{\partial}{\partial t} P_{ij}(\tau, t) = P_{i,j-1}(\tau, t)(j-1)\lambda(t) + P_{ij}(\tau,t)\{-j\,[\lambda(t)+\mu(t)]\}$$
$$+ P_{i,j+1}(\tau, t)(j+1)\mu(t)$$

and

$$\frac{\partial}{\partial \tau} P_{ij}(\tau, t) = -i\lambda(\tau)\, P_{i+1,j}(\tau, t) + i[\lambda(\tau)+\mu(\tau)]\, P_{ij}(\tau, t)$$
$$- i\mu(\tau)P_{i-1,j}(\tau, t). \quad (2.33)$$

3. MATRICES, EIGENVALUES AND DIAGONALIZATION

Before proceeding to derive explicit solutions for the Kolmogorov differential equations, let us briefly review some important concepts from linear algebra (see Birkhoff and MacLane [1953] and Gantmacher [1960]). First, a few definitions are in order.

Let

$$\mathbf{W} = \begin{pmatrix} w_{11} & w_{12} & \cdots & w_{1s} \\ w_{21} & w_{22} & \cdots & w_{2s} \\ \vdots & \vdots & & \vdots \\ w_{s1} & w_{s2} & \cdots & w_{ss} \end{pmatrix} \quad (3.1)$$

be any $s \times s$ matrix of elements w_{ij}; let $\mathbf{W}'$ be its transpose, and let $|\mathbf{W}|$ be its determinant. A *minor* of order r of $\mathbf{W}$ is any $r \times r$ submatrix of $\mathbf{W}$ obtained by crossing out $s - r$ rows and $s - r$ columns.

A *principal minor* is a minor whose diagonal elements lie on the diagonal of **W**. A *cofactor* W_{ij} of the (i,j) element of **W** is $(-1)^{i+j}$ times the determinant of the minor of order $s-1$, which is obtained by deleting from **W** the i-th row and the j-th column.

The determinant $|\mathbf{W}|$ of **W** can be expanded in terms of the cofactors of any row,

$$|\mathbf{W}| = \sum_{j=1}^{s} w_{ij} W_{ij}, \qquad i = 1, \ldots, s, \tag{3.2}$$

or of any column,

$$|\mathbf{W}| = \sum_{i=1}^{s} w_{ij} W_{ij}, \qquad j = 1, \ldots, s. \tag{3.3}$$

On the other hand, if an expansion is made in terms of elements of one row (column) and cofactors of a different row (column), the sum vanishes:

$$\sum_{j=1}^{s} w_{ij} W_{kj} = 0 \qquad \text{if } k \neq i \tag{3.4}$$

$$\sum_{i=1}^{s} w_{ij} W_{ik} = 0 \qquad \text{if } k \neq j. \tag{3.5}$$

We call **W** a *singular matrix* if its determinants $|\mathbf{W}| = 0$, *non-singular* if $|\mathbf{W}| \neq 0$. A matrix **W** is non-singular if all the columns (and, in fact, all the rows) are linearly independent. The *rank* of a matrix is the size of its largest non-singular square submatrix; thus a matrix is of rank r if it has at least one $r \times r$ non-singular submatrix and all larger submatrices are singular.

Let W_{ij} be the cofactors of **W**. The matrix

$$\mathbf{M} = \begin{pmatrix} W_{11} & W_{21} & \cdots & W_{s1} \\ W_{12} & W_{22} & \cdots & W_{s2} \\ \vdots & \vdots & & \vdots \\ W_{1s} & W_{2s} & \cdots & W_{ss} \end{pmatrix} \tag{3.6}$$

is the *adjoint matrix* of **W** (note that the indices are transposed!). It is clear from equations (3.2) and (3.5) that

$$\mathbf{MW} = \begin{pmatrix} W_{11} & W_{21} & \cdots & W_{s1} \\ W_{12} & W_{22} & \cdots & W_{s2} \\ \vdots & \vdots & & \vdots \\ W_{1s} & W_{2s} & \cdots & W_{ss} \end{pmatrix} \begin{pmatrix} w_{11} & w_{12} & \cdots & w_{1s} \\ w_{21} & w_{22} & \cdots & w_{2s} \\ \vdots & \vdots & & \vdots \\ w_{s1} & w_{s2} & \cdots & w_{ss} \end{pmatrix}$$

$$= \begin{pmatrix} |W| & 0 & \cdots & 0 \\ 0 & |W| & \cdots & 0 \\ \vdots & \vdots & & \vdots \\ 0 & 0 & \cdots & |W| \end{pmatrix} = \mathbf{WM}. \tag{3.7}$$

Thus we have

$$\mathbf{MW} = \mathbf{WM} = |W|\mathbf{I}, \tag{3.8}$$

where $\mathbf{I}$ is an $s \times s$ identity matrix.

Suppose $\mathbf{W}$ is non-singular, so that $|W| \neq 0$. Let

$$W^{-1} = \begin{pmatrix} \frac{W_{11}}{|W|} & \frac{W_{21}}{|W|} & \cdots & \frac{W_{s1}}{|W|} \\ \frac{W_{12}}{|W|} & \frac{W_{22}}{|W|} & \cdots & \frac{W_{s2}}{|W|} \\ \vdots & \vdots & & \vdots \\ \frac{W_{1s}}{|W|} & \frac{W_{2s}}{|W|} & \cdots & \frac{W_{ss}}{|W|} \end{pmatrix}. \tag{3.9}$$

From (3.8) we deduce that

$$\mathbf{WW}^{-1} = \mathbf{I} = \mathbf{W}^{-1}\mathbf{W}. \tag{3.10}$$

If $\mathbf{W}$ has an inverse $\mathbf{W}^{-1}$, then $|W||W^{-1}| = |WW^{-1}| = |I| = 1$; therefore the determinant $|W| \neq 0$. Now let w_{jk}^{-1} be the (j, k)th element of an inverse of $\mathbf{W}$, so that $\sum_{j=1}^{s} w_{ij}w_{jk}^{-1} = \delta_{ik}$; from (3.2) and (3.4) we see that $w_{jk}^{-1} = W_{kj}/|W|$. To summarize, we have:

Theorem 2. *A square matrix* $\mathbf{W}$ *has an inverse if and only if the determinant* $|W| \neq 0$, *and the matrix* $\mathbf{W}^{-1}$ *given in* (3.9) *is the unique inverse.*

3.1 Eigenvalues and Eigenvectors.

If a non-zero column vector **t** and a scalar ρ satisfy the equation

$$\mathbf{W}\mathbf{t} = \rho\mathbf{t}, \tag{3.11}$$

then ρ is called an *eigenvalue* or *characteristic root* of **W**, and **t** is an *eigenvector* of **W** corresponding to the eigenvalue ρ. Clearly, an eigenvector of **W** multiplied by a scalar also is an eignenvector of **W** corresponding to the same eigenvalue.

Rewriting (3.11) as

$$(\rho\mathbf{I} - \mathbf{W})\mathbf{t} = \mathbf{0}, \tag{3.12}$$

we see that the equation holds true if and only if the *characteristic matrix* of **W**,

$$(\rho\mathbf{I} - \mathbf{W}) = \mathbf{A}, \tag{3.13}$$

is singular; or if and only if the determinant $|A| = 0$. Hence ρ is an eigenvalue of **W** if and only if

$$|A| = |\rho I - W| = 0. \tag{3.14}$$

Equation (3.14) is the *characteristic equation* of the matrix **W**, and the determinant $|A|$ is the *characteristic polynomial* of **W**. Since $|A|$ is a polynomial of degree s in the unknown ρ, it follows from the fundamental theorem of algebra that (3.14) has exactly s roots, which we denote by $\rho_1, \ldots, \rho_s$.

The characteristic polynomial can be expanded in powers of ρ:

$$|\rho I - W| = \rho^s - b_1\rho^{s-1} + b_2\rho^{s-2} - \ldots + (-1)^{s-1}b_{s-1}\rho + (-1)^s b_s \tag{3.15}$$

where the b_i are constants. Straightforward computations show that the coefficient b_r is the sum of the determinants of all principle minors of **W** of order r. For example, $b_1 = w_{11} + \ldots + w_{ss}$; $b_{s-1} = W_{11} + \ldots + W_{ss}$; and $b_{ss} = |W|$. The coefficient b_1 is called the *trace* or *spur* of W. It is usually written tr W or sp W. The characteristic polynomial may also be written in terms of the roots $\rho_1, \ldots, \rho_s$:

$$|\rho I - W| = (\rho - \rho_1) \ldots (\rho - \rho_s). \tag{3.16}$$

Expanding (3.16) in powers of ρ and equating coefficients of the corresponding powers in (3.15), we find that for each r the coefficient

b_r is equal to the sum of all products of ρ_i taken r at a time. In particular,

$$b_1 = \sum_{i=1}^{s} w_{ii} = \sum_{i=1}^{s} \rho_i,$$

$$b_2 = \sum_{j>i}^{s} \sum_{i=1}^{s-1} \begin{vmatrix} w_{ii} & w_{ij} \\ w_{ji} & w_{jj} \end{vmatrix} = \rho_1\rho_2 + \dots + \rho_{s-1}\rho_s \tag{3.17}$$

$$b_{s-1} = \sum_{i=1}^{s} W_{ii} = \rho_1\rho_2 \dots \rho_{s-1} + \dots + \rho_2\rho_3 \dots \rho_s$$

$$b_s = |W| = \rho_1\rho_2 \dots \rho_s.$$

The eigenvalues ρ_j may be real or complex numbers; they may or may not be distinct. The following theorem applies to distinct eigenvalues:

Theorem 3. *The eigenvectors corresponding to distinct eigenvalues are linearly independent.*

Proof. Let $\rho_1, \dots, \rho_r$ be distinct eigenvalues of $\mathbf{W}$ and $\mathbf{T}_1, \dots, \mathbf{T}_r$ be the corresponding eigenvectors with

$$\mathbf{W}\mathbf{T}_j = \rho_j \mathbf{T}_j, \qquad j = 1, \dots, r. \tag{3.18}$$

We shall prove the theorem by contradiction. Suppose that the eigenvectors are linearly dependent, so that there exist constants c_j, not all of which are zero, such that

$$\sum_{j=1}^{r} c_j \mathbf{T}_j = \mathbf{0}. \tag{3.19}$$

Without loss of generality, we may assume that $c_1 \neq 0$. Now consider the matrix

$$\mathbf{U} = (\rho_2\mathbf{I} - \mathbf{W})(\rho_3\mathbf{I} - \mathbf{W}) \cdots (\rho_r\mathbf{I} - \mathbf{W}), \tag{3.20}$$

and determine the matrix product

$$\mathbf{U}\mathbf{T}_r = (\rho_2\mathbf{I} - \mathbf{W}) \cdots (\rho_{r-1}\mathbf{I} - \mathbf{W})(\rho_r\mathbf{T}_r - \mathbf{W}\mathbf{T}_r) = \mathbf{0}, \tag{3.21}$$

since the last factor vanishes because of (3.18). Similarly, we have

$$\mathbf{U T}_2 = \mathbf{U T}_3 = \cdots = \mathbf{U T}_r = \mathbf{0}. \tag{3.22}$$

On the other hand,

$$\begin{aligned} \mathbf{U T}_1 &= (\rho_2 \mathbf{I} - \mathbf{W}) \cdots (\rho_{r-1}\mathbf{I} - \mathbf{W})(\rho_r \mathbf{T}_1 - \mathbf{W T}_1) \\ &= (\rho_2 \mathbf{I} - \mathbf{W}) \cdots (\rho_{r-1}\mathbf{I} - \mathbf{W})(\rho_r - \rho_1)\mathbf{T}_1 \\ &= (\rho_2 \mathbf{I} - \mathbf{W}) \cdots (\rho_{r-1}\mathbf{T}_1 - \mathbf{W T}_1)(\rho_r - \rho_1) \\ &= (\rho_2 \mathbf{I} - \mathbf{W}) \cdots (\rho_{r-1} - \rho_1)(\rho_r - \rho_1)\mathbf{T}_1 \\ &= \cdots \\ &= (\rho_2 - \rho_1) \cdots (\rho_{r-1} - \rho_1)(\rho_r - \rho_1)\mathbf{T}_1 . \end{aligned} \tag{3.23}$$

From (3.19), (3.22), and (3.23) we see that

$$\begin{aligned} \mathbf{0} = \mathbf{U} \sum_{j=1}^{r} c_j \mathbf{T}_j = \sum_{j=1}^{r} c_j \mathbf{U T}_j = c_1 \mathbf{U T}_1 \\ = c_1(\rho_2 - \rho_1) \cdots (\rho_r - \rho_1)\mathbf{T}_1 . \end{aligned} \tag{3.24}$$

Since the ρ_j are all distinct, (3.24) implies that c_1 must be zero. This result, which contradicts our assumption that $c_1 \neq 0$, proves that eigenvectors are linearly independent.

3.2. Diagonalization of a Matrix.

If all the eigenvalues $\rho_1, \cdots, \rho_s$ of an $s \times s$ matrix $\mathbf{W}$ are distinct, then the matrix of the corresponding eigenvectors

$$\mathbf{T} = (\mathbf{T}_1, \cdots, \mathbf{T}_s) \tag{3.25}$$

has linearly independent columns; it is non-singular, and has an inverse $\mathbf{T}^{-1}$. Therefore, we can form the matrix

$$\mathbf{T}^{-1}\mathbf{W}\,\mathbf{T}. \tag{3.26}$$

To examine the structure of the matrix in (3.26), we use equations (3.25) and (3.18) to write

$$\mathbf{W T} = (\mathbf{W T}_1, \dots, \mathbf{W T}_s) = (\rho_1 \mathbf{T}_1, \dots, \rho_s \mathbf{T}_s) \tag{3.27}$$

and hence

$$\mathbf{T}^{-1}\mathbf{W T} = (\rho_1 \mathbf{T}^{-1}\mathbf{T}_1, \dots, \rho_s \mathbf{T}^{-1}\mathbf{T}_s). \tag{3.28}$$

Now we write the identity $\mathbf{T}^{-1}\mathbf{T} = \mathbf{I}$ as

$$(\mathbf{T}^{-1}\mathbf{T}_1, \ldots, \mathbf{T}^{-1}\mathbf{T}_s) = \begin{pmatrix} 1 & 0 & \cdots & 0 \\ 0 & 1 & \cdots & 0 \\ \vdots & \vdots & & \vdots \\ 0 & 0 & \cdots & 1 \end{pmatrix} \tag{3.29}$$

and apply (3.29) to (3.28) to get

$$\mathbf{T}^{-1}\mathbf{W}\mathbf{T} = \begin{pmatrix} \rho_1 & 0 & \cdots & 0 \\ 0 & \rho_2 & \cdots & 0 \\ \vdots & \vdots & & \vdots \\ 0 & 0 & \cdots & \rho_s \end{pmatrix} = \boldsymbol{\rho}. \tag{3.30}$$

In equation (3.30), $\boldsymbol{\rho}$ is what is known as the diagonalized form of the matrix $\mathbf{W}$.

Theorem 4. *For an $s \times s$ matrix to be diagonalizable, it is necessary and sufficient that it possess s linearly independent eigenvectors; in particular, it is sufficient that the matrix have s distinct eigenvalues.*

Since an eigenvector $\mathbf{T}_j$ multiplied by a non-zero constant also corresponds to the same eigenvalue ρ_j, there is more than one matrix which diagonalizes $\mathbf{W}$. Let $c_j \neq 0$ be non-zero constants, and

$$\mathbf{R} = (c_1\mathbf{T}_1, \ldots, c_s\mathbf{T}_s). \tag{3.31}$$

Then matrix $\mathbf{R}$ also diagonalizes $\mathbf{W}$, or

$$\mathbf{R}^{-1}\mathbf{W}\mathbf{R} = \begin{pmatrix} \rho_1 & 0 & \cdots & 0 \\ 0 & \rho_2 & \cdots & 0 \\ \vdots & \vdots & & \vdots \\ 0 & 0 & \cdots & \rho_s \end{pmatrix}. \tag{3.32}$$

3.3. A Useful Lemma.

In further discussing diagonalized matrices and in deriving solutions for Kolmogorov differential equations, we need Lemma 2 in Chapter 6 which is restated here for easy reference.

Lemma 1: *For any distinct numbers* $\rho_1, \ldots, \rho_s$,

$$\sum_{i=1}^{s} \frac{\rho_i^r}{\prod_{\substack{j=1 \\ j \neq i}}^{s} (\rho_i - \rho_j)} = 0 \qquad for \qquad 0 \le r < s - 1$$

$$= 1 \qquad for \qquad r = s - 1. \tag{3.33}$$

3.4. Matrix of Eigenvectors.

In section 3.2 we were concerned with basic properties of eigenvectors and the role they play in diagonalizing a matrix. The essential problem remaining is to show how to find an eigenvector $\mathbf{T}_j$ for a given eigenvalue ρ_j. In this section we provide such eigenvectors and the matrix $\mathbf{T}$ that serves to diagonalize the original matrix $\mathbf{W}$.

Consider the characteristic matrix

$$\mathbf{A}(\rho_j) = (\rho_j \mathbf{I} - \mathbf{W}), \tag{3.34}$$

which corresponds to ρ_j; and let $A_{ki}(\rho_j)$ be the cofactors of $A(\rho_j)$. A non-zero vector

$$\mathbf{T}_j(k) = \begin{pmatrix} A_{k1}(\rho_j) \\ A_{k2}(\rho_j) \\ \vdots \\ A_{ks}(\rho_j) \end{pmatrix} \tag{3.35}$$

is an eigenvector of $\mathbf{W}$ for $\rho = \rho_j$, whatever may be $k = 1, 2, \ldots, s$. Formally we introduce the following theorem.

Theorem 5. *Any non-zero column of the adjoint matrix of* $\mathbf{A}(\rho_j)$ *is an eigenvector corresponding to eigenvalue* ρ_j.

Proof. For every eigenvalue ρ_j and corresponding eigenvector $\mathbf{T}_j(k)$, we have

$$(\rho_j \mathbf{I} - \mathbf{W})\mathbf{T}_j(k) = \mathbf{A}(\rho_j) \begin{pmatrix} A_{k1}(\rho_j) \\ A_{k2}(\rho_j) \\ \vdots \\ A_{ks}(\rho_j) \end{pmatrix} = \begin{pmatrix} 0 \\ 0 \\ \vdots \\ 0 \end{pmatrix}. \tag{3.36}$$

The last equality in (3.36) is easily justified. For $i \neq k$, the i-th element of the matrix product represents an expansion of $|A(\rho_j)|$ in terms of elements of one row by cofactors of a different row; thus the i-th element must vanish. The k-th element, which is equal to the determinant $|A(\rho_j)|$, must also vanish, because ρ_j is a root of the equation $|\rho I - W| = 0$.

When the eigenvalues $\rho_1, \ldots, \rho_s$, are distinct, we may select any non-zero column from each adjoint matrix of $\mathbf{A}(\rho_j)$, $j = 1, \ldots, s$, to formulate a matrix $\mathbf{T}$ that will diagnonalize $\mathbf{W}$ as in (3.30). However, there is an advantage in selecting the *same* column from each of the adjoint matrices. Take a typical example:

$$\mathbf{T}(k) = \begin{pmatrix} A_{k1}(\rho_1) & A_{k1}(\rho_2) & \cdots & A_{k1}(\rho_s) \\ A_{k2}(\rho_1) & A_{k2}(\rho_2) & \cdots & A_{k2}(\rho_s) \\ \vdots & \vdots & & \vdots \\ A_{ks}(\rho_1) & A_{k2}(\rho_2) & \cdots & A_{ks}(\rho_s) \end{pmatrix}. \tag{3.37}$$

The j-th column in (3.37) is the k-th column of the adjoint matrix of $\mathbf{A}(\rho_j) = (\rho_j \mathbf{I} - \mathbf{W})$, and k is the same for all j. Since we assume the eigenvalues to be distinct, the matrix $\mathbf{T}(k)$ consists of s linearly independent non-zero vectors, and we have

Theorem 6. *If the eigenvalues* $\rho_1, \ldots, \rho_s$, *of* $\mathbf{W}$ *are distinct, then matrix* $\mathbf{T}(k)$ *in equation* (3.37) *diagonalizes* W:

$$\mathbf{T}^{-1}(k)\mathbf{W}\mathbf{T}(k) = \boldsymbol{\rho}, \tag{3.38}$$

where $\boldsymbol{\rho} = \operatorname{diag}[\rho_1, \ldots, \rho_s]$, *as given in equation* (3.30).

The inverse of $\mathbf{T}(k)$ is

$$\mathbf{T}^{-1}(k) = \begin{pmatrix} \dfrac{T_{11}(k)}{|T(k)|} & \cdots & \dfrac{T_{k1}(k)}{|T(k)|} & \cdots & \dfrac{T_{s1}(k)}{|T(k)|} \\ \dfrac{T_{12}(k)}{|T(k)|} & \cdots & \dfrac{T_{k2}(k)}{|T(k)|} & \cdots & \dfrac{T_{s2}(k)}{|T(k)|} \\ \cdot & \cdot & \cdot & \cdot & \cdot \\ \dfrac{T_{1s}(k)}{|T(k)|} & \cdots & \dfrac{T_{ks}(k)}{|T(k)|} & \cdots & \dfrac{T_{ss}(k)}{|T(k)|} \end{pmatrix}, \tag{3.39}$$

where $T_{ij}(k)$ are the cofactors of $\mathbf{T}(k)$. Clearly the matrix $\mathbf{T}(k)$ varies with the choice of k. However, the inverse matrices $\mathbf{T}^{-1}(1), \ldots, \mathbf{T}^{-1}(s)$ have an important feature in common.

Theorem 7. *The k-th column of the inverse matrix* $\mathbf{T}^{-1}(k)$ *defined in* (3.39) *is independent of k and is given by*

$$\begin{pmatrix} \dfrac{T_{11}(1)}{|T(1)|} \\ \\ \dfrac{T_{12}(1)}{|T(1)|} \\ \\ \vdots \\ \\ \dfrac{T_{1s}(1)}{|T(1)|} \end{pmatrix} = \cdots = \begin{pmatrix} \dfrac{T_{s1}(s)}{|T(s)|} \\ \\ \dfrac{T_{s2}(s)}{|T(s)|} \\ \\ \vdots \\ \\ \dfrac{T_{ss}(s)}{|T(s)|} \end{pmatrix} = \begin{pmatrix} \dfrac{1}{\prod\limits_{l=2}^{s}(\rho_1 - \rho_l)} \\ \\ \dfrac{1}{\prod\limits_{\substack{l=1 \\ l\neq 2}}^{s}(\rho_2 - \rho_l)} \\ \\ \vdots \\ \\ \dfrac{1}{\prod\limits_{l=1}^{s-1}(\rho_s - \rho_l)} \end{pmatrix}. \tag{3.40}$$

Before presenting a proof of Theorem 7, let us illustrate it with an example.

Example: $s = 2$. In the illness-death process described in Chapter 11, the matrix $\mathbf{V}$ and its characteristic matrix are

$$\mathbf{V} = \begin{pmatrix} \nu_{11} & \nu_{12} \\ \nu_{21} & \nu_{22} \end{pmatrix}$$

and

$$\mathbf{A}(\rho_j) = \begin{pmatrix} \rho_j - \nu_{11} & -\nu_{12} \\ -\nu_{21} & \rho_j - \nu_{22} \end{pmatrix}.$$

The eigenvalues are

$$\rho_1 = \tfrac{1}{2}\left[(\nu_{11} + \nu_2) + \sqrt{(\nu_{11} - \nu_{22})^2 + 4\nu_{12}\nu_{21}}\,\right]$$

and

$$\rho_2 = \tfrac{1}{2}\left[(\nu_{11} + \nu_{22}) - \sqrt{(\nu_{11} - \nu_{22})^2 + 4\nu_{12}\nu_{21}}\,\right].$$

Case 1: $k = 1$. By taking the first column of each of the adjoint matrices of $\mathbf{A}(\rho_j)$, we have

$$\mathbf{T}(1) = \begin{pmatrix} A_{11}(\rho_1) & A_{11}(\rho_2) \\ A_{12}(\rho_1) & A_{12}(\rho_2) \end{pmatrix} = \begin{pmatrix} \rho_1 - \nu_{22} & \rho_2 - \nu_{22} \\ \nu_{21} & \nu_{21} \end{pmatrix};$$

the determinant is $|T(1)| = \nu_{21}(\rho_1 - \rho_2)$. We can compute the inverse directly:

$$\mathbf{T}^{-1}(1) = \begin{pmatrix} \dfrac{T_{11}(1)}{|T(1)|} & \dfrac{T_{21}(1)}{|T(1)|} \\ \dfrac{T_{12}(1)}{|T(1)|} & \dfrac{T_{22}(1)}{|T(1)|} \end{pmatrix} = \begin{pmatrix} \dfrac{1}{\rho_1 - \rho_2} & -\dfrac{\rho_2 - \nu_{22}}{\nu_{21}(\rho_1 - \rho_2)} \\ \dfrac{1}{\rho_2 - \rho_1} & -\dfrac{\rho_1 - \nu_{22}}{\nu_{21}(\rho_2 - \rho_1)} \end{pmatrix}$$

where the *first* column is given in (3.40).

Case 2: $k = 2$. We take the second column of each of the adjoint matrices of $\mathbf{A}(\rho_j)$ to get

$$\mathbf{T}(2) = \begin{pmatrix} A_{21}(\rho_1) & A_{21}(\rho_2) \\ A_{22}(\rho_1) & A_{22}(\rho_2) \end{pmatrix} = \begin{pmatrix} \nu_{12} & \nu_{12} \\ \rho_1 - \nu_{11} & \rho_2 - \nu_{11} \end{pmatrix};$$

the determinant is $|T(2)| = \nu_{12}(\rho_2 - \rho_1)$. The inverse is

$$\mathbf{T}^{-1}(2) = \begin{pmatrix} \dfrac{T_{11}(2)}{|T(2)|} & \dfrac{T_{21}(2)}{|T(2)|} \\ \dfrac{T_{12}(2)}{|T(2)|} & \dfrac{T_{22}(2)}{|T(2)|} \end{pmatrix} = \begin{pmatrix} -\dfrac{\rho_2 - \nu_{11}}{\nu_{12}(\rho_1 - \rho_2)} & \dfrac{1}{\rho_1 - \rho_2} \\ -\dfrac{\rho_1 - \nu_{11}}{\nu_{12}(\rho_2 - \rho_1)} & \dfrac{1}{\rho_2 - \rho_1} \end{pmatrix}$$

where the *second* column is given in (3.40), and is also equal to the first column of $\mathbf{T}^{-1}(1)$.

Proof of Theorem 7. Use $\mathbf{T}(k)$ as it is given in (3.37) to formulate the following system of simultaneous equations,

$$T(k) \begin{pmatrix} z_1 \\ z_2 \\ \vdots \\ z_s \end{pmatrix} = \begin{pmatrix} \delta_{1k} \\ \delta_{2k} \\ \vdots \\ \delta_{sk} \end{pmatrix}, \tag{3.41}$$

where the components z_j of the column vector $\mathbf{z}$ are unknown constants, and δ_{jk} is the Kronecker delta. Obviously, the solution of (3.41) is

$$z_j = \frac{T_{kj}(k)}{|T(k)|}, \qquad j = 1, \cdots, s. \tag{3.42}$$

We can write equation (3.41) in scalar notation as

$$\left.\begin{array}{l} A_{k1}(\rho_1)z_1 + \cdots + A_{k1}(\rho_s)z_s = 0 \\ \cdot \qquad \cdot \qquad \cdot \quad \cdot \\ A_{kk}(\rho_1)z_1 + \cdots + A_{kk}(\rho_s)z_s = 1 \\ \cdot \qquad \cdot \qquad \cdot \quad \cdot \\ A_{ks}(\rho_1)z_1 + \cdots + A_{ks}(\rho_s)z_s = 0. \end{array}\right\} . \tag{3.43}$$

The cofactors $A_{ki}(\rho_j)$ in (3.43) are then expanded in polynomials of ρ_j as in equation (3.15):

$$\begin{aligned} A_{kk}(\rho_j) &= \rho_j^{s-1} + b_{kk2}\,\rho_j^{s-2} + \cdots + b_{kks}\,\rho_j^0 \\ A_{ki}(\rho_j) &= \qquad\quad b_{ki2}\,\rho_j^{s-2} + \cdots + b_{kis}\,\rho_j^0, \\ & \qquad\qquad i \neq k, \; i = 1, \ldots, s. \end{aligned} \tag{3.44}$$

The coefficients b in (3.44) are functions of w_{ij}, but are independent of ρ_j and j. When (3.44) is introduced in (3.43), and the terms rearranged according to the coefficients b, the resulting equations are

$$\left.\begin{array}{l} b_{k12}\sum_{j=1}^{s} z_j\,\rho_j^{s-2} + \cdots + b_{k1s}\sum_{j=1}^{s} z_j\,\rho_j^0 = 0 \\ \sum_{j=1}^{s} z_j\,\rho_j^{s-1} + b_{kk2}\sum_{j=1}^{s} z_j\,\rho_j^{s-2} + \cdots + b_{kks}\sum_{j=1}^{s} z_j\,\rho_j^0 = 1 \\ \cdot \qquad \cdot \qquad \cdot \qquad \cdot \\ b_{ks2}\sum_{j=1}^{s} z_j\,\rho_j^{s-2} + \cdots + b_{kss}\sum_{j=1}^{s} z_j\,\rho_j^0 = 0. \end{array}\right\} . \tag{3.45}$$

Our problem is to solve (3.45) for z_j. Recalling Lemma 1, we know that whatever may be s distinct numbers $\rho_1, \ldots, \rho_s$,

$$\sum_{j=1}^{s} \frac{\rho_j^r}{\prod_{\substack{l=1 \\ l \neq j}}^{s} (\rho_j - \rho_l)} = 1, \qquad r = s - 1$$

$$= 0, \qquad 0 \leq r < s - 1. \tag{3.33}$$

Therefore the solution of (3.45) is

$$z_j = \frac{1}{\prod_{\substack{l=1 \\ l \neq j}}^{s} (\rho_j - \rho_l)}, \qquad j = 1, \cdots, s. \tag{3.46}$$

Since the determinant of $\mathbf{T}(k)$ is not zero, equation (3.41) has a unique solution; hence solutions (3.42) and (3.46) are equal. Theorem 7 is proven.

4. EXPLICIT SOLUTIONS FOR KOLMOGOROV DIFFERENTIAL EQUATIONS

In this section we consider the Kolmogorov differential equations for time homogeneous finite Markov processes when matrix V has single eigenvalues. We present two explicit solutions for these equations and show that the two solutions are identical. The reasoning used to derive these solutions applies to any finite system of linear, first-order, homogeneous differential equations with constant coefficients. The general solutions also hold for functions other than transition probabilities. We shall study only systems in which all states are communicating states, in the sense that for every i, $j = 1, 2, \ldots$, there exists a $t > 0$ such that $P_{ij}(0, t) > 0$. Systems that incorporate absorbing states as well will be treated in Chapter 16.

Let a Markov process $\{X(t); t \varepsilon [0, \infty)\}$ consist of a finite number s of states, denoted by $1, \ldots, s$, with intensity functions ν_{ij} independent of t. We assume that the system is closed, so that for every i and for every $t > 0$,

$$\sum_{j=1}^{s} P_{ij}(0, t) = 1, \qquad i = 1, \ldots, s, \tag{4.1}$$

or

$$\nu_{ii} = -\sum_{\substack{j=1 \\ j \neq i}}^{s} \nu_{ij}, \qquad i = 1, \ldots, s, \tag{4.2}$$

and the matrix

$$\mathbf{V} = \begin{pmatrix} \nu_{11} & \cdots & \nu_{1s} \\ \vdots & & \vdots \\ \nu_{s1} & \cdots & \nu_{ss} \end{pmatrix} \tag{4.3}$$

is singular with rank $s - 1$.

The Kolmogorov differential equations for a finite Markov process are

$$\frac{d}{dt} P_{ik}(0, t) = \sum_{j=1}^{s} P_{ij}(0, t) \nu_{jk} \tag{4.4}$$

and

$$\frac{d}{dt} P_{ik}(0, t) = \sum_{j=1}^{s} \nu_{ij} P_{jk}(0, t), \tag{4.5}$$

with the initial conditions at $t = 0$,

$$P_{ik}(0, 0) = \delta_{ik}. \tag{4.6}$$

The corresponding matrix equations are

$$D\mathbf{P}(0, t) = \mathbf{P}(0, t)\mathbf{V} \qquad \text{or} \qquad (D - \mathbf{V}')\mathbf{P}'(0, t) = \mathbf{0}, \tag{4.7}$$

$$D\mathbf{P}(0, t) = \mathbf{V}\mathbf{P}(0, t) \qquad \text{or} \qquad (D - \mathbf{V})\mathbf{P}(0, t) = \mathbf{0} \tag{4.8}$$

and

$$\mathbf{P}(0, 0) = \mathbf{I} \tag{4.9}$$

where D is a diagonal matrix with the differentiation operator d/dt on the diagonal line. The matrix $\mathbf{P}(0, t)$ is the transition probability matrix

$$\mathbf{P}(0, t) = \begin{pmatrix} P_{11}(0, t) & \cdots & P_{1s}(0, t) \\ \vdots & & \vdots \\ P_{s1}(0, t) & \cdots & P_{ss}(0, t) \end{pmatrix}. \tag{4.10}$$

Our problem is to derive explicit functions for individual transition probabilities $P_{ik}(0, t)$ satisfying equations (4.4) and (4.5) and the Chapman-Kolmogorov equation

$$P_{ik}(0, \tau + t) = \sum_{j=1}^{s} P_{ij}(0, \tau) P_{jk}(0, t), \qquad i, k = 1, \dots, s. \quad (4.11)$$

4.1. Intensity Matrix V and its Eigenvalues.

Let

$$\mathbf{A} = (\rho \mathbf{I} - \mathbf{V}) \quad (4.12)$$

be the characteristic matrix of **V**, and let

$$|A| = |\rho I - V| = 0 \quad (4.13)$$

be the corresponding characteristic equation. The roots of (4.13) are the eigenvalues of **V**, which we denote by $\rho_1, \dots, \rho_s$. Because matrix **V** is singular, one of the eigenvalues, say ρ_1, is zero. The range of values of ρ is determined in the following theorem.

Theorem 8. *If a matrix* **V** *satisfies the conditions that* $v_{ij} \geq 0$ *for* $i \neq j$ *and* $\sum_{j=1}^{s} v_{ij} = 0$ *for* $i, j = 1, \dots, s$, *then the eigenvalues of* **V** *are non-positive.*

Proof. Let ρ be any real eigenvalue of **V**. There is at least one real non-zero vector

$$\mathbf{C} = \begin{pmatrix} c_1 \\ \vdots \\ c_s \end{pmatrix}$$

for which

$$(\rho \mathbf{I} - \mathbf{V})\mathbf{C} = 0, \quad (4.14)$$

or equivalently,

$$\rho c_i = v_{i1} c_1 + \dots + v_{is} c_s, \qquad i = 1, \dots, s. \quad (4.14a)$$

Let c_k be the largest component in absolute value of vector **C** so that $c_i c_k \leq c_k^2$, $i = 1, \dots, s$. Then from (4.14a) for $i = k$ we have

$$\rho c_k^2 = (v_{k1} c_1 + \dots + v_{ks} c_s) c_k \leq (v_{k1} + \dots + v_{ks}) c_k^2 = 0.$$

Therefore, $\rho \leq 0$.

Theorem 8 is similar to Theorem 1, Chapter 6, which pertains to the eigenvalue of a stochastic matrix P. In the present case, if $0 \le \nu_{ij} < 1$, for $i \neq j$ and $0 < |\nu_{ii}| < 1$, then we can use the result in Chapter 6 to determine a narrower range for values of ρ.

Corollary. *If every diagonal element of matrix* **V** *is less than one in absolute value, then the range of the eigenvalue of* **V** *is* $-2 \le \rho \le 0$.

Proof. Let

$$\lambda = 1 + \rho .$$

Then rewrite the characteristic matrix of **V** as follows:

$$(\rho \mathbf{I} - \mathbf{V}) = (\lambda \mathbf{I} - (\mathbf{I} + \mathbf{V})) . \tag{4.15}$$

Every element of the matrix $(\mathbf{I} + \mathbf{V})$ is between zero and one and each row sum of $(\mathbf{I} + \mathbf{V})$ is equal to one. According to Theorem 1, Chapter 6, the eigenvalue of $(\mathbf{I} + \mathbf{V})$ is $|\lambda| \le 1$. Therefore the range of ρ is $-2 \le \rho \le 0$.

Lemma 2. *Cofactors of elements in the same row of* **V** *are equal; that is,*

$$V_{ij} = V_{ik}, \qquad i, j, k = 1, \ldots, s . \tag{4.16}$$

This lemma is essentially the same as lemma 1 in section 2, Chapter 6. The reader is referred to Chapter 6 for proof of lemma 2.

We have seen in (3.17) that the sum of all products of ρ_i taken $(s - 1)$ at a time is equal to the sum of the cofactors V_{ii},

$$\rho_1 \rho_2 \ldots \rho_{s-1} + \ldots + \rho_2 \rho_3 \ldots \rho_s = V_{11} + \ldots + V_{ss}$$

In the present case, however, $\rho_1 = 0$; therefore

$$\rho_2 \rho_3 \ldots \rho_s = V_{11} + \ldots + V_{ss} . \tag{4.17}$$

4.2. First Solution for Individual Transition Probabilities $P_{ij}(0, t)$.

The solution offered here was given by Chiang [1964a] in a study of competing risks; it is adapted here to a more general case. The Kolmogorov equations,

$$\frac{d}{dt} P_{ik}(0, t) = \sum_{j=1}^{s} P_{ij}(0, t) \nu_{jk}, \qquad i, k = 1, \ldots, s, \tag{4.4}$$

are linear, first order differential equations; thus their solutions are exponential functions of time. Therefore, we begin by looking for solutions that take the form

$$P_{ij}(0, t) = c_{ij} e^{\rho t}, \qquad i, j = 1, \ldots, s. \tag{4.18}$$

Equations (4.4) and (4.18) may be written in matrix notation as

$$(D - \mathbf{V}')\,\mathbf{P}'(0, t) = \mathbf{0} \tag{4.7}$$

and

$$\mathbf{P}(0, t) = \mathbf{C} e^{\rho t} \tag{4.19}$$

respectively, where ρ and the constant matrix

$$\mathbf{C} = \begin{pmatrix} c_{11} & \cdots & c_{1s} \\ \vdots & & \vdots \\ c_{s1} & \cdots & c_{ss} \end{pmatrix} \tag{4.20}$$

are to be determined. Substituting (4.19) in (4.7) and cancelling out the nonvanishing scalar factor $e^{\rho t}$, we obtain s simultaneous equations

$$(\rho\mathbf{I} - \mathbf{V}')\mathbf{C}' = \mathbf{0}. \tag{4.21}$$

In order for $\mathbf{C}'$ to have a non-trivial solution, it is necessary that the matrix $\mathbf{A}' = (\rho\mathbf{I} - \mathbf{V}')$ be singular, or that $|A'| = 0$. This means that the roots of the characteristic equation

$$|\rho I - V'| = 0 \tag{4.22}$$

are the only values of ρ for which (4.19) is a valid solution of (4.7). Since the matrix $\mathbf{V}$ and its transpose $\mathbf{V}'$ have the same eigenvalues, the roots of (4.22) are also the eigenvalues of $\mathbf{V}$. These are denoted by $\rho_1, \ldots, \rho_s$.

For each ρ_l, we use

$$(\rho_l\mathbf{I} - \mathbf{V}')\mathbf{C}'(l) = \mathbf{0} \tag{4.23}$$

to determine the corresponding constant matrix $\mathbf{C}(l)$. Since ρ_l is a solution of (4.22), the matrix

$$\mathbf{A}'(\rho_l) = \begin{pmatrix} \rho_l - \nu_{11} & -\nu_{21} & \cdots & -\nu_{s1} \\ -\nu_{12} & \rho_l - \nu_{22} & \cdots & -\nu_{s2} \\ \vdots & \vdots & & \vdots \\ -\nu_{1s} & -\nu_{2s} & \cdots & \rho_l - \nu_{ss} \end{pmatrix} \tag{4.24}$$

is singular. According to Cramer's rule, the homogeneous equations in (4.23) have non-trivial solutions where c_{ijl} are proportional to the corresponding cofactors $A'_{ij}(\rho_l)$ of $\mathbf{A}'(\rho_l)$, or

$$c_{ijl} = k_{il} A'_{ij}(\rho_l). \tag{4.25}$$

Therefore, for each ρ_l,

$$\begin{aligned} P_{ij}(0, t) &= c_{ijl} e^{\rho_l t} \\ &= k_{il} A'_{ij}(\rho_l) e^{\rho_l t}, \qquad l = 1, \dots, s. \end{aligned}$$

If all the s eigenvalues of $\mathbf{V}$ are distinct, the general solution of (4.4) is

$$P_{ij}(0, t) = \sum_{l=1}^{s} k_{il} A'_{ij}(\rho_l)\, e^{\rho_l t}, \qquad i, j = 1, \dots, s. \tag{4.26}$$

As we pointed out earlier, equation (4.26) is the general solution for any finite system of differential equations of the same type as (4.4), and $P_{ij}(0, t)$ need not represent probabilities.

To derive a particular solution corresponding to the initial conditions in equation (4.6), we set $t = 0$ in (4.26), thereby imposing the conditions on k_{il}:

$$\begin{aligned} \sum_{l=1}^{s} k_{il} A'_{ij}(\rho_l) &= 1, \qquad j = i, \\ &= 0, \qquad j \neq i;\ i, j = 1, \dots, s. \end{aligned} \tag{4.27}$$

To determine the values of k_{il} from (4.27) we expand the cofactors $A'_{ij}(\rho_l)$ in polynomials of ρ_l,

$$A'_{ii}(\rho_l) = \rho_l^{s-1} + b_{ii2}\, \rho_l^{s-2} + \dots + b_{iis}$$

and

$$A'_{ij}(\rho_l) = b_{ij2}\, \rho_l^{s-2} + \dots + b_{ijs}, \qquad j \neq i, \tag{4.28}$$

where the coefficients b are functions of ν_{ij} but are independent of ρ_l and l. Substituting (4.28) in (4.27) and rearranging terms according to coefficients b, the resulting equations are

$$\left.\begin{array}{r} b_{i12}\sum_{l=1}^{s} k_{il}\rho_l^{s-2} + \dots + b_{i1s}\sum_{l=1}^{s} k_{il} = 0 \\ \cdot \quad \cdot \quad \cdot \quad \cdot \quad \cdot \quad \cdot \quad \cdot \\ \sum_{l=1}^{s} k_{il}\rho_l^{s-1} + b_{ii2}\sum_{l=1}^{s} k_{il}\rho_l^{s-2} + \dots + b_{iis}\sum_{l=1}^{s} k_{il} = 1 \\ \cdot \quad \cdot \quad \cdot \quad \cdot \quad \cdot \quad \cdot \quad \cdot \\ b_{is2}\sum_{l=1}^{s} k_{il}\rho_l^{s-2} + \dots + b_{iss}\sum_{l=1}^{s} k_{il} = 0 \end{array}\right\} . \tag{4.29}$$

According to Lemma 1 in section 3.3,

$$\sum_{l=1}^{s} \frac{\rho_l^r}{\prod_{\substack{m=1\\m\neq l}}^{s} (\rho_l - \rho_m)} = 1 \qquad r = s - 1$$

$$= 0 \qquad 0 \leq r < s - 1. \tag{4.30}$$

Therefore, the values of k_{il} that satisfy equation (4.29) are

$$k_{il} = \frac{1}{\prod_{\substack{m=1\\m\neq l}}^{s} (\rho_l - \rho_m)}, \qquad i, l = 1, \dots, s. \tag{4.31}$$

Substituting (4.31) in (4.26) gives us an explicit solution for the Kolmogorov forward differential equations in (4.4):

$$P_{ij}(0, t) = \sum_{l=1}^{s} \frac{A'_{ij}(\rho_l)e^{\rho_l t}}{\prod_{\substack{m=1\\m\neq l}}^{s} (\rho_l - \rho_m)}, \qquad i, k = 1, \dots, s. \tag{4.32}$$

The solution presented in (4.32) is a real function of the intensity functions ν_{ij} and time t even when some of the eigenvalues are complex conjugates. Proof of this assertion is exactly the same as for Theorem 2, Chapter 6; we shall not repeat the argument here.

Theorem 9. *If intensity function matrix* **V** *has distinct eigenvalues* $\rho_1, \ldots, \rho_s$, *then the solution of the Kolmogorov differential equations* (4.4) *and* (4.5) *corresponding to the initial condition* (4.6) *is given in* (4.32). *The solution is a real function of* v_{ij} *even if* **V** *has complex eigenvalues.*

4.3. Second Solution for Individual Transition Probabilities $P_{ij}(0, t)$.

If we ignore the fact that $\mathbf{P}(0, t)$ and $\mathbf{V}$ are matrices, the differential equation

$$D\mathbf{P}(0, t) = \mathbf{P}(0, t)\mathbf{V} \tag{4.7}$$

has the appearance of an ordinary first-order differential equation with a constant coefficient. Formally, this suggests the solution

$$\mathbf{P}(0, t) = e^{\mathbf{V}t}\mathbf{P}(0,0),$$

or, since $\mathbf{P}(0, 0) = \mathbf{I}$,

$$\mathbf{P}(0, t) = e^{\mathbf{V}t}. \tag{4.33}$$

If the matrix exponential is defined by

$$e^{\mathbf{V}t} = \sum_{n=0}^{\infty} \frac{\mathbf{V}^n t^n}{n!}, \tag{4.34}$$

then (4.33) is indeed a solution of (4.7). We can show that the matrix series in (4.34) converges uniformly in t (for proof, see Bellman [1960] and Doob [1953]). Therefore we can take the derivative of the infinite sum in (4.33) with respect to t term by term:

$$D\mathbf{P}(0, t) = \frac{d}{dt} e^{\mathbf{V}t} = \frac{d}{dt} \sum_{n=0}^{\infty} \frac{\mathbf{V}^n t^n}{n!}$$

$$= \sum_{n=1}^{\infty} \frac{\mathbf{V}^{n-1} t^{n-1}}{(n-1)!} \mathbf{V} = e^{\mathbf{V}t}\mathbf{V} = \mathbf{P}(0, t)\mathbf{V}. \tag{4.35}$$

We thus recover the differential equation (4.7). Furthermore, substituting $t = 0$ in (4.33) produces an identity.

The formal solution in (4.33), however, is not very useful from a practical point of view. For purposes of application, we need to find explicit functions for the individual transition probabilities $P_{ij}(0, t)$ that satisfy differential equations (4.4) and (4.5).

Following up the discussion on diagonalization of a matrix in sections 3.2 and 3.4, we let

$$\mathbf{T}_l(k) = \begin{pmatrix} A_{kl}(\rho_l) \\ \cdot \\ \cdot \\ \cdot \\ A_{ks}(\rho_l) \end{pmatrix} \tag{4.36}$$

be a non-zero eigenvector of $\mathbf{V}$ for $\rho = \rho_l$. The matrix

$$\mathbf{T}(k) = [\mathbf{T}_1(k), \ldots, \mathbf{T}_s(k)] \tag{4.37}$$

diagonalizes $\mathbf{V}$ so that

$$\mathbf{T}^{-1}(k)\mathbf{V}\mathbf{T}(k) = \boldsymbol{\rho} \tag{4.38}$$

where $\boldsymbol{\rho}$ is the diagonal matrix given in (3.30). We can rewrite equation (4.38) as

$$\mathbf{V} = \mathbf{T}(k)\boldsymbol{\rho}\mathbf{T}^{-1}(k), \tag{4.39}$$

from which we compute

$$\mathbf{V}^2 = [\mathbf{T}(k)\boldsymbol{\rho}\mathbf{T}^{-1}(k)]\,[\mathbf{T}(k)\boldsymbol{\rho}\mathbf{T}^{-1}(k)] = \mathbf{T}(k)\boldsymbol{\rho}^2\mathbf{T}^{-1}(k). \tag{4.40}$$

Induction shows that, in general,

$$\mathbf{V}^n = \mathbf{T}(k)\boldsymbol{\rho}^n\mathbf{T}^{-1}(k), \qquad n = 1, 2, \ldots. \tag{4.41}$$

Now we use (4.41) to compute the exponential in equation (4.33):

$$e^{\mathbf{V}t} = \sum_{n=0}^{\infty}\frac{\mathbf{V}^n t^n}{n!} = \sum_{n=0}^{\infty}\frac{\mathbf{T}(k)\boldsymbol{\rho}^n\mathbf{T}^{-1}(k)t^n}{n!} = \mathbf{T}(k)\sum_{n=0}^{\infty}\frac{\boldsymbol{\rho}^n t^n}{n!}\mathbf{T}^{-1}(k). \tag{4.42}$$

Since $\boldsymbol{\rho}$ is a diagonal matrix,

$$\boldsymbol{\rho}^n = \begin{pmatrix} \rho_1^n & 0 & \cdots & 0 \\ 0 & \rho_2^n & \cdots & 0 \\ \vdots & \vdots & & \vdots \\ 0 & 0 & \cdots & \rho_s^n \end{pmatrix}; \tag{4.43}$$

hence,

$$\sum_{n=0}^{\infty} \frac{\rho^n t^n}{n!} = \begin{pmatrix} \sum_{n=0}^{\infty} \frac{\rho_1^n t^n}{n!} & 0 & \cdots & 0 \\ 0 & \sum_{n=0}^{\infty} \frac{\rho_2^n t^n}{n!} & \cdots & 0 \\ \cdot & \cdot & & \cdot \\ \cdot & \cdot & & \cdot \\ 0 & 0 & \cdots & \sum_{n=0}^{\infty} \frac{\rho_s^n t^n}{n!} \end{pmatrix}$$

$$= \begin{pmatrix} e^{\rho_1 t} & 0 & \cdots & 0 \\ 0 & e^{\rho_2 t} & \cdots & 0 \\ \cdot & \cdot & & \cdot \\ \cdot & \cdot & & \cdot \\ \cdot & \cdot & & \cdot \\ 0 & 0 & \cdots & e^{\rho_s t} \end{pmatrix}$$

$$= \mathbf{E}(t). \tag{4.44}$$

Where $\mathbf{E}(t)$ is written for the diagonal matrix:

$$\mathbf{E}(t) = \operatorname{diag}\,[e^{\rho_1 t}, \ldots, e^{\rho_s t}]\,. \tag{4.45}$$

Substituting (4.44) in (4.42), we see that the solution in equation (4.33) is

$$\mathbf{P}(0, t) = \mathbf{T}(k)\,\mathbf{E}(t)\,\mathbf{T}^{-1}(k). \tag{4.46}$$

Expanding (4.46) we obtain the second explicit solution for the transition probabilities $P_{ij}(0, t)$

$$P_{ij}(0, t) = \sum_{l=1}^{s} A_{ki}(\rho_l)\,\frac{T_{jl}(k)}{|T(k)|}\,e^{\rho_l t}, \qquad i,\ j = 1, \ldots, s. \tag{4.47}$$

Equation (4.47) holds whatever may be $k = 1, \ldots, s$, as noted in equation (3.35).

The differential equations (4.5) can also be solved in the same way; we leave this to the reader as an exercise.

Theorem 10. *If intensity function matrix* **V** *in equation* (4.3) *has distinct eigenvalues,* $\rho_1, \ldots, \rho_s$, *then the solution of Kolmogorov differential equations* (4.4) *and* (4.5) *corresponding to the initial condition in* (4.6) *is given in* (4.47).

4.4. Identity of the Two Solutions.

We must now show that the two explicit solutions found in (4.32) and (4.47) are identical, or that

$$\sum_{l=1}^{s} \frac{A'_{ij}(\rho_l)}{\prod\limits_{\substack{m=1\\m\neq l}}^{s} (\rho_l - \rho_m)} e^{\rho_l t} = \sum_{l=1}^{s} A_{ki}(\rho_l) \frac{T_{jl}(k)}{|T(k)|} e^{\rho_l t}. \tag{4.48}$$

Since (4.47) holds for any k, we may let $k = j$ and rewrite (4.48) as

$$\sum_{l=1}^{s} \frac{A'_{ij}(\rho_l)}{\prod\limits_{\substack{m=1\\m\neq l}}^{s} (\rho_l - \rho_m)} e^{\rho_l t} = \sum_{l=1}^{s} A_{ji}(\rho_l) \frac{T_{jl}(j)}{|T(j)|} e^{\rho_l t}. \tag{4.49}$$

Clearly (4.49) holds if, for each l,

$$\frac{A'_{ij}(\rho_l)}{\sum\limits_{\substack{m=1\\m\neq l}}^{s} (\rho_l - \rho_m)} = A_{ji}(\rho_l) \frac{T_{jl}(j)}{|T(j)|}. \tag{4.50}$$

Since $\mathbf{A}'(\rho_l)$ is the transpose of $\mathbf{A}(\rho_l)$ so that $A'_{ij}(\rho_l) = A_{ji}(\rho_l)$, equation (4.49) also holds if

$$\frac{1}{\prod\limits_{\substack{m=1\\m\neq l}}^{s} (\rho_l - \rho_m)} = \frac{T_{jl}(j)}{|T(j)|}. \tag{4.51}$$

Therefore, in order to prove that the two solutions in (4.32) and (4.47) are identical, it is sufficient to prove (4.51) for each l. Equation (4.51), however, already has been shown to be true via Theorem 7, equation (3.40); therefore, the proof of the identity is complete.

4.5. Chapman-Kolmogorov Equations.

In deriving Kolmogorov differential equations in section 2, we use the Chapman-Kolmogorov equation (1.6) as a point of departure. In homogeneous processes, the equation is

$$P_{ik}(0, \tau + t) = \sum_{j=1}^{s} P_{ij}(0, \tau) P_{jk}(0, t), \qquad i, k = 1, \dots, s. \quad (4.11)$$

The corresponding matrix representation is

$$\mathbf{P}(0, \tau + t) = \mathbf{P}(0, \tau)\mathbf{P}(0, t). \quad (4.52)$$

We leave it to the reader to verify that solutions (4.32) and (4.47) satisfy equation (4.11) for individual transition probabilities. We shall proceed to verify (4.52).

Substituting solution (4.46) in the right-hand side of (4.52), we compute

$$\begin{aligned} \mathbf{P}(0, \tau)\mathbf{P}(0, t) &= [\mathbf{T}(k)\mathbf{E}(\tau)\mathbf{T}^{-1}(k)]\, [\mathbf{T}(k)\mathbf{E}(t)\mathbf{T}^{-1}(k)] \\ &= \mathbf{T}(k)\mathbf{E}(\tau)\mathbf{E}(t)\mathbf{T}^{-1}(k) = \mathbf{T}(k)\mathbf{E}(\tau + t)\mathbf{T}^{-1}(k) \\ &= \mathbf{P}(0, \tau + t). \end{aligned} \quad (4.53)$$

Equation (4.52) is verified. Thus we have the theorem.

Theorem 11. *The solutions of Kolmogorov differential equations given in equations* (4.32) *and* (4.47) *are identical and satisfy the Chapman-Kolmogorov equation* (4.11).

4.6. Limiting Probabilities.

Theorem 12. *As t approaches infinity, the limiting transition probabilities $P_{ij}(0, t)$ are independent of the initial state i, and are given by*

$$\lim_{t \to \infty} P_{ij}(0, t) = \frac{V_{jj}}{\sum_{l=1}^{s} V_{ll}}, \qquad i, j = 1, \dots, s. \quad (4.54)$$

Therefore, the process is ergodic.

Proof. Since $\rho_k < 0$ for $k = 2, \dots, s$, $e^{\rho_k t}$ tends to zero as t tends to infinity. From equation (4.32), we see that

$$\lim_{t \to \infty} P_{ij}(0, t) = \frac{A'_{ij}(\rho_1)}{\prod_{m=2}^{s} (\rho_1 - \rho_m)}. \quad (4.55)$$

Here $\mathbf{A}'(\rho_1) = (\rho_1 \mathbf{I} - \mathbf{V}')$, $\rho_1 = 0$; and $V_{ji} = V_{jj}$, therefore

$$A'_{ij}(\rho_1) = (-1)^{s-1} V'_{ij} = (-1)^{s-1} V_{ji} = (-1)^{s-1} V_{jj}. \tag{4.56}$$

For the denominator in (4.55), we use equation (4.17) to write

$$(-1)^{s-1} \rho_2 \dots \rho_s = (-1)^{s-1} [V_{11} + \dots + V_{ss}]. \tag{4.57}$$

Substituting (4.56) and (4.57) in (4.55), we recover (4.54).

Remark. In Theorem 3, Chapter 6, we derived a limiting probability distribution for ergodic Markov chains. Theorem 11 is the counterpart in continuous processes. To make the two theorems similar, we restate Theorem 11 below.

Let $\mathbf{P} = (\mathbf{I} + \mathbf{V})$ be a stochastic matrix wherein each row sums to unity. Then one of the eigenvalues of $\mathbf{P}$ is $\lambda = 1$. Let

$$\mathbf{a}(1) = (\mathbf{I} - \mathbf{P})$$

be the characteristic matrix of $\mathbf{P}$ corresponding to $\lambda = 1$. The limiting probabilities are

$$\lim_{t\to\infty} p_{ij}(0, t) = \frac{\mathbf{a}_{jj}(1)}{\sum_{l=1}^{s} \mathbf{a}_{ll}(1)}, \qquad i, j = 1, \dots, s. \tag{4.60}$$

Since $\mathbf{a}_{jj}(1) = V_{jj}$, the formula in (4.60) is the same as that in (4.54).

5. PROBLEMS FOR SOLUTION

1. Show that the value of a determinant is unchanged if a row (or column) is replaced by the sum of all rows (columns).

2. *Linearly independent vectors.* Show that all the column vectors of a square matrix $\mathbf{W}$ are linearly independent if and only if all the row vectors are linearly independent.

3. Show that if matrix $\mathbf{W}$ is nonsingular, then the transpose of the inverse is the inverse of the transpose, $(\mathbf{W}^{-1})' = (\mathbf{W}')^{-1}$.

4. The sum of the diagonal elements of a square matrix $\mathbf{W}$ is called the *trace* of $\mathbf{W}$, *tr* $\mathbf{W}$. In general, the sum of the determinant of all principal minors of $\mathbf{W}$ of order r is called the *spur* of $\mathbf{W}$, $sp_r\,\mathbf{W}$ (see, for example Aitken [1962]). Verify the relations in (3.17) among the coefficients b, the spurs, and the eigenvalues for the following matrix,

$$\mathbf{W} = \begin{pmatrix} 0 & 1 & 0 \\ 0 & 0 & 2 \\ -3 & -1/2 & 4 \end{pmatrix}$$

5. *Cramer's Rule.* Given a system of s simultaneous equations

$$\begin{array}{l} a_{11} Z_1 + \dots + a_{1s} Z_s = c_1 \\ \cdot\cdot \quad \cdots \quad \cdot\cdot \quad \cdot \\ a_{s1} Z_1 + \dots + a_{ss} Z_s = c_s . \end{array}$$

If the c's are not all zero and if the determinant

$$|A| = \begin{vmatrix} a_{11} & \dots & a_{1s} \\ \vdots & & \vdots \\ a_{s1} & \dots & a_{ss} \end{vmatrix} \neq 0$$

then the system has a unique solution. Find the solution and show that the solution is unique.

6. *Continuation.* Show that if in problem 5 the c's are all zero, then a nontrivial solution exists if and only if the determinant $|A| = 0$ and that the solution is proportional to the corresponding cofactors of A; namely

$$Z_j = k A_{ij}, \qquad j = 1, \dots, s,$$

whatever may be $i = 1, \dots, s$.

7. *Diagonalization of matrix.* Let a, b, and c be non-zero real numbers with $a \neq c$ and let

$$\mathbf{W} = \begin{pmatrix} a & 0 \\ b & c \end{pmatrix}.$$

(a) Find the eigenvalues ρ_1 and ρ_2 of $\mathbf{W}$.

(b) Let $\mathbf{A}(\rho_l) = (\rho_l \mathbf{I} - \mathbf{W})$ and take the first column of each adjoint matrix of $\mathbf{A}(\rho_l)$

$$\mathbf{T}_l(1) = \begin{pmatrix} A_{11}(\rho_l) \\ A_{12}(\rho_l) \end{pmatrix}, \qquad l = 1, 2$$

for form the matrix $\mathbf{T}(1) = (\mathbf{T}_1(1), \mathbf{T}_2(1))$. Show that

$$\mathbf{T}^{-1}(1)\mathbf{W}\mathbf{T}(1) = \begin{pmatrix} \rho_1 & 0 \\ 0 & \rho_2 \end{pmatrix}.$$

(c) Find the first column of the inverse $\mathbf{T}^{-1}(1)$ of $\mathbf{T}(1)$.

(d) Take the second column of each adjoint matrix of $\mathbf{A}(\rho_l)$ and form the matrix $\mathbf{T}(2) = (\mathbf{T}_1(2), \mathbf{T}_2(2))$. Find the second column of the inverse $\mathbf{T}^{-1}(2)$ of $\mathbf{T}(2)$.

8. *Continuation.* Given a matrix

$$\mathbf{W} = \begin{pmatrix} -1 & 1 \\ 2 & -2 \end{pmatrix}$$

(a) Determine the eigenvalues

(b) For each eigenvalue ρ_l, $l = 1, 2$, formulate the matrix $\mathbf{A}(\rho_l) = (\rho_l \mathbf{I} - \mathbf{W})$, and show that

$$(\rho_l \mathbf{I} - \mathbf{W}) \begin{pmatrix} A_{k1}(\rho_l) \\ A_{k2}(\rho_l) \end{pmatrix} = \begin{pmatrix} 0 \\ 0 \end{pmatrix}, \qquad k = 1, 2.$$

(c) For any k of your choice formulate the matrix

$$\mathbf{T}(k) = \begin{pmatrix} A_{k1}(\rho_1) & A_{k1}(\rho_2) \\ A_{k2}(\rho_1) & A_{k2}(\rho_2) \end{pmatrix}$$

and show that

$$\mathbf{T}^{-1}(k)\mathbf{W}\mathbf{T}(k) = \begin{pmatrix} \rho_1 & 0 \\ 0 & \rho_2 \end{pmatrix}$$

(d) Verify that the k-th column of the inverse matrix $\mathbf{T}^{-1}(k)$ of $\mathbf{T}(k)$ is equal to

$$\begin{pmatrix} \dfrac{1}{\rho_1 - \rho_2} \\ \dfrac{1}{\rho_2 - \rho_1} \end{pmatrix}$$

9. For $\rho_1 = 1$, $\rho_2 = 2$, $\rho_3 = 3$ show that

$$\frac{\rho_1^r}{(\rho_1 - \rho_2)(\rho_1 - \rho_3)} + \frac{\rho_2^r}{(\rho_2 - \rho_1)(\rho_2 - \rho_3)} + \frac{\rho_3^r}{(\rho_3 - \rho_1)(\rho_3 - \rho_2)} = 0 \qquad r = 0, 1$$

$$= 1 \qquad r = 2.$$

10. *Vandermonde determinant.* (a) Deduce the following expansion of the Vandermonde determinant

$$\mathbf{W} = \begin{vmatrix} 1 & 1 & 1 & 1 \\ \rho_1 & \rho_2 & \rho_3 & \rho_4 \\ \rho_1^2 & \rho_2^2 & \rho_3^2 & \rho_4^2 \\ \rho_1^3 & \rho_2^3 & \rho_3^3 & \rho_4^3 \end{vmatrix} = (\rho_4 - \rho_3)(\rho_4 - \rho_2)(\rho_4 - \rho_1)(\rho_3 - \rho_2)(\rho_3 - \rho_1)(\rho_2 - \rho_1)$$

(b) Let W_{ij} be the (i,j)th cofactor of the Vandermonde determinant in (a). Show that $\sum_{j=1}^{4} W_{ij} = 0$ for $1 < i \leq 4$.

11. Consider the matrix

$$\mathbf{V} = \begin{pmatrix} \nu_{11} & \dots & \nu_{1s} \\ \vdots & & \vdots \\ \nu_{s1} & \dots & \nu_{ss} \end{pmatrix} \tag{4.3}$$

with

$$\nu_{ii} = -\sum_{\substack{j=1 \\ j \neq i}}^{s} \nu_{ij}, \quad i = 1, \dots, s. \tag{4.2}$$

Show that the cofactors of $\mathbf{V}$ satisfy the relation

$$V_{ij} = V_{ik}$$

whatever may $i, j, k = 1, \dots, s$.

12. *The matrix exponential.* (See Bellman [1960] pp. 162–164). For any $s \times s$ matrix $\mathbf{W}$ of elements w_{ij}, define

$$\| W \| = \sum_{i=1}^{s} \sum_{j=1}^{s} | w_{ij} |.$$

(a) Show that if $\mathbf{W}$ and $\mathbf{V}$ are two $s \times s$ matrices, then

$$\| \mathbf{W} + \mathbf{V} \| \leq \| \mathbf{W} \| + \| \mathbf{V} \|$$

and

$$\| \mathbf{W} \mathbf{V} \| \leq \| \mathbf{W} \| \| \mathbf{V} \|.$$

(b) Show that a sufficient condition for the convergence of the matrix series $\sum_{n=1}^{\infty} \mathbf{W}_n$ is that the numerical series $\sum_{n=1}^{\infty} \| \mathbf{W}_n \|$ converges.

(c) Using (a) and (b), show that the matrix exponential defined in (4.34) converges uniformly in any bounded interval $-T \leq t \leq T$.

13. Show that if the eigenvalues ρ_l of $\mathbf{V}$ are distinct, then whatever may be $i, j, l = 1, \dots, s$, the functions

$$P_{ij}(0, t) = \sum_{l=1}^{s} k_{il} A'_{ij}(\rho_l) e^{\rho_l t} \tag{4.26}$$

satisfy the system of differential equations

$$\frac{d}{dt} P_{ih}(0, t) = \sum_{j=1}^{s} P_{ij}(0, t) \nu_{jh}. \tag{4.4}$$

14. Show that the solution

$$P_{ij}(0;t) = \sum_{l=1}^{s} \frac{A'_{ij}(\rho_l)\,e^{\rho_l t}}{\prod_{\substack{m=1\\m\neq l}}^{s}(\rho_l - \rho_m)} \tag{4.32}$$

(a) Satisfy the forward differential equation

$$\frac{d}{dt}P_{ik}(0,t) = \sum_{j=1}^{s} P_{ij}(0,t)\,\nu_{jk} \tag{4.4}$$

(b) and the backward differential equation

$$\frac{d}{dt}P_{ik}(0,t) = \sum_{j=1}^{s} \nu_{ij}P_{jk}(0,t). \tag{2.17}$$

15. Prove that the solution in (4.32) is a real function of the intensity functions ν_{ij}, $i, j = 1, \ldots, s$ when the matrix $\mathbf{V}$ has complex roots.

16. *Solution of backward differential equations.* Derive solution for the backward differential equations

$$\frac{d}{dt}P_{ik}(0,t) = \sum_{j=1}^{s} \nu_{ij}P_{jk}(0,t) \tag{4.5}$$

satisfying the initial conditions at $t = 0$, $P_{ik}(0,0) = \delta_{ik}$, using the approach in section 4.2.

17. Show that the solution

$$P_{ij}(0,t) = \sum_{l=1}^{s} A_{ki}(\rho_l)\frac{T_{jl}(k)}{|T(k)|}e^{\rho_l t} \tag{4.47}$$

satisfies the forward differential equations in (4.4) and the backward differential equations in (2.17).

18. The backward differential equations in (2.17) may be expressed in matrix notation as

$$\frac{d}{dt}\mathbf{P}(0,t) - \mathbf{VP}(0,t).$$

Solve this differential equation to obtain the individual transition probabilities $P_{ij}(0,t)$.

19. Show that the solution in (4.32) in problem 14 satisfies the Chapman-Kolmogorov equation

$$P_{ik}(0,\tau + t) = \sum_{j=1}^{s} P_{ij}(0,\tau)P_{jk}(0,t).$$

20. Show that the solution in (4.47) in problem 4 satisfies the Chapman-Kolmogorov equation.

21. *Limiting probabilities.* Show that as $t \to \infty$, the limiting probability of $P_{ij}(0,t)$ is independent of the initial state i and

$$\lim_{t\to\infty} \sum_{l=1}^{s} A_{ki}(\rho_l) \frac{T_{jl}(k)}{|T(k)|} e^{\rho_l t} = \frac{V_{jj}}{\sum_{h=1}^{s} V_{hh}}$$

22. To illustrate that the solution in (4.47) for the transition probabilities is independent of k, consider the simple illness-death process with

$$\mathbf{V} = \begin{pmatrix} \nu_{11} & \nu_{12} \\ \nu_{21} & \nu_{22} \end{pmatrix}, \quad \mathbf{A}(\rho_l) = (\rho_l \mathbf{I} - \mathbf{V}),$$

where $\nu_{11} + \nu_{12} < 0$ and $\nu_{21} + \nu_{22} < 0$. Find $P_{ij}(0,t)$ from

$$P_{ij}(0,t) = \sum_{l=1}^{2} A_{1i}(\rho_l) \frac{T_{jl}(1)}{|T(1)|} e^{\rho_l t}$$

and

$$P_{ij}(0,t) = \sum_{l=1}^{2} A_{2i}(\rho_l) \frac{T_{jl}(2)}{|T(2)|} e^{\rho_l t},$$

and show that they are equal for given i and j.

23. Consider a singular matrix

$$\mathbf{V} = \begin{vmatrix} -.2 & .1 & .1 \\ .1 & -.4 & .3 \\ .2 & .1 & -.3 \end{vmatrix}$$

(a) Show that the cofactors

$$V_{i1} = V_{i2} = V_{i3}, \quad i = 1, 2, 3.$$

(b) Matrix $\mathbf{V}$ has one zero eigenvalue and two negative eigenvalues. Determine these eigenvalues.

(c) For each eigenvalue ρ_l, formulate the characteristic matrix

$$\mathbf{A}(\rho_l) = (\rho_l \mathbf{I} - \mathbf{V})$$

and compute the cofactors $A_{ij}(\rho_l)$.

(d) Show that whatever may be $k = 1, 2, 3$, the non-zero vector

$$\mathbf{T}_l(k) = \begin{pmatrix} A_{k1}(\rho_l) \\ A_{k2}(\rho_l) \\ A_{k3}(\rho_l) \end{pmatrix}$$

is an eigenvector of $\mathbf{V}$ corresponding to ρ_l.

(e) For a particular k of your choice formulate a matrix

$$\mathbf{T}(k) = (\mathbf{T}_1(k), \mathbf{T}_2(k), \mathbf{T}_3(k)).$$

Verify that

$$\mathbf{T}^{-1}(k)\,\mathbf{V}\,\mathbf{T}(k) = \begin{pmatrix} \rho_1 & 0 & 0 \\ 0 & \rho_2 & 0 \\ 0 & 0 & \rho_3 \end{pmatrix}$$

and

$$\mathbf{T}(k)\begin{pmatrix} \rho_1 & 0 & 0 \\ 0 & \rho_2 & 0 \\ 0 & 0 & \rho_3 \end{pmatrix}\mathbf{T}^{-1}(k) = \mathbf{V}.$$

(f) Compute $\mathbf{V}^2$ and

$$\mathbf{T}(k)\begin{pmatrix} \rho_1^2 & 0 & 0 \\ 0 & \rho_2^2 & 0 \\ 0 & 0 & \rho_3^2 \end{pmatrix}\mathbf{T}^{-1}(k)$$

and show that the two matrices are equal.

(g) Compute $\mathbf{T}^{-1}(k)\ \mathbf{V}^2\mathbf{T}(k)$ and show that it is equal to the diagonal matrix

$$\begin{pmatrix} \rho_1^2 & 0 & 0 \\ 0 & \rho_2^2 & 0 \\ 0 & 0 & \rho_3^2 \end{pmatrix}$$

(h) Substitute the numerical values of ν_{ij} to formulate the system of forward differential equations

$$\frac{d}{dt} P_{ik}(0,t) = \sum_{j=1}^{3} P_{ij}(0,t)\,\nu_{jk}$$

and the backward differential equations

$$\frac{d}{dt} P_{ik}(0,t) = \sum_{j=1}^{3} \nu_{ij} P_{jk}(0,t)$$

assuming $P_{ij}(0,0) = \delta_{ij}$.

(i) Compute

$$P_{ij}(0,t) = \sum_{l=1}^{3} \frac{A_{ij}(\rho_l)}{\prod\limits_{\substack{m=1\\ m\neq l}}^{3}(\rho_l - \rho_m)}\, e^{\rho_l t}, \quad i, j = 1, 2, 3$$

and show that they satisfy the differential equations and the initial conditions in (h).

(j) Solve the differential equations in (h).

(k) Show that $P_{ij}(0,t)$ in (i) satisfies

$$\sum_{j=1}^{3} P_{ij}(0,\tau)P_{jk}(0,t) = P_{ik}(0,\tau+t)$$

for some particular i and k of your choice.

(l) For two values of k of your choice compute

$$\sum_{l=1}^{3} A_{ki}(\rho_l)\frac{T_{jl}(k)}{|T(k)|}e^{\rho_l t}, \quad j = 1, 2, 3.$$

Do they depend on the value of k?

(m) Compare your results in (l) with (i).

(n) Show that

$$\lim_{t\to\infty} P_{ij}(0,t) = \frac{V_{jj}}{\sum_{l=1}^{3} V_{ll}}.$$

24. In section 4.1 we proved that any eigenvalue of $\mathbf{V}$ is nonpositive. We now prove the assertion with a method devised by Myra J. Samuels. Let

$$\mathbf{C} = \begin{pmatrix} c_1 \\ \vdots \\ c_s \end{pmatrix}$$

be a non-zero vector such that

$$(\rho\mathbf{I} - \mathbf{V}')\mathbf{C} = 0,$$

or equivalently

$$c_1 v_{1j} + \dots c_s v_{sj} = \rho c_j, \quad j = 1, \dots, s.$$

Adding the last equation over those j for each $c_j > 0$, denoting this partial sum of $\sum *$, we have

$$c_1 \sum * v_{ij} + \dots + c_s \sum * v_{sj} = \rho \sum * c_j.$$

Show that each of the terms on the left side of the last equation is non-positive and hence $\rho \le 0$.

CHAPTER 15

Kolmogorov Differential Equations and Finite Markov Processes—Continuation

1. INTRODUCTION

In Chapter 14 we presented two solutions for the Kolmogorov differential equations for cases where the intensity function matrix **V** has distinct eigenvalues. We will now show how the formulas for the individual transition probabilities are obtained when the matrix **V** has multiple eigenvalues. We will not derive solutions of the differential equations afresh, but rather will use the results found in equations (4.32) and (4.47), Chapter 14, as a point of departure.

2. FIRST SOLUTION FOR INDIVIDUAL TRANSITION PROBABILITIES $P_{ij}(0, t)$

When the intensity function matrix **V** has single eigenvalues $\rho_1, \ldots, \rho_s$, we presented the first solution of the Kolmogorov differential equations in equation (4.32), Chapter 14:

$$P_{ij}(0,t) = \sum_{l=1}^{s} \frac{A'_{ij}(\rho_l)}{\prod\limits_{\substack{m=1 \\ m \neq l}}^{s} (\rho_l - \rho_m)} e^{\rho_l t}, \qquad i, j = 1, \ldots, s, \tag{2.1}$$

where $A'_{ij}(\rho_l)$ is the (j, i)-th cofactor of the characteristic matrix of **V**, for $\rho = \rho_l$,

$$\mathbf{A}(\rho_l) = (\rho_l \mathbf{I} - \mathbf{V}), \qquad l = 1, \ldots, s. \tag{2.2}$$

Now suppose the matrix $\mathbf{V}$ has multiple eigenvalues. We derive formulas for the transition probabililities $P_{ij}(0, t)$ from equation (2.1). But first recall lemma 1, Chapter 14. According to the lemma, if $\varepsilon_1, \ldots, \varepsilon_s$ are distinct numbers, then

$$\sum_{l=1}^{s} \frac{\varepsilon_l^k}{\prod_{\substack{\alpha=1 \\ \alpha \neq l}}^{s} (\varepsilon_l - \varepsilon_\alpha)} = 1, \quad \text{for} \quad k = s - 1$$

$$= 0, \quad \text{for} \quad k = 0, 1, \ldots, s - 2. \tag{2.3}$$

We state the first solution in the following theorem.

Theorem 1. *If the matrix* $\mathbf{V}$ *has multiple eigenvalues,* $\rho_1, \ldots, \rho_r$, *with the respective multiplicities,* $s_1, \ldots, s_r$, *such that* $s_1 + \ldots + s_r = s$, *then the solution of the differential equations*

$$\frac{d}{dt} P_{ij}(0, t) = \sum_{h=1}^{s} P_{ih}(0, t) \nu_{hj}, \tag{2.4}$$

and

$$\frac{d}{dt} P_{ij}(0, t) = \sum_{h=1}^{s} \nu_{ih} P_{hj}(0, t), \tag{2.5}$$

for $i, j = 1, \ldots, s$, *that correspond to the initial condition*

$$P_{ij}(0, 0) = \delta_{ij} \tag{2.6}$$

is

$$p_{ij}(0,t) = \sum_{l=1}^{r} \frac{e^{\rho_l t}}{\prod_{\substack{\alpha=1 \\ \alpha \neq l}}^{r} (\rho_l - \rho_\alpha)^{s_\alpha}} \sum_{m=0}^{s_l - 1}$$

$$\times \left[\sum \cdots \sum \prod_{\substack{\alpha=1 \\ \alpha \neq l}}^{r} \binom{s_\alpha + m - 1}{m_\alpha} (\rho_\alpha - \rho_l)^{-m_\alpha} \right]$$

$$\times \left[\sum_{n=0}^{s_l - 1 - m} \frac{t^{s_l - 1 - m - n}}{(s_1 - 1 - m - n)!n!} \frac{d^n}{d\rho_l^n} A'_{ij}(\rho_l) \right] \tag{2.7}$$

where $\Sigma \ldots \Sigma$ stands for $r - 1$ summations taken over $m_\alpha = 0, 1, \ldots, m$; $\alpha \neq l$, such that $(m_1 + \ldots + m_r) - m_l = m$, and

$$\frac{d^n}{d\rho_l^n} A'_{ij}(\rho_l), \qquad l = 1, \ldots, r$$

is the n-th derivative of $A'_{ij}(\rho)$ taken at $\rho = \rho_l$. Furthermore, the solution given in (2.7) is a real function of the intensity functions ν_{ij}, even when some of the eigenvalues are complex numbers.

Proof: We order the s distinct eigenvalues of matrix **V**, divide them into r groups: $(\rho_{11}, \ldots, \rho_{1s}), \ldots, (\rho_{r1}, \ldots, \rho_{rs})$, and write equation (2.1) as follows:

$$p_{ij}(0,t) = \sum_{l=1}^{r} \sum_{\beta=1}^{s_l} \frac{A_{ij}(\rho_{l\beta}) e^{\rho_{l\beta} t}}{\sum\limits_{\substack{\delta=1 \\ \delta\neq\beta}}^{s_l} (\rho_{l\beta} - \rho_{l\delta}) \sum\limits_{\substack{\alpha=1 \\ \alpha\neq l}}^{r} \sum\limits_{\gamma=1}^{s_\alpha} (\rho_{l\beta} - \rho_{\alpha\gamma})}$$

$$i,j = 1, \ldots, s. \tag{2.8}$$

We shall derive (2.7) from (2.8) by taking the limit as $\rho_{l\beta} \to \rho_l$, for $\beta = 1, \ldots, s_l$; $l = 1, \ldots, r$. Formally we let $\rho_{l\beta} = \rho_l + \varepsilon_{l\beta}$ and write

$$p_{ij}(0,t) = \sum_{l=1}^{r} \sum_{\beta=1}^{s_l} \frac{A'_{ij}(\rho_l + \varepsilon_{l\beta}) e^{(\rho_l + \varepsilon_{l\beta})t}}{\prod\limits_{\substack{\delta=1 \\ \delta\neq\beta}}^{s_l} (\varepsilon_{l\beta} - \varepsilon_{l\delta}) \prod\limits_{\substack{\alpha=1 \\ \alpha\neq l}}^{r} \prod\limits_{\gamma=1}^{s_\alpha} (\rho_l + \varepsilon_{l\beta} - \rho_\alpha - \varepsilon_{\alpha\gamma})},$$

$$i,j = 1, \ldots s. \tag{2.9}$$

We evaluate the numerator in each term as follows:

$$A'_{ij}(\rho_l + \varepsilon_{l\beta}) = \sum_{n=0}^{s-1} \frac{\varepsilon_{l\beta}^n}{n!} \frac{d^n}{d\rho_l^n} A'_{ij}(\rho_l)$$

and

$$e^{(\rho_l + \varepsilon_{l\beta})t} = e^{\rho_l t} \sum_{h=0}^{\infty} \frac{\varepsilon_{l\beta}^h t^h}{h!}$$

The product is

$$A'_{ij}(\rho_l + \varepsilon_{l\beta})\, e^{(\rho_l+\varepsilon_{l\beta})t} = e^{\rho_l t}\left[\sum_{k=0}^{\infty} \varepsilon_{l\beta}^{k} \sum_{n=0}^{\min[k,s-1]} \frac{t^{k-n}}{(k-n)!\,n!}\,\frac{d^n}{d\rho_l^n} A'_{ij}(\rho_l)\right] \tag{2.10}$$

where min $[k, s - 1]$ represents the smaller of the two numbers k and $s - 1$. As $\varepsilon_{\alpha\gamma} \to 0$, we find from the denominator

$$\left[\prod_{\substack{\alpha=1\\ \alpha\neq l}}^{r} \prod_{\gamma=1}^{s_l} (\rho_l + \varepsilon_{l\beta} - \rho_\alpha - \varepsilon_{\alpha\gamma})\right]^{-1} = \prod_{\substack{\alpha=1\\ \alpha\neq l}}^{r} (\rho_l + \varepsilon_{l\beta} - \rho_\alpha)^{-s_\alpha}$$

$$= \prod_{\substack{\alpha=1\\ \alpha\neq l}}^{r} (\rho_l - \rho_\alpha)^{-s_\alpha} \sum_{m_\alpha=0}^{\infty} \binom{-s_\alpha}{m_\alpha} \varepsilon_{l\beta}^{m_\alpha} (\rho_l - \rho_\alpha)^{-m_\alpha}$$

$$= \frac{1}{\prod\limits_{\substack{\alpha=1\\ \alpha\neq \Pi}}^{r} (\rho_l - \rho_\alpha)^{s_\alpha}} \prod_{\substack{\alpha=1\\ \alpha\neq l}}^{r} \left[\sum_{m_\alpha=0}^{\infty} \binom{s_l + m_l - 1}{m_\alpha} \varepsilon_{l\beta}^{m_\alpha} (\rho_\alpha - \rho_l)^{-m_\alpha}\right]$$

$$= \frac{1}{\prod\limits_{\substack{\alpha=1\\ \alpha\neq l}}^{r} (\rho_l - \rho_\alpha)^{s_\alpha}} \sum_{m=0}^{\infty} \varepsilon_{l\beta}^{m} \left[\sum \cdots \sum \binom{s_l + m_l - 1}{m_\alpha} (\rho_\alpha - \rho_l)^{-m_\alpha}\right] \tag{2.11}$$

where $\Sigma \ldots \Sigma$ stands for $r - 1$ summations taken over $m_\alpha = 0, 1, \ldots, m$; $\alpha \neq l$ such that $(m_1 + \ldots + m_r) - m_l = m$. Substituting (2.10) and (2.11) in (2.9) yields

$$p_{ij}(0,t) = \sum_{l=1}^{r} \frac{e^{\rho_l t}}{\prod_{\substack{\alpha=1 \\ \alpha\neq l}}^{r} (\rho_l - \rho_\alpha)^{s_\alpha}} \sum_{k=0}^{\infty} \sum_{m=0}^{\infty} \sum_{\beta=1}^{s_l} \frac{\varepsilon_{l\beta}^{k+m}}{\sum_{\substack{\delta=1 \\ \delta\neq\beta}}^{s_l} (\varepsilon_{l\beta} - \varepsilon_{l\delta})}$$

$$\times \left[\sum \cdots \sum \sum_{\substack{\alpha=1 \\ \alpha\neq l}}^{r} \binom{s_l + m_l - 1}{m_\alpha} (\rho_\alpha - \rho_l)^{-m_\alpha} \right]$$

$$\times \sum_{n=0}^{\min[k,s-1]} \frac{t^{k-n}}{(k-n)!n!} \frac{d^n}{d\rho_l^n} A'_{ij}(\rho_l) \tag{2.12}$$

According to the lemma in (2.3),

$$\sum_{\beta=1}^{s_l} \frac{\varepsilon_{l\beta}^{k+m}}{\prod_{\substack{\delta=1 \\ \delta\neq\beta}}^{s_l} (\varepsilon_{l\beta} - \varepsilon_{l\delta})} = 0, \qquad \text{for } k + m = 0, 1, \ldots, s_l - 2,$$

$$= 1, \qquad \text{for } k + m = s_l - 1. \tag{2.13}$$

For $k + m > s_l - 1$, we take the limit as $\varepsilon_{l\delta} \to 0$,

$$\lim_{\substack{\varepsilon_{l\beta}\to 0 \\ \beta=1,\ldots,s_l}} \frac{\varepsilon_{l\beta}^{k+m}}{\prod_{\substack{\delta=1 \\ \delta\neq\beta}}^{s_l} (\varepsilon_{l\beta} - \varepsilon_{l\delta})} = 0, \qquad k + m > s_l - 1, \tag{2.14}$$

since the numerator is of a smaller order of magnitude than the denominator. For every $m = 0, 1, \ldots, s_1 - 1$, there is one and only one value of k for which $k + m = s_1 - 1$. That is, $k = s_1 - 1 - m$. Consequently, (2.12) reduces to (2.7), as is required to be shown.

Complex eigenvalues of **V**, if they exist, will appear in complex conjugates, and two conjugates of a complex number will appear with the same multiplicities. We can easily show that, in equation (2.7), the two terms corresponding to complex conjugate eigenvalues are themselves complex conjugates; therefore, their sum is a real function of the intensity functions ν_{ij}. Every term corresponding to a real eigenvalue is real. Therefore the formula in (2.7) is a real function of ν_{ij}. A more explicit justification for a similar assertion is contained in the proof of Theorem 2, Chapter 6. Finally, we can easily show that the probabilities $P_{ij}(0, t)$ as they are given in (2.7) satisfy the differential equations (2.4) and (2.5). Thus proof of Theorem 1 is complete.

3. SECOND SOLUTION FOR INDIVIDUAL TRANSITION PROBABILITIES $P_{ij}(0,t)$[1]

As in section 4.3, Chapter 14, we seek a way to diagonalize matrix **V**. However, when dealing with multiple eigenvalues, the computations are somewhat involved. In this case, the vectors $T_l(k)$ in equation (4.37), Chapter 14, are linearly dependent, and the matrix $\mathbf{T}(k)$ is singular. Consequently, the whole scheme of diagonalizing the matrix **V** collapses; the solution given in equation (4.47), Chapter 14, no longer holds true. We need other devices to generate independent vectors in order to expand the matrix solution

$$\mathbf{P}(0, t) = e^{\mathbf{V}t}.$$

Suppose the matrix **V** has multiple eigenvalues $\rho_1, \ldots, \rho_r$ with the respective multiplicities $s_1, \ldots, s_r$. Let us consider again the character matrix

$$\mathbf{A}(\rho) = (\rho\mathbf{I} - \mathbf{V}) \tag{3.1}$$

and a non-zero eigenvector

$$\begin{pmatrix} A_{k1}(\rho) \\ \vdots \\ A_{ks}(\rho) \end{pmatrix}. \tag{3.2}$$

Take the derivative of the vector in (3.2) with respect to ρ, $(s_l - 1)$ times, and let

$$\mathbf{T}_l^{(j)}(k) = \frac{1}{j!}\frac{d^j}{d\rho^j}\begin{pmatrix} A_{k1}(\rho) \\ \vdots \\ A_{ks}(\rho) \end{pmatrix}\Bigg|_{\rho=\rho_l}, \quad j = 0, 1, \ldots, s_l - 1. \tag{3.3}$$

When $j = 0$,

$$\mathbf{T}_l^{(0)}(k) = \begin{pmatrix} A_{k1}(\rho_l) \\ \vdots \\ A_{ks}(\rho_l) \end{pmatrix} \tag{3.4}$$

[1]The second solution is based on Chiang [1973] but with some revision.

is an eigenvector of $\mathbf{V}$ corresponding to ρ_l. In a system where all s states are communicative, we expect the matrix $\mathbf{V}$ to be such that the cofactors $A_{ki}(\rho_l)$ are not all zero. Therefore, for each ρ_l, we can find a non-zero column as the one in equation (3.4) and get non-zero derivatives as those in (3.3).

Lemma 1. *For an eigenvalue of* $\mathbf{A}(\rho)$, ρ_l, *the vectors* $\mathbf{T}_l^{(0)}(k)$, $\mathbf{T}_l^{(1)}(k)$, ..., $\mathbf{T}_l^{(s_l-1)}(k)$ *as defined in* (3.3) *are linearly independent.*

Proof. First let us formulate an identity in ρ:

$$(\rho\mathbf{I}-\mathbf{V})\begin{pmatrix} A_{k1}(\rho) \\ \vdots \\ A_{ks}(\rho) \end{pmatrix} = |A(\rho)|\,\mathbf{I}_k, \tag{3.5}$$

where $\mathbf{I}_k$ is an $s \times 1$ column vector with Kronecker deltas as its components:

$$\mathbf{I}_k = \begin{pmatrix} \delta_{k1} \\ \vdots \\ \delta_{kk} \\ \vdots \\ \delta_{ks} \end{pmatrix} = \begin{pmatrix} 0 \\ \vdots \\ 1 \\ \vdots \\ 0 \end{pmatrix}. \tag{3.6}$$

Differentiating both sides of (3.5) with respect to ρ, $(s_l - 1)$ times, yields $(s_l - 1)$ equations of the form

$$(\rho\mathbf{I}-\mathbf{V})\frac{d^j}{d\rho^j}\begin{pmatrix} A_{k1}(\rho) \\ \vdots \\ A_{ks}(\rho) \end{pmatrix} + j\frac{d^{j-1}}{d\rho^{j-1}}\begin{pmatrix} A_{k1}(\rho) \\ \vdots \\ A_{ks}(\rho) \end{pmatrix} = |A^{(j)}(\rho)|\,\mathbf{I}_k,$$

$$j = 1, \ldots, s_l - 1, \tag{3.7}$$

where $|A^{(j)}(\rho)|$ is the j-th derivative of $|A(\rho)|$. When $\rho = \rho_l$, the determinant $|A(\rho_l)| = 0$, the right hand sides of both (3.5) and (3.7) vanish. Dividing these equations respectively by $j!$, we get s_l equations of the forms

$$(\rho_l\mathbf{I}-\mathbf{V})\mathbf{T}_l^{(0)}(k) = \mathbf{0} \tag{3.8}$$

and

$$(\rho_l \mathbf{I} - \mathbf{V})\mathbf{T}_l^{(j)}(k) + \mathbf{T}_l^{(j-1)}(k) = \mathbf{0}, \qquad j = 1, \ldots, s_l - 1, \tag{3.9}$$

where $\mathbf{0}$ are $s \times 1$ zero column vectors. We shall use equations (3.8) and (3.9) to prove lemma 1 by contradiction.

Suppose that the vectors in (3.3) are linearly dependent. There then exists a non-zero column vector

$$\mathbf{C} = (c_0, c_1, \ldots, c_{s_l-1})' \tag{3.10}$$

such that

$$c_0 \mathbf{T}_l^{(0)}(k) + c_1 \mathbf{T}_l^{(1)}(k) + c_2 \mathbf{T}_l^{(2)}(k) + \ldots + c_{s_l-1} \mathbf{T}_l^{(s_l-1)}(k) = \mathbf{0}. \tag{3.11}$$

By multiplying every term in (3.11) on the left by $(\rho_l \mathbf{I} - \mathbf{V})$, and substituting (3.8) and (3.9), we find the equation

$$c_1 \mathbf{T}_l^{(0)}(k) + c_2 \mathbf{T}_l^{(1)}(k) + \ldots + c_{s_l-1} \mathbf{T}_l^{(s_l-2)}(k) = \mathbf{0}. \tag{3.12}$$

The term with the constant c_0 has disappeared. Indeed, successively multiplying every term of (3.12) on the left by $(\rho_l \mathbf{I} - \mathbf{V})$, $(s_l - 2)$ times, and substituting in (3.8) and (3.9) after each multiplication, we find that the first $s_l - 1$ terms have vanished, leaving

$$c_{s_l-1} \mathbf{T}_l^{(0)}(k) = \mathbf{0}.$$

Since vector $\mathbf{T}_l^{(0)}(k) \neq 0$, we must have $c_{s_l-1} = 0$. Consequently, equation (3.11) reduces to

$$c_0 \mathbf{T}_l^{(0)}(k) + c_1 \mathbf{T}_l^{(1)}(k) + \ldots + c_{s_l-2} \mathbf{T}_l^{(s_l-2)}(k) = \mathbf{0}. \tag{3.13}$$

Repeated applications of this procedure show that $c_{s_l-1} = 0, \ldots, c_0 = 0$. Therefore in order for equation (3.11) to hold, vector $\mathbf{C}$ in (3.10) must be a zero vector and we reach a contradiction. Thus we proved lemma 1.

In lemma 1, we are concerned with vectors generated from a single eigenvalue ρ_l. If we consider the entire $s_1 + \ldots + s_r = s$ vectors generated from the r distinct eigenvalues $\rho_1, \ldots, \rho_r$, then these s vectors are obviously linearly independent.

Lemma 2. *The s vectors*

$$[\mathbf{T}_1^{(0)}(k), \ldots, \mathbf{T}_1^{(s_1-1)}(k), \ldots, \mathbf{T}_r^{(0)}(k), \ldots, \mathbf{T}_r^{(s_r-1)}(k)] \tag{3.14}$$

generated from r distinct eigenvalues $\rho_1, \ldots, \rho_r$, by means of differentiation as in (3.3), *are linearly independent.*

Now for each ρ_l, we formulate a $s_l \times s_l$ matrix known as a Jordan block:

$$\mathbf{J}_l = \begin{pmatrix} \rho_l & 1 & 0 & \dots & 0 \\ 0 & \rho_l & 1 & \dots & 0 \\ 0 & 0 & \rho_l & \dots & 0 \\ \cdot & \cdot & \cdot & \dots & \cdot \\ 0 & 0 & 0 & \dots & \rho_l \end{pmatrix}, \qquad l = 1, \dots, r. \tag{3.15}$$

The n-th power of a Jordan block as in (3.15) is

$$\mathbf{J}_l^n = \begin{pmatrix} \rho_l^n & \binom{n}{1}\rho_l^{n-1} & \dots & \binom{n}{s_l-1}\rho_l^{n-s_l+1} \\ 0 & \rho_l^n & \dots & \binom{n}{s_l-2}^{n-s_l+2} \\ \cdot & \cdot & \dots & \cdot \\ 0 & 0 & \dots & \rho_l^n \end{pmatrix}, \quad l = 1, \dots, r. \tag{3.16}$$

A matrix with Jordan blocks on the diagonal as in (3.17) is known as a Jordan matrix:

$$\mathbf{J} = \begin{pmatrix} \mathbf{J}_1 & 0 & \dots & 0 \\ 0 & \mathbf{J}_2 & \dots & 0 \\ \cdot & \cdot & \dots & \cdot \\ 0 & 0 & \dots & \mathbf{J}_r \end{pmatrix} \tag{3.17}$$

and is a quasi-diagonal matrix. The n-th power of a Jordan matrix is also a quasi-diagonal matrix:

$$\mathbf{J}^n = \begin{pmatrix} \mathbf{J}_1^n & 0 & \dots & 0 \\ 0 & \mathbf{J}_2^2 & \dots & 0 \\ \cdot & \cdot & \dots & \cdot \\ 0 & 0 & \dots & \mathbf{J}_r^n \end{pmatrix}. \tag{3.18}$$

There is a close connection between the Jordan matrix in (3.18) and the vectors described in Lemma 2. Let us use the vectors defined in (3.3) to formulate an $s \times s$ matrix $\mathbf{T}(k)$,

$$\mathbf{T}(k) = [\mathbf{T}_1^{(0)}(k), \ldots, \mathbf{T}_1^{(s_1-1)}(k), \ldots, \mathbf{T}_r^{(0)}(k), \ldots, \mathbf{T}_r^{(s_r-1)}(k)]. \quad (3.19)$$

The matrix $\mathbf{T}(k)$, which is composed of s linearly independent columns, is non-singular. Therefore, it has the inverse $\mathbf{T}^{-1}(k)$, and we can also form a matrix $\mathbf{T}^{-1}(k)\mathbf{V}\,\mathbf{T}(k)$.

Theorem 2. *The matrix* $\mathbf{V}$ *is similar to the Jordan matrix* $\mathbf{J}$ *as defined in equation* (3.17) *with* $\mathbf{T}(k)$ *as the transformation matrix:*

$$\mathbf{T}^{-1}(k)\mathbf{V}\,\mathbf{T}(k) = \mathbf{J}. \quad (3.20)$$

Proof. In order to prove the validity of the formula in (3.20), we first show that the first s_1 columns of the product $\mathbf{T}^{-1}(k)\mathbf{V}\,\mathbf{T}(k)$ are

$$\mathbf{T}^{-1}(k)\mathbf{V}\,[\mathbf{T}_1^{(0)}(k), \mathbf{T}_1^{(1)}(k), \ldots, \mathbf{T}_1^{(s_1-1)}(k)] = \begin{pmatrix} \mathbf{J}_1 \\ \mathbf{0} \end{pmatrix}, \quad (3.21)$$

where $\mathbf{J}_1$ is an $s_1 \times s_1$ Jordan block as given in (3.15) for $\rho_l = \rho_1$, and $\mathbf{0}$ is an $(s - s_1) \times s_1$ zero matrix.

According to the definition of $\mathbf{T}(k)$ given in equation (3.19), the product $\mathbf{V}\mathbf{T}(k)$ is

$$\mathbf{V}\mathbf{T}(k) = [\mathbf{V}\mathbf{T}_1^{(0)}(k), \ldots \mathbf{V}\mathbf{T}_1^{(s_1-1)}(k), \ldots, \mathbf{V}\mathbf{T}_r^{(0)}(k), \ldots, \mathbf{V}\mathbf{T}_r^{(s_r-1)}(k)]. \quad (3.22)$$

In view of equations (3.8) and (3.9), we see that the first s_1 columns of the product $\mathbf{V}\mathbf{T}(k)$ in (3.22) are

$$\begin{aligned} \mathbf{V}\mathbf{T}_1^{(0)}(k) &= \rho_1 \mathbf{T}_1^{(0)}(k) \\ \mathbf{V}\mathbf{T}_1^{(1)}(k) &= \rho_1 \mathbf{T}_1^{(1)}(k) + \mathbf{T}_1^{(0)}(k) \\ &\vdots \\ \mathbf{V}\mathbf{T}_1^{(s_1-1)}(k) &= \rho_1 \mathbf{T}_1^{(s_1-1)}(k) + \mathbf{T}_1^{(s_1-2)}(k). \end{aligned} \quad (3.23)$$

On the other hand, from the identity

$$\mathbf{T}^{-1}(k)\,[\mathbf{T}_1^{(0)}(k), \ldots, \mathbf{T}_1^{(s_1-1)}(k), \ldots, \mathbf{T}_r^{(0)}(k), \ldots, \mathbf{T}_r^{(s_k-1)}(k)] = \mathbf{I}, \quad (3.24)$$

we have $s \times 1$ column vectors in the first s_1 columns

$$\mathbf{T}^{-1}(k)\mathbf{T}_1^{(0)}(k) = \begin{pmatrix} 1 \\ 0 \\ \vdots \\ 0 \end{pmatrix} \quad (3.25)$$

and

$$\mathbf{T}^{-1}(k)\mathbf{T}_1^{(j)}(k) = \begin{pmatrix} 0 \\ \vdots \\ 1 \\ \vdots \\ 0 \end{pmatrix}, \quad j = 1, \ldots, s_1 - 1. \tag{3.26}$$

The $(j+1)$th component of the vector in (3.26) is 1 and the other components are zero.

We now use the results in (3.23), (3.25) and (3.26) to compute the product $\mathbf{T}^{-1}(k)\mathbf{V}\mathbf{T}(k)$. The first column of the product is

$$\begin{aligned} \mathbf{T}^{-1}(k)\mathbf{V}\mathbf{T}_1^{(0)}(k) &= \mathbf{T}^{-1}(k)\rho_1\mathbf{T}_1^{(0)}(k) \\ &= \rho_1\mathbf{T}^{-1}(k)\mathbf{T}_1^{(0)}(k) \\ &= \begin{pmatrix} \rho_1 \\ 0 \\ 0 \\ \vdots \\ 0 \end{pmatrix}; \end{aligned} \tag{3.27}$$

the second column of the product is

$$\begin{aligned} \mathbf{T}^{-1}(k)\mathbf{V}\mathbf{T}_1^{(1)}(k) &= \mathbf{T}^{-1}(k)\,[\rho_1\mathbf{T}_1^{(1)}(k) + \mathbf{T}_1^{(0)}(k)] \\ &= \rho_1\mathbf{T}^{-1}(k)\mathbf{T}_1^{(1)}(k) + \mathbf{T}^{-1}(k)\mathbf{T}_1^{(0)}(k) \\ &= \begin{pmatrix} 1 \\ \rho_1 \\ 0 \\ 0 \\ \vdots \\ 0 \end{pmatrix}; \end{aligned} \tag{3.28}$$

and in general, the j-th column of the product is

$$
\begin{aligned}
\mathbf{T}^{-1}(k)\,\mathbf{V}\,\mathbf{T}_1^{(j-1)}(k) &= \mathbf{T}^{-1}(k)\,[\rho_1\,\mathbf{T}_1^{(j-1)}(k) + \mathbf{T}_1^{(j-2)}(k)] \\
&= \rho_1\,\mathbf{T}^{-1}(k)\,\mathbf{T}_1^{(j-1)}(k) + \mathbf{T}^{-1}(k)\,\mathbf{T}_1^{(j-2)}(k) \\
&= \begin{pmatrix} 0 \\ \vdots \\ 1 \\ \rho_1 \\ 0 \\ \vdots \\ 0 \end{pmatrix}, \qquad j = 2, \ldots, s_1, \qquad (3.29)
\end{aligned}
$$

where the $(j-1)$th component is 1 and the j-th component is ρ_1. Taking equations (3.27), (3.28) and (3.29) together, we can lay out the first s_1 columns:

$$
\mathbf{T}^{-1}(k)\,\mathbf{V}\,[\mathbf{T}_1^{(0)}(k), \mathbf{T}_1^{(1)}(k), \ldots, \mathbf{T}_1^{(s_1-1)}(k)] = \begin{pmatrix} \rho_1 & 1 & 0 & \ldots & 0 \\ 0 & \rho_1 & 1 & \ldots & 0 \\ 0 & 0 & \rho_1 & \ldots & 0 \\ \cdot & \cdot & \cdot & \ldots & \cdot \\ 0 & 0 & 0 & \ldots & \rho_1 \\ 0 & 0 & 0 & \ldots & 0 \\ \cdot & \cdot & \cdot & \ldots & \cdot \\ 0 & 0 & 0 & \ldots & 0 \end{pmatrix}
$$

$$
= \begin{pmatrix} \mathbf{J}_1 \\ \mathbf{0} \end{pmatrix}. \qquad (3.30)
$$

Hence, equation (3.21) is true. Applying the same multiplication operation and using equations (3.8) and (3.9), we find that the l-th block of s_l columns of the product $\mathbf{T}^{-1}(k)\,\mathbf{V}\mathbf{T}(k)$ is

$$
\mathbf{T}^{-1}(k)\,\mathbf{V}\,[\mathbf{T}_l^{(0)}(k), \mathbf{T}_l^{(1)}(k), \ldots, \mathbf{T}_l^{(s_l-1)}(k)] = \begin{pmatrix} \mathbf{0} \\ \mathbf{J}_l \\ \mathbf{0} \end{pmatrix},
$$

$$
l = 1, \ldots, r. \qquad (3.31)
$$

Consequently,

$$\mathbf{T}^{-1}(k)\,\mathbf{V}\,\mathbf{T}(k) = \begin{pmatrix} \mathbf{J}_1 & \mathbf{0} & \dots & \mathbf{0} \\ \mathbf{0} & \mathbf{J}_2 & \dots & \mathbf{0} \\ \cdot & \cdot & \dots & \cdot \\ \mathbf{0} & \mathbf{0} & \dots & \mathbf{J}_r \end{pmatrix}$$

$$= \mathbf{J}. \tag{3.20}$$

Theorem 2 is proven.

We are now in a position to derive formulas for the individual transition probabilities $P_{ij}(0, t)$ from the exponential solution

$$\mathbf{P}(0, t) = e^{\mathbf{V}t}$$

$$= \sum_{n=0}^{\infty} \frac{\mathbf{V}^n t^n}{n!}. \tag{3.32}$$

Transposing the matrix $\mathbf{T}(k)$ to the right hand side of equation (3.20), we find that

$$\mathbf{V} = \mathbf{T}(k)\,\mathbf{J}\,\mathbf{T}^{-1}(k) \tag{3.33}$$

and

$$\mathbf{V}^n = \mathbf{T}(k)\,\mathbf{J}^n\,\mathbf{T}^{-1}(k). \tag{3.34}$$

Therefore, we can determine the infinite sum in (3.32):

$$\sum_{n=0}^{\infty} \frac{\mathbf{V}^n t^n}{n!} = \sum_{n=0}^{\infty} \frac{\mathbf{T}(k)\,\mathbf{J}^n t^n\,\mathbf{T}^{-1}(k)}{n!}$$

$$= \mathbf{T}(k)\left[\sum_{n=0}^{\infty} \frac{\mathbf{J}^n t^n}{n!}\right]\mathbf{T}^{-1}(k). \tag{3.35}$$

Using the definition of the Jordan matrix in (3.17), we write the last infinite sum in (3.35) as a quasi-diagonal matrix

$$\sum_{n=0}^{\infty} \frac{\mathbf{J}^n t^n}{n!} = \operatorname{diag}\left[\sum_{n=0}^{\infty} \frac{\mathbf{J}_1^n t^n}{n!}, \dots, \sum_{n=0}^{\infty} \frac{\mathbf{J}_r^n t^n}{n!}\right]. \tag{3.36}$$

The n-th power of each Jordan block is given in (3.16). Therefore, the l-th block on the diagonal in equation (3.36) is an upper triangular matrix of rank s_l:

$$\sum_{n=0}^{\infty} \frac{\mathbf{J}_l^n t^n}{n!} = \begin{pmatrix} e^{\rho_l t} & \frac{t}{1!} e^{\rho_l t} & \dots & \frac{t^{s_l - 1}}{(s_l - 1)!} e^{\rho_l t} \\ 0 & e^{\rho_l t} & \dots & \frac{t^{s_l - 2}}{(s_l - 2)!} e^{\rho_l t} \\ \cdot & \cdot & \dots & \cdot \\ 0 & 0 & \dots & e^{\rho_l t} \end{pmatrix}$$

$$= \quad \mathbf{E}_l(t) \qquad l = 1, \dots, r. \tag{3.37}$$

Substituting (3.36), (3.37) in (3.35) yields the final solution

$$\mathbf{P}(0, t) = \mathbf{T}(k) \operatorname{diag} [\mathbf{E}_1(t), \dots, \mathbf{E}_r(t)] \, \mathbf{T}^{-1}(k). \tag{3.38}$$

By expanding the matrix product on the right hand side of (3.38), we obtain the formula for the individual transition probabilities

$$P_{ij}(0, t) =$$

$$\sum_{l=1}^{r} \left\{ \sum_{m=1}^{s_l} \left[\sum_{n=0}^{m-1} \frac{t^{m-1-n}}{(m-1-n)!\,n!} \left(\frac{d^n}{d\rho_l^n} A_{ki}(\rho_l) \right) T^{m'j}(k) \right] \right\} e^{\rho_l t}$$

$$i, j = 1, \dots, s, \tag{3.39}$$

where $m' = s_1 + \dots + s_{l-1} + m$ and $T^{m'j}(k)$ is the (m', j)-th element of the inverse matrix $\mathbf{T}^{-1}(k)$. We summarize the above result in the following theorem.

Theorem 3. *If the matrix* $\mathbf{V}$ *has multiple eigenvalues* $\rho_1, \dots, \rho_r$ *with respective multiplicities* $s_1, \dots, s_r$ *such that* $s_1 + \dots + s_r = s$, *then the solution of Kolmogorov differential equations in* (2.4) *and* (2.5) *corresponding to the initial condition* (2.6) *is given in* (3.39).

4. PROBLEMS FOR SOLUTION

1. Let $Z = x + iy$ and $\bar{Z} = X - iy$ be complex conjugates and let

$$P(Z) = c_0 + c_1 Z + \dots + c_k Z^k$$

be a polynomial of Z with real coefficients c's. Show that the complex conjugate of $P(Z)$, $\bar{P}(Z)$, is a polynomial of $\bar{Z}$, or,

$$\bar{P}(Z) = c_0 + c_1 \bar{Z} + \dots + c_k \bar{Z}^k.$$

2. Show that the solution of $p_{ij}(0, t)$ in (2.7) satisfies the differential equations in (2.4) and in (2.5).

3. Find the limiting probability of $P_{ij}(0,t)$ as $t \to \infty$.
4. Differentiate both sides of

$$(\rho \mathbf{I} - \mathbf{V})\begin{pmatrix} A_{k1}(\rho) \\ \vdots \\ A_{ks}(\rho) \end{pmatrix} = |A(\rho)|\,\mathbf{I}_k \tag{3.5}$$

with respect to ρ to find $(s_l - 1)$ equations in (3.7).

5. Derive equation (3.12) from equation (3.11).
6. Derive the equation

$$c_{s_l-1}\,\mathbf{T}_l^{(0)}(k) = \mathbf{0}$$

from equation (3.12).

7. Show that the coefficients $c_0, c_1, \ldots, c_{s_l-2}$ in equation (3.13) are all equal to zero.
8. Find the n-th power of the following Jordan block

$$\mathbf{J}_1 = \begin{pmatrix} \rho & 1 & 0 \\ 0 & \rho & 1 \\ 0 & 0 & \rho \end{pmatrix}$$

9. Verify the equation

$$\mathbf{T}^{-1}(k)\mathbf{V}\,[\mathbf{T}_l^{(0)}(k), \mathbf{T}_l^{(1)}(k), \ldots, \mathbf{T}_l^{(s_l-1)}(k)] = \begin{pmatrix} 0 \\ \mathbf{J}_l \\ 0 \end{pmatrix} \tag{3.31}$$

10. Expand the matrix product on the right-hand side of (3.38) to obtain the individual transition probabilities $P_{ij}(0,t)$ in (3.39).
11. Show that the solution of $P_{ij}(0,t)$ in (3.39) satisfies the forward differential equations in (2.4) and the backward differential equations in (2.5).

CHAPTER 16

A General Illness-Death Process

1. INTRODUCTION

With the results of Chapter 14 we can now extend the simple illness death process in Chapter 11 to account for variations in intensities of illness and causes of death. In this general model there are s states of health, $s_1, \dots, s_s$, and r states of death, $R_1, \dots, R_r$, for positive integers s and r. A health state might be broadly defined to reflect the absence of illness (an optimal health state), a physical impairment, a single specific disease or stage of disease, or any combination of diseases. A death state, on the other hand, is defined by the cause of death, whether single or multiple. Transition from a health state to a death state specifies not only the cause of death, but also any disease present. For example, an individual in a state of tuberculosis who passes to the death state of pneumonia dies of the latter in the presence of tuberculosis.

Transition from one state to another is determined by the intensities of illness $\nu_{\alpha\beta}$ and the intensities of death $\mu_{\alpha\delta}$, $\alpha \neq \beta$, $\alpha, \beta = 1, \dots, s$, and $\delta = 1, \dots, r$. These intensities are defined in equation (2.1) and (2.2), Chapter 11. They are assumed to be independent of time, therefore the illness-death process is time homogeneous. As in Chapter 11 we let

$$\nu_{\alpha\alpha} = -\left[\sum_{\substack{\beta=1\\ \beta\neq\alpha}}^{s} \nu_{\alpha\beta} + \sum_{\delta=1}^{r} \mu_{\alpha\delta}\right]. \tag{1.1}$$

For convenience we also introduce the *illness intensity matrix.*

$$\mathbf{V} = \begin{pmatrix} \nu_{11} & \cdots & \nu_{1s} \\ \vdots & & \vdots \\ \nu_{s1} & \cdots & \nu_{ss} \end{pmatrix} \tag{1.2}$$

and the *death intensity matrix*

$$\mathbf{U} = \begin{pmatrix} \mu_{11} & \cdots & \mu_{1r} \\ \vdots & & \vdots \\ \mu_{s1} & \cdots & \mu_{sr} \end{pmatrix} \tag{1.3}$$

Now let us define the transition probabilities for a time interval $(0, t)$, $0 \le t < \infty$, as follows:

$$P_{\alpha\beta}(0, t) = \Pr\{\text{an individual in state } S_\alpha \text{ at time 0 will be in health state } S_\beta \text{ at time } t\},$$
$$\alpha, \beta = 1, \dots, s, \tag{1.4}$$

$$Q_{\alpha\delta}(0, t) = \Pr\{\text{an individual in state } S_\alpha \text{ at time 0 will be in death state } R_\delta \text{ at time } t\},$$
$$\alpha = 1, \dots, s;\ \delta = 1, \dots, r. \tag{1.5}$$

At time $t = 0$,

$$P_{\alpha\alpha}(0, 0) = 1, \qquad P_{\alpha\beta}(0, 0) = 0, \qquad Q_{\alpha\beta}(0, 0) = 0,$$
$$\beta \neq \alpha; \quad \alpha, \beta = 1, \dots, s \quad \delta = 1, \dots, r. \tag{1.6}$$

The corresponding matrices are:

$$\mathbf{P}(0,t) = \begin{pmatrix} P_{11}(0,t) & \cdots & P_{1s}(0,t) \\ \vdots & & \vdots \\ P_{s1}(0,t) & \cdots & P_{ss}(0,t) \end{pmatrix}, \tag{1.7}$$

$$\mathbf{Q}(0,t) = \begin{pmatrix} Q_{11}(0,t) & \cdots & Q_{1r}(0,t) \\ \vdots & & \vdots \\ Q_{s1}(0,t) & \cdots & Q_{sr}(0,t) \end{pmatrix}, \tag{1.8}$$

and

$$\mathbf{P}(0,0) = \mathbf{I}, \qquad \mathbf{Q}(0,0) = \mathbf{0}. \tag{1.9}$$

The strict formulation of a real illness-death process requires that two assumptions be made: First that no death takes place without a cause, and second, that at the time of death an individual is affected with the disease from which he dies. A practical consequence of these assumptions would require many of the intensities $\mu_{\alpha\delta}$ to be zero. Furthermore, if an individual is unlikely (with probability $o(\Delta)$) either to contract or to recover from more than one disease within an infinitesimal time interval Δ, many $\nu_{\alpha\beta}$ will also be negligible. Nevertheless, our model will be presented in general form, without deleting any $\nu_{\alpha\beta}$ or $\mu_{\alpha\delta}$, and it will satisfy the following assumptions.

Assumption 1. The system is closed. For every α, and for every $t \geq 0$,

$$\sum_{\beta=1}^{s} P_{\alpha\beta}(0, t) + \sum_{\delta=1}^{r} Q_{\alpha\delta}(0, t) = 1, \tag{1.10}$$

so that the intensities and the transition probabilities have the relationships as in (1.1) where

$$\nu_{\alpha\beta} = \frac{d}{dt} P_{\alpha\beta}(0, t)\Big|_{t=0} \qquad \alpha, \beta = 1, \ldots, s \tag{1.11}$$

and

$$\mu_{\alpha\delta} = \frac{d}{dt} Q_{\alpha\delta}(0, t)\Big|_{t=0} \qquad \delta = 1, \ldots, r. \tag{1.12}$$

Assumption 2. The illness intensity matrix **V** is of rank s, and the death intensity matrix **U** is non-zero. Therefore the health states S_α are all transient states, and the system contains at least one death state R_δ.

2. TRANSITION PROBABILITIES

In this section we present explicit formulas for the transition probabilities and discuss some related problems. Because health transition probabilities $P_{\alpha\beta}(0, t)$ and the ordinary transition probabilities defined in Chapter 14 are essentially the same, we will not repeat the details.

2.1. Health Transition Probabilities $P_{\alpha\beta}(0, t)$.

Using the same reasoning that led to Kolmogorov differential equations in Chapter 14, we establish that the transition probabilities $P_{\alpha\beta}(0, t)$ satisfy the forward differential equations

$$\frac{d}{dt} P_{\alpha\gamma}(0, t) = \sum_{\beta=1}^{s} P_{\alpha\beta}(0, t)\nu_{\beta\gamma} \tag{2.1}$$

and the backward differential equations

$$\frac{d}{dt} P_{\alpha\gamma}(0, t) = \sum_{\beta=1}^{s} \nu_{\alpha\beta} P_{\beta\gamma}(0, t), \qquad \alpha, \gamma = 1, \ldots, s. \tag{2.2}$$

We let $\rho_1, \ldots, \rho_s$ be the roots of the characteristic equation

$$|\rho \mathbf{I} - \mathbf{V}'| = 0, \tag{2.3}$$

and for every $\rho = \rho_l$, we let $\mathbf{A}'(\rho_l) = (\rho_l \mathbf{I} - \mathbf{V}')$ and $A'_{\alpha\beta}(\rho_l)$ be the cofactors of $\mathbf{A}'(\rho_l)$. The solutions for the transition probabilities derived in Chapters 14 and 15 apply here with $\mathbf{V}$ having either single or multiple eigenvalues. For simplicity, we shall consider only the former.

When the eigenvalues $\rho_1, \ldots, \rho_s$ are distinct, then equations (2.1) and (2.2) have the common solution

$$P_{\alpha\beta}(0, t) = \sum_{l=1}^{s} \frac{A'_{\alpha\beta}(\rho_l)}{\prod_{\substack{j=1 \\ j \neq l}}^{s} (\rho_l - \rho_j)} e^{\rho_l t}, \qquad \alpha, \beta = 1, \ldots, s. \tag{2.4}$$

or

$$P_{\alpha\beta}(0, t) = \sum_{l=1}^{s} A_{k\alpha}(l) \frac{T_{\beta l}(k)}{|T(k)|} e^{\rho_l t}, \qquad \alpha, \beta = 1, \ldots, s, \tag{2.5}$$

where $A_{\alpha\beta}(\rho_l)$ is the transpose of $A'_{\alpha\beta}(\rho_l)$, and $T_{\beta l}(k)$ is the cofactor of the non-singular matrix

$$\mathbf{T}(k) = \begin{pmatrix} A_{k1}(\rho_1) & \cdots & A_{k1}(\rho_s) \\ \vdots & & \vdots \\ A_{ks}(\rho_1) & \cdots & A_{ks}(\rho_s) \end{pmatrix}. \tag{2.6}$$

Equation (2.5) may be compactly presented in matrix notation as

$$\mathbf{P}(0, t) = \mathbf{T}(k)\mathbf{E}(t)\mathbf{T}^{-1}(k) \tag{2.7}$$

where $\mathbf{E}(t)$ is a diagonal matrix:

$$\mathbf{E}(t) = \begin{pmatrix} e^{\rho_1 t} & 0 & \cdots & 0 \\ 0 & e^{\rho_2 t} & \cdots & 0 \\ \vdots & \vdots & & \vdots \\ 0 & 0 & \cdots & e^{\rho_s t} \end{pmatrix}. \tag{2.8}$$

Equations (2.4), (2.5) and (2.7) are similar to those in (4.32), (4.47), and (4.46) in Chapter 14. The only difference is the rank of the illness intensity matrix $\mathbf{V}$ as defined in (1.2). In the illness-death process, the rank of matrix $\mathbf{V}$ is s, and at least one row sum is less than zero, whereas in the finite Markov process presented in Chapter 14, the matrix $\mathbf{V}$ is of rank $s - 1$, and every row sum equals zero.

We can show that the probabilities given in (2.4) and (2.5) satisfy the differential equations in (2.1) and (2.2), and the Chapman-Kolmogorov equation

$$P_{\alpha\gamma}(0, \tau + t) = \sum_{\beta=1}^{s} P_{\alpha\beta}(0, \tau)P_{\beta\gamma}(0, t), \qquad \alpha, \gamma = 1, \ldots, s. \tag{2.9}$$

The proof is left to the reader.

2.2 Transition Probabilities Leading to Death, $Q_{\alpha\delta}(0, t)$.

The probability $Q_{\alpha\delta}(0, t)$ that an individual in health state S_α at time 0 will be in death state R_δ at time t derives from probability $P_{\alpha\beta}(0, t)$; the corresponding transition probability matrix $\mathbf{Q}(0, t)$ derives from the matrix $\mathbf{P}(0, t)$. An individual in health state S_α at time 0 may enter the death state R_δ directly from S_α, or by way of some other state S_β, $\beta \neq \alpha$, $\beta = 1, \ldots, s$, at any time τ prior to t. Thus

$$Q_{\alpha\delta}(0, t) = \int_0^t \sum_{\beta=1}^{s} P_{\alpha\beta}(0, \tau)\mu_{\beta\delta}\,d\tau \tag{2.10}$$

[cf., equation (2.29), Chapter 11] or, in terms of the corresponding matrices

$$\mathbf{Q}(0, t) = \int_0^t \mathbf{P}(0, \tau)\mathbf{U}\,d\tau. \tag{2.11}$$

The intensity matrix $\mathbf{U}$ is an $s \times r$ matrix as defined in equation (1.3). The integral in (2.11) calls for integration of each element of the matrix product $\mathbf{P}(\tau)\mathbf{U}$. To derive $\mathbf{Q}(0, t)$ from (2.11), we substitute equation (2.7) in (2.11) and integrate, obtaining

$$\begin{aligned}\mathbf{Q}(0, t) &= \int_0^t \mathbf{T}(k)\mathbf{E}(\tau)\mathbf{T}^{-1}(k)\mathbf{U}\,d\tau \\ &= \mathbf{T}(k)\,[\mathbf{E}(t) - \mathbf{I}]\,\boldsymbol{\rho}^{-1}\mathbf{T}^{-1}(k)\,\mathbf{U}. \end{aligned} \tag{2.12}$$

The unit matrix is $s \times s$ and $\boldsymbol{\rho}$ is an $s \times s$ diagonal matrix defined by

$$\boldsymbol{\rho} = \begin{pmatrix} \rho_1 & 0 & \cdots & 0 \\ 0 & \rho_2 & \cdots & 0 \\ \vdots & \vdots & & \vdots \\ 0 & 0 & \cdots & \rho_s \end{pmatrix} . \tag{2.13}$$

The individual transition probability $Q_{\alpha\delta}(0, t)$ can be obtained directly from (2.10) or by expanding (2.12); either way, this probability is

$$Q_{\alpha\delta}(0, t) = \sum_{l=1}^{s}\sum_{\beta=1}^{s} A_{k\alpha}(\rho_l)\frac{T_{\beta l}(k)}{|T(k)|}\rho_l^{-1}(e^{\rho_l t} - 1)\,\mu_{\beta\delta}. \tag{2.14}$$

Its equivalent form is

$$Q_{\alpha\delta}(0, t) = \sum_{l=1}^{s}\sum_{\beta=1}^{s} \frac{A'_{\alpha\beta}(\rho_l)}{\prod_{\substack{j=1\\ j\neq l}}^{s}(\rho_l - \rho_j)}\,\rho_l^{-1}\,(e^{\rho_l t} - 1)\mu_{\beta\delta} \tag{2.15}$$

$$\alpha = 1, \ldots, s; \qquad \delta = 1, \ldots, r.$$

A Chapman-Kolmogorov type equation can be established also for the transition probabilities $Q_{\alpha\delta}(0, \tau + t)$. There are two possible transitions that will move an individual who is in S_α at time 0 into R_δ at time $\tau + t$: The individual must either enter R_δ prior to τ or else be in some illness state S_β at time τ and enter R_δ sometime between τ and $\tau + t$. Therefore the corresponding transition probabilities satisfy the equation

$$Q_{\alpha\delta}(0, \tau + t) = Q_{\alpha\delta}(0, \tau) + \sum_{\beta=1}^{s} P_{\alpha\beta}(0, \tau)\,Q_{\beta\delta}(0, t) \tag{2.16}$$

[cf., equation (3.6) Chapter 11]. Equation (2.16) holds for $\alpha = 1, \dots, s$ and for $\delta = 1, \dots, r$, and the corresponding matrices satisfy the relationship:

$$\mathbf{Q}(0, \tau + t) = \mathbf{Q}(0, \tau) + \mathbf{P}(0, \tau)\mathbf{Q}(0, t). \tag{2.17}$$

To verify (2.17), we recall the solutions obtained in (2.7) and (2.12) and use these results to write

$$\begin{aligned}\mathbf{Q}(0, \tau) &+ \mathbf{P}(0, \tau)\mathbf{Q}(0, t)\\ &= \mathbf{T}(k)\,[\mathbf{E}(\tau) - \mathbf{I}]\,\boldsymbol{\rho}^{-1}\mathbf{T}^{-1}(k)\mathbf{U} + \\ &\quad [\mathbf{T}(k)\,\mathbf{E}(\tau)\mathbf{T}^{-1}(k)]\,[\mathbf{T}(k)\,\{\mathbf{E}(t) - \mathbf{I}\}\,\boldsymbol{\rho}^{-1}\mathbf{T}^{-1}(k)\mathbf{U}].\end{aligned} \tag{2.18}$$

After multiplication, the right hand side reduces to

$$\begin{aligned}\mathbf{T}(k)\,[\mathbf{E}(\tau) - \mathbf{I}]\,\boldsymbol{\rho}^{-1}\mathbf{T}^{-1}(k)\mathbf{U} &+ \mathbf{T}(k)\,[\mathbf{E}(\tau + t) - \mathbf{E}(\tau)]\,\boldsymbol{\rho}^{-1}\mathbf{T}^{-1}(k)\mathbf{U}\\ &= \mathbf{T}(k)\,[\mathbf{E}(\tau + t) - \mathbf{I}]\,\boldsymbol{\rho}^{-1}\mathbf{T}^{-1}(k)\mathbf{U}\\ &= \mathbf{Q}(0, \tau + t),\end{aligned} \tag{2.19}$$

proving equation (2.17) and hence (2.16) as well.

2.3. An Equality Concerning Transition Probabilities.

An individual who is in health state S_α at time 0 must at time t be either in one of the health states S_β or in one of the death states R_δ; therefore the corresponding transition probabilities must satisfy the equation

$$\sum_{\beta=1}^{s} P_{\alpha\beta}(0, t) + \sum_{\delta=1}^{r} Q_{\alpha\delta}(0, t) = 1, \qquad \alpha = 1, \dots, s. \tag{2.20}$$

Having derived explicit formulas for the transition probabilities, we can verify equation (2.20) directly. By substituting (2.4) and (2.15) in (2.20) we obtain

$$\begin{aligned}\sum_{\beta=1}^{s}\sum_{l=1}^{s} &\frac{A'_{\alpha\beta}(\rho_l)}{\prod\limits_{\substack{j=1\\ j\neq l}}^{s}(\rho_l - \rho_j)}\, e^{\rho_l t}\\ &+ \sum_{\delta=1}^{r}\sum_{\beta=1}^{s}\sum_{l=1}^{s} \frac{A'_{\alpha\beta}(\rho_l)}{\prod\limits_{\substack{j=1\\ j\neq l}}^{s}(\rho_l - \rho_j)\rho_l}\,[e^{\rho_l t} - 1]\,\mu_{\beta\delta} = 1.\end{aligned} \tag{2.21}$$

Since equation (2.21) can be verified by direct computation, its proof is left to the reader. The corresponding matrix equation is verified below.

Equation (2.20) can be summarized in matrix notation as

$$\mathbf{P}(0, t)\begin{pmatrix}1\\ \vdots\\ 1\end{pmatrix}_s + \mathbf{Q}(0, t)\begin{pmatrix}1\\ \vdots\\ 1\end{pmatrix}_r = \begin{pmatrix}1\\ \vdots\\ 1\end{pmatrix}_s. \tag{2.22}$$

The first and third column vectors are $s\times 1$, the second column vector is $r\times 1$, and all the components are one. To verify equation (2.22) we substitute equation (2.7) for the term $\mathbf{P}(0, t)$ and equation (2.12) for the term $\mathbf{Q}(0, t)$; the left hand side of (2.22) becomes

$$\mathbf{T}(k)\mathbf{E}(t)\mathbf{T}^{-1}(k)\begin{pmatrix}1\\ \vdots\\ 1\end{pmatrix}_s + \mathbf{T}(k)\,[\mathbf{E}(t)-\mathbf{I}]\,\boldsymbol{\rho}^{-1}\mathbf{T}^{-1}(k)\mathbf{U}\begin{pmatrix}1\\ \vdots\\ 1\end{pmatrix}_r. \tag{2.23}$$

From (1.1), (1.2) and (1.3) we deduce the relationship

$$\mathbf{U}\begin{pmatrix}1\\ \vdots\\ 1\end{pmatrix}_r = -\mathbf{V}\begin{pmatrix}1\\ \vdots\\ 1\end{pmatrix}_s; \tag{2.24}$$

and hence we can rewrite (2.23) as

$$\mathbf{T}(k)\,\mathbf{E}(t)\mathbf{T}^{-1}(k)\begin{pmatrix}1\\ \vdots\\ 1\end{pmatrix}_s - \mathbf{T}(k)\,[\mathbf{E}(t)-\mathbf{I}]\boldsymbol{\rho}^{-1}\mathbf{T}^{-1}(k)\;\mathbf{V}\begin{pmatrix}1\\ \vdots\\ 1\end{pmatrix}_s. \tag{2.25}$$

From equation (3.30), Chapter 14, we see that $\mathbf{T}(k)$, as defined in (2.6), transforms matrix $\mathbf{V}$ into a diagonal matrix:

$$\mathbf{T}^{-1}(k)\mathbf{V}\mathbf{T}(k) = \boldsymbol{\rho} \tag{2.26}$$

where $\boldsymbol{\rho}$ is the diagonal matrix in (2.13). Therefore,

$$\boldsymbol{\rho}^{-1}\mathbf{T}^{-1}(k)\mathbf{V} = \mathbf{T}^{-1}(k). \tag{2.27}$$

Substituting (2.27) in (2.25) and canceling out the first two terms, we get

$$\mathbf{T}(k)\mathbf{I}\,\mathbf{T}^{-1}(k)\begin{pmatrix}1\\ \vdots\\ 1\end{pmatrix}_s = \begin{pmatrix}1\\ \vdots\\ 1\end{pmatrix}_s, \tag{2.28}$$

thus proving equation (2.22).

2.4. Limiting Transition Probabilities.

We proved in section 4.1, Chapter 14, that if $\nu_{\alpha\beta} \geq 0$ for $\alpha \neq \beta$ and $\sum_{\beta} \nu_{\alpha\beta} \leq 0$ for each α, then any eigenvalue of $\mathbf{V}$ is nonpositive. In the present case, $\mathbf{V}$ is a rank s; all its eigenvalues are negative. Consequently, as t approaches infinity, the transition probabilities become

$$P_{\alpha\beta}(0, \infty) = \lim_{t\to\infty} \sum_{l=1}^{s} \frac{A'_{\alpha\beta}(\rho_l)}{\prod_{\substack{j=1\\ j\neq l}}^{s} (\rho_l - \rho_j)} e^{\rho_l t} = 0,$$

$$\alpha, \beta = 1, \ldots, s, \tag{2.29}$$

and

$$Q_{\alpha\delta}(0,\infty) = \lim_{t\to\infty} \sum_{\beta=1}^{s} \sum_{l=1}^{s} \frac{A'_{\alpha\beta}(\rho_l)\mu_{\beta\delta}}{\prod_{\substack{j=1\\ j\neq l}}^{s} (\rho_l - \rho_j)\rho_l} (e^{\rho_l t} - 1)$$

$$= -\sum_{\beta=1}^{s} \sum_{l=1}^{s} \frac{A'_{\alpha\beta}(\rho_l)\mu_{\beta\delta}}{\prod_{\substack{j=1\\ j\neq l}}^{s} (\rho_l - \rho_j)\rho_l}, \qquad \delta = 1, \ldots, r. \tag{2.30}$$

It follows from (2.21) that

$$\sum_{\delta=1}^{r} Q_{\alpha\delta}(0, \infty) = 1. \tag{2.31}$$

Thus we say that starting from any health state S_α at any given time, the probability is one that an individual will eventually enter a death state.

2.5. Expected Durations of Stay in Health and Death States.

Given an individual in health state S_α at time 0, what is the expected length of stay in each of the states within the time interval $(0, t)$? This important concept was introduced and defined in the context of simple illness-death processes in Chapter 11. For easy reference, however, we shall here restate the pertinent symbols.

For an individual in S_α at time 0, let

$$e_{\alpha\beta}(t) = \text{the expected duration of stay in } S_\beta \text{ during the interval } (0, t), \quad \beta = 1, \ldots, s, \tag{2.32}$$

and

$$\varepsilon_{\alpha\beta}(t) = \text{the expected duration of stay in } R_\delta \text{ during the interval } (0, t), \quad \delta = 1, \ldots, r. \tag{2.33}$$

By the same reasoning used in Chapter 11, we find that

$$e_{\alpha\beta}(t) = \int_0^t P_{\alpha\beta}(0, \tau)\,d\tau \tag{2.34}$$

and

$$\varepsilon_{\alpha\delta}(t) = \int_0^t Q_{\alpha\delta}(0, \tau)\,d\tau. \tag{2.35}$$

Substituting formulas (2.4) and (2.15) for the transition probabilities, we compute

$$e_{\alpha\beta}(t) = \int_0^t \sum_{l=1}^{s} \frac{A'_{\alpha\beta}(\rho_l)}{\prod_{\substack{j=1\\ j\neq l}}^{s} (\rho_l - \rho_j)} e^{\rho_l \tau}\,d\tau$$

$$= \sum_{l=1}^{s} \frac{A'_{\alpha\beta}(\rho_l)}{\prod_{\substack{j=1\\ j\neq l}}^{s} (\rho_l - \rho_j)\rho_l} [e^{\rho_l t} - 1], \quad \alpha, \beta = 1, \ldots, s, \tag{2.36}$$

and

$$\varepsilon_{\alpha\delta}(t) = \int_0^t \sum_{l=1}^{s} \sum_{\beta=1}^{s} \frac{A'_{\alpha\beta}(\rho_l)\mu_{\beta\delta}}{\prod_{\substack{j=1\\ j\neq l}}^{s} (\rho_l - \rho_j)\rho_l} (e^{\rho_l \tau} - 1)d\tau$$

$$= \sum_{l=1}^{s} \sum_{\beta=1}^{s} \frac{A'_{\alpha\beta}(\rho_l)\mu_{\beta\delta}}{\prod_{\substack{j=1\\ j\neq l}}^{s} (\rho_l - \rho_j)\rho_l} \left[\frac{1}{\rho_l}(e^{\rho_l t} - 1) - t\right],$$

$$\alpha = 1, \dots, s; \quad \delta = 1, \dots, r. \tag{2.37}$$

Since an individual in S_α at time 0 must be in one and only one of the $s + r$ states at any given instant during the interval $(0, t)$, we can say that

$$\sum_{\beta=1}^{s} e_{\alpha\beta}(t) + \sum_{\delta=1}^{r} \varepsilon_{\alpha\delta}(t) = t. \tag{2.38}$$

We can show equation (2.38) quite easily by substituting equations (2.34) and (2.35) in (2.38). As a result we find

$$\sum_{\beta=1}^{s} e_{\alpha\beta}(0,t) + \sum_{\delta=1}^{r} \varepsilon_{\alpha\delta}(0,t) =$$

$$\int_0^t \left[\sum_{\beta=1}^{s} P_{\alpha\beta}(0, \tau) + \sum_{\delta=1}^{r} Q_{\alpha\delta}(0, \tau)\right] d\tau. \tag{2.39}$$

The integrand is unity, and therefore the integral equals t.

2.6. Population Sizes in Health States and Death States.

At time 0, let there be i_α individuals in state S_α, $\alpha = 1, \dots, s$, so that

$$i = i_1 + \dots + i_s \tag{2.40}$$

is the initial size of the total population. During the time interval $(0, t)$, these i individuals will travel independently from one health state to another, and some will enter a death state. At the end of the interval, there will be $X_\beta(t)$ individuals in S_β and $Y_\delta(t)$ in R_δ, $\beta = 1, \dots, s$; $\delta = 1, \dots, r$. We are interested in finding the joint probability distribution of all the random variables $X_\beta(t)$ and $Y_\delta(t)$. As we pointed out in section 5, Chapter 11, the random variables $X_\beta(t)$ and $Y_\delta(t)$ can be characterized according to their initial state at time 0. This is expressed by the formula

$$X_\beta(t) = X_{1\beta}(t) + \dots + X_{s\beta}(t), \tag{2.41}$$

where $X_{\alpha\beta}(t)$ is the number of people in state S_β at time t who were in state S_α at time 0. Also,

$$Y_\delta(t) = Y_{1\delta}(t) + \dots + Y_{s\delta}(t) \tag{2.42}$$

where $Y_{\alpha\delta}(t)$ is the number of people in state R_δ at time t who were in state S_α at time 0.

Each of the i_α people in state S_α at time 0 must be in one of the health states or in one of the death states at time t; thus

$$i_\alpha = \sum_{\beta=1}^{s} X_{\alpha\beta}(t) + \sum_{\delta=1}^{r} Y_{\alpha\delta}(t). \tag{2.43}$$

According to (2.20),

$$1 = \sum_{\beta=1}^{s} P_{\alpha\beta}(0, t) + \sum_{\delta=1}^{r} Q_{\alpha\delta}(0, t). \tag{2.20}$$

Equations (2.43) and (2.20) together determine that, given i_α, the random variables on the right side of (2.43) have the joint multinomial distribution. Letting $X_{\alpha\beta}(t)$ and $Y_{\alpha\delta}(t)$ assume the values of $x_{\alpha\beta}$ and $y_{\alpha\delta}$, respectively, their joint probability distribution is

$$\frac{i_\alpha!}{\prod_{\beta=1}^{s} x_{\alpha\beta}! \prod_{\delta=1}^{r} y_{\alpha\delta}!} \prod_{\beta=1}^{s} [P_{\alpha\beta}(t)]^{x_{\alpha\beta}} \prod_{\delta=1}^{r} [Q_{\alpha\delta}(t)]^{y_{\alpha\delta}}, \tag{2.44}$$

where $x_{\alpha\beta}$ and $y_{\alpha\delta}$ are non-negative integers satisfying the condition

$$\sum_\beta x_{\alpha\beta} + \sum_\delta y_{\alpha\delta} = i_\alpha. \tag{2.45}$$

For $\alpha = 1, \dots, s$, the joint probability distribution of $X_\beta(t)$ and $Y_\delta(t)$ is the convolution of the distribution in (2.44). That is

$$\Pr\{X_1(t) = x_1, \ldots, X_s(t) = x_s;\ Y_1(t) = y_1, \ldots, Y_r(t) = y_r | i_1, \ldots, i_s\}$$

$$= \Sigma \prod_{\alpha=1}^{s} \frac{i_\alpha!}{\prod_{\beta=1}^{s} x_{\alpha\beta}! \prod_{\delta=1}^{r} y_{\alpha\delta}!} \prod_{\beta=1}^{s} [P_{\alpha\beta}(t)]^{x_{\alpha\beta}} \prod_{\delta=1}^{r} [Q_{\alpha\delta}(t)]^{y_{\alpha\delta}}, \quad (2.46)$$

where $x_{\alpha\beta}$ and $y_{\alpha\delta}$ are non-negative integers that satisfy equation (2.45). The summation is taken over all $x_{\alpha\beta}$ and $y_{\alpha\delta}$ so that

$$\sum_{\alpha=1}^{s} x_{\alpha\beta} = x_\beta \quad \text{and} \quad \sum_{\alpha=1}^{s} y_{\alpha\delta} = y_\delta . \quad (2.47)$$

The expected population sizes of the states and the corresponding variances and covariances are obtained easily from (2.47) by using familiar theorems introduced in our discussion of the multinomial distribution in Chapter 1. The expectations, for example, are

$$E[X_\beta(t)] = \sum_{\alpha=1}^{s} i_\alpha P_{\alpha\beta}(t) \quad (2.48)$$

and

$$E[Y_\delta(t)] = \sum_{\alpha=1}^{s} i_\alpha Q_{\alpha\delta}(0, t) . \quad (2.49)$$

As t approaches infinity, $P_{\alpha\beta}(0, t)$ tends to zero, and the probability distribution in (2.46) reduces to

$$\Sigma \prod_{\alpha=1}^{s} \frac{i_\alpha!}{\prod_{\delta=1}^{r} y_{\alpha\delta}!} \prod_{\delta=1}^{r} [Q_{\alpha\delta}(0, \infty)]^{y_{\alpha\delta}}, \quad (2.50)$$

and the expectation

$$E[Y_\delta(\infty)] = \sum_{\alpha=1}^{s} i_\alpha Q_{\alpha\delta}(0, \infty) \quad (2.51)$$

with $Q_{\alpha\delta}(0, \infty)$ as given in (2.30).

3. MULTIPLE TRANSITION PROBABILITIES

The transition probabilities $P_{\alpha\beta}(0, t)$ presented in section 2 relate only to the end results of an individual's movement over a given period of time. They are inadequate to describe the pattern of movement during the interval. In dealing with the simple illness-death process in Chapter 12, we resolve this problem by studying the multiple transition probabilities. We shall consider the same problem for the general model, but let us first review some symbols and definitions.

The probability that an individual who is in state S_α at time 0 will be in state S_β at time t is $P_{\alpha\beta}(0, t)$. During the interval $(0, t)$ the individual will travel continuously from one state to another; he or she may *exit* from S_α a number of times, or may *enter* S_β a number of times. There are two kinds of random variables associated with transitions that an individual makes during a time interval $(0, t)$. We define $M_{\alpha\beta}(0, t)$ as the *number of exit transitions from* S_α, and $N_{\alpha\beta}(0, t)$ as *the number of entrance transitions into* S_β. Both $M_{\alpha\beta}(0, t)$ and $N_{\alpha\beta}(0, t)$ are random variables with the respective probabilities denoted by $P_{\alpha\beta}^{(m)}(0, t)$ and $p_{\alpha\beta}^{(n)}(0, t)$, so that

$$\begin{aligned} P_{\alpha\beta}^{(m)}(0, t) &= \Pr\{M_{\alpha\beta}(0, t) = m\} \\ &= \Pr\{\text{an individual in } S_\alpha \text{ at time 0 will } \textit{leave } S_\alpha\, m \text{ times} \\ &\qquad \text{during } (0, t) \text{ and will be in } S_\beta \text{ at time } t\} \\ &\qquad m = 0, 1, \ldots; \qquad \alpha, \beta = 1, \ldots, s \end{aligned} \tag{3.1}$$

and

$$\begin{aligned} p_{\alpha\beta}^{(n)}(0, t) &= \Pr\{N_{\alpha\beta}(0, t) = n\} \\ &= \Pr\{\text{an individual in } S_\alpha \text{ at time 0 will } \textit{enter } S_\beta\, n \text{ times} \\ &\qquad \text{during } (0, t) \text{ and will be in } S_\beta \text{ at time } t\} \\ &\qquad n = 0, 1, \ldots; \qquad \alpha, \beta = 1, \ldots, s. \end{aligned} \tag{3.2}$$

Because an individual may travel between S_α and other states in the system without ever entering S_β the random variables $M_{\alpha\beta}(0, t)$ and $N_{\alpha\beta}(0, t)$ have different probability distributions. When $\alpha = \beta$, however,

$$\Pr\{M_{\alpha\alpha}(0, t) = m\} = \Pr\{N_{\alpha\alpha}(0, t) = m\}, \tag{3.3}$$

whatever may be $m = 0, 1, \ldots$. In any case, we have

$$\sum_{m=0}^{\infty} P_{\alpha\beta}^{(m)}(0, t) = \sum_{n=0}^{\infty} p_{\alpha\beta}^{(n)}(0, t) = P_{\alpha\beta}(0, t). \tag{3.4}$$

Since $P_{\alpha\beta}(0, t) < 1$, $M_{\alpha\beta}(0, t)$ and $N_{\alpha\beta}(0, t)$ are improper random variables. Explicit formulas for the multiple transition probabilities are difficult to obtain for a system that incorporates an arbitrary number of health states, but formulas can be derived for the corresponding probability generating functions.

3.1 Multiple Exit Transition Probabilities $P_{\alpha\beta}^{(m)}(0, t)$.

Let the p.g.f. of $P_{\alpha\beta}^{(m)}(0, t)$ be defined by

$$g_{\alpha\beta}(s; t) = \sum_{m=0}^{\infty} s^m P_{\alpha\beta}^{(m)}(0, t). \tag{3.5}$$

At $s = 1$,

$$g_{\alpha\beta}(1, t) = P_{\alpha\beta}(0, t). \tag{3.6}$$

Using an approach similar to that described in section 3, Chapter 12, we establish the following differential equations for the multiple exit transition probabilities:

$$\frac{d}{dt} P_{\alpha\alpha}^{(m)}(0, t) = P_{\alpha\alpha}^{(m)}(0, t)\nu_{\alpha\alpha} + \sum_{\substack{\beta \neq \alpha \\ \beta=1}}^{s} P_{\alpha\beta}^{(m)}(0, t)\nu_{\beta\alpha}$$

and

$$\frac{d}{dt} P_{\alpha\gamma}^{(m)}(0, t) = P_{\alpha\alpha}^{(m-1)}(0, t)\nu_{\alpha\gamma} + \sum_{\substack{\beta \neq \alpha \\ \beta=1}}^{s} P_{\alpha\beta}^{(m)}(0, t)\nu_{\beta\gamma}$$

$$m = 0, 1, \ldots; \qquad \gamma \neq \alpha; \quad \alpha, \gamma = 1, \ldots, s. \tag{3.7}$$

From (3.7) direct computations show that the p.g.f.'s satisfy the differential equations

$$\frac{\partial}{\partial t} g_{\alpha\alpha}(s; t) = \sum_{\beta=1}^{s} g_{\alpha\beta}(s; t)\nu_{\beta\alpha}$$

$$\frac{\partial}{\partial t} g_{\alpha\gamma}(s; t) = s g_{\alpha\alpha}(s; t)\nu_{\alpha\gamma} + \sum_{\substack{\beta \neq \alpha \\ \beta=1}}^{s} g_{\alpha\beta}(s; t)\nu_{\beta\gamma}. \tag{3.8}$$

Since $P_{\alpha\alpha}^{(0)}(0, 0) = 1$, $P_{\alpha\gamma}^{(0)}(0, 0) = 0$, $\gamma \neq \alpha$, and $P_{\alpha\gamma}^{(m)}(0, 0) = 0$, $m = 1, \ldots,$ the initial conditions for the differential equations in (3.8) are

$$g_{\alpha\alpha}(s; 0) = 1 \quad \text{and} \quad g_{\alpha\gamma}(s; 0) = 0, \qquad \gamma \neq \alpha; \quad \alpha, \gamma = 1, \ldots, s. \tag{3.9}$$

The system of differential equations in (3.8) represents s^2 differential equations which we can solve as the system of equations in (2.1). However, because of the presence of s as the coefficient of $g_{\alpha\gamma}(s; t)$ in some but not all of the equations, it is difficult to use matrix notation in order to present the solution in a compact form. Nevertheless, for each α, we can rewrite (3.8) as follows:

$$
\begin{aligned}
&(D - \nu_{11})g_{\alpha 1} - \nu_{21}g_{\alpha 2} - \dots - s\nu_{\alpha 1}g_{\alpha\alpha} - \dots - \nu_{s1}g_{\alpha s} = 0\\
&-\nu_{12}g_{\alpha 1} + (D - \nu_{22})g_{\alpha 2} - \dots - s\nu_{\alpha 2}g_{\alpha\alpha} - \dots - \nu_{s2}g_{\alpha s} = 0\\
&\quad\cdot \qquad \cdot \qquad \cdot \qquad \cdot \qquad \cdot \qquad \cdot\\
&-\nu_{1\alpha}g_{\alpha 1} - \nu_{2\alpha}g_{\alpha 2} - \dots + (D - \nu_{\alpha\alpha})g_{\alpha\alpha} - \dots - \nu_{s\alpha}g_{\alpha s} = 0\\
&\quad\cdot \qquad \cdot \qquad \cdot \qquad \cdot \qquad \cdot \qquad \cdot\\
&-\nu_{1s}g_{\alpha 1} - \nu_{2s}g_{\alpha 2} - \dots - s\nu_{\alpha s}g_{\alpha\alpha} - \dots + (D - \nu_{ss})g_{\alpha s} = 0.
\end{aligned}
\tag{3.10}
$$

For simplicity, the symbol D is introduced to designate the differentiation $\partial/\partial t$, and $g_{\alpha\beta}$ designates $g_{\alpha\beta}(s; t)$. The corresponding characteristic equation is

$$
|A'(\alpha)| = \begin{vmatrix}
(\rho - \nu_{11}) & -\nu_{21} & \cdots & -s\nu_{\alpha 1} & \cdots & -\nu_{s1}\\
-\nu_{12} & (\rho - \nu_{22}) & \cdots & -s\nu_{\alpha 2} & \cdots & -\nu_{s2}\\
\cdot & \cdot & \cdot & \cdot & \cdot & \cdot\\
-\nu_{1\alpha} & -\nu_{2\alpha} & \cdots & (\rho - \nu_{\alpha\alpha}) & \cdots & -\nu_{s\alpha}\\
\cdot & \cdot & \cdot & \cdot & \cdot & \cdot\\
-\nu_{1s} & -\nu_{2s} & \cdots & -s\nu_{\alpha s} & \cdots & (\rho - \nu_{ss})
\end{vmatrix}
= 0. \tag{3.11}
$$

In equation (3.11), the index s appears in the α-th column, except in the diagonal element. Now suppose that the characteristic equation has distinct roots, $\rho_1(\alpha), \dots, \rho_s(\alpha)$. Following the steps for solving the Kolmogorov differential equations in (4.4), Chapter 14, we obtain the general solution of (3.10)

$$
g_{\alpha\gamma}(s; t) = \sum_{i=1}^{s} k_{\alpha i} A'_{\alpha\gamma}(\alpha, i)\, e^{\rho_i(\alpha)t}, \tag{3.12}
$$

where $A'_{\alpha\gamma}(\alpha, i)$ are cofactors of $|A'(\alpha, i)|$ with $\rho = \rho_i(\alpha)$, α, β, $i = 1$,

$\dots, s$. Substituting (3.12) in (3.9) for $t = 0$, and solving the resulting simultaneous equations for $k_{\alpha i}$ yields

$$k_{\alpha i} = \frac{1}{\prod_{\substack{j \neq i \\ j=1}}^{s} [\rho_i(\alpha) - \rho_j(\alpha)]} . \tag{3.13}$$

Hence the solution for the differential equations in (3.8) is

$$g_{\alpha\gamma}(s; t) = \sum_{i=1}^{s} \frac{A'_{\alpha\gamma}(\alpha, i)}{\prod_{\substack{j \neq i \\ j=1}}^{s} [\rho_i(\alpha) - \rho_j(\alpha)]} e^{\rho_i(\alpha)t} . \tag{3.14}$$

For given α and γ, $\rho_i(\alpha)$ and $A'_{\alpha\gamma}(\alpha, i)$ are functions of the argument s. When $s = 1$, $|A'(\alpha)|$ in (3.11) becomes identical to $|\rho\mathbf{I} - \mathbf{V}'|$ in (2.3), and the p.g.f. $g_{\alpha\gamma}(1, t)$ is equal to the transition probability $P_{\alpha\gamma}(0, t)$ in (2.4).

The individual multiple transition probabilities are obtained from the corresponding p.g.f.'s in (3.14) by taking the appropriate derivatives

$$P_{\alpha\gamma}^{(m)}(0, t) = \frac{1}{m!} \frac{\partial^m}{\partial s^m} g_{\alpha\gamma}(s; t) \bigg|_{s=0} . \tag{3.15}$$

However, the computations are overwhelming, even for a moderate number of health states and transitions.

3.2 Multiple Transition Probabilities Leading to Death, $Q_{\alpha\delta}^{(m)}(0, t)$.

Consider again an individual in S_α at time 0. Let $D_{\alpha\delta}(0, t)$ be the number of times the individual leaves S_α before reaching a death state R_δ at some time prior to t. Let

$$Q_{\alpha\delta}^{(m)}(0, t) = \Pr\{D_{\alpha\delta}(0, t) = m\} \qquad m = 1, \dots$$
$$\alpha = 1, \dots, s$$
$$\delta = 1, \dots, r, \tag{3.16}$$

be the probability and

$$h_{\alpha\delta}(s; t) = \sum_{m=1}^{\infty} s^m Q_{\alpha\delta}^{(m)}(0, t) \tag{3.17}$$

be the corresponding p.g.f. We shall derive explicit formulas for $h_{\alpha\delta}(s; t)$. Obviously, $Q_{\alpha\delta}^{(m)}(0, t)$ and $P_{\alpha\beta}^{(m)}(0, t)$ have the relation expressed in the formula

$$Q_{\alpha\delta}^{(m)}(0, t) = \int_0^t P_{\alpha\alpha}^{(m-1)}(0, \tau)\mu_{\alpha\delta}\,d\tau + \int_0^t \sum_{\substack{\beta \neq \alpha \\ \beta=1}}^{s} P_{\alpha\beta}^{(m)}(0, \tau)\,\mu_{\beta\delta}\,d\tau \tag{3.18}$$

(c.f., equation (8.3), Chapter 12). Substituting (3.18) in (3.17) yields

$$h_{\alpha\delta}(s; t) = \sum_{m=1}^{\infty} s^m \left\{ \int_0^t P_{\alpha\alpha}^{(m-1)}(0, \tau)\mu_{\alpha\delta}\,d\tau + \int_0^t \sum_{\substack{\beta \neq \alpha \\ \beta=1}}^{s} P_{\alpha\beta}^{(m)}(0, \tau)\,\mu_{\beta\delta}\,d\tau \right\}. \tag{3.19}$$

In (3.19) the infinite series converges absolutely. If we interchange the summation and integral signs and write

$$\begin{aligned} h_{\alpha\delta}(s;t) = &\int_0^t \left\{ \sum_{m=1}^{\infty} s^{m-1} P_{\alpha\alpha}^{(m-1)}(0, \tau) \right\} s\mu_{\alpha\delta}\,d\tau \\ &+ \int_0^t \sum_{\substack{\beta \neq \alpha \\ \beta=1}}^{s} \left\{ \sum_{m=1}^{\infty} s^m P_{\alpha\beta}^{(m)}(0, \tau) \right\} \mu_{\beta\delta}\,d\tau, \end{aligned} \tag{3.20}$$

then each infinite sum in (3.20) is the same as the p.g.f. in (3.5), whose solution is given in (3.14). Substituting (3.14) in (3.20) and integrating the resulting expression yields the formulas

$$\begin{aligned} h_{\alpha\delta}(s;t) = &\sum_{i=1}^{s} \frac{A'_{\alpha\alpha}(\alpha; i)\, s\mu_{\alpha\delta}}{\prod\limits_{\substack{j \neq i \\ j=1}}^{s} [\rho_i(\alpha) - \rho_j(\alpha)]\,\rho_i(\alpha)} [e^{\rho_i(\alpha)t} - 1] \\ &+ \sum_{\substack{\beta \neq \alpha \\ \beta=1}}^{s} \sum_{i=1}^{s} \frac{A'_{\alpha\beta}(\alpha; i)\,\mu_{\beta\delta}}{\prod\limits_{\substack{j \neq i \\ j=1}}^{s} [\rho_i(\alpha) - \rho_j(\alpha)]\,\rho_i(\alpha)} [e^{\rho_i(\alpha)t} - 1]. \end{aligned} \tag{3.21}$$

When $s = 1$, $h_{\alpha\delta}(1; t) = Q_{\alpha\delta}(0, t)$ is given in equation (2.15).

3.3 Multiple Entrance Transition Probabilities, $p_{\alpha\beta}^{(n)}(0, t)$.

In the general illness-death model with more than two health states, the number of exit transitions from a state S_α and the number of entrance transitions into another state S_β are not only conceptually different, they also have different probability distributions. Let

$$g_{\alpha\beta}(s; t) = \sum_{n=0}^{\infty} s^n p_{\alpha\beta}^{(n)}(0, t) \tag{3.22}$$

be the p.g.f. of the entrance transition probability $p_{\alpha\beta}^{(n)}(0, t)$ defined in (3.2). Following the procedure outlined in section 9, Chapter 12, we derive the differential equations for the probabilities defined in (3.2),

$$\frac{d}{dt} p_{\alpha\gamma}^{(n)}(0, t) = \sum_{\substack{\beta \neq \gamma \\ \beta=1}}^{s} \nu_{\alpha\beta} p_{\beta\gamma}^{(n)}(0, t) + \nu_{\alpha\gamma} p_{\gamma\gamma}^{(n-1)}(0, t)$$

and

$$\frac{d}{dt} p_{\gamma\gamma}^{(n)}(0, t) = \sum_{\beta=1}^{s} \nu_{\gamma\beta} p_{\beta\gamma}^{(n)}(0, t). \tag{3.23}$$

The corresponding p.g.f.'s satisfy the differential equations

$$\frac{d}{dt} g_{\alpha\gamma}(s; t) = \sum_{\substack{\beta \neq \gamma \\ \beta=1}}^{s} \nu_{\alpha\beta} g_{\beta\gamma}(s; t) + \nu_{\alpha\gamma} s g_{\gamma\gamma}(s; t) \tag{3.24}$$

and

$$\frac{d}{dt} g_{\gamma\gamma}(s; t) = \sum_{\beta=1}^{s} \nu_{\gamma\beta} g_{\beta\gamma}(s; t)$$

with the conditions that, at $t = 0$,

$$g_{\alpha\gamma}(s; 0) = 0, \qquad g_{\gamma\gamma}(s; 0) = 1. \tag{3.25}$$

The corresponding characteristic equation is

$$|A(\gamma)| = \begin{vmatrix} (\rho - \nu_{11}) & -\nu_{12} & \cdots & -\nu_{1\gamma} s & \cdots & -\nu_{1s} \\ -\nu_{21} & (\rho - \nu_{22}) & \cdots & -\nu_{2\gamma} s & \cdots & -\nu_{2s} \\ \cdot & \cdot & \cdot & \cdot & \cdot & \cdot \\ -\nu_{\gamma 1} & -\nu_{\gamma 2} & \cdots & (\rho - \nu_{\gamma\gamma}) & \cdots & -\nu_{\gamma s} \\ \cdot & \cdot & \cdot & \cdot & \cdot & \cdot \\ -\nu_{s1} & -\nu_{s2} & \cdots & -\nu_{s\gamma} s & \cdots & (\rho - \nu_{ss}) \end{vmatrix}$$

$$= 0. \tag{3.26}$$

When equation (3.26) has distinct roots $\rho_1(\gamma), \ldots, \rho_s(\gamma)$, the differential equations in (3.24) have the solution

$$g_{\alpha\gamma}(s; t) = \sum_{i=1}^{s} \frac{A_{\alpha\gamma}(\gamma; i)}{\prod_{\substack{j\neq i\\ j=1}}^{s} [\rho_i(\gamma) - \rho_j(\gamma)]} e^{\rho_i(\gamma)t},$$

$$\alpha, \gamma = 1, \ldots, s, \tag{3.27}$$

where $A_{\alpha\gamma}(\gamma; i)$ is the (α, γ)th cofactor of $\mathbf{A}(\gamma; i)$, for $\rho = \rho_i(\gamma)$.

The characteristic equation (3.26) plays a role similar to that of the characteristic equation (3.11) for the exit transition probabilities. Here the index s appears in the γ-th column of the determinant $|A(\gamma)|$, whereas in (3.11) s is in the α-th column of the transpose $|A'(\alpha)|$. Consequently, the p.g.f.'s in (3.27) are different from the p.g.f.'s in (3.41); the entrance transition probabilities are different from the exit transition probabilities.

4. AN ANNUAL HEALTH INDEX

Health of an individual is a dynamic phenomenon; it varies with time over a continuum extending from some optimum state of well-being through illness to death. An individual's health at any given moment may be represented by a point on the continuum and its variation over time by a path which the point travels. A collection of such paths for people in a population forms a visual description of the population's health status over the period in question. To quantify this conceptual description of health, we divide the continuum into a set of ordered categories, call them states of health, and denote them by $(S_1, \ldots, S_s, R)$. An individual who is in excellent health is said to be in S_1; if the person's health declines, he or she enters one of the states S_2 through S_s; if the person dies, he or she enters state R. A modified version of states proposed by Belloc, Breslow, and Hochstim [1971] consists of S_1: optimum health; S_2: adequate health; S_3: mild discomfort; S_4: symptomatic condition; S_5: single chronic condition; S_6: multiple chronic condition; S_7: moderate disability; S_8: severe disability; and R: death. Based on the general illness-death process described in this chapter, we shall briefly describe how an annual health index is developed. Terminology used is somewhat different: The intensity functions $\nu_{\alpha\beta}$ and μ_α $(=\mu_{\alpha 1} + \ldots + \mu_{\alpha r})$ are referred to as *incidence rates*; the transition probabilities

$P_{\alpha\beta}(0, t)$ and $Q_\alpha(0, t)$ are measures of *prognosis*; and the proportions of people in health states at any time t $(\pi_1(t), \ldots, \pi_s(t))$ are called *prevalence rates.*

Since the duration and level of well-being enjoyed by an individual forms the basis for any judgment of that person's health, the health of an individual during a year should be judged not by any one health condition apparent at a particular moment but by the length of time the person spends in each of the health states. To accommodate this intuitively appealing idea, we begin our formulation of annual health indices with the expected duration of stay.

For an individual who is in S_α at the beginning of a year, let $e_{\alpha\beta}$ be the expected fraction of the year that the individual will be in S_β. Let ε_α be the fraction of the year the individual will be in R. Let $\pi_1, \ldots, \pi_s$ be the proportion of people in a population who are initially in $S_1, \ldots, S_s$, respectively. Then

$$e_\beta = \pi_1 e_{1\beta} + \ldots + \pi_s e_{s\beta}, \tag{4.1}$$

is the fraction of a year an individual picked at random will be in S_β, $\beta = 1, \ldots, s$, and

$$\varepsilon = \pi_1 \varepsilon_1 + \ldots + \pi_s \varepsilon_s \tag{4.2}$$

is the fraction of a year the individual will be in R. The sum $e_1 + \ldots + e_r + \varepsilon$ is equal to one year.

Now let $h_1, \ldots, h_s$ and h_r be measures of the health of an individual who is in states $S_1, \ldots, S_s$ or R. The linear function

$$H = e_1 h_1 + e_2 h_2 + \ldots + e_s h_s + \varepsilon h_r \tag{4.3}$$

which is a measure of the health of the individual over a calendar year is called the *annual index of health.* If $h_1 = 1$ is the value assigned to the state of optimum health S_1 and $h_r = 0$ is the value assigned to the death state, R, then the health index is

$$H = e_1 + e_2 h_2 + \ldots + e_s h_s, \tag{4.4}$$

where $h_2, \ldots, h_s$ signify the health condition of people in $S_2, \ldots, S_s$ relative to those in S_1. If everyone in a population is perfectly healthy (i.e., in S_1) throughout the year, then $e_1 = 1$, $e_2 = \ldots = e_s = 0$ and the index of health assumes the value of one. When persons in a population experience varying degrees of health and illness, then $e_1 < 1$, $e_2, \ldots, e_s$, have positive values, and the index for the population is less than one.

The index of health defined in (4.4) incorporates three sets of parameters: The proportions of people π_α in state S_α at the beginning of the year; the intensity functions $\nu_{\alpha\beta}$ and μ_α; and the measures of health $h_2, \ldots, h_s$. The proportions π_α can easily be determined in an actual situation. And formulas for estimates of the intensity functions $\nu_{\alpha\beta}$ and μ_α will be described shortly. A more intricate problem, however, is the assignment of numerical values to $h_2, \ldots, h_s$. The health condition of an individual in a state S_α may be measured by the degree of rapidity with which he or she returns to perfect health, i.e., to state S_1. The incidence rate $\nu_{\alpha 1}$, on the other hand, is a measure of an individual's instantaneous recovery; i.e., from S_α to S_1. Therefore, the measure h_α should be directly proportional to $\nu_{\alpha 1}$, for $\alpha = 2, \ldots, s$. Letting c be the constant of proportionality, we have the formula for the health index:

$$H = e_1 + c\, e_2 \nu_{21} + \ldots + c\, e_s \nu_{s1}. \tag{4.5}$$

When $c = 1$,

$$H = e_1 + e_2 \nu_{21} + \ldots + e_s \nu_{s1}. \tag{4.6}$$

To estimate the intensity functions for a population for which a health index is to be computed, we take a sample of N people and select a time period out of a year for each individual in the sample. The N periods are of fixed length T (such as six weeks) and are evenly distributed over the year. During the period we monitor the health condition and changes in health status of each individual. At the end of the period, we ascertain the duration of stay in each health state and the number of transitions from one state to another. For the i-th individual in the sample, we let

$t_{\alpha i}$ = the total length of time the i-th individual stays in state S_α;

$m_{\alpha\beta i}$ = the number of transitions from S_α to S_β made by the i-th individual; and

$d_{\beta i}$ = 1, if the i-th individual enters the state of death R from S_β.

For each individual, t_{α_i}, $m_{\alpha\beta_i}$, and $d_{\beta i}$ are random variables; their likelihood function is

$$\prod_{\beta=1}^{s} \prod_{\alpha=1}^{s} e^{\nu_{\alpha\alpha} t_{\alpha i}} \nu_{\alpha\beta}^{m_{\alpha\beta i}} \mu_\beta^{d_{\beta i}}, \qquad i = 1, \ldots, N; \tag{4.7}$$

The likelihood function for the entire sample is

$$L = \prod_{i=1}^{N} \left(\prod_{\alpha=1}^{s} \prod_{\beta=1}^{s} e^{\nu_{\alpha\alpha} t_{\alpha i}} \nu_{\alpha\beta}^{m_{\alpha\beta i}} \mu_{\beta}^{d_{\beta i}} \right). \tag{4.8}$$

From (4.8), we obtain the maximum likelihood estimators of the incidence rates

$$\hat{\nu}_{\alpha\beta} = \frac{\sum_{i=1}^{N} m_{\alpha\beta i}}{\sum_{i=1}^{N} t_{\alpha i}}, \qquad \alpha, \beta = 1, \ldots, s, \tag{4.9}$$

and

$$\hat{\mu}_{\beta} = \frac{\sum_{i=1}^{N} d_{\beta i}}{\sum_{i=1}^{N} t_{\beta i}}, \qquad \beta = 1, \ldots, s. \tag{4.10}$$

The estimator of $\nu_{\alpha\alpha}$ is derived from

$$\hat{\nu}_{\alpha\alpha} = -\left[\sum_{\substack{\beta=1 \\ \beta\neq\alpha}}^{s} \hat{\nu}_{\alpha\beta} + \hat{\mu}_{\alpha} \right], \qquad \alpha = 1, \ldots, s. \tag{4.11}$$

Each of the estimators in (4.9) is a ratio of the total number of transitions from S_{α} to S_{β} to the total length of stay in S_{α}. A similar interpretation holds for the estimators in (4.10). (Reference is made also to equation (7.14a), Chapter 3). The sample variances of the estimators are

$$S_{\hat{\nu}_{\alpha\beta}}^2 = \frac{\sum_{i}^{N} m_{\alpha\beta i}}{\left(\sum_{i}^{N} t_{\alpha i} \right)^2}, \qquad \alpha, \beta = 1, \ldots, s; \tag{4.12}$$

and

$$S^2_{\hat{\mu}_\beta} = \frac{\sum_{i=1}^{N} d_{\beta i}}{\left(\sum_i^N t_{\beta i}\right)^2}, \qquad \beta = 1, \ldots, s, \tag{4.13}$$

respectively. Using the estimates of the incidence rates obtained in (4.9), (4.10) and (4.11), and the estimates of $\pi_1, \ldots, \pi_s$, we can determine the expected durations of stay from (4.1) and (4.2). We then compute the health index for the population based on the formula in (4.6).

5. PROBLEMS FOR SOLUTION

1. Show that the probability

$$P_{\alpha\beta}(t) = \sum_{l=1}^{s} A_{kl}(l) \frac{T_{\beta l}(k)}{|T(k)|} e^{\rho_l t} \tag{2.5}$$

satisfy the backward differential equations

$$\frac{d}{dt} P_{\alpha\gamma}(t) = \sum_{l=1}^{s} \nu_{\alpha\beta} P_{\beta\gamma}(t). \tag{2.2}$$

2. When $t = 0$, equation (2.4) becomes

$$P_{\alpha\beta}(0, 0) = \sum_{l=1}^{s} \frac{A'_{\alpha\beta}(\rho_l)}{\prod_{\substack{j=1 \\ j \neq l}}^{s} (\rho_l - \rho_j)}.$$

Show that $P_{\alpha\alpha}(0,0) = 1$ and $P_{\alpha\beta}(0,0) = 0$ for $\beta \neq \alpha$.

3. Verify the equation

$$\int_0^t \mathbf{T}(k)\mathbf{E}(\tau)\mathbf{T}^{-1}(k)\mathbf{U}\, d\tau = \mathbf{T}(k)[\mathbf{E}(t) - \mathbf{I}]\,\rho^{-1}\mathbf{T}^{-1}(k)\mathbf{U}. \tag{2.12}$$

4. Derive the individual transition probabilities $Q_{\alpha\delta}(0,t)$ in (2.14) from the matrix product

$$Q(0,t) = \mathbf{T}(k)\,[\mathbf{E}(t) - I]\,\rho^{-1}\mathbf{T}^{-1}(k)\mathbf{U}. \tag{2.12}$$

5. Use formulas (2.4) and (2.15) to prove the following Chapman-Kolmogorov equation

$$Q_{\alpha\delta}(0,\tau+t)=Q_{\alpha\delta}(0,\tau)+\sum_{\beta=1}^{s}P_{\alpha\beta}(0,\tau)\,Q_{\beta\delta}(0,t). \qquad (2.16)$$

6. Use formulas (2.5) and (2.14) to prove (2.16) in problem 5.

7. Verify the equality in (2.21).

8. Substitute (2.30) in (2.31) and verify the resulting equation.

9. Substitute (2.36) and (2.37) in (2.38) and prove the resulting equation.

10. Let $\|e_{ij}(t)\|$ be the matrix of the expected durations of stay. We can derive $\|e_{ij}(t)\|$ from the matrix of the transition probabilities $\mathbf{P}(0,t)$ from the following equation (P. Rust)

$$\|e_{ij}(t)\|=\int_0^t P(0,\tau)\,d\tau$$

or from

$$\|e_{ij}(t)\|=\int_0^t e^{V\tau}\,d\tau.$$

Derive from the last equation the individual expectations $e_{ij}(t)$.

11. Derive the partial differential equations in (3.8) from the differential equations in (3.7).

12. Show that the formula for the p.g.f. $g_{\alpha\gamma}(s;t)$ in (3.14) satisfies the differential equations in (3.8).

13. Find the first renewal probability $P_{\alpha\alpha}^{(1)}(0,t)$ and the first passage probability from S_α to S_β $P_{\alpha\beta}^{(1)}(0,t)$ for $\alpha \neq \beta$.

14. Derive a formula for the p.g.f. $h_{\alpha\delta}(s;t)$ in (3.21) from the p.g.f.'s in (3.14).

15. A system has three transient states, s_1, s_2, s_3, and one absorbing state R, with the intensity matrices

$$\mathbf{V}=\begin{pmatrix}-.4 & .1 & .2\\ .1 & -.3 & .1\\ .1 & 0 & -.2\end{pmatrix}$$

and

$$\mathbf{U}=\begin{pmatrix}-.1\\ -.1\\ -.1\end{pmatrix}$$

(a) Find the eigenvalues of **V**.

(b) State the differential equations for the transition probabilities $P_{\alpha\beta}(0, t)$, $\alpha, \beta = 1, 2, 3$.

(c) Solve the differential equations in (b) to obtain the transition probabilities.

(d) Derive with the result in (c) the transition probabilities $Q_{\delta}(0, t)$.

(e) Find the expected durations of stay in the interval $(0, t)$, $e_{\alpha\beta}(t)$ and $\varepsilon_{\alpha}(t)$.

CHAPTER 17

Migration Process and Birth-Illness-Death Process

1. INTRODUCTION

In Chapter 16, our emphasis was on transition probabilities rather than on population sizes, which we obtained only as a byproduct. In this chapter we are concerned exclusively with population sizes in health states, and we will derive directly the corresponding probability distributions. Furthermore, we will allow the populations of various states to also change through birth, death, and migration. Movement of individuals between states (internal migration) is retained through transition as before.

We again use $s_1, \ldots, s_s$ to denote the health states. We let the population sizes of the states be represented at the initial time 0 by a constant column vector

$$\mathbf{i} = \begin{pmatrix} i_1 \\ \vdots \\ i_s \end{pmatrix} \tag{1.1}$$

and at time t by a random vector

$$\mathbf{X}_t = \begin{pmatrix} X_{1t} \\ \vdots \\ X_{st} \end{pmatrix}, \tag{1.2}$$

so that X_{1t}, for example, is the population size in state S_1 at time t. The value of $\mathbf{X}_t$ is represented by a constant vector

$$\mathbf{j} = \begin{pmatrix} j_1 \\ \vdots \\ j_s \end{pmatrix}, \tag{1.3}$$

where the elements j_α are non-negative integers. We are interested in the conditional probability

$$P_{\mathbf{i},\mathbf{j}}(0, t) = \Pr\{\mathbf{X}_t = \mathbf{j} \text{ given } \mathbf{X}_0 = \mathbf{i}\}. \tag{1.4}$$

In the models to be considered in this chapter, the probability distribution in equation (1.4) depends not only on the initial size $\mathbf{i}$ and on the health-death transitions, but also on birth and migration occurring within the interval $(0, t)$. In section 2, migration processes are discussed in detail and their relation to the general illness-death process noted. In section 3 we briefly present a birth-illness-death process. For the moment, let us consider a general case.

For each τ, $0 \le \tau < t$, a change in the population size of each state S_α during the time interval $(\tau, \tau + \Delta)$ is assumed to take place according to the following instantaneous probabilities:

$$\begin{aligned}
\lambda_\alpha^*(\tau)\Delta + o(\Delta) &= \Pr\{\text{the size of state } S_\alpha \text{ will increase by one during the interval } (\tau, \tau+\Delta) \text{ through immigration or birth}\},\\
\nu_{\alpha\beta}^*(\tau)\Delta + o(\Delta) &= \Pr\{\text{one individual will move from state } S_\alpha \text{ to } S_\beta \text{ during the interval } (\tau, \tau+\Delta)\},\ \beta \ne \alpha,\\
\mu_\alpha^*(\tau)\Delta + o(\Delta) &= \Pr\{\text{the size of state } S_\alpha \text{ will decrease by one during the interval } (\tau, \tau+\Delta) \text{ through emigration or death}\}.
\end{aligned} \tag{1.5}$$

We let

$$\nu_{\alpha\alpha}^*(\tau) = -\left[\sum_{\beta \ne \alpha} \nu_{\alpha\beta}^*(\tau) + \mu_\alpha^*(\tau)\right] \tag{1.6}$$

and introduce a column vector

$$\boldsymbol{\delta}_\alpha = \begin{pmatrix} \delta_{1\alpha} \\ \vdots \\ \delta_{s\alpha} \end{pmatrix}. \tag{1.7}$$

The components of $\boldsymbol{\delta}_\alpha$ in (1.7) are Kronecker deltas so that $\delta_{\alpha\alpha} = 1$ and $\delta_{\alpha\beta} = 0$ for $\alpha \neq \beta$. It is easy to see that the probabilities in (1.4) satisfy the following system of differential equations such that

$$\begin{aligned}\frac{d}{dt} P_{\mathbf{i},\mathbf{j}}(0, t) = &-P_{\mathbf{i},\mathbf{j}}(0, t) \sum_{\alpha=1}^{s} [\lambda_\alpha^*(t) - \nu_{\alpha\alpha}^*(t)] \\ &+ \sum_{\alpha=1}^{s} P_{\mathbf{i},\mathbf{j}-\boldsymbol{\delta}_\alpha}(0, t)\, \lambda_\alpha^*(t) \\ &+ \sum_{\alpha=1}^{s} \sum_{\substack{\beta=1 \\ \alpha\neq\beta}}^{s} P_{\mathbf{i},\mathbf{j}+\boldsymbol{\delta}_\alpha-\boldsymbol{\delta}_\beta}(0, t)\, \nu_{\alpha\beta}^*(t) \\ &+ \sum_{\alpha=1}^{s} P_{\mathbf{i},\mathbf{j}+\boldsymbol{\delta}_\alpha}(0, t)\, \mu_\alpha^*(t). \end{aligned} \tag{1.8}$$

At $t = 0$, the initial conditions are

$$P_{\mathbf{i},\mathbf{i}}(0, 0) = 1, \qquad P_{\mathbf{i},\mathbf{j}}(0, 0) = 0 \qquad \text{for} \qquad \mathbf{j} \neq \mathbf{i}. \tag{1.9}$$

The system of differential equations in (1.8) describes the growth of a population in general. Various models can be derived from (1.8) by making appropriate assumptions regarding $\lambda_\alpha^*(t)$, $\nu_{\alpha\beta}^*(t)$, and $\mu_\alpha^*(t)$. Table 1 lists some of the stochastic processes discussed in this book in terms of the general system of differential equations in (1.8).

2. EMIGRATION-IMMIGRATION PROCESSES—POISSON-MARKOV PROCESSES

We have pointed out early in Chapter 16 that in stochastic processes emigration may be treated as death. But, the term immigration has a meaning different from that of birth although the basis for distinction is arbitrary. An increase in a population within a small time interval $(t, t + \Delta)$ is regarded as the result of birth if the corresponding instantaneous probability is a function of the size of the population at time t; otherwise it is treated as immigration. Migration processes have applications to practical problems. They serve as useful analytic models for predicting population sizes, for forecasting future demographic composition, and for making other demographic studies. An early study of the process was made by Bartlett [1949]. Patil [1957] considered a migration process model in the study of sperma-

Table 1. Stochastic processes concerned with birth, illness, migration and death

Type of process	Number of states s	$\lambda_\alpha^*(t)$	$\nu_{\alpha\beta}^*(t)$	$\mu_\alpha^*(t)$
Poisson process	1	λ	—	0
	1	$\lambda(t)$	—	0
Pure birth process	1	$j\lambda$	—	0
	1	$j\lambda(t)$	—	0
Pure death process	1	0	—	$(i-j)\mu(t)$
Polya process	1	$\dfrac{\lambda+\lambda aj}{1+\lambda at}$	—	0
Linear growth	1	$j\lambda$	—	$j\mu$
General birth-death process	1	$j\lambda(t)$	—	$j\mu(t)$
Simple illness-death process	2	0	$j_\alpha\nu_{\alpha\beta}$	$j_\alpha(\mu_{\alpha 1}+\ldots+\mu_{\alpha r})$
Finite Markov process	s	—	ν_{ij}	—
General illness-death process	s	0	$j_\alpha\nu_{\alpha\beta}$	$j_\alpha(\mu_{\alpha 1}+\ldots+\mu_{\alpha r})$
Migration process	s	$\lambda_\alpha(t)$	$j_\alpha\nu_{\alpha\beta}$	$j_\alpha\mu_\alpha$
Birth-illness-death process	s	$j_\alpha\lambda_\alpha$	$j_\alpha\nu_{\alpha\beta}$	$j_\alpha\mu_\alpha$

tozoa counts. The following presentation is based on Chiang [1964] and [1972].

Let us consider a migration process in which an increase in population during a time interval $(t, t+\Delta)$ is independent of the existing population size, so that for state S_α,

$$\lambda_\alpha^*(t) = \lambda_\alpha(t), \qquad \alpha = 1, \ldots, s. \tag{2.1}$$

The transition of an individual from one state to another is assumed to be independent of transitions made by other individuals,

$$\nu_{\alpha\beta}^*(t) = j_\alpha \nu_{\alpha\beta}, \qquad \alpha \neq \beta;\ \alpha, \beta = 1, \ldots, s. \tag{2.2}$$

A decrease in the population size of state S_α either through death or emigration is measured by the intensity function

$$\mu_\alpha^*(t) = j_\alpha \mu_\alpha, \qquad \alpha = 1, \ldots, s. \tag{2.3}$$

We again define

$$\nu_{\alpha\alpha} = -\left[\sum_{\substack{\beta=1 \\ \beta\neq\alpha}}^{s} \nu_{\alpha\beta} + \mu_\alpha\right], \qquad \alpha \neq \beta;\ \alpha, \beta = 1, \ldots, s, \tag{2.4}$$

where j_α is the population size of state S_α at time t. When $\nu_{\alpha\beta}$ and μ_α are independent of time and $\lambda_\alpha(t)$ is a function of t, there is an explicit solution of the probability distribution $P_{\mathbf{i},\mathbf{j}}(0, t)$. In demography, $\lambda_\alpha(t)$ is known as the *immigration rate* (into state S_α), $\nu_{\alpha\beta}$ as the *internal migration rate* (from S_α to S_β), and μ_α as the *emigration rate* (from S_α). We shall use two approaches to obtain the solution for the probabilities $P_{ij}(0, t)$.

2.1. First Approach.

We again let

$$\mathbf{V} = ||\nu_{\alpha\beta}||_{\alpha,\beta=1,\ldots,s} \tag{2.5}$$

be the matrix of $\nu_{\alpha\beta}$ and $\rho_1, \ldots, \rho_s$ be the eigenvalues of $\mathbf{V}$. For each ρ_l, we let

$$\mathbf{A}(\rho_l) = ||\rho_l \mathbf{I} - \mathbf{V}||, \qquad l = 1, \ldots, s, \tag{2.6}$$

be the corresponding characteristic matrix of $\mathbf{V}$ as before. For simplicity, we shall also assume in this chapter that $\rho_1, \ldots, \rho_s$ are distinct eigenvalues.

We are interested in the explicit formulas for the probabilities $P_{\mathbf{i},\mathbf{j}}(0, t)$ and in the probability generating function

$$G_{\mathbf{X}(t)}(\mathbf{u}; t) = \sum_{j_1} \cdots \sum_{j_s} u_1^{j_1} \cdots u_s^{j_s} P_{\mathbf{i},\mathbf{j}}(0, t). \tag{2.7}$$

Random vector $\mathbf{X}(t)$ is composed of two vectors $\mathbf{Y}(t)$ and $\mathbf{Z}(t)$; that is

$$\mathbf{X}(t) = \mathbf{Y}(t) + \mathbf{Z}(t). \tag{2.8}$$

The components of $\mathbf{Y}(t)$,

$$\mathbf{Y}(t) = \begin{pmatrix} Y_1(t) \\ Y_2(t) \\ \vdots \\ Y_s(t) \end{pmatrix}, \tag{2.9}$$

are the numbers of survivors of the original cohort $\mathbf{i} = (i_1, \ldots, i_s)$ in the respective states $s_1, \ldots, s_s$ at time t; the components of $\mathbf{Z}(t)$,

$$\mathbf{Z}(t) = \begin{pmatrix} Z_1(t) \\ Z_2(t) \\ \vdots \\ Z_s(t) \end{pmatrix}, \tag{2.10}$$

are the numbers of survivors among those who immigrated into the population during the interval $(0, t)$. Let $g_{\mathbf{Y}(t)}(\mathbf{u}; t)$ and $h_{\mathbf{Z}(t)}(\mathbf{u}; t)$ be the probability generating functions of $\mathbf{Y}(t)$ and $\mathbf{Z}(t)$ respectively. Since $\mathbf{Y}(t)$ and $\mathbf{Z}(t)$ are obviously independent vectors under the present model, the p.g.f. of $\mathbf{X}(t)$, $\mathbf{Y}(t)$ and $\mathbf{Z}(t)$ have the usual relationship

$$G_{\mathbf{X}(t)}(\mathbf{u}; t) = g_{\mathbf{Y}(t)}(\mathbf{u}; t)\, h_{\mathbf{Z}(t)}(\mathbf{u}; t). \tag{2.11}$$

From section 2, Chapter 16, we know that the joint probability distribution of the components of vector $\mathbf{Y}(t)$ is the convolution of s multinomial distributions, each generated from the initial population size i_α in state S_α, $\alpha = 1, \ldots, s$. Therefore the probability generating function of $\mathbf{Y}(t)$ is

$$g_{\mathbf{Y}(t)}(\mathbf{u}; t) = \prod_{\alpha=1}^{s} [\pi_{\alpha 0}(0, t) + \pi_{\alpha 1}(0, t)u_1 + \ldots + \pi_{\alpha s}(0, t)u_s]^{i_\alpha}, \tag{2.12}$$

where $\pi_{\alpha\beta}(0, t)$ is the transition probability, or internal migration probability from S_α at $t = 0$ to S_β at t. It is given by[1]

$$\pi_{\alpha\beta}(0, t) = \sum_{l=1}^{s} \frac{A'_{\alpha\beta}(\rho_l)}{\prod_{\substack{m=1 \\ m \neq l}}^{s} (\rho_l - \rho_m)} e^{\rho_l t}, \qquad \alpha, \beta = 1, \dots, s, \tag{2.13}$$

and $\pi_{\alpha 0}(0, t) = [1 - \pi_{\alpha 1}(0, t) - \dots - \pi_{\alpha s}(0, t)]$ is the probability that an individual in S_α at 0 will die during $(0, t)$. The joint probability of $(Y_1(t), \dots, Y_s(t))$ is

$$\Pr\{Y_1(t) = k_1, \dots, Y_s(t) = k_s\}$$

$$= \Sigma \prod_{\alpha=1}^{s} \frac{i_\alpha!}{k_{\alpha 1}! \dots k_{\alpha s}! k_{\alpha 0}!} [\pi_{\alpha 1}(0, t)]^{k_{\alpha 1}} \dots [\pi_{\alpha s}(0, t)]^{k_{\alpha s}} [\pi_{\alpha 0}(0, t)]^{k_{\alpha 0}} \tag{2.14}$$

for $k_{\alpha\beta} = 0, 1, \dots, \min[i_\alpha, k_\beta]$. Here $k_{\alpha\beta}$ is the number of individuals in state S_β at time t who were initially in state S_α at $t = 0$, $\alpha, \beta = 1, \dots, s$. The value $k_{\alpha 0}$ is the number of those who died during $(0, t)$. The summation in (2.14) is taken over all possible values of $k_{\alpha\beta}$ such that the sum

$$k_{\alpha 0} + k_{\alpha 1} + \dots + k_{\alpha s} = i_\alpha, \qquad \alpha = 1, \dots, s, \tag{2.15}$$

is the initial population size of state S_α;

$$k_{1\beta} + k_{2\beta} + \dots + k_{s\beta} = k_\beta, \qquad \beta = 1, \dots, s, \tag{2.16}$$

is the population size of state S_β at time t; and the sum

$$k_{10} + k_{20} + \dots + k_{s0} = k_0 \tag{2.17}$$

is the number who died during the interval $(0, t)$.

Vector $\mathbf{Z}(t)$ is the outcome of sequences of events of immigration, internal migration, and survival or death. Since the sequence of events occuring to one individual is independent of events occuring to other individuals, and is also independent of population sizes in various

[1] To avoid confusion in notation, we have introduced symbols $\mathbf{Y}(t)$ to denote survivors, $\pi_{\alpha\beta}(0, t)$ to replace the transition probability $P_{\alpha\beta}(0, t)$ and $\pi_{\alpha\beta}(0, t)$ to replace $Q_\alpha(0, t)$ as they were defined in Chapter 16.

states, $\mathbf{Z}(t)$ has the multiple Poisson distribution. This means that the probability generating function of $\mathbf{Z}(t)$ is

$$h_{\mathbf{Z}(t)}(\mathbf{u}; t) = \exp\left\{ -\sum_{\beta=1}^{s} (1 - u_\beta)\theta_\beta(t) \right\}, \tag{2.18}$$

where $\theta_\beta(t)$ is the Poisson parameter, or the expected population size in state S_β at time t,

$$E[Z_\beta(t)] = \theta_\beta(t), \qquad \beta = 1, \ldots, s. \tag{2.19}$$

To determine $\theta_\beta(t)$, let us recall the events involved and the corresponding probabilities. An individual who is in S_β at time t must (1) immigrate to a state S_α during some time interval $(\tau, \tau + d\tau)$, for $0 \le \tau \le t$, and (2) be in state S_β at time t. The probability of the former event is $\lambda_\alpha(\tau)d\tau$; the probability of the latter is $\pi_{\alpha\beta}(\tau, t)$. Therefore, the probability for the occurrence of the sequence is

$$\lambda_\alpha(\tau)d\tau\,\pi_{\alpha\beta}(\tau, t). \tag{2.20}$$

For distinct values of $\alpha = 1, 2, \ldots, s$, and for distinct values of τ, $0 \le \tau \le t$, the corresponding sequences are mutually independent; the addition theorem gives

$$\theta_\beta(t) = \sum_{\alpha=1}^{s} \int_0^t \lambda_\alpha(\tau)\pi_{\alpha\beta}(\tau, t)\,d\tau \tag{2.21}$$

where the transition probabilities are

$$\pi_{\alpha\beta}(\tau, t) = \sum_{l=1}^{s} \frac{A'_{\alpha\beta}(\rho_l)}{\prod_{\substack{m=1\\ m\neq l}}^{s} (\rho_l - \rho_m)} e^{\rho_l(t-\tau)}, \quad \alpha, \beta = 1, \ldots, s. \tag{2.22}$$

When the migration rate $\lambda_\alpha(\tau) = \lambda_\alpha$ is independent of time,

$$\theta_\beta(t) = \sum_{\alpha=1}^{s} \int_0^t \lambda_\alpha \sum_{l=1}^{s} \frac{A'_{\alpha\beta}(\rho_l)}{\prod_{\substack{m=1\\ m\neq l}}^{s} (\rho_l - \rho_m)} e^{\rho_l(t-\tau)} d\tau$$

$$= \sum_{\alpha=1}^{s} \sum_{l=1}^{s} \lambda_\alpha \frac{A'_{\alpha\beta}(\rho_l)}{\prod_{\substack{m=1\\ m\neq l}}^{s} (\rho_l - \rho_m)\rho_l} (e^{\rho_l t} - 1), \quad \beta = 1, \ldots, s. \tag{2.23}$$

In either case, the probability distribution of vector $\mathbf{Z}(t)$ is

$$\Pr\{Z_1(t) = m_1, \ldots, Z_s(t) = m_s\} = \prod_{\beta=1}^{s} \frac{e^{-\theta_\beta(t)}[\theta_\beta(t)]^{m_\beta}}{m_\beta!}. \tag{2.24}$$

Consequently, we have the theorem.

Theorem 1. *The joint probability distribution of vector* $\mathbf{X}(t)$ *is the convolution of the multinomial distributions in equation* (2.14) *and the multiple Poisson distribution in equation* (2.24). *The probability generating function of* $\mathbf{X}(t)$ *is given by*

$$G_{\mathbf{X}(t)}(\mathbf{u};t) = \prod_{\alpha=1}^{s} [\pi_{\alpha 0}(0,t) + \pi_{\alpha 1}(0,t)u_1 + \ldots + \pi_{\alpha s}(0,t)u_s]^{i_\alpha}$$
$$\times \exp\left\{-\sum_{\beta=1}^{s}(1-u_\beta)\theta_\beta(t)\right\}, \tag{2.25}$$

where the transition probabilities $\pi_{\alpha\beta}(0,t)$ *are given in* (2.13) *and the Poisson parameters* $\theta_\beta(t)$ *are derived from* (2.21) *when the immigration rate* $\lambda_\alpha(t)$ *is time dependent; they are given in* (2.23) *when* $\lambda_\alpha(t) = \lambda_\alpha$.

From the p.g.f. in (2.25), we compute the expectations

$$E[X_\beta(t)] = \sum_{\alpha=1}^{s} i_\alpha \pi_{\alpha\beta}(0,t) + \theta_\beta(t), \tag{2.26}$$

the variances

$$V[X_\beta(t)] = \sum_{\alpha=1}^{s} i_\alpha \pi_{\alpha\beta}(0,t)[1-\pi_{\alpha\beta}(0,t)] + \theta_\beta(t), \tag{2.27}$$

and the covariances

$$\text{Cov}[X_\beta(t), X_\gamma(t)] = -\sum_{\alpha=1}^{s} i_\alpha \pi_{\alpha\beta}(0,t)\pi_{\alpha\gamma}(0,t) \tag{2.28}$$

for $\beta \neq \gamma$, $\beta, \gamma = 1, \ldots, s$.

2.2. Second Approach[2]

The derivation of the p.g.f. $G_{\mathbf{X}}(u;t)$ in (2.25) is simple and straightforward, but it deviates from the ordinary approach to obtaining

---

[2]The advanced reader should omit this section.

probability generating functions. In order to acquaint the reader with mathematical manipulation in this rather complex situation, we shall now recompute equation (2.25) using differential equations. The computations involved, as the reader will see, are quite lengthy.

2.2.1. Differential Equation for the Probability Generating Function.

Under the assumptions described in equation (2.1) through (2.4) the probability function of the random vector $\mathbf{X}(t)$ satisfies the following system of differential equations:

$$\begin{aligned}\frac{d}{dt}P_{\mathbf{i},\mathbf{j}}(0,t) = &-P_{\mathbf{i},\mathbf{j}}(0,t)\sum_{\alpha=1}^{s}[\lambda_\alpha(t) - j_\alpha \nu_{\alpha\alpha}] \\ &+ \sum_{\alpha=1}^{s} P_{\mathbf{i},\mathbf{j}-\boldsymbol{\delta}_\alpha}(0,t)\lambda_\alpha(t) \\ &+ \sum_{\alpha=1}^{s}\sum_{\substack{\beta=1\\ \alpha\neq\beta}}^{s} P_{\mathbf{i},\mathbf{j}+\boldsymbol{\delta}_\alpha-\boldsymbol{\delta}_\beta}(0,t)(j_\alpha+1)\nu_{\alpha\beta} \\ &+ \sum_{\alpha=1}^{s} P_{\mathbf{i},\mathbf{j}+\boldsymbol{\delta}_\alpha}(0,t)(j_\alpha+1)\mu_\alpha. \end{aligned} \tag{2.29}$$

Taking the derivative of the p.g.f. in (2.7) with respect to t, we get

$$\frac{\partial}{\partial t}G_{\mathbf{X}_t}(\mathbf{u};t) = \sum_{j_1}\cdots\sum_{j_s} u_1^{j_1}\cdots u_s^{j_s}\frac{\partial}{\partial t}P_{\mathbf{i},\mathbf{j}}(0,t). \tag{2.30}$$

Introducing (2.29) for the derivatives of $P_{\mathbf{i},\mathbf{j}}(0,t)$ yields the partial differential equation for the generating function

$$\begin{aligned}\frac{\partial}{\partial t}G_{\mathbf{X}_t}(\mathbf{u};t) = &-\sum_{\alpha=1}^{s}\lambda_\alpha(t)G_{\mathbf{X}_t}(\mathbf{u};t) + \sum_{\alpha=1}^{s}\nu_{\alpha\alpha}u_\alpha\frac{\partial}{\partial u_\alpha}G_{\mathbf{X}_t}(\mathbf{u};t) \\ &+ \sum_{\alpha=1}^{s}\lambda_\alpha(t)u_\alpha G_{\mathbf{X}_t}(u;t) + \sum_{\alpha=1}^{s}\sum_{\substack{\beta=1\\ \alpha\neq\beta}}^{s}\nu_{\alpha\beta}u_\beta\frac{\partial}{\partial u_\alpha}G_{\mathbf{X}_t}(\mathbf{u};t) \\ &+ \sum_{\alpha=1}^{s}\mu_\alpha\frac{\partial}{\partial u_\alpha}G_{\mathbf{X}_t}(u;t), \end{aligned} \tag{2.31}$$

with the derivatives

$$\frac{\partial}{\partial u_\alpha}G_{\mathbf{X}_t}(\mathbf{u};t) = \sum_{j_1}\cdots\sum_{j_s}u_1^{j_1}\cdots u_s^{j_s}j_\alpha u_\alpha^{-1}P_{\mathbf{i},\mathbf{j}}(0,t)$$

$$\alpha = 1, \ldots, s.$$

After collecting terms in (2.31), we find that

$$\frac{\partial}{\partial t} G_{\mathbf{X}_t}(\mathbf{u};t) = -\sum_{\alpha=1}^{s} \lambda_\alpha(t)(1-u_\alpha)\, G_{\mathbf{X}_t}(\mathbf{u};t) + \sum_{\alpha=1}^{s}\left[\sum_{\beta=1}^{s} \nu_{\alpha\beta} u_\beta + \mu_\alpha\right]\frac{\partial}{\partial u_\alpha} G_{\mathbf{X}_t}(\mathbf{u};t). \tag{2.32}$$

Since (2.4) implies that $\mu_\alpha = -(\nu_{\alpha 1} + \ldots + \nu_{\alpha s})$, we can rewrite equation (2.32) as

$$\frac{\partial}{\partial t} G_{\mathbf{X}_t}(\mathbf{u};t) = -\sum_{\alpha=1}^{s} \lambda_\alpha(t)(1-u_\alpha)\, G_{\mathbf{X}_t}(\mathbf{u};t) - \sum_{\alpha=1}^{s}\sum_{\beta=1}^{s} \nu_{\alpha\beta}(1-u_\beta)\frac{\partial}{\partial u_\alpha} G_{\mathbf{X}_t}(\mathbf{u};t) \tag{2.33}$$

which, on substitution of

$$z_\alpha = 1 - u_\alpha, \tag{2.34}$$

becomes

$$\frac{\partial}{\partial t} G_{\mathbf{X}_t}(\mathbf{z};t) = -\sum_{\alpha=1}^{s} \lambda_\alpha(t) z_\alpha\, G_{\mathbf{X}_t}(\mathbf{z};t) + \sum_{\alpha=1}^{s}\sum_{\beta=1}^{s} \nu_{\alpha\beta} z_\beta \frac{\partial}{\partial z_\alpha} G_{\mathbf{X}_t}(\mathbf{z};t). \tag{2.35}$$

At $\mathbf{t} = 0$, the initial condition is

$$G_{\mathbf{X}_t}(\mathbf{z};0) = \prod_{\alpha=1}^{s} (1 - z_\alpha)^{i_\alpha}. \tag{2.36}$$

2.2.2. Solution for the Probability Generating Function.

Differential equation (2.35) can be solved in the manner described in section 7, Chapter 8. The auxiliary equations are:

$$-\frac{dt}{1} = \frac{dz_1}{\sum_\beta \nu_{1\beta} z_\beta} = \ldots = \frac{dz_s}{\sum_\beta \nu_{s\beta} z_\beta} = \frac{dG_{\mathbf{X}_t}(\mathbf{z};t)}{\sum_\alpha \lambda_\alpha(t)\, z_\alpha\, G_{\mathbf{X}_t}(\mathbf{z};t)}. \tag{2.37}$$

There are $s + 1$ equations in (2.37); the first s equations are

$$-\frac{dt}{1} = \frac{dz_\alpha}{\sum_{\beta=1}^{s} \nu_{\alpha\beta} z_\beta}, \qquad \alpha = 1, \dots, s,$$

or

$$\frac{dz_\alpha}{dt} + \sum_{\beta=1}^{s} \nu_{\alpha\beta} z_\beta = 0, \qquad \alpha = 1, \dots, s, \tag{2.37a}$$

and the last equation is

$$-\frac{dt}{1} = \frac{d\,G_{\mathbf{x}_t}(\mathbf{z};t)}{\sum_{\alpha=1}^{s} \lambda_\alpha(t) z_\alpha G_{\mathbf{x}_t}(\mathbf{z};t)} \qquad \beta = 1, \dots, s,$$

or

$$\frac{d}{dt} \ln G_{\mathbf{x}_t}(\mathbf{z};t) = -\sum_{\alpha=1}^{s} \lambda_\alpha(t) z_\alpha. \tag{2.37b}$$

We shall use matrix notation to simplify the presentation. Let

$$\boldsymbol{\lambda}(t) = \begin{pmatrix} \lambda_1(t) \\ \vdots \\ \lambda_s(t) \end{pmatrix}, \qquad \mathbf{z} = \begin{pmatrix} z_1 \\ \vdots \\ z_s \end{pmatrix}, \tag{2.38}$$

and

$$\mathbf{V} = \begin{pmatrix} \nu_{11} & \cdots & \nu_{1s} \\ \vdots & & \vdots \\ \nu_{s1} & \cdots & \nu_{ss} \end{pmatrix}, \tag{2.39}$$

and let D be a diagonal matrix with the differentiation operator d/dt on the diagonal line. We can rewrite equations (2.37a) and (2.37b) as follows:

$$(D + \mathbf{V})\mathbf{z} = \mathbf{0} \tag{2.40}$$

and

$$d \ln G_{\mathbf{x}_t}(\mathbf{z};t) = -\boldsymbol{\lambda}'(t)\mathbf{z}\,dt, \tag{2.41}$$

where $\mathbf{0} = (0, \ldots, 0)'$ is an $s \times 1$ column vector and $\boldsymbol{\lambda}'(t) = (\lambda_1(t), \ldots, \lambda_s(t))$ is an $1 \times s$ row vector. Equation (2.40) is of the same type as Kolmogorov differential equations in (4.7) and (4.8), Chapter 14. We can use the result in Chapter 14 to obtain the solution for vector $\mathbf{Z}$. For the sake of clarity, but at the expense of repetition, we shall solve (2.40) directly.

Equation (2.40) is a system of s linear, first order, homogeneous differential equations with constant coefficients. Therefore, the solution is of the form

$$\mathbf{z} = e^{\rho t}\mathbf{c}, \tag{2.42}$$

where constant ρ and constant vector

$$\mathbf{c} = \begin{pmatrix} c_1 \\ c_2 \\ \vdots \\ c_s \end{pmatrix} \tag{2.43}$$

are to be determined. Substituting (2.42) in (2.40) and factoring out the non-vanishing exponentials yields the equation

$$(\rho\mathbf{I} + \mathbf{V})\mathbf{c} = \mathbf{0}, \tag{2.44}$$

where $\mathbf{I}$ is an $s \times s$ unit matrix. This means that the values of ρ and $\mathbf{c}$ that satisfy (2.44) are the only values for which (2.42) is a valid solution of $\mathbf{z}$.

For a given ρ, (2.44) represents a system of s homogeneous equations. It has a non-trivial solution for vector $\mathbf{c}$ only if the determinant

$$|\rho\mathbf{I} + \mathbf{V}| = 0. \tag{2.45}$$

Equation (2.45) represents a restriction on possible values of ρ for the solution of $\mathbf{Z}$. We denote the roots of equation (2.45) by $-\rho_1, \ldots, -\rho_s$. For each ρ_j, we let

$$\mathbf{A}(\rho_j) = (\rho_j\mathbf{I} - \mathbf{V}) \tag{2.46}$$

and denote cofactors of $\mathbf{A}(\rho_l)$ by $A_{k\alpha}(\rho_j)$. The non-zero vector

$$\mathbf{T}_j(k) = \begin{pmatrix} A_{k1}(\rho_j) \\ \vdots \\ A_{ks}(\rho_j) \end{pmatrix} \tag{2.47}$$

is an eigenvector of $\mathbf{V}$ corresponding to ρ_j, so that

$$(\rho_j \mathbf{I} - \mathbf{V})\mathbf{T}_j(k) = \mathbf{0}. \tag{2.48}$$

We use $\mathbf{T}_j(k)$ to form a matrix

$$\mathbf{T}(k) = (\mathbf{T}_1(k), \ldots, \mathbf{T}_s(k)). \tag{2.49}$$

Now for each ρ_j, there is a corresponding solution for (2.40):

$$\mathbf{z} = e^{-\rho_j t}\mathbf{c}(j) \tag{2.50}$$

where

$$\mathbf{c}(j) = \begin{pmatrix} c_{1j} \\ \vdots \\ c_{sj} \end{pmatrix}. \tag{2.51}$$

When (2.50) is introduced in (2.40), we obtain the equation

$$(\rho_j \mathbf{I} - \mathbf{V})\mathbf{c}(j) = \mathbf{0}, \tag{2.52}$$

or, by the definition of $\mathbf{A}(\rho_l)$ in (2.46),

$$\mathbf{A}(\rho_j)\mathbf{c}(j) = \mathbf{0}. \tag{2.53}$$

Since $-\rho_j$ is a solution of (2.45), the determininant $|A(\rho_j)|$ is equal to zero. Cramer's rule implies that the solution $\mathbf{c}(j)$ is proportional to the cofactors of elements in a same row of $\mathbf{A}(\rho_j)$. That is

$$\mathbf{c}(j) = b_j \begin{pmatrix} A_{k1}(\rho_j) \\ \vdots \\ A_{ks}(\rho_j) \end{pmatrix} \tag{2.54}$$

or, from (2.47), that

$$\mathbf{c}(j) = b_j \mathbf{T}_j(k), \qquad j = 1, \ldots, s, \tag{2.55}$$

where b_j is an arbitrary constant. Substituting (2.55) in (2.50) gives

$$\mathbf{z} = e^{-\rho_j t} b_j \mathbf{T}_j(k), \qquad j = 1, \ldots, s, \tag{2.56}$$

When the eigenvalues $-\rho_j$ are distinct, the general solution of the auxiliary equations in (2.40) is the sum

$$\mathbf{z} = \sum_{j=1}^{s} e^{-\rho_j t} b_j \mathbf{T}_j(k). \tag{2.57}$$

To express (2.57) in matrix form, we introduce the diagonal matrix

$$\mathbf{E}(t) = \begin{pmatrix} e^{\rho_1 t} & 0 & \cdots & 0 \\ 0 & e^{\rho_2 t} & \cdots & 0 \\ \vdots & \vdots & & \vdots \\ 0 & 0 & \cdots & e^{\rho_s t} \end{pmatrix} \tag{2.58}$$

and the column vector

$$\mathbf{b} = \begin{pmatrix} b_1 \\ \vdots \\ b_s \end{pmatrix}, \tag{2.59}$$

and rewrite the solution in (2.57) as

$$\mathbf{z} = \mathbf{T}(k)\mathbf{E}^{-1}(t)\mathbf{b}. \tag{2.60}$$

Equation (2.60) is now substituted into auxiliary equation (2.41) to yield

$$d \ln G_{\mathbf{x}_t}(\mathbf{z};t) = -\boldsymbol{\lambda}'(t)\mathbf{T}(k)\mathbf{E}^{-1}(t)\mathbf{b}\,dt. \tag{2.61}$$

Hence, the generating function

$$G_{\mathbf{x}_t}(\mathbf{z};t) = c\exp\left\{-\int_0^t \boldsymbol{\lambda}'(\xi)\mathbf{T}(k)\mathbf{E}^{-1}(\xi)\mathbf{b}\,d\xi\right\} \tag{2.62}$$

where $\ln c$ is the constant of integration. The integral in (2.62) is

$$\int_0^t \boldsymbol{\lambda}'(\xi)\mathbf{T}(k)\mathbf{E}^{-1}(\xi)\mathbf{b}\,d\xi = \boldsymbol{\eta}'(t)\mathbf{b} \tag{2.63}$$

where

$$\boldsymbol{\eta}'(t) = \int_0^t \boldsymbol{\lambda}'(\xi)\mathbf{T}(k)\mathbf{E}^{-1}(\xi)\,d\xi. \tag{2.64}$$

Its components are

$$\eta_l(t) = \sum_{\alpha=1}^{s} A_{k\alpha}(\rho_l)\int_0^t \lambda_\alpha(\xi)e^{-\rho_l\xi}\,d\xi, \qquad l = 1, \ldots, s. \tag{2.65}$$

At $t = 0$,

$$\boldsymbol{\eta}'(0) = (0, \dots, 0). \tag{2.66}$$

Substituting (2.63) in (2.62) gives

$$G_{\mathbf{x}_t}(\mathbf{z};t) = c\exp\{-\boldsymbol{\eta}'(t)\mathbf{b}\}. \tag{2.67}$$

Rearranging (2.60) as

$$\mathbf{b} = \mathbf{E}(t)\mathbf{T}^{-1}(k)\mathbf{z} \tag{2.68}$$

and expressing the constant c in (2.67) as a function Φ of the constant vector $\mathbf{b}$, we have

$$c = \Phi\{\mathbf{b}\} = \Phi\{\mathbf{E}(t)\mathbf{T}^{-1}(k)\mathbf{z}\}. \tag{2.69}$$

When (2.68) and (2.69) are substituted in (2.67), we obtain the general solution for the differential equation in (2.31):

$$G_{\mathbf{x}_t}(\mathbf{z};t) = \Phi\{\mathbf{E}(t)\mathbf{T}^{-1}(k)\mathbf{z}\}\exp\{-\boldsymbol{\eta}'(t)\mathbf{E}(t)\mathbf{T}^{-1}(k)\mathbf{z}\}. \tag{2.70}$$

For the particular solution corresponding to the initial condition

$$G_{\mathbf{x}_t}(\mathbf{z};0) = \prod_{\alpha=1}^{s}[1 - z_\alpha]^{i_\alpha}, \tag{2.36}$$

we need to determine the function Φ. If we set $t = 0$, then $\boldsymbol{\eta}(0) = \mathbf{0}$, the exponential function in (2.70) vanishes, and we can use (2.36) to write equation (2.70) as

$$G_{\mathbf{x}_t}(\mathbf{z};0) = \Phi\{\mathbf{E}(0)\mathbf{T}^{-1}(k)\mathbf{z}\} = \prod_{\alpha=1}^{s}[1 - z_\alpha]^{i_\alpha} \tag{2.71}$$

where $\mathbf{E}(0)$, as it is defined in (2.58) with $t = 0$, is a unit matrix. Therefore we use the equation

$$\Phi\{\mathbf{T}^{-1}(k)\mathbf{z}\} = \prod_{\alpha=1}^{s}[1 - z_\alpha]^{i_\alpha} \tag{2.72}$$

to determine function Φ.

Let

$$\mathbf{T}^{-1}(k)\mathbf{z} = \mathbf{b}_0; \tag{2.73}$$

then

$$\mathbf{z} = \mathbf{T}(k)\mathbf{b}_0. \tag{2.74}$$

For every $\mathbf{b}_0$ such that each component of $\mathbf{z}$ in (2.74) is less than or equal to one in absolute value, function Φ is given by

$$\Phi\{\mathbf{b}_0\} = \prod_{\alpha=1}^{s} [1 - z_\alpha]^{i_\alpha}; \tag{2.75}$$

where z_α are components of $\mathbf{z}$ as given in (2.74). In (2.70) we have

$$\mathbf{b}_t = \mathbf{E}(t)\mathbf{T}^{-1}(k)\mathbf{z}. \tag{2.76}$$

Substituting $\mathbf{b}_t$ for $\mathbf{b}_0$ in (2.74) and letting

$$\boldsymbol{\zeta} = \mathbf{T}(k)\mathbf{E}(t)\mathbf{T}^{-1}(k)\mathbf{z}, \tag{2.77}$$

we find that

$$\Phi\{\mathbf{E}(t)\mathbf{T}^{-1}(k)\mathbf{z}\} = \prod_{\alpha=1}^{s} [1 - \zeta_\alpha]^{i_\alpha} \tag{2.78}$$

where ζ_α are components of $\boldsymbol{\zeta}$ in (2.77). Substituting (2.78) in (2.70) yields the particular solution required

$$G_{\mathbf{x}_t}(\mathbf{z};t) = \prod_{\alpha=1}^{s} [1 - \zeta_\alpha]^{i_\alpha} \exp\{-\boldsymbol{\eta}'(t)\mathbf{E}(t)\mathbf{T}^{-1}(k)\mathbf{z}\}. \tag{2.79}$$

We can now expand the factor $[1 - \zeta_\alpha]^{i_\alpha}$ and the exponential function in (2.79) to get a more explicit formula for the probability generating function. The components of $\mathbf{z}$ introduced in (2.34) are $z_\alpha = 1 - u_\alpha$, and the matrix product $\mathbf{T}(k)\mathbf{E}(t)\mathbf{T}^{-1}(k)$ in (2.77) is exactly the same as that in equation (4.46), Chapter 14. Expanding (2.77) yields components of vector $\boldsymbol{\zeta}$:

$$\zeta_\alpha = \sum_{\beta=1}^{s}\sum_{l=1}^{s} A_{k\alpha}(\rho_l)\frac{T_{\beta l}(k)}{|T(k)|} e^{\rho_l t}(1 - u_\beta), \qquad \alpha = 1, \dots, s. \tag{2.80}$$

In section 4.4, Chapter 14, we also have shown that

$$\sum_{\alpha=1}^{s} A_{k\alpha}(\rho_l)\frac{T_{\beta l}(k)}{|T(k)|} e^{\rho_l t} = \sum_{l=1}^{s} \frac{A'_{\alpha\beta}(\rho_l)}{\prod_{\substack{m=1\\ m\neq l}}^{s} (\rho_l - \rho_m)} e^{\rho_l t} \tag{2.81}$$

is the transition probability that an individual in S_α at time $t = 0$ will be in S_β at time t. Denote this probability by $\pi_{\alpha\beta}(0, t)$ as in the preceding section,

$$\pi_{\alpha\beta}(0, t) = \sum_{l=1}^{s} \frac{A'_{\alpha\beta}(\rho_l)}{\prod_{\substack{m=1 \\ m \neq l}}^{s} (\rho_l - \rho_m)} e^{\rho_l t}, \qquad \alpha, \beta = 1, \ldots, s, \quad (2.13)$$

and let $\pi_{\alpha 0}(0, t) = 1 - \sum_{\beta=1}^{s} \pi_{\alpha\beta}(0, t)$ be the probability that an individual will die or emigrate from the population during interval $(0, t)$. The component ζ_α in (2.80) can be written as

$$\zeta_\alpha = \sum_{\beta=1}^{s} \pi_{\alpha\beta}(0, t)(1 - u_\beta), \qquad \alpha = 1, \ldots, s, \quad (2.82)$$

and the product in (2.79) is simply

$$\prod_{\alpha=1}^{s} [1 - \zeta_\alpha]^{i_\alpha} = \prod_{\alpha=1}^{s} [\pi_{\alpha 0}(0, t) + \pi_{\alpha 1}(0, t) u_1 + \ldots + \pi_{\alpha s}(0, t) u_s]^{i_\alpha}. \quad (2.83)$$

The exponential function in (2.79) depends on the immigration rate $\lambda_\alpha(t)$. When $\lambda_\alpha(t) = \lambda_\alpha$, then $\mathbf{E}^{-1}(\xi)$ is the only factor in (2.64) that involves time ξ. Recalling the formula for $\mathbf{E}(\xi)$ in (2.58), we integrate (2.64) to obtain

$$\boldsymbol{\eta}'(t) = \boldsymbol{\lambda}'\mathbf{T}(k) \int_0^t \mathbf{E}^{-1}(\xi) d\xi = \boldsymbol{\lambda}'\mathbf{T}(k) [\mathbf{I} - \mathbf{E}^{-1}(t)] \boldsymbol{\rho}^{-1}, \quad (2.84)$$

where $\boldsymbol{\rho}^{-1}$ is the inverse of the diagonal matrix

$$\boldsymbol{\rho} = \text{diag}[\rho_1, \ldots, \rho_s]. \quad (2.85)$$

Thus, since $\boldsymbol{\rho}^{-1}$ and $\mathbf{E}(t)$ are diagonal matrices, $\boldsymbol{\rho}^{-1}\mathbf{E}(t) = \mathbf{E}(t)\boldsymbol{\rho}^{-1}$, the exponential in (2.79), can be rearranged:

$$\begin{aligned} -\boldsymbol{\eta}'(t) \mathbf{E}(t) \mathbf{T}^{-1}(k) \mathbf{z} &= \boldsymbol{\lambda}'\mathbf{T}(k) [\mathbf{I} - \mathbf{E}^{-1}(t)] \boldsymbol{\rho}^{-1} \mathbf{E}(t) \mathbf{T}^{-1}(k) \mathbf{z} \\ &= -\boldsymbol{\lambda}'\mathbf{T}(k) [\mathbf{E}(t) - \mathbf{I}] \boldsymbol{\rho}^{-1} \mathbf{T}^{-1}(k) \mathbf{z}. \quad (2.86) \end{aligned}$$

Expanding the matrix product in (2.86) and recalling $z_\beta = 1 - u_\beta$ yields

$$-\boldsymbol{\lambda}'\mathbf{T}(k)\,[\mathbf{E}(t)-\mathbf{I}]\,\boldsymbol{\rho}^{-1}\mathbf{T}^{-1}(k)\mathbf{z} = -\sum_{\beta=1}^{s}\theta_\beta(t)(1-u_\beta) \quad (2.87)$$

where

$$\theta_\beta(t) = \sum_{\alpha=1}^{s}\sum_{l=1}^{s}\lambda_\alpha A_{k\alpha}(\rho_l)\frac{T_{\beta l}(k)}{|T(k)|}\rho_l^{-1}(e^{\rho_l t}-1) \quad (2.88)$$

or, because of (2.81),

$$\theta_\beta(t) = \sum_{\alpha=1}^{s}\sum_{l=1}^{s}\lambda_\alpha \frac{A'_{\alpha\beta}(\rho_l)}{\prod_{\substack{m=1\\ m\neq l}}^{s}(\rho_l-\rho_m)\rho_l}(e^{\rho_l t}-1). \quad (2.89)$$

Equation (2.89) is the same as equation (2.23). Substituting (2.83) and (2.87) in (2.79), we arrive at the formula

$$G_{\mathbf{X}(t)}(\mathbf{u};t) = \prod_{\alpha=1}^{s}[\pi_{\alpha 0}(0,t)+\pi_{\alpha 1}(0,t)u_1+\ldots+\pi_{\alpha s}(0,t)u_s]^{i_\alpha}$$
$$\times\exp\left\{-\sum_{\alpha=1}^{s}\theta_\beta(t)(1-u_\beta)\right\} \quad (2.25)$$

which was given in Theorem 1.

3. A BIRTH-ILLNESS-DEATH PROCESS

The migration processes discussed in section 2 were developed under the assumption in (2.1) that $\lambda_\alpha^*(t) = \lambda(t)$. An increase in population in each state is due either to immigration or internal migration. When $\lambda_\alpha^*(t)$ is a function of the population size j_α of state S_α at time t, we have a birth-illness-death process. A simple example is

$$\lambda_\alpha^*(t) = j_\alpha\lambda_\alpha, \qquad \nu_{\alpha\beta}^* = j_\alpha\nu_{\alpha\beta}, \qquad \mu_\alpha^* = j_\alpha\mu_\alpha, \quad (3.1)$$

where λ_α, $\nu_{\alpha\beta}$, and μ_α are independent of t and the process is time homogeneous.

The only difference between the birth-illness-death process and the migration process described in section 2 is in the assumption regarding $\lambda_\alpha^*(t)$. In (3.1), $\lambda_\alpha^*(t)$ is proportional to the population size j_α; in (2.1), $\lambda_\alpha^*(t)$ is independent of j_α. This slight difference, however, greatly changes the complexity of the problem. Not only do we lack an easy avenue toward an explicit solution, but also the differential equations involved are unmanageable, as we shall see presently.

Under the assumptions in (3.1), the probabilities $P_{\mathbf{i},\mathbf{j}}(0, t)$ satisfy the differential equations

$$\frac{d}{dt}P_{\mathbf{i},\mathbf{j}}(0, t) =$$

$$- P_{\mathbf{i},\mathbf{j}}(0, t)\sum_{\alpha=1}^{s} j_\alpha(\lambda_\alpha - \nu_{\alpha\alpha}) + \sum_{\alpha=1}^{s} P_{\mathbf{i},\mathbf{j}-\boldsymbol{\delta}_\alpha}(0, t)(j_\alpha - 1)\lambda_\alpha$$

$$+ \sum_{\substack{\alpha=1 \\ \alpha\neq\beta}}^{s}\sum_{\beta=1}^{s} P_{\mathbf{i},\mathbf{j}+\boldsymbol{\delta}_\alpha-\boldsymbol{\delta}_\beta}(0, t) j_\alpha \nu_{\alpha\beta} + \sum_{\alpha=1}^{s} P_{\mathbf{i},\mathbf{j}+\boldsymbol{\delta}_\alpha}(0, t) j_\alpha \mu_\alpha. \quad (3.2)$$

Since (3.2) is also not directly solvable, we again resort to the probability generating function. The differential equation of the p.g.f. is

$$\frac{\partial}{\partial t} G_{\mathbf{X}(t)}(\mathbf{u}; t) = - \sum_{\alpha=1}^{s} \lambda_\alpha u_\alpha(1 - u_\alpha)\frac{\partial}{\partial u_\alpha} G_{\mathbf{X}(t)}(\mathbf{u}; t)$$

$$+ \sum_{\alpha=1}^{s} u_\alpha \nu_{\alpha\alpha}\frac{\partial}{\partial u_\alpha} G_{\mathbf{X}(t)}(\mathbf{u}; t)$$

$$+ \sum_{\substack{\alpha=1 \\ \alpha\neq\beta}}^{s}\sum_{\beta=1}^{s} u_\beta \nu_{\alpha\beta}\frac{\partial}{\partial u_\alpha} G_{\mathbf{X}(t)}(\mathbf{u}; t)$$

$$+ \sum_{\alpha=1}^{s} \mu_\alpha \frac{\partial}{\partial u_\alpha} G_{\mathbf{X}(t)}(\mathbf{u}; t). \quad (3.4)$$

We proceed to use the method outlined in section 7, Chapter 8, to find the solution for the partial differential equations in (3.4). We let $z_\alpha = 1 - u_\alpha$ and introduce the relation $\mu_\alpha = -\sum_\beta \nu_{\alpha\beta}$ in (3.4) to rewrite the differential equation as

$$\frac{\partial}{\partial t} G_{\mathbf{X}(t)}(\mathbf{z}; t) = \sum_{\alpha=1}^{s}\left[\lambda_\alpha z_\alpha(1 - z_\alpha) + \sum_{\beta=1}^{s} \nu_{\alpha\beta} z_\beta\right]\frac{\partial}{\partial z_\alpha} G_{\mathbf{X}(t)}(\mathbf{z}; t). \quad (3.5)$$

The auxiliary equations are

$$-\frac{dt}{1} = \frac{dz_\alpha}{\lambda_\alpha z_\alpha(1 - z_\alpha) + \sum_{\beta=1}^{s} \nu_{\alpha\beta} z_\beta}, \qquad \alpha = 1, \dots, s, \tag{3.6}$$

and

$$-\frac{dt}{1} = \frac{dG_{\mathbf{X}(t)}(\mathbf{z}; t)}{0}. \tag{3.7}$$

As in section 2, we need to solve the two sets of equations in (3.6) and (3.7) to find a functional relationship between the probability generating function and the parameters λ_α and $\nu_{\alpha\beta}$. However, when we rewrite equation (3.6) as

$$\frac{dz_\alpha}{dt} = -\lambda_\alpha z_\alpha(1 - z_\alpha) - \sum_{\beta} \nu_{\alpha\beta} z_\beta, \qquad \alpha = 1, \dots, s, \tag{3.6a}$$

we find that the right hand side of (3.6a) is a quadratic function of z_α for each α, and that the equations in (3.6a) cannot be solved by known methods. Thus, with the mathematics we now possess, we cannot obtain explicit formulas either for the p.g.f. $G_{\mathbf{X}(t)}(u; t)$ or the probabilities $P_{\mathbf{i},\mathbf{j}}(0, t)$. For practical applications, numerical methods are used to resolve this problem.

4. PROBLEMS FOR SOLUTION

1. Derive the differential equations in (1.8).

2. Let j be the number of people living at t. Derive from (1.8) the differential equations for

(a) the pure birth process by letting

$$\lambda_\alpha^*(t) = j\lambda(t) \quad \text{and} \quad \mu_\alpha^*(t) = 0.$$

(b) the Polya process by letting

$$\lambda_\alpha^*(t) = (\lambda + \lambda a j)/(1 + \lambda a t) \quad \text{and} \quad \mu_\alpha^*(t) = 0$$

(c) the simple illness-death process by letting

$$\lambda^*(t) = 0, \; \nu_{\alpha\beta}^*(t) = j \quad \text{and} \quad \mu_\alpha^*(t) = j_\alpha(\mu_{\alpha 1} + \dots + \mu_{\alpha r}).$$

3. *Backward differential equations.* Derive a system of backward differential equations for the transition probabilities $p_{\mathbf{i},\mathbf{j}}(0, t)$ in the emigration-immigration process using (2.2), (2.3) and assuming $\lambda_\alpha(t) = \lambda_\alpha$.

4. *Continuation.* Derive the partial differential equation for the p.g.f. of $p_{\mathbf{i},\mathbf{j}}(0, t)$ in problem 3.

5. *Continuation.* Solve the partial differential equation in problem 4 and compare your result with that in equation (2.25).

6. In deriving explicit solutions in section 2, we have assumed that the eigenvalues of the matrix **V** are distinct. Find the solution when **V** has multiple eigenvalues.

7. Derive the differential equation in (2.35) from (2.31).

8. Integrate (2.64) to obtain the components of the vector $\boldsymbol{\eta}(t)$.

9. Show that the p.g.f. $\mathbf{G}_{\mathbf{x}_t}(\mathbf{u}; t)$ in (2.25) satisfies the differential equation in (2.31)

10. Find the variance of $X_\beta(t)$ in (2.27) and the covariance of $X_\beta(t)$ and $X_\gamma(t)$ in (2.28).

(a) from the p.g.f. in (2.25), and

(b) from the probability functions in (2.14) and (2.24).

11. Find the limiting probability distribution of $\mathbf{X}(t)$ as $t \to \infty$.

12. Consider three points on the time axis $0 < t_1 < t_2$ and let the corresponding population sizes of the health states be denoted by the vectors

$$\mathbf{X}_0 = \begin{pmatrix} x_{10} \\ \vdots \\ x_{s0} \end{pmatrix}, \quad \mathbf{X}_1 = \begin{pmatrix} x_{11} \\ \vdots \\ x_{21} \end{pmatrix}, \quad \mathbf{X}_2 = \begin{pmatrix} x_{12} \\ \vdots \\ x_{s2} \end{pmatrix},$$

respectively.

(a) Derive the p.g.f of the joint distributions of the random vectors $\mathbf{X}_1$ and $\mathbf{X}_2$ for the case of constant immigration, $\boldsymbol{\lambda}(t) = \boldsymbol{\lambda}$.

(b) Derive from the p.g.f in (a) the joint probability distribution of $\mathbf{X}_1$ and $\mathbf{X}_2$.

(c) Find the covariance between the components of $\mathbf{X}_1$ and $\mathbf{X}_2$.

Bibliography

Bailey, N. T. J. [1963]. The simple stochastic epidemic: a complete solution in terms of known functions, *Biometrika,* **50,** 235–240.

Bailey, N. T. J. [1964]. *The Elements of Stochastic Processes with Applications to the Natural Sciences.* Wiley, New York.

Barlett, M. S. [1949]. Some evolutionary stochastic processes, *J. Royal Statist. Soc.,* **B11,** 211–229.

Bartlett, M. S. [1956a]. *An Introduction to Stochastic Processes.* Cambridge University Press.

Bartlett, M. S. [1956b]. Deterministic and stochastic models of recurrent epidemics, *Proceedings of the Third Berkeley Symposium on Mathematical Statistics and Probability,* (J. Neyman, editor), University of California Press, Berkeley, **4,** 81–109.

Bates, G. E. and J. Neyman [1952]. Contribution to the theory of accident proneness. I. An optimistic model of the correlation between light and severe accidents, *University of California Publication in Statistics,* **1,** University of California Press, Berkeley, 215–254.

Belloc, N. B., L. Breslow and J. R. Hochstim [1971]. Measurement of physical health in a general population survey, *Amer. J. Epidemiol.,* **93,** 328–336.

Bharucha-Reid, A. T. [1960]. *Elements of the Theory of Markov Processes and their Applications.* McGraw-Hill, New York.

Birkhoff, G. and S. MacLane [1953]. *A Survey of Modern Algebra* (rev. ed.). Macmillan, New York.

Blackwell, D. [1948]. A renewal theorem, *Duke Math. J.,* **15,** 145–150.

Brockmeyer, E., H. L. Halstom, and H. Jensen [1948]. *The Life and Works of A. K. Erlang.* Copenhagen Telephone Co., Copenhagen.

Buck, R. [1965]. *Advanced Calculus* (2nd ed). McGraw-Hill, New York.

Burke, P. J. [1956]. The output of a queueing system, *Operations Research,* **4,** 699–704.

Chiang, C. L. [1964a]. A birth-illness-death process, *Ann. Math. Statist.,* **35,** 1390–1391 (abstract).

Chiang, C. L. [1964b]. A stochastic model of competing risks of illness and competing risks of death, *Stochastic Models in Medicine and Biology,* (J. Gurland, editor), University of Wisconsin Press, Madison, 323–354.

Chiang, C. L. [1965]. An index of health: Mathematical models, *Vital and Health Statistics,* series 2, no. 5, National Center for Health Statistics, 1–19.

Chiang, C. L. [1966]. On the expectation of the reciprocal of a random variable, *J. Am. Statist. Assoc.,* **20** (4), 38.

Chiang, C. L. [1968]. *Introduction to Stochastic Processes in Biostatistics.* Wiley, New York.

Chiang, C. L. [1972]. A general migration process, *Population Dynamics* (T. N. E. Greville, editor), Academic Press, 333–355.

Chiang, C. L. [1973]. A solution of Kolmogorov differential equations—A preliminary report, *Bull. International Statist. Inst.*, **45,** 264–270.

Chiang, C. L. [1974]. An equality in stochastic processes and its applications, *Progress in Statistics,* **1,** (J. Gani, K. Sarkadi, I. Vincze, editors), North-Holland, 145–151.

Chiang, C. L. [1977]. An algebraic treatment of finite Markov chains, (presented at the Second Vilnius Conference on Probability Theory and Mathematical Statistics, Lithuania, July, 1977).

Chiang, C. L. [1979]. Survival and stages of disease, *Mathematical Biosciences,* **43,** 159–171.

Chiang, C. L. and J. P. Hsu [1976]. On multiple transition time in a simple illness-death process—A Fix-Neyman model, *Mathematical Biosciences,* **30,** 55–71.

Chiang, C. L. and J. P. Hsu [1977]. An alternating renewal process with an absorbing state, *Applications of Statistics,* (P. R. Krishnaish, editor), North-Holland, 109–121.

Chiang, C. L. and S. Raman [1973]. On a solution of Kolmogorov differential equations, *Proceedings of the Fourth Conference on Probability Theory,* Editura Academici Republiclii Socialiste Romania, Bucuresti, Romania, 129–136.

Chung, K. L. [1960]. *Markov Chains with Stationary Transition Probabilities.* Springer-Verlag, Berlin.

Cohen, J. W. [1956]. On the queueing processes of lanes, *Philips Tech. Rept.*

Cox, D. R. [1962]. *Renewal Theory.* Methuen, London.

Cox, D. R. and H. D. Miller [1965]. *The Theory of Stochastic Processes.* Wiley, New York.

Doob, J. [1945]. Markoff chains—denumerable case. *Trans. Am. Math. Soc.,* **58,** 455–473.

Doob, J. L. [1948]. Renewal theory from the point of view of the theory of probability, *Trans. Amer. Math. Soc.,* **63,** 422–438.

Doob, J. L. [1953]. *Stochastic Processes.* Wiley, New York.

Du Pasquier [1913]. Mathematische theorie der invaliditatsversicherung, *Milt. Verein. Schweiz. Versich.—Math.,* **8,** 1–153.

Epstein, B. and M. Sobel [1953]. Life testing, *J. Amer. Statist. Assoc.,* **48,** 486–502.

Erlang, A. K. [1909]. Probability and telephone calls, *Nyt Tidsskr. Mat.,* **B20,** 33–39.

Feller, W. [1936]. Zur theorie der stochastischen prozesse, *Math. Ann.,* **113,** 113–160.

Feller, W. [1940]. On the integrodifferential equations of purely discontinuous Markoff Processes, *Trans. Amer. Math. Soc.,* **48,** 488–515.

Feller, W. [1941]. On the integral equation of renewal theory, *Ann. Math. Statist.,* **12,** 243–267.

Feller, W. [1949]. Fluctuation theory of recurrent events, *Trans. Amer. Math. Soc.,* **67,** 98–119.

Feller, W. [1966]. *An Introduction to Probability Theory and its Applications,* Vol. II. Wiley, New York.

Feller, W. [1968] (3rd edition). *An Introduction to Probability Theory and its Applications.* Wiley, New York.

Fisher, R. A. [1922]. On the dominance ratio, *Proc. Royal Soc. (Edinburgh),* **42,** 321–341.

Fisher, R. A. [1930]. The distribution of gene ratios for rare mutations, *Proc. Royal Soc. (Edinburgh),* **50,** 204–219.

Fix, E. and J. Neyman [1951]. A simple stochastic model of recovery, relapse, death

and loss of patients, *Human Biology*, **23**, 205–241.
Ford, L. R. [1933]. *Differential Equations*, McGraw-Hill, New York.
Forsyth, A. R. [1961] (6th edition). *A Treatise on Differential Equations.* Macmillan, London.
Gantmacher, F. R. [1959]. *The Theory of Matrices.* Chelsea, New York.
Gompertz, B. [1825]. On the nature of the function expressive of the law of human mortality. *Phil. Trans. Royal Soc. (London)*, **115**, 513–583.
Haight, F. A. [1957]. Queueing with balking, *Biometrika*, **44.**
Haldane, J. B. S. [1927]. A mathematical theory of natural and artificial selection. Part V: Selection and mutation, Proc. Royal Soc. (Edinburgh), **23**, 838–844.
Halley, E. [1693]. An estimation of the degrees of mortality of mankind, drawn from curious tables of the births and funerals at the City of Breslau, *Phil. Trans. Royal Soc. (London)*, **17**, 596–610.
Hardy, G. H. [1908]. Mendelian proportion in a mixed population, *Science*, **28**, 49–50.
Harris, T. E. [1963]. *The Theory of Branching Processes.* Springer-Verlag, Berlin.
Karlin, S. [1966]. *A First Course in Stochastic Processes.* Academic Press, New York.
Kendall, D. G. [1948]. On the generalized birth-and-death process, *Ann. Math. Statist.*, **19**, 1–15.
Kendall, D. G. [1956]. Deterministic and stochastic epidemics in a closed population, *Proceedings of the Third Berkeley Symposium on Mathematical Statistics and Probability* (J. Neyman, editor), University of California Press, **4**, 149–165.
Kolmogorov, A. M. [1931]. Uber die analytischen methoden in der wahrscheinlichkeitsrechnung, *Mathematische Annln*, **104**, 415–458.
Kolmogorov, A. M. [1937]. Markov chains with a countable number of possible states (Russian), *Bull. Math. Univ. Moscow*, **1**, 16 pp.
Levy, Paul [1951]. Systemes markoviens et stationnaires. Cas denombrable. *Ann. Sci. Ecole Norm. Sup.*, **68**, 340–391.
Li, C. C. [1968]. *Population Genetics.* University of Chicago Press, Chicago.
Lundberg, O. [1940]. *On Random Processes and their Applications to Sickness and Accident Statistics.* Uppsala.
Makeham, W. M. [1860]. On the law of mortality and the construction of annuity tables, *J. Inst. Actuaries*, **8.**
Markov, A. A. [1906]. Extension of the law of large numbers to dependent events (Russian), *Bull. Soc. Phys. Math. Kazan*, **2**, 135–156.
McKendrick, A. M. [1926]. Applications of mathematics to medical problems, *Proc. Edinburgh Math. Soc.*, **44**, 1–34.
Miller, F. H. [1941]. *Partial Differential Equations* (11th printing, 1965). Wiley, New York.
Neyman, J. and E. L. Scott [1964]. A stochastic model of epidemics, *Stochastic Models in Medicine and Biology* (J. Gurland, editor), University of Wisconsin Press, Madison, pp. 45–83.
Parzen, E. [1962]. *Stochastic Processes.* Holden-Day, San Francisco.
Patil, V. T. [1957]. The consistency and adequacy of the Poisson-Markoff model for density fluctuations, *Biometrika*, **44**, 43–56.
Ploya, G. and G. Szego [1964]. *Aufgaben und Lehrsatze aus der Analysis*, Vol. 2. Spring-Verlag, Berlin.
Prabhu, N. U. [1965]. *Stochastic Processes.* Macmillian, New York.
Pyke, R. [1958]. On renewal processes related to type I and type II counter models, *Ann. Math. Statist.*, **29**, 737–754.

Pyke, R. [1961a]. Markov renewal processes: Definitions and preliminary properties, *Ann. Math. Statist.*, **32**, 1231–1242.

Pyke, R. [1961b]. Markov renewal processes with finitely many states, *Ann. Math. Statist.*, **32**, 1243–1259.

Race, R. R. and R. Sanger [1958]. *Blood Groups in Man.* Blackell, Oxford, England.

Reich, E. [1957]. Waiting time when queues are in tandem, *Ann. Math. Statist.*, **28**, 768–773.

Riordan, J. [1958]. *An Introduction to Combinatorial Analysis.* Wiley, New York.

Rudin, W. [1953]. *Principles of Mathematical Analysis.* McGraw-Hill, New York.

Sacks, S. T. and C. L. Chiang [1977]. A transition probability model for the study of chronic diseases, *Mathematical Biosciences,* **34**, 325–346.

Singh, V. P. [1968]. Queueing systems with balking and heterogeneous servers. Ph.D. thesis. *Tech. Memo,* #113, Department of Operations Research, Case Western Reserve University, Cleveland.

Singh, V. P. [1970]. Two-server Markovian queues with balking: Heterogeneous vs. homogeneous servers, *Operations Research,* **18**, 145–159.

Smith, W. L. [1957]. On renewal theory, counter problems and quasi-Poisson processes, *Proc. Cambridge Phil. Soc.*, **53**, 175–193.

Smith, W. L. [1958]. Renewal theory and its ramifications, *J. Roy. Statist. Soc., Ser. B,* **20**, 243–302.

Stern, Curt [1969] (2nd edition). *Principles of Human Genetics.* Freeman, San Francisco.

Sverdrup, E. [1965]. Estimates and test procedures in connection with stochastic models for deaths, recoveries and transfers between different states of health, *Skad. Aktuarietidskrift,* **44**, 184–211.

Takács, L. [1954]. Some investigations concerning recurrent stochastic processes of a certain type (in Hungarian), *Magyar Tud. Akad. Alkalm. Mat. Int. Kozl,* **3**, 115–128.

Takács, L. [1956]. On the sequence of events, selected by a counter from a recurrent process of events, *Teor. Veroyatnost. i Primenen,* **1**, 90–102.

Takács, L. [1960]. *Stochastic Processes.* Methuen, London.

Uspansky, J. V. [1937]. *Introduction to Mathematical Probability.* McGraw-Hill, New York.

Wald, A. [1947]. *Sequential Analysis.* Wiley, New York.

Weinberg, W. [1908]. Uber den nachweis der vererbung beim menshcen, *Jahreshefte Verein f. Veterl. Naturk, in Wurttemberg,* **64**, 368–382.

Yang, G. L. and C. L. Chiang [1971]. A time dependent simple stochastic epidemic, *Proceedings of the Sixth Berkeley Symposium on Mathematical Statistics and Probability,* (J. Neyman, editor), University of California Press, Berkeley, **4**, 147–158.

Yule, G. U. [1924]. A mathematical theory of evolution based on the conclusion of Dr. J. C. Willis, F. R. S., *Phil. Trans. Royal Soc. (London),* **B213**, 21–87.

Author Index

Subject Index

Shenghui Chu
1/14/1981
U of M.

ck

JAN 14 6027

$0 006.85Mt
$0 034.65Mt

S$0 041.50TL
$0 001.64Tx

*$0 043.14TL